v. 109-119, 55 - 76

Surface Wave Filters

SURFACE WAVE FILTERS

DESIGN, CONSTRUCTION, AND USE

Herbert Matthews, *Editor*

Consultant, Sperry Research Center
Sudbury, Massachusetts

A WILEY-INTERSCIENCE PUBLICATION

JOHN WILEY & SONS, New York · London · Sydney · Toronto

Library of Congress Cataloging in Publication Data:

Main entry under title:

Surface wave filters.

"A Wiley-Interscience publication."
Includes bibliographies and index.
1. Acoustic surface wave filters. 2. Signal processing. 3. Radar. 4. Spread spectrum communications.
I. Matthews, Herbert.

TK7872.F5S88   621.38'043   77-3913
ISBN 0-471-58030-9

Printed in the United States of America

10 9 8 7 6 5 4 3 2 1

Contributors

DELMAR T. BELL, JR., Texas Instruments, Inc., Dallas, Texas

LEWIS T. CLAIBORNE, Texas Instruments, Inc., Dallas, Texas

ADRIAN J. DEVRIES, Zenith Radio Corporation, Elk Grove Village, Illinois

GERALD W. FARNELL, Faculty of Engineering, McGill University, Montreal, Canada

HENRY M. GERARD, Hughes Aircraft Company, Fullerton, California

J. DENNIS MAINES, Royal Signals and Radar Establishment, Great Malvern, Worcestershire, England

R. F. MILSOM, Allen Clark Research Center, The Plessey Company Ltd., Caswell, Towcester, Northants, England

MARTIN REDWOOD, Department of Electrical and Electronic Engineering, Queen Mary College, University of London, London, England

N. H. C. REILLY, Department of Electrical and Electronic Engineering, Queen Mary College, University of London, London, England

HENRY I. SMITH, Lincoln Laboratory, Massachusetts Institute of Technology, Lexington, Massachusetts

PHILIP B. SNOW, Tektronix, Inc., Beaverton, Oregon

ROGER H. TANCRELL, Raytheon Research Division, Waltham, Massachusetts

MANFRED G. UNKAUF, Raytheon Company, Wayland, Massachusetts

RICHARD C. WILLIAMSON, Lincoln Laboratory, Massachusetts Institute of Technology, Lexington, Massachusetts

Preface

This book teaches the art of designing, making, and using the new class of signal processing devices based on elastic surface waves. The book is not a review of the immense work done on surface wave phenomena and devices since the initial inventions about 15 years ago. Rather, the topics presented provide a working knowledge of surface wave devices for bandpass filtering and for generating and correlating complicated waveforms. These devices have proved practical and are used in operating radar and communications equipment.

Elastic waves are the basis of a useful class of filters because they travel in suitable solids with negligible loss and at velocities, typically, 10^3 to 10^4 m/sec, that lead to operating frequencies from 30 to 800 MHz for practical surface wave filters. When a solid is piezoelectric, an elastic wave traveling on its surface generates an electric wave, so that a traveling electric field extends above the surface and can interact with metal electrodes on it. Electrode structures made by photolithographic techniques can be quite complicated, and therefore filters for a wide range of signal processing functions can be constructed. Filters based on these principles not only perform necessary signal processing functions within strict specifications but also are small, rugged, reproducible, and cheap.

This book was written by experts. Each has made creative and useful contributions to the theory, design, construction, or application of surface wave filters. Individually each chapter is a special treatise on its subject. Together the chapters are a text for engineers and technicians newly interested in the subject. The initial chapters present principles and methods that guide design and construction of all surface wave filters. The next chapters describe design and performance of bandpass filters, binary and chirp sequence filters, and reflective array compressors. The concluding chapters discuss the use of these devices in radar and communications equipment. Readers with education or experience equivalent to a bachelor's degree in electrical engineering or physics will understand most of the presentation easily, but a few sections require more advanced preparation.

A group of remarkably keen and hard-working men in 15 years converted a good idea about elastic surface waves into a vast array of brilliant studies and clever devices. There are too many men to list here, but I will note the basic patent was applied for in 1963 by John Rowen of the Bell Telephone Laboratories. Invention and development of new surface wave devices are still vigorously pursued, and the form these devices will have 15 years hence can be only dimly perceived. I have tried to gather under one cover what I believe is lasting and fundamental to a working knowledge of surface wave filters. I thank the authors of this book for joining me in this project, and I compliment them for their patience, energy, and ability. I thank also Jennifer Matthews for her considerable help in preparing the final manuscript.

HERBERT MATTHEWS

Wayland, Massachusetts
January 1977

Contents

Chapter 1   Elastic Surface Waves   **1**

     1.1   Elastic Waves, 2
     1.2   Free Surfaces, 11
     1.3   Solution Procedure and Isotropic Substrates, 14
     1.4   Anisotropic Free Surfaces, 20
     1.5   Thin Layers and Perturbations, 31
     1.6   Diffraction and Attenuation, 43

Chapter 2   The Interdigital Transducer   **55**

     2.1   Field Analysis of Generation and Detection, 57
     2.2   Equivalent Electrical Circuits and Other
           Simplified Models, 76
     2.3   Analysis by Chain Matrices, 90
     2.4   Nonuniform Arrays, 97

Chapter 3   Principles of Surface Wave Filter Design   **109**

     3.1   Transversal Filters and Their Surface Wave
           Implementation, 111
     3.2   Filter Design and Synthesis, 135
     3.3   Input Impedance and Distortion, 146

Chapter 4   Surface Wave Device Fabrication   **165**

     4.1   Substrates and Polymer Film Preparation, 167
     4.2   Photolithography, 175
     4.3   Etching and Lift-off, 188

4.4   Electron Lithography, 195
4.5   X-Ray Lithography, 205
4.6   Ion Beam Etching of Surface Relief
       Gratings, 210

Chapter 5   Matching Networks and Packaging Structures   219

5.1   Criteria for Matching Network Design, 219
5.2   Passive Matching Networks, 233
5.3   The Packaging Structure and the Crystal
       Substrate, 243
5.4   Other Packaging Design Considerations, 253

Chapter 6   Surface Wave Bandpass Filters   263

6.1   Selectivity of a Surface Wave Transducer, 264
6.2   Filter Response by Means of Admittance
       Parameters, 281
6.3   Bandpass Filter Design, 290

Chapter 7   Phase Code Generators and Correlators   307

7.1   Code Properties, 310
7.2   Design of Devices for Phase-Coded
       Waveforms, 319
7.3   Constraints on the Uses of Phase Coded
       Devices, 339

Chapter 8   Surface Wave Interdigital Electrode Chirp Filters   347

8.1   Surface Wave Transversal Filters and Chirp
       Filter Applications, 348
8.2   Design of Interdigital Electrode Chirp
       Filters, 350
8.3   FM Filter Performance, 362
8.4   The Status of Interdigital Chirp Filters, 375

Chapter 9   Reflection Grating Filters   381

9.1   Physics of Surface Wave Reflections, 386
9.2   Grating Geometries and Their Relation to Filter
       Response, 412
9.3   Examples of Reflection-Grating Devices 431

Chapter 10 Surface Wave Devices for Radar Equipment   443

      10.1 Radar: Basic Concepts, 444
      10.2 Surface Wave Devices and Their Significance
            in Radar Systems, 450
      10.3 Systems Applications of Surface Wave
            Devices, 463

Chapter 11 Surface Wave Devices in Spread Spectrum Systems   477

      11.1 Spread Spectrum Communications, 478
      11.2 Communication System Techniques, 489
      11.3 Application to the Dispersive Channel, 498
      11.4 The Burst Communication Modem, 502

Index   511

Surface Wave
Filters

ONE
Elastic Surface Waves

G. W. FARNELL

McGill University
Montreal, Quebec, Canada

In an unbounded isotropic solid elastic waves can propagate with the material displacement polarized in the direction of propagation or transverse to it, each mode having a characteristic velocity dependent on the elastic properties of the material but typically between 10^3 and 10^4 m/sec. When boundaries or interfaces are introduced along the direction of propagation, modes other than these simple bulk waves become possible. Of central interest here is the so-called Rayleigh wave, which can propagate along the free surface of a solid. The amplitude of the displacement of the material due to the passage of this wave is largest right at the free surface and decays exponentially with depth into the solid, so that the mechanical energy transported by the wave is concentrated in a region of the order of a wavelength in depth below the surface. The dispersionless velocity of propagation of this type of wave is somewhat less than the velocity of a transversely polarized bulk elastic wave. If the solid substrate is a piezoelectric, the deformations produced by the elastic wave induce local electric fields. These fields propagate along with the mechanical wave and extend into the space above the surface of the solid. The electric field will interact with any metal electrodes placed on the surface, and such electrodes can be connected to external circuits. Most of this book deals with the realization of useful devices through the interactions between metal electrodes on the surface of a piezoelectric solid and an elastic surface wave propagating under the electrodes.

1

   This chapter summarizes the theory of elastic wave propagation along the surface of piezoelectric solids and presents the characteristics of elastic surface waves that underlie the filters described in later chapters.

1.1   Elastic Waves

In the absence of any disturbance each point or small region of a solid remains at its equilibrium position, which is defined by a set of cartesian coordinates (x_1, x_2, x_3). An elastic wave propagating in the solid displaces each point from this equilibrium position. The displacement vector that gives the departure from the unperturbed position has three components, u_1, u_2, and u_3, parallel to the respective cartesian axes, and each of these components is a function of time and of the spatial coordinates x_1, x_2, and x_3 of the point considered. For the conditions of interest here the displacements can be considered infinitesimal, so the change of size or shape of any elementary volume is small, and, moreover, any rotation of this volume element is neglected. Thus a very useful measure of the deformation of the volume element is given by the symmetric strain tensor

$$S_{ij} = \frac{1}{2} \left(\frac{\partial u_i}{\partial x_j} + \frac{\partial u_j}{\partial x_i} \right) \tag{1.1}$$

The lower case subscripts i, j, k, and so on, separately take on the values 1, 2, and 3 corresponding to the three axes x_1, x_2, and x_3.

   If we have a plane wave with displacement in the x_1 direction only, propagating in this x_1 direction with a phase velocity v and angular frequency ω, or wave vector $k = \omega/v$, the displacement is represented by

$$u_1 = \alpha e^{ik(x_1 - vt)}, \qquad u_2 = u_3 = 0 \tag{1.2}$$

and the only component of strain in this "compressional" or "longitudinal" wave is $S_{11} = iku_1$, in phase quadrature with the displacement. On the other hand, if the only displacement component in the uniform plane wave propagating along x_1 were in a transverse direction, say x_2, the displacement vector would be

$$u_1 = 0, \qquad u_2 = \beta e^{ik(x_1 - vt)}, \qquad u_3 = 0 \tag{1.3}$$

and now we have a "transverse" or "shear" wave, and the strain tensor has two off-diagonal or shear components

$$S_{12} = S_{21} = \tfrac{1}{2} iku_2 \tag{1.4}$$

Thus a small region that was square in cross section in the (x_1, x_2) plane with sides parallel to the x_1 and x_2 axes under equilibrium conditions is deformed periodically into a rhombus elongated alternately along one diagonal, then the other. For more general types of plane or inhomogeneous waves all the six independent components of the symmetric strain tensor can be present.

The forces acting on an infinitesimal cube in the solid considered as a free body, as shown in Fig. 1.1, can be divided into body forces acting directly on the material in the cube and traction forces transmitted across the bounding surfaces. The latter are expressed as the components T_{ij} of a stress tensor. The component T_{ij} is the ith component of the force per unit area acting on the positive side of the ith face of the infinitesimal cube located at (x_1, x_2, x_3), as illustrated in Fig. 1.1. In ultrasonic applications there are no body torques exerted on the infinitesimal cubes and thus the second-rank stress tensor is symmetric.

$$T_{ij} = T_{ji} \tag{1.5}$$

For the infinitesimal volume of Fig. 1.1 the stresses can be expanded in Taylor series in δx_1, δx_2, and δx_3 about their values at the central point (x_1, x_2, x_3), so that the net force due to these stresses on the boundaries acting in, say, the x_2 direction is

$$\left(\frac{\partial T_{21}}{\partial x_1} + \frac{\partial T_{22}}{\partial x_2} + \frac{\partial T_{23}}{\partial x_3}\right) \delta x_1 \, \delta x_2 \, \delta x_3 \tag{1.6}$$

Thus, if there are no body forces acting on the material within the cube, and if ρ is the mass density of the solid, Newton's third law gives for the

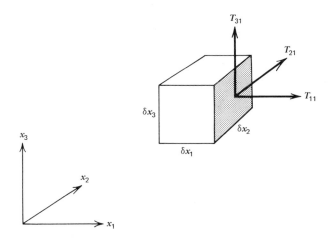

Figure 1.1 Infinitesimal volume of solid showing stress components on one face.

equation of motion of the small volume and, hence, of each region of the solid considered as a continuum

$$\rho \frac{\partial^2 u_i}{\partial t^2} = \sum_{j=1}^{3} \frac{\partial T_{ij}}{\partial x_i} \tag{1.7}$$

Summations over the coordinate axes as found in (1.7) occur so frequently in acoustic wave propagation that it is convenient to adopt the summation convention wherein a repeated subscript in a given term implies summation of that term over the three values of the repeated subscript. For example, the ith equation of motion becomes in such a notation

$$\rho \frac{\partial^2 u_i}{\partial t^2} = \frac{\partial T_{ij}}{\partial x_j} \tag{1.8}$$

Note that here the term on the right-hand side is summed on the dummy subscript j but not on the free subscript i.

Elastic Constants. As noted previously, the stresses and strains associated with elastic waves in solids are small, well below the elastic limits, and for nonpiezoelectric solids the stress field can be taken as proportional to the strain field. In tensor notation with the preceding summation convention

$$T_{ij} = c_{ijkl} S_{kl} \tag{1.9}$$

where c_{ijkl} is one component of the fourth-rank *"elastic constant"* or *"stiffness"* tensor. Not all of these elastic constants are independent for a given solid. Because both the stress and strain tensors have been taken as symmetric, $c_{ijkl} = c_{jikl}$ and $c_{ijkl} = c_{ijlk}$. Moreover because energy considerations require that $c_{ijkl} = c_{klij}$, there is a maximum of 21 independent elastic constants for the most general crystalline symmetry.

It is convenient in many instances to use a contracted notation for the pairs of subscripts that occur in the stress, strain, and elastic constant tensors. When the contracted notation is used the strain components form a column matrix of six elements in which

$$\begin{matrix} S_1 = S_{11} & S_2 = S_{22} & S_3 = S_{33} \\ S_4 = 2S_{23} = 2S_{32} & S_5 = 2S_{13} = 2S_{31} & S_6 = 2S_{12} = 2S_{21} \end{matrix} \tag{1.10}$$

(note the factors of two in the shear strains), and the stress components are

$$\begin{matrix} T_1 = T_{11} & T_2 = T_{22} & T_3 = T_{33} \\ T_4 = T_{23} = T_{32} & T_5 = T_{13} = T_{31} & T_6 = T_{12} = T_{21} \end{matrix} \tag{1.11}$$

The contraction allows the stiffness tensor to be written as a 6×6 symmetric matrix when the subscript pairs are rewritten as follows: 1 for 11, 2 for 22, 3 for 33, 4 for 23 or 32, 5 for 13 or 31, and 6 for 12 or 21. For example, c_{1123} becomes c_{14}, which is always equal to c_{41}, and c_{1231} becomes $c_{56} = c_{65}$.

Although in general there are 21 independent elements in the elastic constant matrix, crystalline symmetry of the solid with respect to the chosen coordinate axes appreciably reduces this number. For example, if the axes x_1, x_2, x_3 are chosen parallel to the crystalline axes X, Y, Z of a cubic crystal, there are three independent constants, as indicated by the first entry of Table 1.1. Values of elastic constants for several solids important in ultrasonics are given in Table 1.2. It is seen that bismuth germanium oxide ($Bi_{12}GeO_{20}$, written BGO) and silicon are examples of cubically symmetric crystals—the former is piezoelectric but the latter is not. The piezoelectric and dielectric constants are discussed in the next section. The elastic constant matrix for an isotropic solid is the same as that of a cubic solid, but any choice of coordinates axes can be used. Moreover, for an isotropic material $c_{44} = \frac{1}{2}(c_{11} - c_{12})$, and thus there are only two independent elastic constants. The piezoelectric ceramics, such as lead zirconium titanate (PZT), which are useful in low frequency ultrasonic applications, are polycrystalline and hence elastically isotropic. If x_3 is taken along the Z axis of a hexagonal crystal such as CdS or ZnO, there are five independent elastic constants, as shown by the central entry of Table 1.1. Some trigonal materials that are important as propagation or excitation media for surface waves are quartz, lithium niobate ($LiNbO_3$) and sapphire, crystal classes 32, 3 m, and $\bar{3}$ m, respectively. The elastic constant matrix in the crystalline axes for these trigonal crystals is shown by the right hand entry of Table 1.1.

Equations of Motion. In certain crystals mechanical strain produces a proportional electric polarization and, conversely, an applied electric field produces a proportional mechanical strain. Such crystals are said to be *piezoelectric*, and a necessary condition for this effect is that the crystal does not belong to a class that has inversion symmetry. For solids in which the piezoelectric effect is of significant magnitude, the mechanical and dielectric properties are intercoupled. The separate constitutive relations of the elastic behavior, $T_{ij} = c_{ijkl}S_{kl}$, and of the electromagnetic behavior, $D_i = \epsilon_{ij}E_j$, where $\mathbf{D}$ and $\mathbf{E}$ are the electric displacement and electric field, respectively, become the coupled set

$$T_{ij} = c_{ijkl}^E S_{kl} - e_{kij}E_k$$
$$D_i = \epsilon_{ij}^S E_j + e_{ijk}S_{jk} \qquad (1.12)$$

Table 1.1 Nonzero Elements of Elastic Constant Matrices in Crystalline Axes

Cubic Crystals (All Cubic Classes)	Hexagonal Crystals (All Hexagonal Classes)	Trigonal Crystals (Classes 32, 3 m, and $\bar{3}$ m)

$$
\begin{pmatrix}
c_{11} & c_{12} & c_{12} & \cdot & \cdot & \cdot \\
c_{12} & c_{11} & c_{12} & \cdot & \cdot & \cdot \\
c_{12} & c_{12} & c_{11} & \cdot & \cdot & \cdot \\
\cdot & \cdot & \cdot & c_{44} & \cdot & \cdot \\
\cdot & \cdot & \cdot & \cdot & c_{44} & \cdot \\
\cdot & \cdot & \cdot & \cdot & \cdot & c_{44}
\end{pmatrix}
$$

$$
\begin{pmatrix}
c_{11} & c_{12} & c_{13} & \cdot & \cdot & \cdot \\
c_{12} & c_{11} & c_{13} & \cdot & \cdot & \cdot \\
c_{13} & c_{13} & c_{33} & \cdot & \cdot & \cdot \\
\cdot & \cdot & \cdot & c_{44} & \cdot & \cdot \\
\cdot & \cdot & \cdot & \cdot & c_{44} & \cdot \\
\cdot & \cdot & \cdot & \cdot & \cdot & c_{66}
\end{pmatrix}
$$

$$
c_{66} = \tfrac{1}{2}(c_{11} - c_{12})
$$

$$
\begin{pmatrix}
c_{11} & c_{12} & c_{13} & c_{14} & \cdot & \cdot \\
c_{12} & c_{11} & c_{13} & -c_{14} & \cdot & \cdot \\
c_{13} & c_{13} & c_{33} & \cdot & \cdot & \cdot \\
c_{14} & -c_{14} & \cdot & c_{44} & \cdot & \cdot \\
\cdot & \cdot & \cdot & \cdot & c_{44} & c_{14} \\
\cdot & \cdot & \cdot & \cdot & c_{14} & c_{66}
\end{pmatrix}
$$

$$
c_{66} = \tfrac{1}{2}(c_{11} - c_{12})
$$

Table 1.2 Elastic Constants for Several Solids Important in Ultrasonics

Material	Crystal Class	Elastic Constants c^E 10^{10} Newton/m²						Piezoelectric Constants, Coulomb/m²						Permittivity		Density kg/m³
		c_{11}	c_{33}	c_{44}	c_{12}	c_{13}	c_{14}	e_{11}	e_{14}	e_{15}	e_{22}	e_{31}	e_{33}	$\frac{\epsilon_{11}}{\epsilon_0}$	$\frac{\epsilon_{33}}{\epsilon_0}$	ρ
LiNbO$_3$	3 m	20.3	24.5	6.0	5.3	7.5	0.9			3.7	2.5	0.2	1.3	44	29	4700
Quartz	32	8.674	10.72	5.794	0.699	1.191	−1.791	0.171	−0.0436					4.5	4.6	2651
BGO	23	12.80		2.55	3.05				0.99					38		9200
CdS	6 mm	9.07	9.38	1.504	5.81	5.10				−0.21		−0.24	0.44	9.02	9.53	4820
ZnO	6 mm	20.97	21.09	4.247	12.11	10.51				−0.48		−0.573	1.32	8.55	10.2	5680
PZT-5H	uniaxial	12.6	11.7	2.30	7.95	8.41				17.0		−6.5	23.3	1700	1470	7500
GaAs	$\bar{4}$3 m	11.88		5.94	5.38				0.154					12.5		5307
Al$_2$O$_3$	$\bar{3}$ m	49.4	49.6	14.5	15.8	11.4	−2.3							9.34	11.54	3986
Fused silica	isot	7.85		3.12										3.78		2200
Si	m 3 m	16.57		7.956	6.39									11.7		2332

[a] Data from Auld "Acoustic Fields and Waves in Solids." Only independent constants shown; for others see Tables 1.1 and 1.3.

Here the superscript on the elastic constants indicates they are measured at constant electric field, and the superscript on the components of the permittivity tensor indicates these components are measured under constant strain conditions. The coupling is provided by the third-rank piezoelectric constant tensor, which relates the vector electric quantity to the second-rank tensor mechanical quantity. Note that the first subscript on each coefficient e refers to the electric component. Again the "mechanical" pair of subscripts can be contracted and the piezoelectric tensor rewritten as a matrix of three rows and six columns. Crystalline symmetry considerations reduce the number of independent constants in such matrices, and Table 1.3 indicates the possible nonzero independent elements for several crystal classes of importance in ultrasonics. The chosen geometrical axes x_1, x_2, x_3 are again parallel to the crystal axes X, Y, Z. Typical examples of materials corresponding to these crystal classes are BGO for 23; GaAs for $\bar{4}3$ m; CdS or poled PZT when the x_3 axis is taken as the poling axis for 6 mm; quartz for 32; and LiNbO$_3$ for 3 m. The dielectric tensor for each of the preceding crystals is diagonal with $\epsilon_{22} = \epsilon_{11}$, but for the last three ϵ_{33} is not necessarily equal to ϵ_{11}.

Thus in the general problem of elastic waves propagating in a piezoelectric medium, there are two systems of equations, the mechanical equations of motion (1.8), and Maxwell's equations for the electrical behavior. These are relatively weakly intercoupled by the constitutive relations (1.12). The solutions of interest are predominantly mechanical and propagate with velocities many orders of magnitude less than the velocities of the solutions that are predominantly electromagnetic. As a

Table 1.3 Nonzero Elements of Pieozelectric Constant Matrices in Crystalline Axes

Cubic Classes (23 and $\bar{4}3$ m)	Hexagonal Class (6 mm, and poled ceramics with x_3 as poling axis)
$\begin{pmatrix} \cdot & \cdot & \cdot & e_{14} & \cdot & \cdot \\ \cdot & \cdot & \cdot & \cdot & e_{14} & \cdot \\ \cdot & \cdot & \cdot & \cdot & \cdot & e_{14} \end{pmatrix}$	$\begin{pmatrix} \cdot & \cdot & \cdot & \cdot & e_{15} & \cdot \\ \cdot & \cdot & \cdot & e_{15} & \cdot & \cdot \\ e_{31} & e_{31} & e_{33} & \cdot & \cdot & \cdot \end{pmatrix}$
Trigonal Class (32)	Trigonal Class (3 m)
$\begin{pmatrix} e_{11} & -e_{11} & \cdot & e_{14} & \cdot & \cdot \\ \cdot & \cdot & \cdot & \cdot & -e_{14} & -e_{11} \\ \cdot & \cdot & \cdot & \cdot & \cdot & \cdot \end{pmatrix}$	$\begin{pmatrix} \cdot & \cdot & \cdot & \cdot & e_{15} & -e_{22} \\ -e_{22} & e_{22} & \cdot & e_{15} & \cdot & \cdot \\ e_{31} & e_{31} & e_{33} & \cdot & \cdot & \cdot \end{pmatrix}$

result the predominantly electromagnetic solutions can be ignored here, and in the predominantly mechanical solutions the electric field can be assumed to be the gradient of a scalar but time varying potential; that is,

$$E_i = -\frac{\partial \varphi}{\partial x_i} \tag{1.13}$$

Combining the definition of strain (1.1), the mechanical equation of motion (1.8), the constitutive relation (1.12), $\nabla \cdot \mathbf{D} = 0$ from Maxwell's equations, and the quasistatic approximation (1.13) gives the appropriate system of four coupled wave equations for the electric potential and the three components of elastic displacement in a charge-free piezoelectric crystal.

$$\rho \frac{\partial^2 u_j}{\partial t^2} - c_{ijkl} \frac{\partial^2 u_k}{\partial x_i \partial x_l} - e_{kij} \frac{\partial^2 \varphi}{\partial x_i \partial x_k} = 0$$

$$e_{ikl} \frac{\partial^2 u_k}{\partial x_i \partial x_l} - \epsilon_{ik} \frac{\partial^2 \varphi}{\partial x_i \partial x_k} = 0 \tag{1.14}$$

Transformation of Coordinates. In the preceding equations of motion the tensors representing the material parameters are expressed in terms of axes x_i usually selected for convenience in expressing boundary and excitation conditions. However the tabulated values of these tensors are normally expressed in terms of the crystalline axes X_i, and it is necessary to transform the tabulated material parameters to the set of axes imposed by the problem geometry. If a_{ij} is an element of the transformation matrix between the "new" system of axes x_i^{new} and the "old" system x_i^{old}, that is, a_{ij} is the direction cosine of the axis x_i^{new} with respect to x_j^{old}, a point in the original system transforms to a point in the new by $x_i^{\text{new}} = a_{ij} x_j^{\text{old}}$. Similarly the transformations for various tensors are

First rank (vector) $\qquad u_i^{\text{new}} = a_{ij} u_j^{\text{old}}$

Second rank $\qquad T_{ij}^{\text{new}} = a_{ik} a_{jl} T_{kl}^{\text{old}}$

Third rank $\qquad e_{ijk}^{\text{new}} = a_{il} a_{jm} a_{kn} e_{lmn}^{\text{old}}$

Fourth rank $\qquad c_{ijkl}^{\text{new}} = a_{im} a_{jn} a_{ko} a_{lp} c_{mnop}^{\text{old}}$

Each of these coordinate transformations for the material tensors can also be expressed in a transformation matrix that is directly applicable to the matrix or contracted subscript representation of the tensor.

In many instances the required transformation of coordinates is merely an interchange of axes, and in such cases the transformed tensors can be written down directly by an interchange of subscripts. For example, suppose that the axes x_1, x_2, x_3, are, respectively, the crystalline axes X, $-Z$, Y, and that the elastic constants are known in the XYZ system of axes. It is convenient to construct a table as shown below (a minus sign indicates the sign of the element is to be reversed). In this example c_{22} in the new system is equal to c'_{33} of the old, $c_{26} = -c'_{35}$, and so on.

New Contracted Subscripts	New Tensor Subscripts	Transformation $(1 \rightarrow 1, 2 \rightarrow -3, 3 \rightarrow 2)$	Old Tensor Subscripts	Old Contracted Subscripts
	11	11	11	1
2	22	$(-3)(-3)$	33	3
3	33	22	22	2
4	23	$(-3)2$	$(-)23$	$(-)4$
5	13	12	12	6
6	12	$1(-3)$	$(-)13$	$(-)5$

In the analysis of certain experiments it is convenient to have the stress rather than the strain as the independent mechanical variable in the constitutive relations. Equation (1.13) is then replaced by

$$S_{ij} = s_{ijkl}T_{kl} + d_{kij}E_k$$
$$D_i = \epsilon_{ij}^T E_j + d_{ijk}T_{jk} \tag{1.15}$$

in which s_{ijkl} is the elastic "compliance" tensor measured at constant electric field. If the stiffness tensor is expressed as a 6×6 matrix, the corresponding compliance matrix is the inverse of this stiffness matrix. The elements of the dielectric permittivity matrix at constant strain are related to those measured at constant stress by

$$\epsilon_{ij}^S = \epsilon_{ij}^T - d_{ikl}d_{jmn}c_{klmn} \tag{1.16}$$

and the piezoelectric coupling tensor between electric field and stress is related to that between electric field and strain by

$$e_{ijk} = d_{imn}c_{mnjk} \tag{1.17}$$

or

$$d_{ijk} = e_{imn}s_{mnjk} \tag{1.18}$$

Energy Flow. Important characteristics of the propagation of elastic waves are the energy carried by the wave, the direction of the flow of this energy, and its distribution over the cross section of the wave. Such energy considerations are expressed in terms of a mechanical Poynting vector. For piezoelectric solids there is in general an electric field that accompanies a propagating elastic wave, and part of the transported energy is in electric form. If the time variation is $e^{-i\omega t}$, the time average of the power flow per unit area across a surface normal to x_i is given by

$$P_i' = -\tfrac{1}{2} \operatorname{Re} \{T_{ij}u_j^* - i\omega\varphi D_i^*\} \tag{1.19}$$

In this expression the electric second term and the electromechanical contribution contained in the stress (1.12) are zero for elastic waves in nonpiezoelectric solids. They are also small relative to the mechanical contributions for most propagation conditions in piezoelectric solids. As discussed in Section 1.4, the anisotropy of the elastic properties (and to a minor extent of the piezoelectric coupling) results, in general, in energy flow that is not collinear with the phase velocity of the propagating wave.

1.2 Free Surfaces

The prototype geometry for elastic surface wave propagation is shown in Fig. 1.2, where the surface $x_3 = 0$ forms the interface between the infinitely deep solid substrate and the free space above. Within the solid the mechanical displacements and the electric potential at each point must satisfy the equations of motion (1.4) in which the elastic constants, the piezoelectric coefficients, and the permittivity components are all expressed in the axes of Fig. 1.2. In this prototype problem the solutions of the equations of motion should be "surface waves" in that the mechanical displacements, which of course exist only in the solid, must vanish at large depths, and the electric potential, if it exists, must vanish for $x_3 \rightarrow \pm\infty$.

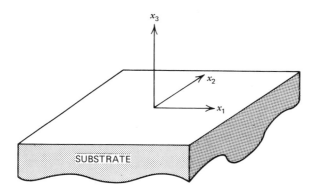

Figure 1.2 Coordinate system for surface wave propagation. The propagation vector lies along x_1. The sagittal plane, which contains the wave vector and the surface normal, is the $x_1 x_3$ plane.

Moreover, if x_1 is the direction of propagation of the wave solutions, there can be no dependence of displacement or potential on the x_2 coordinate because the surface is here assumed infinite. Surface waves satisfying the latter condition may be called *straight-crested*.

Boundary Conditions.   With the mechanically free surface of Fig. 1.2 there is no component of force in the x_3 direction at $x_3 = 0$, and thus the mechanical boundary conditions are

$$T_{31} = T_{32} = T_{33} = 0, \qquad \text{at} \qquad x_3 = 0 \tag{1.20}$$

Various types of electrical boundary conditions can exist at $x_3 = 0$ when the solid is piezoelectric, but for device applications only two forms of boundary conditions are of prime importance. In one form the surface is assumed covered by a thin conducting layer that does not affect the mechanical boundary conditions, but does force the surface to be equipotential and thus the propagating potential to be zero at $x_3 = 0$. In the other form the surface is assumed to be electrically free, and thus the spatially varying part of the potential above the surface satisfies Laplace's equation. Both the potential and D_3 are then continuous at $x_3 = 0$. The propagating potential must be of the form

$$\varphi = \Phi(x_3) e^{-ik(x_1 - vt)} \tag{1.21}$$

where, for $x_3 \geq 0$,

$$\frac{d^2\Phi}{dx_3^2} - k^2 \Phi = 0 \tag{1.22}$$

and hence the potential for $x_3 \geq 0$ is

$$\varphi = \Phi(0) e^{-kx_3} e^{-ik(x_1 - vt)} \tag{1.23}$$

which becomes vanishingly small as $x_3 \to +\infty$.

Partial Waves.   There are several different methods for solving this prototype surface wave problem. All involve numerical computation and can be illustrated by the approach considered here. The wave solution is assumed to be linear combinations of partial waves given by

$$\begin{aligned}
u_j^{(m)} &= \alpha_j^{(m)} \exp{(ikb^{(m)}x_3)} \exp{[ik(x_1 - vt)]} \\
\varphi^{(m)} &= \alpha_4^{(m)} \exp{(ikb^{(m)}x_3)} \exp{[ik(x_1 - vt)]}
\end{aligned} \tag{1.24}$$

wherein each partial wave is to satisfy the wave equation (1.14) and decay to zero as $x_3 \to -\infty$. The weighting coefficients of the linear combinations are chosen to satisfy the mechanical (1.20) and electrical (1.23) boundary conditions at $x_3 = 0$.

Substituting the partial waves (1.24) into the wave equation gives the following matrix equation

$$
\begin{pmatrix}
\Gamma_{11}-\rho v^2 & \Gamma_{12} & \Gamma_{13} & \Gamma_{14} \\
\Gamma_{12} & \Gamma_{22}-\rho v^2 & \Gamma_{23} & \Gamma_{24} \\
\Gamma_{13} & \Gamma_{23} & \Gamma_{33}-\rho v^2 & \Gamma_{34} \\
\Gamma_{14} & \Gamma_{24} & \Gamma_{34} & \Gamma_{44}
\end{pmatrix}
\begin{pmatrix}
\alpha_1 \\ \alpha_2 \\ \alpha_3 \\ \alpha_4
\end{pmatrix}
= 0
\qquad (1.25)
$$

in which the elements Γ of the upper left 3×3 block are associated with the elastic constants and intercouple the mechanical displacements

$$
\begin{aligned}
\Gamma_{11} &= c_{55}b^2 + 2c_{15}b + c_{11} \\
\Gamma_{22} &= c_{44}b^2 + 2c_{46}b + c_{66} \\
\Gamma_{33} &= c_{33}b^2 + 2c_{35}b + c_{55} \\
\Gamma_{12} &= c_{45}b^2 + (c_{14}+c_{56})b + c_{16} \\
\Gamma_{13} &= c_{35}b^2 + (c_{13}+c_{55})b + c_{15} \\
\Gamma_{23} &= c_{34}b^2 + (c_{36}+c_{45})b + c_{56}
\end{aligned}
\qquad (1.26)
$$

The term Γ_{44} is the purely electric term and in the quasistatic approximation is given by

$$
\Gamma_{44} = -(\epsilon_{33}b^2 + 2\epsilon_{13}b + \epsilon_{11})
\qquad (1.27)
$$

The remaining terms are associated with the piezoelectric properties of the solid and couple the electric potential to the mechanical displacements, that is, α_4 to α_1, α_2, and α_3.

$$
\begin{aligned}
\Gamma_{14} &= e_{35}b^2 + (e_{15}+e_{31})b + e_{11} \\
\Gamma_{24} &= e_{34}b^2 + (e_{14}+e_{36})b + e_{16} \\
\Gamma_{34} &= e_{33}b^2 + (e_{13}+e_{35})b + e_{15}
\end{aligned}
\qquad (1.28)
$$

In order to have nontrivial solutions the determinant of the coefficients of α in (1.25) must vanish. For each value of the phase velocity v, setting this determinant equal to zero gives an eighth-order algebraic equation in the decay constants b, and thus for each value of v there are eight values of b. These eight roots are either purely real or members of conjugate pairs. Since surface waves are of concern here only the roots lying within the lower half of the complex plane are retained, because only these roots lead to partial waves that decay with depth. There are four such roots in the general case, and for each there is a four-component eigenvector $\boldsymbol{\alpha}$.

Thus the general solution is of the form

$$u_j = \left\{ \sum_m C_m \alpha_j^{(m)} \exp\left(ikb^{(m)}x_3\right) \right\} \exp\left[ik(x_1 - vt)\right]$$

$$\varphi = \left\{ \sum_m C_m \alpha_4^{(m)} \exp\left(ikb^{(m)}x_3\right) \right\} \exp\left[ik(x_1 - vt)\right]$$

(1.29)

wherein the weighting factors C and the value of phase velocity v, which is contained explicitly in the propagating factor and implicitly in the roots b and the eigenvectors $\boldsymbol{\alpha}$, are to be chosen to satisfy the boundary conditions at the surface.

Boundary Condition Matrix. If the assumed solution is substituted into the boundary conditions, ordered as $T_{33} = T_{31} = T_{32} = 0$ and D_3 continuous, for a free surface, the following homogeneous equations result for the coefficients C_m:

$$\begin{pmatrix} \cdots & (c_{33i1} + c_{33i3}b^m)\alpha_i^m + (e_{133} + e_{333}b^m)\alpha_4^m & \cdots \\ \cdots & (c_{31i1} + c_{31i3}b^m)\alpha_i^m + (e_{131} + e_{331}b^m)\alpha_4^m & \cdots \\ \cdots & (c_{32i1} + c_{32i3}b^m)\alpha_i^m + (e_{132} + e_{332}b^m)\alpha_4^m & \cdots \\ \cdots & (e_{3i1} + e_{3i3}b^m)\alpha_i^m - (\epsilon_{31} + \epsilon_{33}b^m - i\epsilon_0)\alpha_4^m & \cdots \end{pmatrix} \begin{pmatrix} C_1 \\ C_2 \\ C_3 \\ C_4 \end{pmatrix} = 0$$

(1.30)

Here only the general mth column is shown, and the potential for $x_3 \geq 0$ has been taken to be of the form given in (1.23). If the free surface is shorted, equating the potential to zero at $x_3 = 0$ reduces the general term of the last row to α_4^m.

At this stage the computational problem is to find the value of phase velocity v for which the determinant of the coefficients in (1.30) vanishes. Even for cases of high crystalline symmetry in which large numbers of the material constants disappear, it is not possible to find an explicit expression for v. As a result some convergent numerical search technique is usually employed to obtain this velocity by trying successive values of v until the determinant of the coefficients in the boundary conditions is sufficiently close to zero. For this final value of v the weighting coefficients C can be evaluated and inserted in (1.29) to give the displacements and the potential.

1.3 Solution Procedure and Isotropic Substrates

The general procedure outlined in the paragraphs on partial waves and the boundary conditions matrix are summarized in this section as a series of enumerated steps. At each step the form of the results is illustrated for the simplest case, that of an isotropic, nonpiezoelectric solid. This latter case is of course the fundamental one and illustrates most of the basic properties of elastic surface waves. By following this case through the separate steps one can visualize how anisotropy and piezoelectricity modify and intercouple the isotropic solutions.

One general solution procedure consists of the following 10 steps:

1. *Rotate the elastic, piezoelectric, and permittivity tensors from the crystalline axes to the geometric axes of Fig.* 1.2

For an isotropic, nonpiezoelectric solid the elements of the piezoelectric tensor are all zero, the rotated elastic stiffness tensor is of the form of the left-hand entry of Table 1.1 with $c_{44} = \frac{1}{2}(c_{11} - c_{12})$, and the permittivity tensor is diagonal with $\epsilon_{11} = \epsilon_{22} = \epsilon_{33}$.

2. *Express the coefficients Γ of Eq.* (1.25) *in terms of* b

For the isotropic, nonpiezoelectric case the wave equation (1.25) becomes

$$\begin{pmatrix} c_{44}b^2 + c_{11} - \rho v^2 & 0 & (c_{12} + c_{44})b & 0 \\ 0 & c_{44}(b^2 + 1) - \rho v^2 & 0 & 0 \\ (c_{12} + c_{44})b & 0 & c_{11}b^2 + c_{44} - \rho v^2 & 0 \\ 0 & 0 & 0 & -\epsilon_{11}(b^2 + 1) \end{pmatrix} \begin{pmatrix} \alpha_1 \\ \alpha_2 \\ \alpha_3 \\ \alpha_4 \end{pmatrix}$$

$$= 0 \quad (1.31)$$

3. *Note any separation of the eigenvector components that will allow parts to be considered separately*

In the isotropic, nonpiezoelectric wave equation (1.31) there is a separation into three independent parts, one that involves the sagittal displacements α_1 and α_3 intercoupled,

$$\begin{pmatrix} c_{44}b^2 + c_{11} - \rho v^2 & (c_{12} + c_{44})b \\ (c_{12} + c_{44})b & c_{11}b^2 + c_{44} - \rho^2 \end{pmatrix} \begin{pmatrix} \alpha_1 \\ \alpha_3 \end{pmatrix} = 0 \quad (1.32)$$

one that involves transverse displacements α_2 only,

$$\{c_{44}(b^2 + 1) - \rho v^2\}\alpha_2 = 0 \quad (1.33)$$

and a third related to the potential only,

$$\epsilon_{11}(b^2 + 1)\alpha_4 = 0 \quad (1.34)$$

4. *Choose a reasonable value of v and solve for the eight values of* b

Here in the isotropic, nonpiezoelectric problem the roots can be expressed explicitly in terms of b because of the separation at step 3. Four roots,

$b = \pm i\{1 - (v/v_l)^2\}^{1/2}$ and $b = \pm i\{1 - (v/v_t)^2\}^{1/2}$, arise from (1.32), two more, $b = \pm i\{1 - (v/v_t)^2\}^{1/2}$, from (1.33), and the last two, $b = \pm i$, from (1.34). In these expressions $v_t = (c_{44}/\rho)^{1/2}$ and $v_l = (c_{11}/\rho)^{1/2}$ are the phase velocities of shear and longitudinal plane waves, respectively, in the bulk of the isotropic, nonpiezoelectric solid.

5. *Retain the roots in the lower half of the complex plane and determine the corresponding eigenvectors*

For our isotropic, nonpiezoelectric case the retained roots and eigenvectors are

$$b^{(1)} = -i\left\{1 - \left(\frac{v}{v_l}\right)^2\right\}^{1/2} \qquad \boldsymbol{\alpha}^{(1)} = (1, 0, b^{(1)}, 0)$$

$$b^{(2)} = -i\left\{1 - \left(\frac{v}{v_t}\right)^2\right\}^{1/2} \qquad \boldsymbol{\alpha}^{(2)} = (-b^{(2)}, 0, 1, 0)$$

$$\hspace{8cm}(1.35)$$

$$b^{(3)} = -i\left\{1 - \left(\frac{v}{v_t}\right)^2\right\}^{1/2} \qquad \boldsymbol{\alpha}^{(3)} = (0, 1, 0, 0)$$

$$b^{(4)} = -i \qquad\qquad\qquad \boldsymbol{\alpha}^{(4)} = (0, 0, 0, 1)$$

6. *Form a linear combination (1.29) of the partial waves and substitute into the boundary conditions (1.30)*

When the solid is isotropic and nonpiezoelectric (1.30) becomes

$$\begin{pmatrix} c_{11}b^{(1)2} + c_{12} & 2c_{44}b^{(2)} & 0 & 0 \\ 2c_{44}b^{(1)} & c_{44}(1 - b^{(2)2}) & 0 & 0 \\ 0 & 0 & c_{44}b^{(3)} & 0 \\ 0 & 0 & 0 & \epsilon_{11}b^{(4)} - i\epsilon_0 \end{pmatrix} \begin{pmatrix} C_1 \\ C_2 \\ C_3 \\ C_4 \end{pmatrix} = 0$$

$$\hspace{11cm}(1.36)$$

7. *Evaluate the boundary condition determinant noting any decoupling of partial waves*

For the isotropic, nonpiezoelectric case, (1.36) can be separated, and the determinant of the coefficients is zero if any of the following expressions are zero:

$$c_{44}(1 - b^{(2)2})(c_{12} + c_{11}b^{(1)2}) - 4c_{44}^2 b^{(1)}b^{(2)}$$

$$c_{44}b^{(3)} \quad \text{or} \quad (\epsilon_{11}b^{(4)} - i\epsilon_0)$$

This separation corresponds to the uncoupling of components in step 3; that is, the boundary conditions do not recouple the eigenvector components that are uncoupled in the wave equation, and this situation is general for free surface conditions.

8. *If the boundary condition determinant is not zero, select the other values of* v *until it is so*

In our isotropic, nonpiezoelectric case there is one value of $v = v_R$ for which the first expression in step 7 is zero. This value leads to a surface wave solution that is discussed later. In order to have $c_{44}b^{(3)} = 0$, $b^{(3)}$ must be zero or $v = v_t$. This root corresponds to a shear wave polarized parallel to the surface that satisfies the boundary conditions but does not decay with depth and thus does not satisfy the definition of a surface wave. Finally, it is not possible with any choice of v to have $(\epsilon_{11}b^{(4)} - i\epsilon_0)$, that is, $i(\epsilon_{11} + \epsilon_0)$, equal to zero; thus, as should be anticipated for a non-piezoelectric solid, there is no solution that involves the potential.

9. *Evaluate the weighting factors* C *at the surface wave velocity*

Here for the isotropic, nonpiezoelectric substrate two of the weighting factors associated with the surface wave are in the ratio $C_1/C_2 = -(1 - b^{(2)2})/2b^{(1)}$ evaluated at $v = v_R$. The weighting factor C_3 for $v = v_t$ is arbitrary, but the solution is a bulk wave, and the weighting factor C_4 is zero for all values of v.

10. *Substitute values of* C, α, b, *and* v *into general expressions for the displacements and the potential,* (1.29)

The physical characteristics of the surface wave solution for the isotropic, nonpiezoelectric substrate are considered in the next section. Later sections treat examples of solutions of the wave equation for anisotropic and piezoelectric substrates. Examples are also given of the procedural modifications and of the solutions when layers are deposited on the substrate surface.

Solution for Isotropic Substrates. As indicated earlier, the simplest surface wave geometry, the free surface of any isotropic, nonpiezoelectric solid half-space, admits a surface wave solution in which only the sagittal plane displacement components are involved. The sagittal plane is defined in Fig. 1.2. The phase velocity and the group velocity also, because the system is nondispersive, of this so-called Rayleigh wave is obtained by equating to zero the expression obtained in step 7 of the previous section. The phase velocity v_R is then given implicitly by

$$\left\{2 - \left(\frac{v_R}{v_t}\right)^2\right\}^2 = 4\left\{1 - \left(\frac{v_R}{v_l}\right)^2\right\}^{1/2}\left\{1 - \left(\frac{v_R}{v_t}\right)^2\right\}^{1/2} \qquad (1.37)$$

in which v_t and v_l are again the velocities of transverse and longitudinal bulk waves in the material of the substrate. The Rayleigh wave velocity is

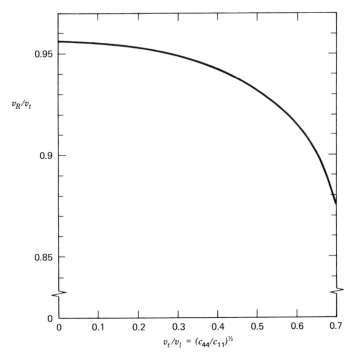

Figure 1.3 Rayleigh wave velocity for isotropic substrates. Here v_t is the velocity of a bulk shear wave and v_l the velocity of a bulk longitudinal wave, Eq. (1.37). Reprinted, with permission, from *Physical Acoustics*, Vol. 9, Academic Press, New York, 1972, p. 49.

plotted in normalized form in Fig. 1.3 for the complete range of values of v_t/v_l allowed for isotropic solids. The plot shows that the surface wave velocity is approximately equal to but always less than the velocity of shear waves in the bulk of the material. Since v_R is less than the velocity of any bulk wave in the solid, there is no coupling with the bulk waves, because the latter cannot satisfy a phase-match condition at any angle of tilt. Coupling between surface waves and bulk waves due to various perturbations of the free surface is discussed in later chapters.

The displacement components of a Rayleigh wave propagating in the x_1 direction are

$$u_1 = C[\exp(kb_1 x_3) - A \exp(kb_2 x_3)] \exp ik(x_1 - v_R t)$$

$$u_3 = -ikb_1 C[\exp(kb_1 x_3) - A^{-1} \exp(kb_2 x_3)] \exp ik(x_1 - v_R t) \quad (1.38)$$

where $b_1 = \{1 - (v_R/v_l)^2\}^{1/2}$, $b_2 = \{1 - (v_R/v_t)^2\}^{1/2}$, and $A = (b_1 b_2)^{1/2}$ are all positive real values, and C is an arbitrary constant depending on the excitation. Because the two square brackets of (1.38) are real, the longitudinal u_1 and vertical u_3 displacement components are in phase quadrature for each value of x_3. The elastic displacement is elliptical, and the polarization precession at the free surface is retrograde. The two curves of Fig. 1.4 show the depth dependence of the factors multiplying the propagation term in (1.38). They show that the displacement amplitudes exist only in a region that extends a few wavelengths from the surface. If the Poynting vector (1.19) is calculated for this Rayleigh wave, it is found to be parallel to x_1 everywhere and to decrease rapidly with depth. Figure 1.5, which shows the relative amplitude of the Poynting vector per unit transverse width, emphasizes the crucial Rayleigh wave property—the wave energy is near the surface.

The material displacements are illustrated further in Fig. 1.6, which shows the distortion at an instant of time of a rectangular grid in a sagittal plane section of the substrate as produced by a Rayleigh wave. The time and x_1 phase quadrature of the displacements are evident along with the

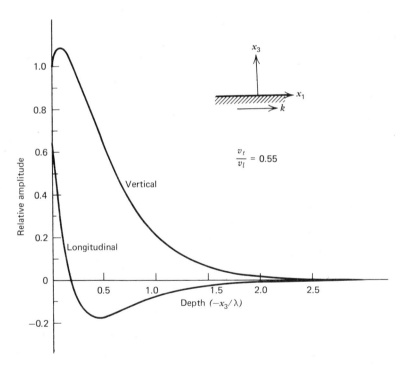

Figure 1.4 Displacement components of a Rayleigh wave on an isotropic substrate, Eq (1.38). Reprinted, with permission, from *Physical Acoustics*, *Vol.* 6, Academic Press, New York, 1970, p. 116.

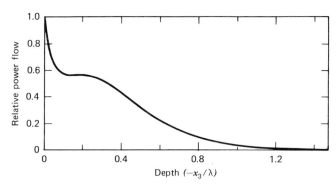

Figure 1.5 Relative power flow per unit area as a function of depth for a Rayleigh wave on an isotropic substrate.

retrograde elliptical displacement of a point on the surface. The displacement amplitudes are greatly exaggerated in the diagram. In practical devices such amplitudes are very small with respect to the wavelength, of the order of 10^{-5} λ.

1.4 Anisotropic Free Surfaces

For surface wave filters it is usually necessary to use single crystals as the propagation medium, sometimes to reduce the high-frequency attenuation characteristic of polycrystalline materials, sometimes to permit

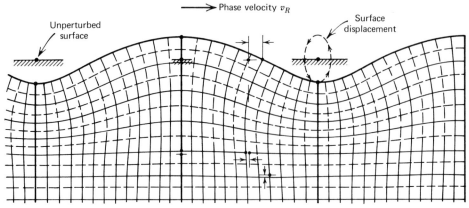

Figure 1.6 Distortion of a square grid in the sagittal plane by a Rayleigh wave. Displacement amplitudes are exaggerated.

piezoelectric effects for electromechanical coupling to the surface waves, and sometimes to introduce specific propagation or intercoupling properties. When the propagation medium is anisotropic, elastic surface waves can still exist. Their dominant properties are the same as the properties of Rayleigh waves outlined in the previous section. The waves are elliptically polarized at each depth and the displacement amplitude decreases with depth; the wave energy is confined to a region close to the surface; the phase velocity is independent of frequency and is of the order of the velocities of the shear waves that propagate in the same direction in the bulk of the same material. However, anisotropy introduces many differences of detail in the form and properties of such waves. For example, in an anisotropic medium the phase velocity depends on the direction of propagation, and the direction of energy flow is not in general parallel to the wave vector. Moreover, the plane of the elliptical polarization of the displacement is not necessarily the sagittal plane, and even when it is the principal axes of the ellipse are not necessarily x_1 and x_3. Furthermore, although the decay with depth of the amplitude of each displacement component in the isotropic case is the sum of simple exponentials, in general the decay with depth of each displacement component in the anisotropic case is the sum of exponentially damped sinusoids. If the substrate is piezoelectric in addition, there is in general an electric potential propagating along with the three components of mechanical displacement, and the velocity of propagation of the wave is dependent somewhat on the electrical conditions at or near the surface.

Although the possible combinations of crystalline substrate, orientation of surface, and direction of propagation are limitless, surface wave filters using single crystals usually have a combination of crystal cut and propagation direction that has relatively high crystalline symmetry. This choice is dictated in large part by a desire to have any "beam" of elastic energy created by an electromechanical transducer propagate parallel to the wave vector, that is, normal to the line of constant phase defined by the transducer.

If phase velocity is plotted as a function of the angle of the propagation vector in the free surface, the curve in general exhibits maxima and minima. The energy flow is parallel to the propagation vector for all extrema of this curve. Some of these extrema are "accidental" in the sense that they depend on the numerical values of the elastic and piezoelectric constants; other extrema are imposed by the crystal symmetry alone. Two symmetry conditions always produce the preceding extrema or "pure-mode axes," but lead to certain decoupling of the various displacement components and the potential from each other in the wave equation (1.14) and the boundary conditions (1.30). Specifically

(a) If the sagittal plane ($x_1 x_3$ plane) is a plane of mirror symmetry of the crystal, x_1 is a pure-mode direction, and the displacement component u_2 is independent of the remaining coupled components u_1, u_3 and φ.

(b) If the sagittal plane is perpendicular to an axis of twofold rotation of the crystal, x_1 is a pure-mode direction, and the coupled displacement components u_1 and u_3 are independent of the other two coupled components u_2 and φ.

Let us now consider three separate examples, the first of which satisfies both of the symmetry conditions (a) and (b), the second only (a), and the third only (b).

Example Satisfying Symmetry Conditions (a) and (b): Silicon. If both of the symmetry conditions (a) and (b) are satisfied simultaneously, the crystal must contain a center of inversion symmetry and thus cannot be piezoelectric. The potential is therefore zero. A typical example is propagation along a crystal axis on a basal plane of a nonpiezoelectric cubic crystal. For this case the wave equation separates in exactly the same manner as illustrated for the isotropic substrate (1.31) and (1.32) of the steps 1, 2, and 3 of the general solution procedure in Section 1.3, except that here $c_{44} \neq (c_{11} - c_{12})/2$. The uncoupled component u_2, (1.33), leads again to a bulk shear wave satisfying the boundary conditions, as in the isotropic case. Here for the cubic substrate the secular equation from (1.32) is again biquartic, but, because $c_{44} \neq (c_{11} - c_{12})/2$, the values of the decay constants b of steps 4 and 5 are not necessarily on the negative imaginary axis. As a specific illustration, if the cubic material is silicon, the search procedure steps 5 to 9, yields a surface wave solution with a phase velocity of 4917 m/sec. For this wave the decay constants are $b^{(1)} = -b^{(2)*} = -0.481 - i0.456$ with the result that each term in the displacement amplitude has an oscillatory factor associated with the real part of b as well as an exponentially decaying factor associated with the imaginary part. The variation of displacement with depth for propagation along a [100] axis of a (001) plane of silicon is shown in Fig. 1.7. Here the general form is similar to the isotropic case Fig. 1.4, but note that the components change sign periodically. For other materials the ratios of the real to the imaginary parts of the roots b are different, and thus details of the decay curves are also different.

It should be noted in passing that if the propagation is on the basal plane of a cubic crystal such as in the previous silicon example, but the

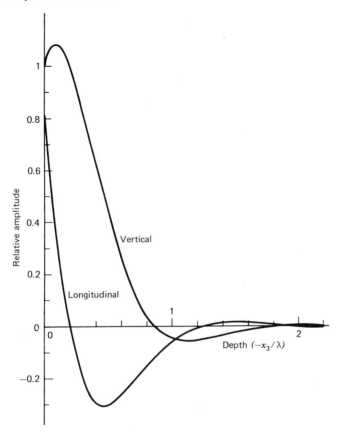

Figure 1.7 Displacement components as a function of depth for a surface wave propagating along a cubic axis on the basal plane of silicon. The actual displacements in meters are $3.51 \times 10^{-6}\,(P/\omega)$ times the displacements shown, where P is the power in the wave per unit length in the x_2 direction.

propagation vector is at an angle to the cubic axis, neither of the symmetry conditions (a) and (b) is satisfied. All three displacement components are present in the solution, and the wave equation does not separate. The velocity depends on the angle between the propagation vector and the crystalline axis. For silicon this dependence is small for small angles ($<1\%$ velocity change for $\pm 20°$) but, as is shown later, the variation of phase velocity with angle can be large for many crystals and is important in device design.

Example Satisfying Symmetry (a): YZ LiNbO$_3$.   Let us turn now from the preceding cubic example, which satisfied both symmetry conditions (a) and (b), to an example that satisfies condition (a) only; that is, the sagittal plane is a plane of mirror symmetry. This is an important case because many surface wave filters are fabricated with a crystalline geometry that falls into this category, namely, propagation along the Z axis of the XZ plane of the strongly piezoelectric, low-loss crystal lithium niobate (LiNbO$_3$ class 3 m). For this so-called YZ geometry in lithium niobate the first symbol Y is used because the crystal is Y cut; that is, the XZ plane is the free surface. The second symbol Z indicates the direction of propagation, as indicated in the insert of Fig. 1.8. The wave equation separates because $\Gamma_{12} = \Gamma_{23} = \Gamma_{24} = 0$ in (1.25), and thus there are two separate problems beginning in step 3 of the general solution procedure of Section 1.3. Again the decoupled part u_2 alone leads to a wave solution satisfying the boundary condition. This is again a bulk wave polarized perpendicular to the sagittal plane independent of the piezoelectric nature of the substrate. However, this bulk wave differs from the previous examples in that it has a propagation vector (phase velocity) tilted at an angle down from the surface, but a Poynting vector parallel to the surface (in the x_1 direction).

The other solution for the YZ geometry is the surface wave. It contains the potential and the two displacement components u_1 and u_3. The presence of piezoelectricity, and hence the potential, increases the velocity of this Rayleigh-type wave above the value it would have if the piezoelectric tensor were null, and thus this solution is often called a *stiffened Rayleigh wave*. The velocity and the detailed form of the solution depend on the electrical boundary conditions imposed at the mechanically free surface. If the surface is also electrically free, so that the permittivity for $x_3 > 0$ in Fig. 1.2 is ϵ_0 and D_3 is continuous, the general solution procedure gives a velocity of 3485 m/sec for LiNbO$_3$. The potential and displacement amplitude are shown by the solid curves of Fig. 1.8. The variation of displacement amplitude with depth is similar to that of the isotropic case, as shown in Fig. 1.4, and the potential, shown in Fig. 1.9, also decays to zero within a few wavelengths of the surface.

The power per unit width carried in the surface wave is found by integration of the Poynting vector (1.19) across the vertical extent of the wave

$$P_i = -\tfrac{1}{2} \operatorname{Re} \left\{ \int_{-\infty}^{0} T_{ij} \dot{u}_j^* \, dx_3 - i\omega \int_{-\infty}^{\infty} \varphi D_i \, dx_3 \right\}, \qquad i = 1, 2 \quad (1.39)$$

For the pure-mode geometry involved here, YZ LiNbO$_3$, only the component P_1 is nonzero, which indicates the energy flow is parallel to the propagation vector. This power per unit width is the normalization used in the curves of Figs. 1.8 and 1.9.

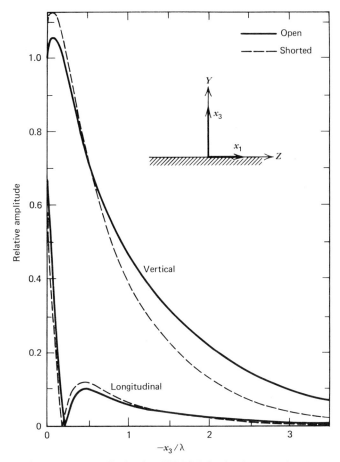

Figure 1.8 Displacement amplitudes for YZ LiNbO$_3$ for free and for shorted electrical boundary conditions. The actual displacements are 2.62×10^{-6} $(P/\omega)^{1/2}$ times the values shown (P defined in Fig. 1.7).

If the electrical boundary conditions are the shorted conditions, as would be produced by a thin, highly conducting layer placed on the surface, the potential must be zero for $x_3 \geq 0$, but the mechanical boundary conditions remain unchanged. The surface wave propagation velocity is decreased from 3485 to 3405 m/sec by the change from free to shorted electrical conditions at the surface, and the displacement and potential distributions are changed to the values given by the broken curves of Figs. 1.8 and 1.9. It is seen that the mechanical displacements are altered little, but the potential is greatly reduced, to zero at the surface of course, but also by a factor of about 4 in the region immediately below the surface.

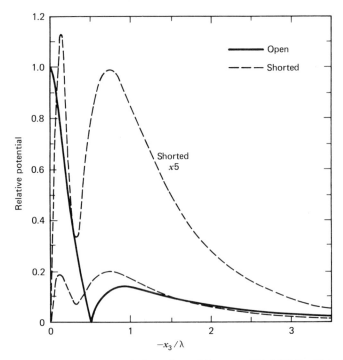

Figure 1.9 Potential for open and shorted conditions on YZ LiNbO$_3$. Potential scale should be multiplied by $1.45 \times 10^4 \, (P/\omega)^{1/2}$ volts.

The change in the surface wave solution produced by the change in electrical boundary condition from free to short circuit is a measure of the efficiency with which a surface wave propagating on a piezoelectric interacts with electrodes placed on the surface. The interaction efficiency is an important factor in the choice of substrate material and propagation geometry for practical surface wave devices, and it is desirable to represent it by a single parameter that can be easily calculated and measured. The parameter used is the fractional change in the phase velocity of a surface wave (propagating in a given direction on a given surface of a given crystal) produced by a change in the electrical boundary condition from free to short circuit.

$$\frac{\Delta v}{v} = \frac{v_{\text{short}} - v}{v} \tag{1.40}$$

With plane bulk waves in piezoelectric solids the phase velocity can be determined through the use of *stiffened elastic constants*, which are of the form $c_{ij}(1 + K_{ij}^2)$, where K_{ij}^2 is an electromechanical coupling factor dimensionally of the form $e^2/c\epsilon$. The appropriate constants depend on the direction of propagation and the polarization. The fractional change of elastic wave velocity due to the piezoelectricity is given by $\Delta v/v = -K^2/2$ for the appropriate K. An example is given in (1.44). By analogy with the bulk wave case it has become common to define an effective electromechanical coupling factor for Rayleigh-type surface waves by

$$K^2 = -2\frac{\Delta v}{v} \qquad (1.41)$$

where $\Delta v/v$ is the fractional change of velocity produced by shorting the surface potential as defined in (1.40). The coupling factor depends on the substrate material and propagation geometry. It is shown later that such device characteristics as insertion loss, transducer efficiency, and bandwidth can often be expressed as an explicit function of the value of the coupling factor. One of the highest values obtainable for pure-mode surface wave propagation on a substrate suitable for high-frequency operation is provided by YZ LiNbO$_3$, where

$$K^2 = -2\left(\frac{3405 - 3485}{3485}\right) = 0.046$$

Table 1.4 lists the surface wave velocities and $\Delta v/v$ values for the stiffened Rayleigh mode on YZ LiNbO$_3$ and also for a few other crystal orientations. The BGO and GaAs geometries have stiffened Rayleigh mode propagation with the sagittal plane displacement components coupled to the electric potential. The X axis on the ST cut of quartz (surface normal in the YZ plane at $132.75°$ to the Z axis) is also a pure-mode axis with the energy flow parallel to the wave vector, but this

Table 1.4 Rayleigh Waves on Piezoelectric Crystals[a]

Substrate	Cut	Propagation Direction	Phase Velocity, m/sec	$-\dfrac{\Delta v}{v}$ (Eq. 1.40) $\times 10^3$	β (Eq. 1.71)	Attenuation, dB/cm at 1 GHz
LiNbO$_3$	Y	X	3488	24	0.54	2.6
BGO	001	110	1681	6.8	0.15	8.6
GaAs	110	X	2822	0.08	0.27	13.4
Quartz	ST	X	3158	0.58	-0.19	8.2

[a] Data from Slobodnick, *IEEE Trans.*, **SU 20**, p. 315.

case satisfies neither symmetry condition (a) nor (b), and all three components of displacement as well as the electric potential are present. The data given in the last two columns of Table 1.4 are explained in later sections of this chapter.

Design of most surface wave filters is based on a pure Rayleigh type wave as the propagating mode, but diffraction considerations and permissible misalignment tolerances require knowledge of propagation conditions for wave vectors oriented at an angle to the design pure-mode direction. For example, the curve of Fig. 1.10 shows the angular variation of the phase velocity for propagation on the XZ plane near the much-used YZ design direction of LiNbO$_3$. A useful polar plot exhibits the reciprocal of the phase velocity as a function of angle of propagation. Such a *slowness* curve is important because the direction of energy flow (1.39) is perpendicular to it. For Y-cut LiNbO$_3$ the slowness curve near

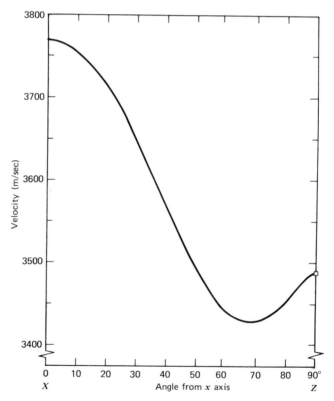

Figure 1.10 Surface-wave velocity on the XZ plane of LiNbO$_3$ for free surface conditions. Here □ indicates YZ pure-mode propagation.

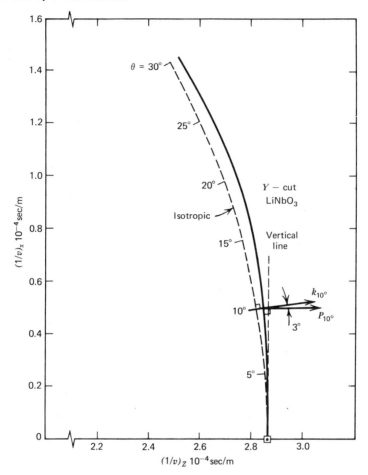

Figure 1.11 Slowness curve for Y-cut LiNbO$_3$ for propagation near Z axis. Also shown are a vertical line and a circular arc (isotropic case).

the Z axis is shown by the solid curve of Fig. 1.11. When, for instance, the wave vector is $10°$ from the Z axis, the Poynting vector makes an angle of some $3°$ with respect to the wave vector. The particular slowness curve shown is almost linear and perpendicular to the Z axis for a rather wide range of angles near the pure-mode axis, and this characteristic leads to unusual diffraction effects. For example, it is shown in Section 1.6 that there is a large degree of autocollimation, and the radiation pattern produced by a transducer of a given effective aperture on YZ LiNbO$_3$ retains its beamlike, or Fresnel region, properties for distances many wavelengths further than would result from the same transducer on an isotropic medium.

Example Satisfying Symmetry (b): Bleustein–Gulyaev Wave. Earlier in this section we listed certain symmetry conditions and discussed examples of anisotropic surface wave propagation along or near crystalline axes that satisfy both the symmetry conditions (a) and (b) and then (a) alone. Now we turn to an example that satisfies condition (b) alone; that is, we have a piezoelectric crystal and a propagation geometry for which the sagittal plane is perpendicular to a crystalline axis of twofold rotation. For all such cases $\Gamma_{12} = \Gamma_{14} = \Gamma_{34} = 0$, and the wave equation (1.25) in the transformed coordinates separates at steps 2 and 3 of the general solution procedure of Section 1.3. The part with u_1 and u_3 intercoupled leads to a pure-mode surface wave of the Rayleigh-type that propagates independently of the piezoelectric properties of the substrate. It is the other part of the solution that is of concern here, the part containing the transverse component of displacement u_2 and the potential φ.

In the particular example of YX geometry on the shorted surface of a 6 mm crystal such as ZnO or CdS, the algebra for the later steps of the general procedure can be carried out explicitly for this stiffened transversely polarized surface wave. Such algebra gives

$$u_2 = C \exp{(kK_1^2 x_3)} \exp{ik(x_1 - vt)} \tag{1.42}$$

$$\varphi = C \frac{e_{15}}{\epsilon_{11}} (\exp{kx_3} - \exp{kK_1^2 x_3}) \exp{ik(x - vt)}$$

with a phase velocity

$$v = \bar{v}_t (1 - K_1^4)^{1/2} \tag{1.43}$$

where $\bar{v}_t = \{c_{44}(1 + K^2)/\rho\}^{1/2}$ is the stiffened velocity of a transversely polarized bulk wave,

$$K^2 = \frac{e_{15}^2}{\epsilon_{11} c_{44}} \tag{1.44}$$

is the electromechanical coupling factor for transverse bulk waves in this geometry, and

$$K_1^2 = \frac{e_{15}^2}{\epsilon_{11} c_{44}(1 + K^2)} \tag{1.45}$$

The factor K_1^2 is much less than unity for all crystals, and thus the velocity of propagation for this so-called Bleustein–Gulyaev mode is only slightly less than that of bulk shear waves of the same polarization propagating in the same direction. Similarly, again because $K_1^2 \ll 1$, the penetration of the

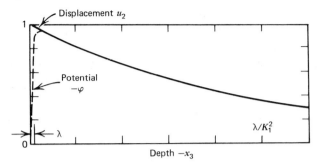

Figure 1.12 Displacement and potential profiles for a Bleustein–Gulyaev wave with a shorted surface on a 6 mm crystal. Here K_1^2 as defined in Eq. (1.45) is approximately 0.02.

potential and of the displacement is quite large relative to the wavelength, as indicated by Fig. 1.12.

If the surface is electrically free rather than shorted in the preceding example, the phase velocity is

$$v = \bar{v}_t \left\{ 1 - K_1^4 \left(\frac{\epsilon_0}{\epsilon_0 + \epsilon_{11}} \right)^2 \right\}^{1/2} \tag{1.46}$$

Because for most piezoelectrics $\epsilon_{11} \gg \epsilon_0$ this velocity is much closer to the shear value $\bar{v}_t$ than for the shorted case. Also the penetration of the disturbance is much deeper, and thus the wave resembles more closely a slightly perturbed bulk shear wave satisfying the surface boundary conditions. For either open or shorted conditions the surface wave degenerates continuously into the transverse bulk waves as the piezoelectric coupling constant e_{15} approaches zero.

The general character of the type of wave encountered on the [110] direction of a ($\bar{1}$10) plane of a piezoelectric cubic crystal, another geometry satisfying symmetry condition (b), is similar to that given by (1.42) to (1.46), but the expressions for K and v are somewhat more complicated. The Bleustein–Gulyaev wave offers some possibilities in device design where a transversely polarized surface wave is desired or where a somewhat deeper penetration than that of a Rayleigh-type wave is required.

1.5 Thin Layers and Perturbations

In some devices the surface or part of it is covered by a thin layer instead of being mechanically free as in the previous examples. This structure is encountered in certain dispersive delay lines where the characteristic dimension furnished by the layer thickness leads to dispersion that can provide, for example, a time delay varying linearly with frequency. Thin layers are found in a type of transducer structure having the coupling electrodes embedded in a piezoelectric layer for excitation of surface waves on a nonpiezoelectric substrate, and, most importantly, in the analysis of the perturbations produced by the loading effects of deposited electrode structures.

Wave Equation and Boundary Conditions.   In the general problem of elastic wave propagation in thin layers there is a piezoelectric, anisotropic layer of a certain crystalline orientation and thickness h on a piezoelectric, anisotropic substrate of some other crystalline orientation. The method of solution can be of the same form as in Sections 1.2 and 1.3, but the numerical complexity at each step is increased greatly. There are two different wave equations (1.14): one is for the substrate material, from which four partial waves are obtained with decay constants b lying in the lower half of the complex plane, and a second wave equation corresponds to the layer material, from which eight partial waves are obtained. Eight are obtained because the layer is finite and none of the values of b can be discarded. Similarly, if the form of potential used in (1.23) is again used above the free surface at $x_3 = h$, there are 12 boundary conditions to be satisfied by two linear combinations of the partial waves, one combination for the layer and one for the substrate. These boundary conditions are: the continuity of the stresses T_{3i} at the substrate-layer interface $x_3 = 0$ and the top surface $x_3 = h$ (six conditions), the continuity of the displacements u_i at the interface (three conditions), and three electric conditions such as the continuity of D_3 at $x_3 = 0$ and $x_3 = h$ and the continuity of φ at the interface. The solution can again be obtained by choosing successive values of the phase velocity until the boundary condition determinant (1.30), now 12×12, becomes zero. The wave velocity depends on the layer thickness as well as on the crystal orientation. Moreover, for a given layer thickness there can be several different solutions or modes at different velocities.

As found for the unlayered substrate, the complexity of the problem is greatly reduced if the propagation geometry satisfies certain symmetry restrictions. In particular, if for both materials, substrate and layer, the sagittal plane is a plane of reflection symmetry, the modes are of two types. In one type there is no potential, and there are only transverse displacements. These so-called Love modes are generalizations of the shear wave satisfying the boundary conditions of the substrate without layer. In the other type there are sagittal plane displacements and an accompanying potential if either substrate or layer is piezoelectric; such modes are generalizations of the stiffened Rayleigh wave. On the other hand, if for both materials the sagittal plane is perpendicular to planes of twofold rotation, there is again separation into two types of modes: stiffened Love modes that involve transverse mechanical displacements and the potential as generalizations of the Bleustein–Gulyaev wave, and modes involving sagittal mechanical displacements only as generalizations of the uncoupled Rayleigh modes in a piezoelectric substrate satisfying symmetry (b).

Most characteristics of waves propagating in a layered medium can be illustrated by consideration of the simplest case, an isotropic, non-piezoelectric layer on an isotropic, nonpiezoelectric substrate. Here the wave equation separates into two independent parts. There is a set of modes, Rayleigh modes, involving sagittal plane displacements u_1 and u_3, and a second set, Love modes, involving the transverse displacement u_2.

Isotropic Love Modes. Turning first to the simpler set of isotropic layer modes, the Love modes, most of the algebra involved in the general solution procedure can be carried out explicitly. Solutions of this type exist only if the bulk shear wave velocity of the layer material $\hat{v}_t$ is less than that of the substrate material v_t. When this condition is met, the dependence of the phase velocity on the relative layer thickness kh is given by the dispersion relation

$$\tan \hat{b}kh = \frac{rb}{\hat{b}} \tag{1.47}$$

in which $\hat{b} = [(v/\hat{v}_t)^2 - 1]^{1/2}$, $b = [1 - (v/v_t)^2]^{1/2}$, and $r = c_{44}/\hat{c}_{44}$, where c_{44} and $\hat{c}_{44}$ are elastic constants of the substrate and layer, respectively. The phase velocity of the mode satisfies $v_t > v > \hat{v}_t$. A graph of this dispersion relation for gold on fused quartz is shown in Fig. 1.13. Introduction of a characteristic dimension, the layer thickness, causes the phase velocity to depend on the frequency of excitation, the group velocity to differ from the phase velocity, and the appearance of multiple modes. The dispersion curve for each mode starts at the substrate shear velocity for some specified cutoff value of kh and becomes asymptotic to the layer shear velocity for large values of kh. As $kh \to 0$, the first or all-pass Love mode degenerates into the transverse bulk shear wave that satisfies free surface boundary conditions, as discussed in Section 1.3, step 8.

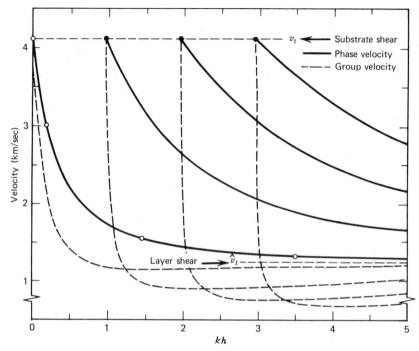

Figure 1.13 Phase velocity of the Love wave for a gold layer on a fused quartz substrate. Displacement profiles for circled points are given in Fig. 1.14. Reprinted, with permission, from *Physical Acoustics*, Vol. 9, Academic Press, New York, 1972, p. 68.

The Love mode displacements are given by

$$u_2 = C \exp (bkx_3) \exp [ik(x_1 - vt)] \tag{1.48}$$

in the substrate, and

$$\hat{u}_2 = C \left[\frac{\cos \hat{b}k(h - x_3)}{\cos \hat{b}kh} \right] \exp [ik(x_1 - vt)] \tag{1.49}$$

in the layer. These displacements are shown for the first mode and for several different values of kh in Fig. 1.14. The decay into the substrate is a simple exponential function of depth, and as kh is increased more of the energy is concentrated within the layer. The same statements are true for the higher modes, but in addition there is more sinusoidal structure within the layer for each successive mode.

Isotropic Rayleigh Modes. The other set of modes for isotropic layer and substrate have sagittal plane displacements only, and thus can be

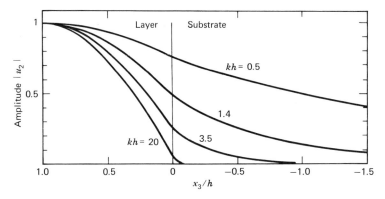

Figure 1.14 Displacement u_2 for the first Love mode of Fig. 1.13 for different relative layer thicknesses. Reprinted, with permission, from *Physical Acoustics, Vol.* 9, Academic Press, New York, 1972, p. 69.

labeled as Rayleigh modes. Such modes exist for all combinations of layer and substrate materials, but we will consider their characteristics for only the two major cases: The shear wave velocity in the layer is appreciably greater than in the substrate and it is appreciably smaller. The several anomalies that occur when these two velocities are approximately equal are ignored here. If the layer shearwave velocity is appreciably greater than the substrate shear wave velocity, the layer is said to *stiffen* the substrate, whereas if $\hat{v}_t < v_t$ the layer is said to *load* the substrate. Little of the algebra in the general procedure can be done explicitly for the Rayleigh modes even when the layer and substrate are isotropic, and although the perturbation techniques discussed later are useful for determining the changes produced by very thin layers, the characteristics of propagation in layers of thickness appreciable with respect to the wavelength are determined numerically.

For the case in which the layer stiffens the substrate, $\hat{v}_t > v_t$, there is only one mode with real value of k. It exists only for a limited range of kh as indicated for an isotropic silicon layer on an isotropic ZnO substrate in Fig. 1.15. Here the dispersion curve starts for $kh = 0$, at of course the Rayleigh velocity of a free surface of the substrate material, and it reaches a limit for confined propagation when it rises to the shear wave velocity of the substrate material. With this and higher velocities the Rayleigh type mode can phase match and couple to a bulk shear wave. In Fig. 1.16 the relative amplitudes of the mechanical displacements u_3 and u_1 corresponding to points a and b of the dispersion curve Fig. 1.15 are plotted. For point a the displacement components are in phase quadrature and of a distribution similar to that for a Rayleigh wave on a free

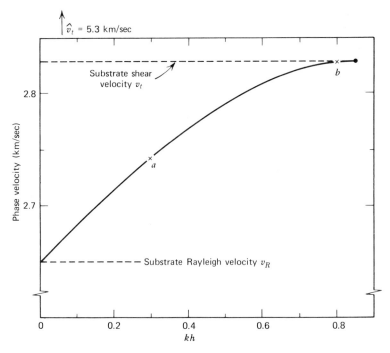

Figure 1.15 Phase velocity of isotropic Rayleigh-type mode when layer stiffens substrate, here ZnO on silicon. Displacement profiles for points a and b are shown in Fig. 1.16.

surface (compare with Fig. 1.4). However, for point b near cutoff the penetration of the u_3 component becomes large and the wave attains the character of a sagittally polarized bulk shear wave slightly perturbed at and near the layer.

We now turn to the case in which the layer loads the substrate, $\hat{v}_t < v_t$. There are many independent Rayleigh type modes, as illustrated in Fig. 1.17 for an isotropic gold layer on a fused quartz substrate. The mode labeled R_1 degenerates into the simple Rayleigh mode on the free surface of the substrate material when the relative layer thickness kh, vanishes. For increasing values of kh the phase velocity of this first mode decreases, crosses the layer shear velocity, and becomes asymptotic to the velocity of a Rayleigh wave on the free surface of an infinitely deep substrate made of the layer material. The corresponding transition in the displacement distribution is illustrated in Fig. 1.18, which shows the relative amplitude of the vertical displacement u_3 as a function of depth for five different values of kh. At small kh most of the mechanical energy is carried in the substrate, and the displacement is characteristic of a

Rayleigh wave on a fused quartz free surface. For large values of kh the energy of this mode propagates in the layer close to the free surface, and the displacement becomes that of a simple Rayleigh wave on gold. The evolution of the longitudinal displacements corresponds to that of the vertical.

Each of the higher Rayleigh type modes for this *slow on fast* combination has a minimum value of kh below which solutions with real k are not allowed, and at this value of kh the phase velocity becomes that of a bulk shear wave in the substrate material. For large values of kh the phase velocity of each higher mode becomes asymptotic to the bulk shear velocity of the layer material. Very close to cutoff the displacements are those of a sagitally polarized bulk shear wave, that is, u_3 existing deep into the substrate, perturbed in and near the layer. In the other limit, for large kh the displacement distributions approach those of sagittal plane

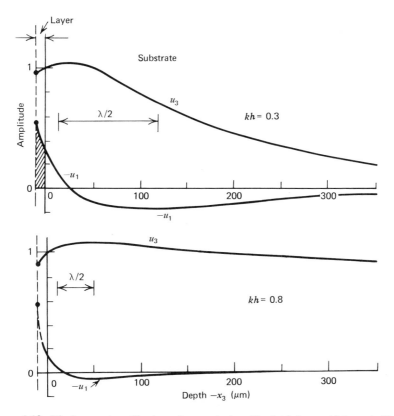

Figure 1.16 Displacement profiles for points marked on Fig. 1.15. Layer thickness is 10 μ.

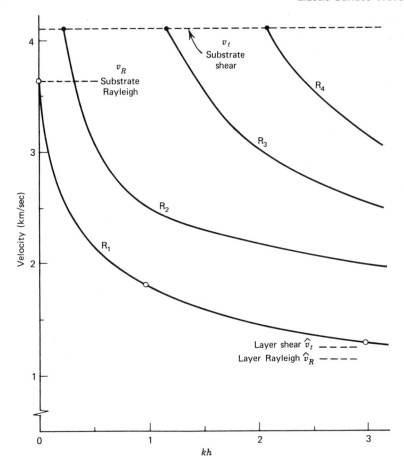

Figure 1.17 Phase velocity of Rayleigh-type modes when layer loads substrate, here gold on fused quartz. Displacement profiles for circled points are shown in Fig. 1.18. Reprinted, with permission, from *Physical Acoustics*, Vol. 9, Academic Press, New York, 1972, p. 60.

plate modes in the layer material perturbed by the presence of the substrate. The amount of structure in the displacement distribution within the layer increases with the mode number.

Surface Perturbations. Frequently in surface wave filters the propagating medium is only slightly perturbed from some known simpler case. For example, placing thin metal electrodes on a free surface of a piezoelectric only perturbs the boundary conditions for surface waves, and thus the dominant characteristics of the surface wave are not radically changed (see Fig. 1.9). Similarly, if the layer changes the mechanical boundary conditions, the changes in the solution are small if the layer is thin (see Figs. 1.13 to 1.18 for small values of kh). It is thus useful to have a perturbation theory that allows the calculation of small changes produced in known solutions by small changes in the boundary conditions. We consider here only the perturbation of the phase velocity.

Assume that in the prototype free surface geometry of Fig. 1.2, the surface wave solution is known. Each of the space dependent quantities, such as a displacement component or the potential, is of the form $f(x_3) \exp[-i(kx_1 - \omega t)]$ for an $\exp(i\omega t)$ time dependence, with $k = \omega/v$ and the appropriate $f(x_3)$ known. Assume now that the perturbed solution due to the perturbation of the boundary is of the same form, $f'(x_3) \exp(-i(k'x_1 - \omega t))$, where the primes refer to perturbed quantities. Thus the unperturbed vertical displacement and potential are

$$u_3 = \bar{u}_3(x_3) \exp[-i(kx_1 - \omega t)] \qquad \text{and} \qquad \varphi = \bar{\varphi}(x_3) \exp[-i(kx_1 - \omega t)]$$

whereas the corresponding perturbed values are

$$u_3' = \bar{u}_3'(x_3) \exp[-i(k'x_1 - \omega t)] \qquad \text{and} \qquad \varphi = \bar{\varphi}'(x_3) \exp[-i(k'x_1 - \omega t)]$$

The perturbed boundary conditions are assumed to impose some extra constraint on the mechanical quantities (displacement, stress, and strain) on the plane $x_3 = 0$, as shown in Fig. 1.19, and some extra constraint on

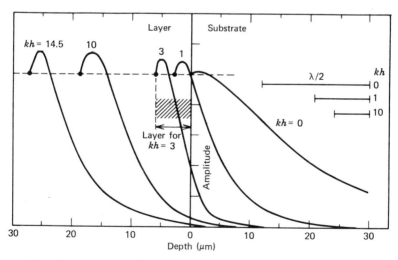

Figure 1.18 Displacement profiles of vertical component for first Rayleigh mode of Fig. 1.17. Dots indicate position of free surface of layer and $f = 100$ MHz.

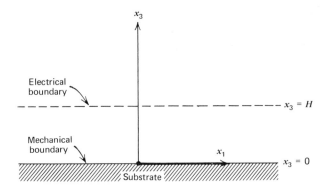

Figure 1.19 Electrical and mechanical boundary condition planes for application of surface wave perturbation theory, Eq. (1.50).

the electrical quantities (potential and electric displacement) on a plane $x_3 = H$ at or above the surface.

The change in wave vector is related to the perturbed and unperturbed solutions by

$$k' - k = \frac{-\omega}{4P_1} [-\bar{T}'_{i3}(0)\bar{u}^*_i(0) + \bar{u}'_i(0)\bar{T}^*_{i3}(0)$$

$$+ \bar{\varphi}'(H)\bar{D}^*_3(H) - \bar{D}'_3(H)\bar{\varphi}^*(H)] \quad (1.50)$$

where the asterisks denote complex conjugates and P_1 is the power flow in the x_1 direction per unit width in the x_2 direction. Because the unperturbed, unprimed quantities are known, if the perturbed quantities can be determined from the perturbed mechanical and electrical boundary conditions, the change in wave vector or velocity can be evaluated from this expression. We will consider only two examples of this approach, one involving only the mechanical terms in (1.50), and the other involving only the electrical terms.

Mechanical Perturbation by a Thin Isotropic Layer. Consider that the Rayleigh solution for the substrate of Fig. 1.20 in the absence of the layer is known, and that although this substrate may be piezoelectric as well as anisotropic the electrical conditions remain unaltered by the layer. The problem is to determine the change in velocity produced by a thin isotropic, nonpiezoelectric layer deposited on the previously free surface, in effect to determine the slope at $kh = 0$ of the dispersion curve for the first mode as in, say, Fig. 1.17.

In the unperturbed case the surface is free and $\bar{T}_{i3}(0) = 0$; thus (1.50) reduces to

$$k' - k = \frac{\omega}{4P_1} \bar{T}'_{i3}(0)\bar{u}_i^*(0) \qquad (1.51)$$

and it is necessary to relate the perturbed stresses at $x_3 = 0$ to the unperturbed displacements on the same plane. If the displacement components in the layer are expanded in a power series

$$u_i = [u_i^{(0)} + u_i^{(1)}(h - x_3) + u_i^{(2)}(h - x_3)^2 + \ldots]e^{-ik'x_1} \qquad 0 \le x_3 \le h \quad (1.52)$$

and substituted into the isotropic form of the wave equation (1.14) and Hooke's law (1.9) all evaluated at the free surface $x_3 = h$, the resulting six algebraic equations can be truncated at the second order in the expansion coefficients and used to express each first and second-order coefficient $u_i^{(1)}$ and $u_i^{(2)}$ in terms of the zero order coefficients $u_j^{(0)}$. Now power series (1.52) is used again in Hooke's law (1.9) to determine the stress at any depth in the layer and in particular at the interface $x_3 = 0$:

$$\bar{T}'_{13}(0) = -h\left(k^2 \frac{c_{11}^2 - c_{12}^2}{c_{11}} - \rho\omega^2\right)u_1^{(0)}$$

$$\bar{T}'_{23}(0) = -h(k^2 c_{44} - \rho\omega^2)u_2^{(0)} \qquad (1.53)$$

$$\bar{T}'_{33}(0) = h\rho\omega^2 u_3^{(0)}$$

The c's and ρ refer to the layer material, and it has been assumed that for calculating the perturbation $k' = k$. Now if $h = 0$, we have the unperturbed surface and from (1.52) $u_i^{(0)}$ is the surface displacement in the absence of the layer $\bar{u}_i(0)$. Equation (1.53), which expresses the stress on the interface in the presence of the layer in terms of the unperturbed displacements, can be substituted into (1.51) to give the fractional

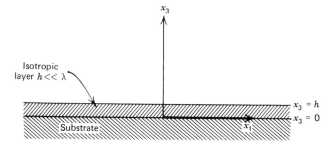

Figure 1.20 Geometry for surface wave perturbation by a thin, isotropic, nonpiezoelectric layer.

change in velocity caused by the thin isotropic layer:

$$\frac{\Delta v}{v} = \frac{v' - v}{v} = -\frac{k' - k}{k} = \frac{\omega}{4P_1} kh\left[\left(\frac{c_{11}^2 - c_{12}^2}{c_{11}} - \rho v^2\right)|\bar{u}_1(0)|^2\right.$$
$$\left. + (c_{44} - \rho v^2)|\bar{u}_2(0)|^2 - \rho v^2|\bar{u}_3(0)|^2\right] \quad (1.54)$$

For example, with a YZ LiNbO$_3$ substrate, $v = 3488$ m/sec, $u_2(0) = 0$, and from Fig. 1.8 $|u_1(0)|^2 \omega/P_1 = 3.16 \times 10^{-12}$ (joules/m^3)$^{-1}$ and $|u_3(0)|^2 \omega/P_1 = 6.86 \times 10^{-12}$. It is seen from (1.54) most layers will have a negative value of $\Delta v/v$, a decrease in velocity due to the "mass loading" ρv^2 terms. However for very stiff layer materials with shear velocity much larger than v, the term $(c_{11}^2 - c_{12}^2)/c_{11} = 2c_{44}[1 + (c_{12}/c_{22})] \cong 2c_{44}$ can dominate and give positive values of $\Delta v/v$ (see Fig. 1.15).

Electrical Boundary Perturbation. As a second example of a perturbation calculation let us assume that the perturbation is the imposition of some electrical condition on the plane $x_3 = H$, Fig. 1.19, and that this condition leaves the stress field in the piezoelectric substrate unaffected. In this case (1.50) reduces to

$$k' - k = \frac{-\omega}{4P_1}[\bar{\varphi}'(H)\bar{D}_3^*(H) - \bar{D}_3'(H)\varphi^*(H)] \quad (1.55)$$

and relations between the perturbed electrical quantities φ' and D_3' and the known unperturbed φ and D_3 on the plane $x_3 = H$ are needed.

Substituting the constitutive relation (1.16) into $\nabla \cdot \mathbf{D} = 0$ once for the unperturbed potential φ in the substrate, once for the perturbed potential, and subtracting the two resulting equations cancels the stress terms and gives

$$\epsilon_{ij}\frac{\partial^2 \psi}{\partial x_i \, \partial x_j} = 0, \qquad x_3 \leq 0 \quad (1.56)$$

where $\psi = \varphi' - \varphi$ and ϵ_{ij} is the permittivity at constant stress.

In calculating the perturbation we again assume that all quantities have a propagation term e^{ikx_1}, so that the solution of (1.56), which vanishes as $x_3 \to -\infty$, is

$$\bar{\psi}(x_3) = A e^{mx_3} \quad (1.57)$$

with $m = k[(\epsilon_p + i\epsilon_{13})/\epsilon_{33}]$ and $\epsilon_p = (\epsilon_{11}\epsilon_{33} - \epsilon_{13}^2)^{1/2}$. From (1.57) the perturbed electrical quantities at the substrate surface are

$$\bar{\varphi}'(0) = \bar{\varphi}(0) + \bar{\psi}(0) = \varphi(0) + A$$
$$\bar{D}_3'(0) = \bar{D}_3(0) - \epsilon_{3j}\frac{\partial \psi}{\partial x_j}\bigg|_{x_3=0} = \bar{D}_3(0) - k\epsilon_p A \quad (1.58)$$

The latter comes from (1.16) and (1.57) with the constant A as yet undetermined.

In the region $0 < x_3 < H$ of Fig. 1.19 the perturbed potential must satisfy

$$\frac{d^2 \bar{\varphi}'}{dx_3^2} - k^2 \bar{\varphi}' = 0 \tag{1.59}$$

so that

$$\bar{\varphi}'(x_3) = B e^{kx_3} + C e^{-kx_3}$$
$$\bar{D}_3'(x_3) = -\epsilon_0 k (B e^{kx_3} - C e^{-kx_3}) \tag{1.60}$$

Matching $\bar{\varphi}'(0)$ and $\bar{D}'(0)$ from (1.60) with the corresponding quantities from (1.58) eliminates the constants A and C to give

$$\bar{\varphi}'(H) = B[e^{kH} - r e^{-kH}] + \bar{\varphi}(0) e^{-kH}$$
$$\bar{D}_3'(H) = -B \epsilon_0 k[e^{kH} + r e^{-kH}] + \epsilon_0 k \bar{\varphi}(0) e^{-kH} \tag{1.61}$$

where $r \equiv (\epsilon_p - \epsilon_0)/(\epsilon_p + \epsilon_0)$ and B is determined by the electrical impedance at $x_3 = H$.

For example, if the plane $x_3 = H$ in Fig. 1.19 is highly conducting, $\bar{\varphi}'(H) = 0$ and

$$B = \frac{-\bar{\varphi}(0) \epsilon^{-kH}}{e^{kH} - r e^{-kH}}$$

In particular if the short circuit is at the substrate surface, the perturbation formula (1.55) then gives

$$\frac{\Delta v}{v} = -(\epsilon_0 + \epsilon_p) |\bar{\varphi}(0)|^2 \frac{\omega}{4 P_1} \tag{1.62}$$

For a YZ LiNbO$_3$ substrate the quantity $|\bar{\varphi}(0)|^2 \omega/4P_1$ can be obtained from Fig. 1.9, and if $\epsilon_p^T = 50.2$, (1.62) gives $\Delta v/v = -0.024$ (see also Table 1.4).

1.6 Diffraction and Attenuation

Because of size restrictions and impedance requirements surface wave transducers have a limited dimension transverse to the direction of the excited beam. This dimension, which determines the width of the radiated beam, is typically 10 to 100 wavelengths in magnitude. To first order with simple interdigital transducers, there is two-dimensional diffraction analogous to the diffraction encountered in optics when a plane wave illuminates a long slit. In the elastic case the end of the transducer plays the role of the determining dimension $2a$ analogous to the slit width. In both cases there is a region, the Fresnel region, extending from the aperture to a distance of the order of a^2/λ, within which the radiation pattern is beamlike, and a region beyond, the Fraunhofer region, within which the pattern has a constant angular form. Most surface wave filters operate within the Fresnel region so the energy from one transducer propagates as a more or less parallel beam. This allows almost the entire energy radiated into the beam to be captured by a receiving transducer of aperture comparable to that of the transmitter. However, some devices involve long propagation paths, and appreciable energy is lost by diffraction spreading of the beam. In many other devices the variations in intensity across the beam produced by diffraction influence the transfer functions of the overall device.

Angular Spectrum of Plane Waves. As in the scalar theory of optical diffraction one can assume for the surface waves that the radiated field can be represented by some scalar quantity, perhaps the amplitude of one of the components of displacement. The values of the amplitude and phase of this quantity are determined by the transducer, and hence are known at each point along the line taken as the effective aperture of the transducer. However, in contrast to the classic optical case, the propagation medium is frequently highly anisotropic, and the resulting variation of phase velocity with direction must be taken into account in diffraction calculations. The actual aperture illumination can be represented by various combinations of elementary radiators (point sources, Gaussian beams, etc.) to assist in the evaluation of the diffraction pattern. For illustration here, and consistent with the approach used for the unrestricted beams of the previous sections of this chapter, the equivalent of an "angular spectrum of plane waves" is used to represent the aperture illumination.

Figure 1.21 shows a coordinate system on the surface of a substrate with an aperture lying along the line $x = 0$. The parallel lines represent a typical straight-crested wave of the type discussed in previous sections. The velocity of this wave can be calculated once the direction of the wave normal and the crystalline geometry have been specified. One component of displacement of such a wave, say the vertical component measured on the free surface, will be given in the coordinate system of Fig. 1.21 by a constant times the propagation factor $\exp[i(k_x x + k_y y)]$, with the time dependence $\exp[-i\omega t]$ understood. But for a straight-crested wave propagating at an angle θ to the x axis, the velocity $v(\theta)$ is known and so is

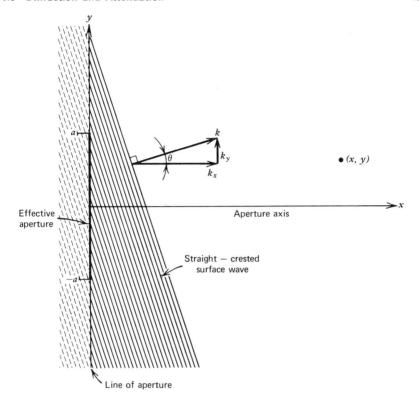

Figure 1.21 Coordinate system for diffraction calculations. Here (x, y) is the field point. The equally spaced lines indicate one of the straight-crested surface waves of which the aperture distribution is composed.

the magnitude of the propagation vector at a given frequency,

$$k(\theta) = \frac{\omega}{v(\theta)} \tag{1.63}$$

In (1.63) $k(\theta)$ is the radius vector of the slowness curve for surface waves propagating in this particular xy plane. The locus of real values of a typical slowness curve is illustrated in Fig. 1.22. Thus for these propagating waves

$$k_x^2 + k_y^2 = k^2(\theta) \tag{1.64}$$

It is now assumed that the displacement at a field point (x, y) on the surface is given by a suitably weighted sum of straight-crested waves of

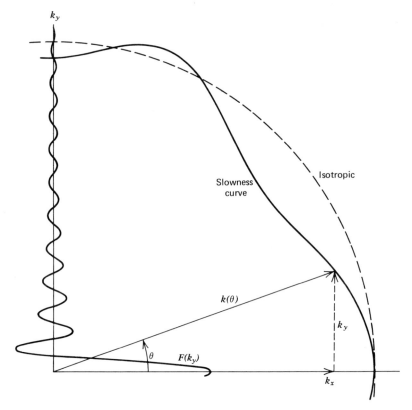

Figure 1.22 Slowness curve for an anisotropic substrate showing the definition of k_x and k_y and the weighting function $F(k_y)$ of Eq. (1.69) for a 20 λ aperture.

this type for all possible real values of k_y; that is,

$$u(x, y) = \int_{-\infty}^{\infty} F(k_y) \exp\{i[k_x(k_y)x + k_y y]\, dk_y, \qquad x \geq 0 \qquad (1.65)$$

in which k_x is regarded as a function of k_y given by

$$k_x^2(k_y) = k^2(\theta) - k_y^2 \qquad (1.66)$$

For values of k_y outside of the slowness curve, such as sketched in Fig. 1.22, the values of k_x are imaginary, and the sign of the square root giving evanescent waves in (1.65) is used. It is shown later that the contributing values of k_y lie well within the slowness curve except for apertures less than a few wavelengths wide.

For x equal to zero (1.65) becomes

$$u(0, y) = \int_{-\infty}^{\infty} F(k_y) e^{ik_y y} \, dk_y \qquad (1.67)$$

and from the properties of Fourier transforms, the weighting function is given by

$$F(k_y) = \frac{1}{2\pi} \int_{-\infty}^{\infty} u(y') e^{-ik_y y'} \, dy' \qquad (1.68)$$

where $u(y')$ is the aperture illumination measured along the line $x = 0$. Thus if the illumination is known, the weighting function from (1.68) can be substituted into (1.65) and the scalar quantity u determined at any point by carrying out the double integration.

For simple illumination functions the transformation (1.68) can be carried out explicitly before substitution into (1.65); but even for isotropic substrates integration of (1.65) cannot be done explicitly, and it is necessary to use numerical calculation. With numerical computation it is frequently advantageous to integrate with respect to k_y before integrating with respect to y', even when $F(k_y)$ can be expressed in closed form.

Uniform Illumination. If the illumination $u(y')$ is assumed to be of constant amplitude and constant phase over a linear aperture of width $2a (-a \leq y' \leq a)$, the weighting function is

$$F(k_y) = \frac{a}{\pi} \frac{\sin k_y a}{k_y a} \qquad (1.69)$$

It should be noted that if $k_0 = 2\pi/\lambda_0$ is the axial value of $|k|$ on the chosen substrate at the operating frequency, and if the aperture is N wavelengths wide, $a = (N/2)\lambda_0$, the first zero of $F(k_y)$ occurs at $k_y = \pm k_0/N$, which gives an indication of the spread of $F(k_y)$. For example, Fig. 1.22 shows a sketch of the weighting function for an aperture 20 wavelengths wide. It is seen that contributions to the diffraction integral (1.65) come almost entirely from the region of k_y near the origin. Thus, despite integration over an infinite range of k_y in (1.65), the predominant contribution comes from that part of the slowness surface near the k_x axis. The form of the diffraction pattern for a given illumination is thus determined by a small portion of the slowness surface, unless the aperture width is less than a few wavelengths.

When the substrate is an isotropic free surface and the illumination is uniform, substitution of (1.69) and $k_x^2 = k_0^2 - k_y^2$ into (1.65) gives the diffraction integrals of slit diffraction in scalar optics. It is useful to introduce a dimensionless parameter

$$W = \frac{\lambda_0}{a^2} x \tag{1.70}$$

as a measure of distance from the aperture because the form of the intensity profile is the same for equal values of W for different relative apertures. Figure 1.23 shows such intensity profiles for different values of W. In the Fresnel region $W < 1$, the intensity distribution is beamlike. Most of the energy is contained in a width $-a < y < a$, and the phase across the beam width is approximately constant; that is, the phase varies much less than $\pi/2$ except near $y = \pm a$. On the other hand, for $W > 1$ the intensity profiles become the radially spreading Fraunhofer pattern, and the amplitude is proportional to $(\sin \gamma)/\gamma$, $\gamma = ka \sin \alpha \cong ka\alpha$, where α is the off-axis angle of the field point. The phase is constant over a radial arc in the main lobe. This pattern can be seen developing near $W = 1$ in Fig. 1.23. Note that for $a = 1$ mm and $f = 100$ MHz on an isotropic substrate with $v_R = 3300$ m/sec, the aperture is 60 λ wide, and $W = 1.0$ corresponds to 3 cm.

Diffraction on Anisotropic Media. As noted, for reasonable relative apertures only a small part of the slowness curve influences the radiation pattern. Thus it is often convenient and accurate to approximate the actual anisotropic slowness curve in the significant region by an analytic expression. For example, if the beam direction, the x axis of Fig. 1.21, is along a pure-mode axis for which the phase velocity is v_0, a convenient approximation for neighboring directions is often

$$v(\theta) = v_0(1 - \beta\theta^2) \tag{1.71}$$

In this so-called parabolic approximation, valid for small values of θ, (1.66) becomes

$$k_x^2(k_y) \cong k_0^2 - (1 - 2\beta)k_y^2 \tag{1.72}$$

where $k_0 = \omega/v_0$. When this expression is substituted into (1.65) and the factor $e^{ik_0 x}$ removed from the integral, the remaining integral is the same as that for the isotropic case but with x replaced by $(1 - 2\beta)x$. Thus the diffraction profiles are displaced by $1 - 2\beta$, and if the dimensionless parameter of (1.70) is redefined as

$$W = \frac{\lambda_0}{a^2}(1 - 2\beta)x \tag{1.73}$$

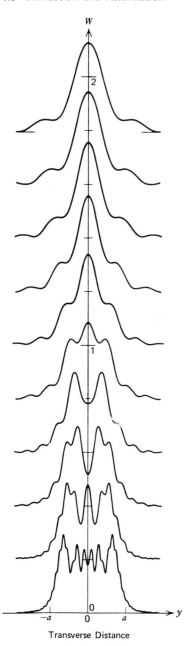

Figure 1.23 Intensity profiles at successive values of the normalized distance W for two-dimensional diffraction on an isotropic substrate.

then equal values of W give similar intensity profiles. As long as the parabolic approximation is valid, the diffraction field is given by the profiles of Fig. 1.23. Positive values of β result in a given profile occurring further from the aperture than in the isotropic case.

Similar scaling applies to focusing of a circularly converging wavefront at the effective aperture. (An interdigital transducer having fingers shaped as portions of circular arcs can produce such a wavefront.) The converging wavefront reaches a geometrical focus at some distance f from the aperture, and on an isotropic medium there is a characteristic intensity profile along the transverse line through the geometrical focus. On an anisotropic medium this characteristic profile occurs at a distance $f/(1 - 2\beta)$ from the aperture.

For constant-phase apertures it is important to note that positive values of β lead to increased Fresnel zone lengths; in other words, the beam is collimated by the anisotropy. In particular, the length of the Fresnel zone approaches infinity as β approaches 0.5 in the parabolic approximation. More generally, when k_x is independent of k_y over the contributing region, near $k_y = 0$, so that the slowness curve is a straight line perpendicular to k_x over this region, the diffraction integral (1.65) becomes

$$u(x, y) = e^{ik_x x} \int_{-\infty}^{\infty} F(k_y) e^{ik_y} \, dk_y \qquad (1.74)$$

But the integral in this expression is recognized from (1.67) as the aperture illumination $u(0, y)$ itself. Thus, under these conditions we have true autocollimation in that the diffraction profile at any distance x is just the aperture illumination with a phase shift appropriate to the distance. Real solids of course cannot have k_x independent of k_y for all values of k_y, as required for perfect autocollimation, but some cases do approach this condition. For example, Fig. 1.11 shows that for propagation near the Z axis on Y-cut $LiNbO_3$, the slowness curve is almost a straight line normal to this Z axis for an angular range of some ± 7 degrees. Thus for apertures many wavelengths in width, so that only this range contributes to the diffraction integral, the cross section of the beam is similar to the cross section at the aperture for distances from the aperture far greater than for an isotropic medium. With a uniformly illuminated aperture 40λ wide, the beam retains essentially its aperture shape for distances more than 10 times greater than for the same aperture on an isotropic substrate. The parabolic approximation of (1.71) is not however itself a good approximation to the velocity curve near the Z axis for this Y-cut $LiNbO_3$.

Another useful crystal orientation providing low loss and high electromechanical coupling for surface wave devices is a basal plane cut of bismuth germanium oxide with propagation along a $\langle 110 \rangle$ axis. Here the parabolic approximation is valid over a relatively wide angle with a value of β about 0.15 (Table 1.4), and thus this orientation is somewhat autocollimating, but not nearly as completely as the YZ LiNbO$_3$. On the other hand, for another useful geometry, X axis propagation on the ST cut of quartz, the value of β is negative (Table 1.4), and the Fraunhofer diffraction spreading of the beam will develop closer to the aperture than for an isotropic medium.

Surface Wave Attenuation. Several types of signal loss can occur in a surface wave filter and potentially result in degradation of the performance of that device. For example, consider a simple delay line consisting of an input and an output transducer on a single-crystal piezoelectric substrate. The amplitude of the surface wave beam launched by the input transducer depends on the transducer design and the frequency of the input signal. The surface wave energy propagates toward the receiving transducer where the electrical signal output depends on the fraction and profile of the beam intercepted, the details of the transducer design, and the electrical matching at the output. The response functions and losses associated with transducers themselves are considered in the following chapter, but it should be noted here that diffraction effects cause a signal loss because of the spreading of the beam and because of the departure of the transverse phase from a constant value. The diffraction losses are reduced if the crystal geometry is autocollimating. Relative misalignment of the two transducers can also cause signal loss. In anisotropic media geometrically aligned transducers can have an extra loss introduced by any departure of the axis of the combination from the pure-mode crystal axis, because then the ultrasonic beam does not follow the transducer axis.

Any surface roughness or discontinuity in or on the surface within the transmission path results in reflections of the propagating surface wave and in excitation of bulk waves radiating into the substrate.

There is also a fundamental elastic loss mechanism in the substrate whereby the coherent surface wave beam is coupled to the incoherent thermal vibrations of the solid. The attenuation factor for this type of loss is proportional to the square of the frequency with the proportionality constant depending on the material chosen. Representative values for the attenuation of certain piezoelectric materials at a frequency of 1 GHz are given in Table 1.4. Because of the quadratic frequency dependence, the attenuation caused by mechanical losses in the substrate can be neglected for frequencies below 1 GHz for YZ LiNbO$_3$. In general, polycrystalline materials have higher attenuation at a given frequency than similar single crystals; for example, the attenuation of fused silica is some 40 dB/cm.

For certain of the surface wave filters we discuss in later chapters, the variation of the phase velocity with temperature is important. The phase velocity depends on the temperature primarily because of the changes produced in the elastic constants and the density. The fractional change in phase velocity $[(1/v)(\partial v/\partial T)]$ is -87 ppm/°C for YZ LiNbO$_3$ and 14 ppm/°C for ST quartz. The large temperature dependence in YZ LiNO$_3$ presents one of the few disadvantages of this material relative to other currently available substrates for surface wave filters. It is interesting to note that if delay time ($\tau = l/v$ where l is the path length) is the important criterion, the fractional change in delay time $[(1/\tau)(\partial \tau/\partial T)]$ is approximately zero for ST quartz whereas it is 94 ppm/°C for YZ LiNbO$_3$.

Bibliography

B. A. Auld, *Acoustic Fields and Waves in Solids*, Wiley, New York, 1973. Chapters 1, 2, 3, 6, and 7 comprise a discussion particularly helpful to those with a microwave engineering background. Chapter 5 contains a recommended discussion of elastic wave energy flow. Chapter 12 is useful resource for readers looking for instruction on calculating the effects of perturbations on surface wave propagation.

D. A. Berlincourt, D. R. Curran, and H. Jaffe, "Piezoelectric and piezomagnetic materials and their function in transducers," in W. P. Mason, Ed., *Physical Acoustics*, Vol. 1A, Academic, New York, 1964, pp. 169–270. A helpful source of information about wave propagation in piezoelectrics.

W. L. Bond, "Mathematics of the physical properties of crystals." *Bell Syst. Tech. J.* **22,** 1 (1943). A useful aid to calculations of physical constants referred to arbitrary axes.

L. M. Brekhovskikh, *Waves in Layered Media*, Academic, New York, 1960. Chapters 1, 2, and 5: One of the classic treatments, suggested for further study of the influence of thin layers on surface wave propagation.

W. G. Cady, *Piezoelectricity*, McGraw-Hill, New York, 1946. Chapters 1 to 11. An old, but classic, treatment of wave propagation in piezoelectrics.

W. M. Ewing, W. S. Jardetsky, and F. Press, *Elastic Waves in Layered Media*, McGraw-Hill, New York, 1957. Chapters 1, 2, and 4: Written for geologists, but a helpful source for surface wave device engineers.

G. W. Farnell, "Elastic surface waves," in W. P. Mason and R. N. Thurston, Eds., *Physical Acoustics*, Vol. 6, Academic, New York, 1970, pp. 109–166. Recommended for readers seeking more instruction about the characteristics of surface waves.

G. W. Farnell and E. L. Adler. "Elastic wave propagation in thin layers," in W. P. Mason and R. N. Thurston, Eds., *Physical Acoustics*, Vol. 9, Academic, New York, 1972, pp. 35–127. The source for the discussion of waves on thin-layered surfaces included in this chapter.

F. I. Federov. *Theory of Elastic Waves in Crystals*, Plenum, New York, 1968. Chapters 1, 2, and 4: A helpful source for intensive study of elastic wave propagation in solids.

R. F. S. Hearmon, *Introduction to Applied Anisotropic Elasticity*, Oxford University Press, Oxford, 1961. Chapters 1–3: Recommended for further study of elasticity and elastic wave propagation.

M. S. Kharusi and G. W. Farnell. "On diffraction and focusing in anisotropic crystals." *Proc. IEEE* **60**, 945 (1972). An important source of the discussion in this chapter.

P. G. Klemens. Effect of thermal and phonon processes on Ultrasonic attenuation, ' in W. P. Mason, Ed., *Physical Acoustics*, Vol. 3B, Academic, New York, 1965, pp. 201–234. A discussion of the physical processes underlying the attenuation of waves traveling in solids.

K. M. Lakin. "Perturbation theory for electromagnetic coupling to elastic surface waves on piezoelectric substrates." *J. Appl. Phys.* **42**, 899 (1971). A useful addition to the treatment included in this chapter.

I. M. Mason and E. A. Ash. "Acoustic surface wave beam diffraction on anisotropic substrates." *J. Appl. Phys.* **42**, 5343 (1971). Recommended to amplify the discussion in this chapter.

W. P. Mason, *Physical Acoustics and the Properties of Solids*, Van Nostrand, Princeton, 1958. A classic. Chapter 2 and Appendices: Suggested for further study of elasticity and elastic wave propagation. Chapters 7, 8, and 10: Recommended for further study of elastic wave attenuation.

M. J. P. Musgrave, *Crystal Acoustics*, Holden-Day, San Francisco, 1970. Chapters 3 and 12. Suggested for further reading about elasticity and elastic wave propagation.

G. Nadeau. *Introduction to Elasticity*, Holt, Rinehart & Winston, New York, 1964. Chapter 2: A lucid discussion of the energy flow accompanying elastic wave propagation.

J. F. Nye. *Physical Properties of Crystals*, Oxford University Press, London, 1957. Chapters 1–7. A complete and admirably clear presentation of the notation used in crystal physics.

M. Redwood. *Mechanical Waveguides*, Pergamon, Oxford, 1960. Chapters 1 and 2: A clear discussion of elasticity and elastic waves with a view toward practical applications.

A. J. Slobodnick, Jr.,"A review of material trade-offs in the design of acoustic surface wave devices at VHF and Microwave Frequencies." *IEEE Trans.* **SU-20**, 315 (1973). Contains a helpful discussion of the influence of attenuation on surface wave filter design.

A. J. Slobodnick, Jr., R. T. Delmonico, and E. D. Conway. *Microwave Acoustics Handbook*, Air Force Cambridge Research Laboratories, Bedford, Mass. Vol. 1, 1970, and Vol. 2, 1974. An indispensable source for measured values of physical constants for all solids used in surface wave filters and for calculated properties of surface waves.

H. F. Tiersten, *Linear Piezoelectric Plate Vibrations*, Plenum, New York, 1969. Chapters 1–7: A detailed and authoritative treatment of waves in piezoelectric materials.

I. A. Viktorov. *Rayleigh and Lamb Waves*, Plenum, New York, 1967. Chapter 1: A well-known and classic presentation of surface wave properties from a practical viewpoint.

TWO
The Interdigital Transducer

R. F. MILSOM,* M. REDWOOD, AND N. H. C. REILLY

Queen Mary College
University of London
London, England

The most efficient and widely used means of generating and detecting surface elastic waves for electronic applications is the interdigital transducer. In its simplest form it consists of a series of parallel metal electrodes periodically spaced on the surface of a piezoelectric substrate as illustrated in Fig. 2.1. The transducer is a two terminal device with alternate electrodes interconnected. When a voltage is applied to these terminals electric fields are set up within the substrate, and these excite alternating stress patterns via the piezoelectric effect. The electric field is reversed at each electrode, and therefore at frequencies for which the periodic length λ of the array is an odd number of wavelengths, elastic surface waves are launched in both directions normal to the electrodes. If v_s is the surface wave velocity for the piezoelectric material concerned, the frequencies of elastic resonance are $(2n-1)v_s/\lambda$, where n is an integer. For simple analysis the interdigital structure may be regarded as an end-fire array,[1] so that the frequency response of an M-period transducer is of the form $\sin[M(f-f_0)]/(f-f_0)$ for frequencies close to the

---

* Now at The Allen Clark Research Centre, The Plessey Company Limited, Caswell, Towcester, Northants, England.

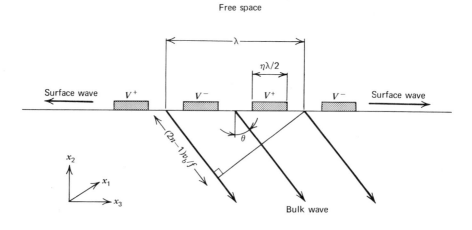

Figure 2.1 Edge view of interdigital transducer electrodes on a piezoelectric solid together with graphic meaning of symbols defined in text. Note coordinate axes.

resonance f_0. This response can, however, be modified considerably by varying the geometry of the array. Detection is achieved by means of a second transducer where the piezoelectric effect causes the elastic stress to be converted back to an electrical voltage.

In addition to launching surface waves the interdigital array acts as a source of bulk waves that propagate into the substrate. Once again simple array theory shows that a bulk wave of velocity v_b propagates at angles θ ($= \sin^{-1}(2n-1)v_b/f\lambda$) for which conditions of constructive interference exist. This implies that efficient generation of bulk waves might only occur above a "cut off" frequency equal to v_b/λ, but, in fact, for transducers with a finite number of electrodes there is a continuous distribution of radiation with angle at all frequencies. As a result there is some conversion of electrical energy to bulk waves at the surface wave fundamental, even though this frequency is usually below the cut off frequency of the slowest bulk wave. Bulk waves cause problems in surface wave devices in three distinct ways. First, bulk wave generation at the input transducer creates loss by reducing the energy available for surface wave generation. Second, there is coupling between surface and bulk modes that modifies the surface wave radiation. Third, bulk waves traveling close to the surface carry some energy to the output transducer and interfere with its response to the surface wave. Bulk wave generation is a particularly serious problem for large bandwidth transducers. Other spurious signals can also be caused by reflections of bulk waves from the lower face, and both surface and bulk waves from the ends of the substrate. However these can often be eliminated by using absorbers or scatterers.⟩

In this chapter we describe two distinct ways of analyzing transducers. First, we consider field analysis, which is essential to an understanding of the physical processes involved. Second, we consider analysis by equivalent circuits, which are somewhat easier to handle and capable of dealing with very much larger arrays.

2.1 Field Analysis of Generation and Detection

We now consider the theoretical analysis of the fields associated with the interdigital transducer. This leads to an approximate expression for the input admittance of a uniform transducer and is followed by a discussion of more exact methods of analysis, which include the full effect of coupling to both surface and bulk waves. A variational method is applied to the infinite periodic array and the results are used to derive parameter values for the electrical equivalent circuits described later. Finally, the method is extended to nonuniform finite arrays and predictions are compared directly with experimental measurements.

Field Equations and Boundary Conditions for Interdigital Transducers. A rigorous theoretical analysis of the interdigital transducer proceeds from the equations of motion for elastic and electric fields in a piezoelectric solid. These equations are derived and discussed in Chapter 1, and displayed there as equations (1.14). They are repeated here with slightly different notation.

$$\rho \ddot{u}_j - c_{ijkl}^E u_{k,li} - e_{kij} \varphi_{,ki} = 0$$
$$e_{ikl} u_{k,li} - \epsilon_{ik}^s \varphi_{,ki} = 0 \tag{2.1}$$

The meaning of the letter symbols is the same here as in Chapter 1. Dots denote differentiation with respect to time, and commas denote partial differentiation with respect to spatial variables in the usual tensor notation. Thus, for instance, $u_{i,jk}$ means $\partial u_i / \partial x_j \partial x_k$.

Our discussion of the boundary conditions for the interdigital transducer is aided by Fig. 2.1. The two half-spaces $x_2 < 0$ and $x_2 > 0$ are occupied by the piezoelectric solid and free space, respectively. The electrodes are parallel to the x_1 axis. In obtaining a solution to the coupled field equations (2.1) it is necessary to take into account both mechanical and electrical boundary conditions. Since in practice the electrodes are thin metal films, it is a common approximation to assume they are perfectly conducting and have zero thickness and mass. The surface $x_2 = 0$

is therefore stress free on the electrodes as well as over the unelectroded regions. This homogeneous mechanical boundary condition may be written

$$N_2 T_{i2} = 0, \quad \text{at} \quad x_2 = 0 \tag{2.2}$$

where N_2 is the unit vector normal to the surface and T_{i2} denotes the components of stress on the surface.

The electrical boundary conditions are more complicated, because they are nonhomogeneous and provide most of the problems in attempts to obtain an accurate solution to the field equations. In the unelectroded regions the free charge density at the surface must be zero (i.e., D_2 must be continuous), and at each instant of time the potential must be constant over all interconnected electrodes (i.e., equal to V^- over one set of electrodes and V^+ over the remaining set). (V^- and V^+ are dependent only on time t.) In addition, continuity of charge requires the total electrical currents in the two sets of electrodes to be equal and opposite, and this current and the potential difference $(V^+ - V^-)$ must satisfy the appropriate conditions for the external circuit. This is discussed more fully later when we consider separately generation and detection. Finally, the potential must be continuous throughout space and in particular at the interface $x_2 = 0$ between solid and free space.

Effective Permittivity. Before going on to describe methods of finding accurate descriptions of the wave fields excited by an interdigital array, we derive in detail the effective permittivity function, first defined by Greebe et al.[2] This function embodies an exact solution to the field equations (2.1) and the mechanical boundary condition (2.2). Once it has been found for a particular material, cut, and direction of propagation, only an electrical boundary value problem remains for each prescribed interdigital array. All the mechanics is removed from the problem without making any significant approximations apart from those already mentioned. The other assumption we make is that the electrodes in Fig. 2.1 are of sufficient length in the x_1 direction to make all differentials with respect to x_1 negligible. Only continuous wave problems are considered, so that all the field variables vary as exp $(j\omega t)$, where ω is the angular frequency of excitation. This time dependence is suppressed in all the equations.

Initially we define the one dimensional Fourier transform and inverse transform

$$\bar{\psi}(k, x_2) = \frac{1}{2\pi} \int_{-\infty}^{\infty} \psi(x_3, x_2) \exp{(jkx_3)} \, dx_3 \tag{2.3}$$

$$\psi(x_3, x_2) = \int_{-\infty}^{\infty} \bar{\psi}(k, x_2) \exp{(-jkx_3)} \, dk \tag{2.4}$$

where ψ is any mechanical or electrical field variable. For the present we assume that the field quantities vary as $\exp(\alpha k x_2)$ in the x_2 direction, where α is a dimensionless decay coefficient, so that the transformed equations (2.1) become

$$
\begin{bmatrix}
\alpha^2 c_{66}^E - 2j\alpha c_{56}^E - c_{55}^E + \rho v^2 & \alpha^2 c_{62}^E - c_{54}^E - j\alpha(c_{64}^E + c_{52}^E) \\
\alpha^2 c_{62}^E - c_{54}^E - j\alpha(c_{64}^E + c_{52}^E) & \alpha^2 c_{22}^E - 2j\alpha c_{24}^E - c_{44}^E + \rho v^2 \\
\alpha^2 c_{46}^E - c_{53}^E - j\alpha(c_{63}^E + c_{54}^E) & \alpha^2 c_{24}^E - c_{43}^E - j\alpha(c_{23}^E + c_{44}^E) \\
\alpha^2 e_{26} - e_{35} - j\alpha(e_{25} + e_{36}) & \alpha^2 e_{22} - e_{34} - j\alpha(e_{24} + e_{32})
\end{bmatrix}
$$

$$
\begin{bmatrix}
\alpha^2 c_{46}^E - c_{53}^E - j\alpha(c_{63}^E + c_{54}^E) & \alpha^2 e_{26} - e_{35} - j\alpha(e_{25} + e_{36}) \\
\alpha^2 c_{24}^E - c_{43}^E - j\alpha(c_{23}^E + c_{44}^E) & \alpha^2 e_{22} - e_{34} - j\alpha(e_{24} + e_{32}) \\
\alpha^2 c_{44}^E - 2j\alpha c_{34}^E - c_{33}^E + \rho v^2 & \alpha^2 e_{24} - e_{33} - j\alpha(e_{23} + e_{34}) \\
\alpha^2 e_{24} - e_{33} - j\alpha(e_{23} + e_{34}) & \epsilon_{33}^S - \alpha^2 \epsilon_{22}^S + 2j\alpha \epsilon_{23}^S
\end{bmatrix}
\begin{bmatrix}
\bar{u}_1 \\
\bar{u}_2 \\
\bar{u}_3 \\
\bar{\varphi}
\end{bmatrix} = 0 \quad (2.5)
$$

where $v\,(=\omega/k)$ is the component of phase velocity in the x_3 direction corresponding to the wave number k and where the material constants c^E, e and ϵ^S have been reduced to the standard matrix notation.[3] A nontrivial solution to this system of linear equations can only exist if the determinant of the left hand matrix is zero, so that for any given value of v possible values of α are restricted to the roots of what is in general an eighth order polynomial in α. Any one of the eight roots gives a solution to (2.5) representing an elementary mode of the system. However, for the given boundary conditions only four of these modes are permissible, since for positive k (or v), real or complex roots must have positive real parts representing modes decaying away from the surface. Imaginary roots representing nondecaying bulk modes must be positive, so that the wave is traveling at an angle *into* the material. Conversely, if k (or v) is negative, the remaining four roots must be chosen.

The elementary solutions to (2.5) may therefore be written as $\bar{u}_i^{(n)}$ $\exp(\alpha_n k x_2)$, in which i, $n = 1, 2, 3, 4$ and $\bar{\varphi}$ has been rewritten as $\bar{u}_4$ for convenience. The superscript refers to the solution corresponding to the chosen root α_n. Each solution may be normalized with respect to $\bar{u}_4^{(n)}$, which is arbitrarily put equal to 1. A more general solution to (2.5) is given by a linear combination of the elementary solutions. Thus

$$
\bar{u}_i = \sum_{n=1}^{4} A_n \bar{u}_i^{(n)} \exp(\alpha_n k x_2) \quad (2.6)
$$

where A_n are as yet unknown constant amplitudes. This result, together with transformed equations (1.12), yields the following expressions for the stress $\bar{T}_{ij}$ and electric displacement $\bar{D}_i$.

$$\bar{T}_{ij} = k \sum_{n=1}^{4} A_n[(\alpha_n c_{ijk2}^E - jc_{ijk3}^E)\bar{u}_k^{(n)} + (\alpha_n e_{2ij} - je_{3ij})\bar{u}_4^{(n)}] \exp(k\alpha_n x_2) \quad (2.7)$$

$$\bar{D}_i = k \sum_{n=1}^{4} A_n[(\alpha_n e_{ik2} - je_{ik3})\bar{u}_k^{(n)} - (\alpha_n \epsilon_{i2}^S - j\epsilon_{i3}^S)\bar{u}_4^{(n)}] \exp(k\alpha_n x_2) \quad (2.8)$$

From the expression for the stress and the boundary condition (2.2) we obtain a system of three linear equations that may be solved for the ratios A_j/A_4 $(j = 1, 2, 3)$ to give a solution satisfying the stress-free boundary condition.

We now consider some of the electrical terms. From (2.6) the transformed potential at the surface $x_2 = 0$ is

$$\bar{\varphi}|_{x_2=0} = \sum_{n=1}^{4} A_n \bar{u}_4^{(n)} = \sum_{n=1}^{4} A_n \quad (2.9)$$

The potential in the external field must satisfy Laplace's equation $\varphi_{,ii} = 0$ and must also be continuous with the potential in the solid; therefore

$$\bar{\varphi} = \sum_{n=1}^{4} A_n \exp(-|k|x_2), \qquad x_2 \geqslant 0 \quad (2.10)$$

and

$$\bar{D}_2 = -\epsilon_0 \bar{\varphi}_{,2} = \epsilon_0 |k| \sum_{n=1}^{4} A_n \exp(-|k|x_2), \qquad x_2 \geqslant 0 \quad (2.11)$$

where ϵ_0 is the permittivity of free space. From (2.8) and (2.11) it can be seen there is a discontinuity in the normal component of flux density D_2. This must be accounted for by a residual free charge distribution at the surface $x_2 = 0$ given by

$$\begin{aligned}
\bar{\sigma} &= \bar{D}_2|_{x_2=0+} - \bar{D}_2|_{x_2=0-} \\
&= k \sum_{n=1}^{4} A_n\left[\left(\alpha_n \epsilon_{22}^S - j\epsilon_{23}^S + \frac{|k|\epsilon_0}{k}\right) - (\alpha_n e_{2k2} - je_{2k3})\bar{u}_k^{(n)}\right]
\end{aligned} \quad (2.12)$$

The effective permittivity of the surface is now defined by

$$\epsilon_s = \frac{\bar{\sigma}}{|k||\bar{\phi}|_{x_2=0}} \quad (2.13)$$

Therefore from (2.9), (2.12), and (2.13),

$$\epsilon_s = \epsilon_0 + \frac{\dfrac{k}{|k|} \displaystyle\sum_{n=1}^{4} A_n[\alpha_n \epsilon_{22}^s - j\epsilon_{23}^s - (\alpha_n e_{2k2} - je_{2k3})\bar{u}_k^{(n)}]}{\displaystyle\sum_{n=1}^{4} A_n} \quad (2.14)$$

Our definition of effective permittivity differs very slightly from that of Greebe et al.,[2] but (2.13) is a useful form for the analysis that is to follow. It can now be appreciated that ϵ_s is a function only of phase velocity v, yet represents an exact solution to the mechanical part of the problem regardless of the electrical boundary conditions. In fact it is convenient to treat ϵ_s as a function of slowness $s(=1/v)$ rather than phase velocity.

Figure 2.2 shows a typical form of ϵ_s, which is an even function in this case, the Z-propagating direction of Y-cut lithium niobate. The poles at $\pm s_s$ and zeros at $\pm s_0$ corresponding to zero $\bar{\varphi}$ and $\bar{\sigma}$ are, respectively, the metalized and unmetalized traveling Rayleigh wave slownesses as found by Campbell and Jones[4] using essentially the same analysis. The discontinuities in $d\epsilon_s/ds$ at $\pm s_1$ and $\pm s_2$ are the cut off slownesses of bulk longitudinal and vertically polarized bulk shear waves. Below the discontinuity at s_1 the decay coefficient α_1 is imaginary, and the corresponding mode is bulk longitudinal. Above s_1 this mode degenerates into a surface mode with α_1 complex. Similarly α_2 is imaginary below s_2 and represents the bulk shear mode, but α_2 is complex above s_2. The decay coefficient associated with the electrostatic field is α_3, it is complex (almost purely real) for all values of s. The type of bulk wave associated with each

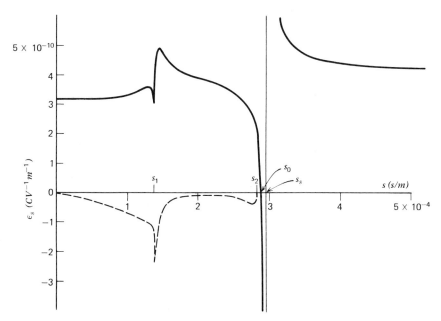

Figure 2.2 Effective permittivity ϵ_s for YZ lithium niobate as a function of the wave slowness $s = 1/v$. Real part given by solid line; imaginary part by dashed line.

imaginary α_n is identified by examining the direction of the particle displacement vector $\bar{u}_i^{(n)}$. For YZ lithium niobate the third type of bulk wave, horizontally polarized shear, which is associated with the decay coefficient α_4, is decoupled from the electric field components and therefore does enter into the effective permittivity.

Approximate Array Analysis. A number of analytical techniques have been employed to find approximate solutions to the interdigital array problem. Among these, the most common approximation is to ignore the piezoelectric coupling at some stage of the analysis. We now examine the consequences of making such an approximation and compare the results with those obtained from the more accurate method described later.

The approach we adopt is to analyze the electrostatic field associated with an infinite uniform array and to assume the charge distribution on each electrode of a finite array is equal to that on a corresponding electrode of the infinite array. Moreover the charge is assumed unperturbed by piezoelectric coupling to the elastic waves. The electrostatic solution to the infinite array has been obtained by Engan[5] using Fourier analysis and the properties of Legendre polynomials. This yields the following expression for the charge density at the surface:

$$\sigma(x_3) = \frac{2\pi V_i \epsilon_s^{(\infty)}}{\lambda K(\cos \eta\pi/2)} \sum_{m=1}^{\infty} P_{m-1}(\cos \eta\pi) \sin 2\pi(2m-1)\frac{x_3}{\lambda} \quad (2.15)$$

where λ is the spatial periodicity of the array, the width of each electrode is $\eta\lambda/2$, V_i is the applied voltage, $\epsilon_s^{(\infty)}$ is the value of effective permittivity for zero velocity (infinite slowness), K is the complete elliptic integral of the first kind, and P_m are the Legendre polynomials. The expression on the right of (2.15) is zero in the space between electrodes, and the corresponding expression for potential in the solution is equal to $\pm V_i/2$ on alternate electrodes, as required by the electrical boundary conditions. This charge distribution is shown in Fig. 2.3a. It is compared with the actual charge on a four-electrode-pair transducer on YZ lithium niobate operated at its surface wave center frequency shown in Fig. 2.3b. The more exact solution was obtained using the accurate numerical method of analysis described later. Figure 2.3b(i) shows that the component of charge in phase with the applied voltage differs slightly from the electrostatic charge assumed, particularly at the ends of the array. Whereas Fig. 2.3b(ii) shows that additional charge in quadrature with the applied voltage is generated piezoelectrically by the excited elastic waves. For larger arrays the significance of ignoring end effects is reduced, but the

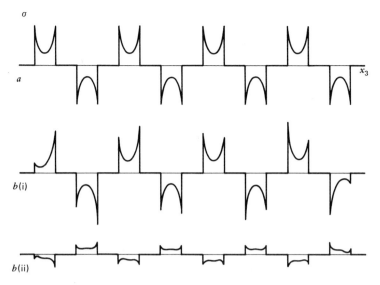

Figure 2.3 Charge distribution σ for a four-electrode-pair transducer on YZ lithium niobate. (*a*) Approximate distribution as given by (2.15). (*b*) Numerically computed exact distribution at surface wave center frequency. (i) Component in phase with applied voltage. (ii) Component in quadrature with applied voltage.

distortion caused by piezoelectric coupling is increased because of the greater amplitude of the surface wave.

We now use the approximation of (2.15) to obtain an expression for the input admittance of a uniform interdigital transducer. The electrical input power at the surface $x_2 = 0$ for any transducer structure of uniform finger length W is given by

$$P_{in} = \tfrac{1}{2} W \operatorname{Re} \int_{-\infty}^{\infty} \varphi(x_3) i(x_3)^* \, dx_3 \qquad (2.16)$$

where * indicates complex conjugate and φ and i are, respectively, voltage and current density at the surface. Applying the convolution theorem[6] to (2.16) and substituting $j\omega\sigma = i$

$$P_{in} = -\pi\omega W \operatorname{Re} \int_{-\infty}^{\infty} j\bar{\varphi}(k)\bar{\sigma}(k)^* \, dk \qquad (2.17)$$

We now substitute for $\bar{\varphi}(k)$ using the effective permittivity (2.13). Thus

$$P_{in} = -\pi\omega W \operatorname{Re} \int_{-\infty}^{\infty} \frac{j\bar{\sigma}(k)\bar{\sigma}(k)^* \, dk}{|k|\epsilon_s} \qquad (2.18)$$

At this point it is convenient to introduce the slowness by making the substitutions $\omega s = k$ and $\omega\, ds = dk$, giving

$$P_{\text{in}} = -\pi\omega W \operatorname{Re} \int_{-\infty}^{\infty} \frac{j\bar{\sigma}(s)\bar{\sigma}(s)^*}{|s|\,\epsilon_s}\, ds \tag{2.19}$$

We now define a new function of slowness

$$\Gamma(s) = \frac{1}{|s|\,\epsilon_s} \tag{2.20}$$

so that

$$P_{\text{in}} = -\pi\omega W \operatorname{Re} \int_{-\infty}^{\infty} j\Gamma(s)\bar{\sigma}(s)\bar{\sigma}(s)^*\, ds \tag{2.21}$$

If the peak applied voltage is V_{in}, the input conductance G_{in} of the transducer is given by

$$G_{\text{in}} = \frac{2P_{\text{in}}}{V_{\text{in}}^2} = -\frac{2\pi\omega W}{V_{\text{in}}^2} \operatorname{Re} \int_{-\infty}^{\infty} j\Gamma(s)\bar{\sigma}(s)\bar{\sigma}(s)^*\, ds \tag{2.22}$$

From Fig. 2.2 and (2.20) it is apparent that $\Gamma(s)$ is a purely real function for numerical vaues of s greater than the cutoff slowness of the slowest bulk wave s_N and has poles at the surface wave slownesses $\pm s_0$. (The number of different bulk waves N is equal to 2 for YZ lithium niobate.) To obtain the contribution to the integral from the poles, we subtract from the integrand a function that contains identical poles but that is otherwise analytic and then apply the theorem of residues[7] to this function. But first we introduce an infinitesimal dissipation into the material, which displaces the positive pole from the real axis into the lower half of the Argand diagram and the negative pole into the upper half. The contour of integration is then taken along the real axis with indentations passing the poles at $-s_0$ and $+s_0$ in the upper and lower half-planes, respectively. The remainder of the integrand is finite and can therefore be integrated numerically. Hence

$$G_{\text{in}} = \frac{2\pi\omega W}{V_{\text{in}}^2} \left[\operatorname{Im} \int_{-s_N}^{s_N} \Gamma(s)\bar{\sigma}(s)\bar{\sigma}(s)^*\, ds \right.$$

$$\left. - \pi G_s \bar{\sigma}(s_0)\bar{\sigma}(s_0)^* - \pi G_s \bar{\sigma}(-s_0)\bar{\sigma}(-s_0)^* \right] \tag{2.23}$$

where $\pm G_s$ are the residues of $\Gamma(s)$ at $\pm s_0$, and

$$G_s = \frac{1}{s_0 (d\epsilon_s/ds)_{s=s_0}} \tag{2.24}$$

The first term in the conductance (2.23) is due to the radiation of bulk waves, whereas the second and third terms are due to surface waves traveling in the positive and negative x_3 directions.

For narrow band transducers operated at their surface wave center frequency (i.e., for numbers of electrode pairs above, say, 20) very little power is transferred to bulk waves, because $\bar{\sigma}(s)$ in (2.23) is concentrated almost entirely in the region of s_0 and does not extend significantly below the highest bulk wave cutoff slowness s_N. Physically this low coupling to bulk waves occurs because the center frequency is below the minimum frequency for Bragg-type reinforcement of bulk waves. Transforming the approximate charge density (2.15), substituting this into (2.23), and ignoring the bulk wave term give for the input conductance at the nth odd harmonic frequency ω_n

$$G_{\text{in}}(\omega_n) = -\pi^2 \omega_n M^2 W \epsilon_s^{(\infty)2} G_s \frac{P_{n-1}^2(\cos \eta\pi)}{K^2(\cos \eta\pi/2)} \tag{2.25}$$

where $\omega_n = 2\pi(2n-1)/\lambda s_0$, M is the number of electrode pairs, and W is the length of the electrodes. Ingebrigtsen[8] has made the further assumption that in the region of s_0 the effective permittivity may be approximated by

$$\epsilon_s \simeq \epsilon_s^{(\infty)} \frac{s - s_0}{s - s_s} \tag{2.26}$$

so that from (2.24)

$$G_s \simeq \frac{s_0 - s_s}{\epsilon_s^{(\infty)} s_0} = \frac{v_s - v_0}{\epsilon_s^{(\infty)} v_s} \tag{2.27}$$

where $v_s = 1/s_s$ and $v_0 = 1/s_0$. A coupling coefficient for surface waves k_s is then defined by

$$k_s^2 = -2\epsilon_s^{(\infty)} G_s = \frac{2(v_0 - v_s)}{v_s} = \frac{2\,\Delta v}{v} \tag{2.28}$$

giving, on substitution into (2.25),

$$G_{\text{in}}(\omega_n) = \tfrac{1}{2}\pi^2 \omega_n M^2 W \epsilon_s^{(\infty)} k_s^2 \frac{P_{n-1}^2(\cos \eta\pi)}{K^2(\cos \eta\pi/2)} \tag{2.29}$$

Equation (2.28) has come to be accepted as the definition of coupling coefficient for surface waves although it bears no direct relation to the more fundamental definitions based on energy considerations.[9] Coupling coefficients computed from energy definitions would be somewhat larger than k_s and could only be realized in practice if the electric field caused by the transducer was identical to the field that is piezoelectrically coupled to the traveling wave. It must be stressed therefore that the coupling coefficient defined by (2.28) is only appropriate in the context of interdigital arrays. In fact, the approximation (2.27) is unnecessary from an analytical point of view, because it is no more difficult to compute the exact value of G_s from (2.24). This gives a more accurate expression for the effective coupling coefficient.

$$k_s^2 = -\frac{2\epsilon_s^{(\infty)}}{s_0(d\epsilon_s/ds)_{s=s_0}} \tag{2.30}$$

The definitions (2.28) and (2.30) give values of 0.049 and 0.0474, respectively, for YZ lithium niobate, so that in this particular instance the approximation is quite reasonable. The only justification for using the less accurate definition is that values of the two velocities may be either measured experimentally or taken from previously computed results. In addition to finding the input conductance G_{in} using the approximation for charge (2.15), we may also find the static capacitance C_0 of the array. Thus integrating the charge on one set of electrodes and dividing by the applied voltage V_{in} we obtain

$$C_0 = MW\epsilon_s^{(\infty)}\frac{K(\sin \eta\pi/2)}{K(\cos \eta\pi/2)} \tag{2.31}$$

Substituting (2.31) into (2.29) and assuming that the susceptance B_{in} at the center frequency is due entirely to the static capacitance C_0 (since the mechanical part of the admittance is purely resistive at resonance), we obtain concise expressions for the real and imaginary parts of the input admittance Y_{in}. Thus

$$\text{Re } Y_{in}(\omega_n) = G_{in}(\omega_n) = \tfrac{1}{2}\pi^2\omega_n C_0 M k_s^2 \frac{P_{n-1}^2(\cos \eta\pi)}{K(\cos \eta\pi/2)K(\sin \eta\pi/2)} \tag{2.32}$$

$$\text{Im } Y_{in}(\omega_n) = B_{in}(\omega_n) = \omega_n C_0 \tag{2.33}$$

Figure 2.4 shows values for the radiation conductance at the fundamental frequency $G_{in}(\omega_1)$ as a function of number of electrode pairs M on YZ lithium niobate. There is fair agreement with experimental measurements made by Smith et al.[10] and also with more exact theory up to 25 electrode pairs. The exact theory discussed later, shows that the error obtained using the present approximation is due largely to the exclusion of the piezoelectrically generated charge and to a lesser extent to the exclusion of bulk waves. One would not expect the approximate theory to be so accurate for much larger arrays, because no account is taken of internal reflections, which place an upper limit on the radiation conductance.

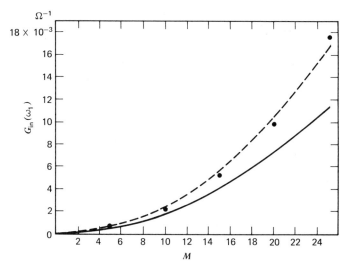

Figure 2.4 Input conductance $G_{in}(\omega_1)$ at the center frequency versus number of electrode pairs M for an interdigital transducer with periodicity $\lambda = 32.4$ mm, metalization $\eta = 0.5$, and electrode length $W = 1.25$ mm on YZ lithium niobate. Solid line according to approximate theory (2.25); dashed line, exact theory; dots are experimental data from Reference 10. Copyright 1969 by The Institute of Electrical and Electronic Engineers, Inc. Reprinted, with permission, from *IEEE Trans.* **MTT-17**, 1969, p. 859.

Accurate Infinite Array Analysis. We now consider the more accurate methods of analysis that take full account of piezoelectricity and include all elastic modes coupled to the electric field. In this section the analysis of infinite uniform transducers is discussed, and in the following section this is extended to nonuniform finite transducers. Although some of the results of the infinite array theory cannot be applied directly to finite arrays, they do provide sufficient information to determine parameter values for the electrical equivalent circuits used to analyze large nonuniform arrays. In addition, the analysis leads to modifications of the basic circuit model that are also suggested in a qualitative way by physical considerations.[11] This is the variable model described in Section 2.2.

The exact solution for an infinite array is obtained using the Ritz variational method.[12] This is made possible by adapting the variational principle for piezoelectric materials described by Holland and Eer Nisse[9]. In its original form this method involves performing volume integrals of trial functions for the fields over the whole piezoelectric solid. However the difficulties resulting from the solid filling an infinite half-space are overcome by using special trial solutions that individually satisfy the equations of motion and the mechanical boundary conditions. That is to say, the surface voltage φ and free charge density σ associated with each trial solution satisfy (2.13). Under these conditions the volume integrals vanish and the variational principle reduces to the surface integral[13]

$$\int_{S_f} \sigma \delta \varphi^* \, dS - \int_{S_m} (\varphi - V) \delta \sigma^* \, dS = 0 \qquad (2.34)$$

where s_m and s_f are, respectively, the metalized and free parts of the surface $x_2 = 0$, $\delta \varphi$ and $\delta \sigma$ are the first variations of φ and σ, and V is the known voltage on the electrodes. In applying the Ritz method the obvious choice of trial solution for σ on an infinite periodic array is a Fourier series representing the spatial harmonics, the corresponding solution for φ being found by substituting into (2.13). Thus

$$\sigma = \sum_{m=1}^{\infty} B_m \sin (k_m x_3) \qquad (2.35)$$

$$\varphi = \sum_{m=1}^{\infty} \frac{B_m}{k_m \epsilon_s (k_m/\omega)} \sin (k_m x_3)$$

where $k_m = (2m - 1)\pi/\lambda$ and B_m are unknown complex amplitudes. The variations are achieved by varying in turn each of the B_m by δB_m, giving

$$\delta \sigma = \delta B_m \sin (k_m x_3)$$
$$\delta \phi = \frac{\delta B_m}{k_m \epsilon_s (k_m/\omega)} \sin (k_m x_3) \qquad (2.36)$$

Taking a finite number of terms M of the Fourier series and substituting (2.35) and (2.36) into (2.34) gives a system of M linear equations that are solved for the constants B_m. The solution is made as accurate as we like by using an appropriately large number of terms M. This analysis was applied to arrays on a surface of PZT 4 ceramic normal to the polar axis. Figure 2.5 shows a typical frequency response with metalization factor $\eta = 0.5$. Because the array is infinite in length the only loss that occurs is due to radiation of bulk waves into the substrate, the Rayleigh wave being purely a standing wave. For this reason the fundamental resonance at f_1 is lossless, but the third and fifth harmonic resonances at f_3 and f_5 are lossy, because these have frequencies greater than the bulk wave cut-off frequencies f_t (vertically polarized shear) and f_l (longitudinal). The coupling to the third harmonic is negligibly small for this value of metalization factor.

Perhaps the most important use of infinite array theory is to evaluate accurately the parameters of the electrical equivalent circuits used for analysis of large arrays.[11] This is discussed more fully in Section 2.2.

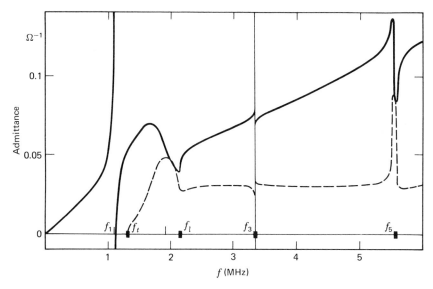

Figure 2.5 Input admittance per half-periodic section of an infinite period transducer with periodicity $\lambda = 2$ mm and metalization $\eta = 0.5$ for PZT-4 with surface normal to polar axis. Solid line gives susceptance B_{in} per unit electrode length; dashed line, conductance G_{in}.

Some of these parameters can be found by other means, for instance by comparison with the approximate theory described earlier. However, apart from being more accurate, the variational method can be applied to any infinite periodic arrangement of electrodes and is not restricted to the simple structure discussed here.

Extension to Finite Array Analysis. Most of the results of the infinite array theory can be applied only indirectly, via the equivalent circuit, to describe generation and detection by finite arrays. The theory, however, can be extended to analyze finite arrays directly. We have already shown that once the effective permittivity for the material is known, the analysis is reduced to finding the electric field variables σ and φ such that (2.13) and the appropriate electrical boundary conditions are satisfied simultaneously. Substituting (2.13) into (2.20) and expressing the Fourier transforms as functions of slowness $s (= k/\omega)$ and the inverse transforms as functions of $X (= \omega x_3)$,

$$\bar{\varphi}(s) = \frac{1}{\omega} \Gamma(s) \bar{\sigma}(s) \qquad (2.37)$$

from which, application of the convolution theorem gives

$$\varphi(X) = \frac{1}{\omega} \int_{-\infty}^{\infty} G(X - X') \sigma(X') \, dX' \tag{2.38}$$

where

$$G(X) = \frac{1}{2\pi} \int_{-\infty}^{\infty} \Gamma(s) \exp(-j\omega X) \, ds \tag{2.39}$$

The purpose of obtaining this Green's function G as a function of X is to eliminate frequency and so give us a function that is purely a property of the material, cut, and direction of propagation. To obtain the relationship between $\varphi(x_3)$ and $\sigma(x_3)$ at arbitrary frequency ω, we resubstitute x_3 for X/ω, giving

$$\varphi(x_3) = \int_{-\infty}^{\infty} G(x_3 - x_3') \sigma(x_3') \, dx_3' \tag{2.40}$$

where G is now frequency dependent.

Equation (2.40) provides considerable insight into the physical process involved in the piezoelectric generation and detection of elastic waves. Note that $G(x_3)$ is the total potential field at the surface resulting from a line source of charge. Examination of (2.20) and (2.39), and the form of the effective permittivity in Fig. 2.2 shows that the contributions to the Green's function from the various modes can be distinguished from one another, because each is associated with a singularity of the integrand. The electrostatic part of the potential field is due to the pole of $\Gamma(s)$ at $s = 0$. The potential fields associated with the forward and backward traveling surface waves are due to the poles at $\pm s_0$, and the fields associated with the bulk waves are due to the discontinuities at $\pm s_1$ and $\pm s_2$. In (2.39) we integrate the poles analytically and the remaining function numerically, giving

$$G(x_3) = -\frac{1}{\pi \epsilon_s^{(0)}} \ln |x_3| - jG_s \exp(-j\omega s_0 |x_3|) + G_b(\omega |x_3|) \tag{2.41}$$

where the bulk wave term $G_b(\omega |x_3|)$ is obtained from the numerical integration. This part of the function is shown in Fig. 2.6, which illustrates the longitudinal and shear waves beating together as they decay with distance from the source. The first term in (2.41), which is the electrostatic potential, is independent of frequency; $\epsilon_s^{(0)}$ is the value of effective permittivity at zero slowness; and the amplitude of the surface wave G_s is given by (2.24).

In order to solve the problem of generation by an interdigital array it is necessary to find the charge distribution that on substitution into (2.40)

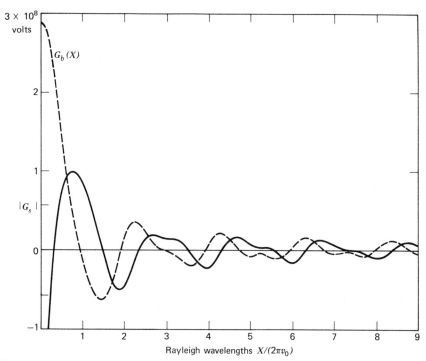

Figure 2.6 Total bulk wave contribution to the Green's function $G(X)$ for YZ lithium niobate. Solid line gives real part; dashed line, imaginary part. The Rayleigh wave amplitude $|G_s|$ is noted.

gives a potential function equal to the known potential on the electrodes. We have developed a numerical technique for computing this charge distribution,[14] but a full description is outside the scope of the present work. A typical example of charge distribution obtained in this way for a four-electrode-pair transducer on YZ lithium niobate is shown in Fig. 2.3b. This shows that the purely electrostatic charge on the array is considerably modified at the center frequency by piezoelectrically generated charge. Failure to include this component of the charge is responsible for most of the error in the approximate method of analysis discussed earlier.

If the computed charge on the input transducer is substituted back into (2.40) we can find the potential field outside the array, and it is therefore possible to extend the method to analyze detection of this field by a second transducer. The potentials on the two sets of electrodes of the detecting array are unknown initially, but the two extra equations required to find these unknowns are provided by continuity of charge and the relationship between charge and voltage in the external circuit. The potential that must be made constant on the electrodes is now the sum of that due to the known charge on the input transducer and the unknown charge on the output transducer. The solution is obtained with the same numerical technique as that used for generation. It is commonly assumed that the theorem of reciprocity may be used to deduce the solution to the detection problem from the solution for generation, and indeed that is true if surface waves only are included in the analysis. If detection of bulk waves is to be taken into account, however, the reciprocity theorem is impossible to apply, and it is necessary to use a more fundamental approach such as that described here.

We have already shown that the full solution to the mechanical part of the problem follows from a knowledge of either the charge or the voltage distribution at the surface. We can therefore substitute our solution for the charge back into the original equations to determine the power carried by each elastic mode and, in the case of bulk waves, the distribution of this power with angle into the substrate.

We now consider the results of applying this accurate theory to arrays on YZ lithium niobate. From a design point of view it is useful to know the input impedance of a transducer in order to achieve optimum electrical matching. The contribution to this impedance from bulk waves is therefore important. In Fig. 2.7 the theoretical proportions of the input power converted to the three types of elastic wave are shown as functions of number of electrode pairs for uniform transducers operated at their center frequency. The electrode-space ratio is 1:1 in all cases. Note that the ratio of surface wave to bulk wave power increases with transducer length.

The theory for both generation and detection is now applied to a surface wave delay line having interdigital transducers for both input and output. The relationship between the insertion loss of the line and the voltages on the two transducers is given by (2.64). Figure 2.8 shows both the theoretical and measured responses of a typical delay line on YZ lithium niobate up to the third harmonic. Each transducer had four electrode pairs with a 1:1 electrode-space ratio and was terminated by a 50Ω resistance. The electrodes were aluminum and about 1000Å thick. The transducer separation was 37.6 periods. Agreement between theory and experiment is seen to be good over the entire frequency range. At approximately twice the center frequency there is a strong signal caused by longitudinal waves, which is 25.5 dB down on the surface wave. Further agreement concerning spurious modes was also obtained. Predicted values of 33 dB for relative shear wave detection and 36.8 dB for triple transit echo (defined in Section 2.3) compared with measured values

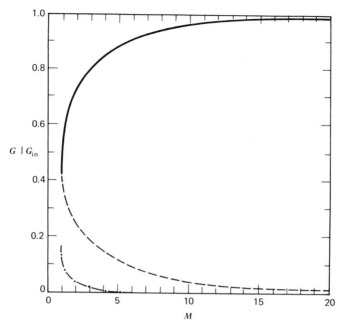

Figure 2.7 Fraction of the input electrical power converted to Rayleigh wave power G_s/G_T (solid line), bulk shear wave power G_t/G_T (dashed line), and bulk longitudinal wave power G_l/G_T (dotted and dashed line) versus number of electrode pairs M. Input power proportional to total input conductance $G_T = G_s + G_t + G_l$. Reprinted, with permission, from *Electron. Lett.* **9**, 1973, *p.* 419.

of 35 dB and 37 dB, respectively. Figure 2.9a shows the bulk shear wave radiation pattern of the input transducer at the center frequency (30 MHz), whereas Figs. 2.9b and c show the radiation patterns of both types of bulk wave at the longitudinal wave frequency (60 MHz). The radiation patterns illustrate clearly the main lobes close to the surface. These are responsible for the signals detected at the output transducer. Also at twice the center frequency there are the additional shear wave lobes at $-34°$ and $+36°$ to the normal. These contribute significantly to the total loss as described previously. The asymmetry of bulk wave radiation into the substrate for this cut is also clearly illustrated. However it must be stressed that the electric field associated with the bulk waves is symmetrical at the surface, so that the signal detected at the output transducer does not depend on whether this is to the left or right of the input transducer.

These results show that the full theory, which takes coupling to all modes into account, is generally accurate over a wide range of frequencies. It should

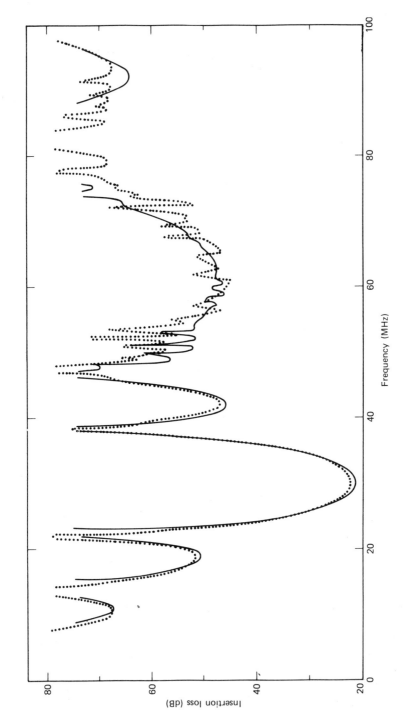

Figure 2.8 Frequency dependence of the insertion loss of a *YZ* lithium niobate delay line. The identical transducers are separated by 4.35 mm, have four electrode pairs, periodicity $\lambda = 0.1156$ mm, metalization $\eta = 0.5$, electrode length $W = 12.49$ mm, and are terminated by 50 Ω resistive.

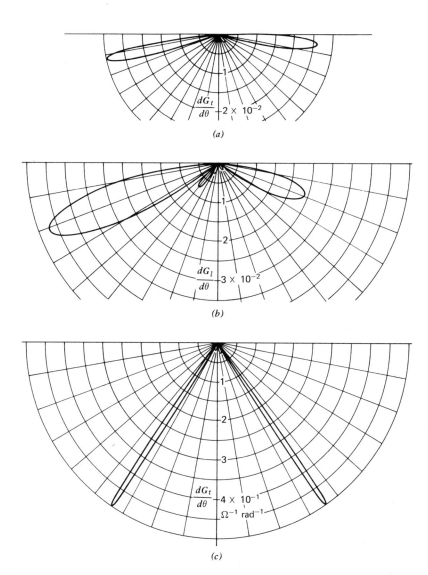

Figure 2.9 Angular distribution of bulk wave power for a four-electrode-pair 30 MHz transducer on YZ lithium niobate. (*a*) Distribution of bulk shear wave power at 30 MHz. (*b*) Distribution of bulk longitudinal wave power at 60 MHz. (*c*) Distribution of bulk shear wave power at 60 MHz.

be remembered that some second-order effects—notably electrode mass, electrode resistance, and diffraction in the surface plane—have been ignored in this analysis. These effects can become significant under certain circumstances. Application of the method is limited by available computer store to comparatively small arrays with less than 30 electrode pairs. Many of the more approximate field theories can, however, be applied to larger arrays, but a more useful method at present is to use the electrical equivalent circuits described in the next section.

2.2 Equivalent Electrical Circuits and Other Simplified Models

The exact field patterns associated with an interdigital transducer have been discussed at some length in the previous section. Although, in principle, the exact method of solution could be applied to the large, non-uniform interdigital transducers in use today, it would require a prohibitive amount of computer time. We therefore turn our attention to simplified field patterns and equivalent circuits.

Simplified Field Patterns and Analogies with Bulk Wave Transducers. The two models used are shown in Fig. 2.10 along with a sketch of the correct field pattern. The models are based on the simplified field patterns shown in Figs. 2.10b and 2.10c. It is natural to call one the in-line field model because the electric field vectors and the direction of propagation are parallel, and to call the other, the cross-field model because the electric field vectors and propagation direction are perpendicular. These two field patterns are the same as those associated with a piezoelectric plate and a piezoelectric bar, respectively.[15]

The great advantage of this simplification is that it is possible to use the Mason equivalent circuit[16] to represent each periodic section of the transducer and to represent the whole transducer by a set of cascaded periodic sections connected electrically in parallel. Figure 2.11 shows a piezoelectric bar and a piezoelectric plate together with their equivalent circuit; $\dot{\xi}$ is particle velocity, F is force, L is the length of equivalent transmission line, v is·the phase velocity of the wave, Z_c is the mechanical characteristic impedance of the line ($\rho v A$ for the plate, $\rho v A_2$ for the bar), C_0 is the static capacitance of the device, and ϕ is the ratio of a transformer that converts from electrical to mechanical quantities. For both models $\phi^2 = k^2 C_0 v Z_c / L$ where k is the piezoelectric coupling coefficient, one definition of which is given by (2.28).

The most significant difference between the bar and the plate is that the bar has no negative capacitor in its equivalent circuit ($\alpha = 0$). This reflects

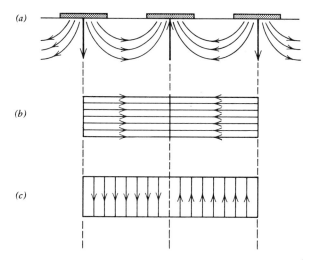

Figure 2.10 Comparison of interdigital transducer electric field patterns. (a) Simplified actual field pattern. (b) Pattern assumed for in-line field model. (c) Pattern assumed for cross-field model.

the fact that a bar is a voltage-driven device, whereas a plate is a current driven device. This can be seen from the circuits by redrawing the equivalent circuit of Fig. 2.11 in the form of Fig. 2.12. To obtain these circuits the transmission line and its terminations have been reflected through the transformer and represented by the impedance Z. Figure 2.12a represents a bar, and Fig. 2.12b represents a plate. However, by Thevenin's theorem, the current source of Fig. 2.12b in parallel with C_0 may be transformed to the voltage source of Fig. 2.12c in series with C_0. In both Fig. 2.12a and 2.12c the voltage across Z is independent of Z. Because Z is the same impedance for both the bar and the plate, representing acoustic wave propagation in both cases, we obtain the same frequency response from a bar driven by a constant voltage source and a plate driven by a constant current source.

A further consequence of the negative capacitor is its effect on the reflection coefficient at port 1 when port 2 is terminated in the characteristic impedance of the line Z_c, and port 3 (the electrical port) is open or short circuited. We first consider the plate ($\alpha = 1$ in Fig. 2.11c). If port 3 is open circuited the static capacitance C_0 is reflected through the transformer and appears as C_0/ϕ^2 in series with the negative capacitor $-C_0/\phi^2$. Thus with port 3 open circuited the outer sheath of the transmission line is grounded, and the reflection coefficient at port 1 is zero when port 2 is terminated in Z_c. Conversely, if port 3 is short circuited the

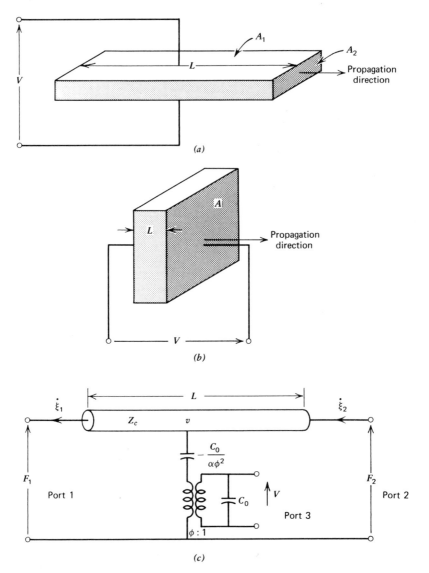

Figure 2.11 (*a*) Schematic representation of a piezoelectric bar. (*b*) Schematic representation of a piezoelectric plate. (*c*) The general equivalent circuit. When $\alpha = 0$, the circuit corresponds to a bar and the in-line field model. When $\alpha = 1$, the circuit corresponds to a plate and the cross-field model.

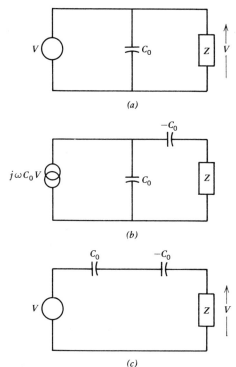

(a)

(b)

(c)

Figure 2.12 Circuit obtained from general equivalent circuit when transmission line and its termination are reflected through the transformer and represented by Z. (a) Bar driven by a voltage source. (b) Plate driven by a current source. (c) Current source for plate transformed to voltage source.

outer sheath of the transmission line is connected to ground via the negative capacitor, so that there is an impedance mismatch and hence a nonzero reflection coefficient at port 1.

An important consequence of this is the phenomenon of regeneration (sometimes also referred to as interaction), whereby a wave generated at some distant point is received and reradiated by any transducer in its path, thus distorting the effective amplitude of any waves generated by that transducer. Clearly this reradiation appears as the finite reflection coefficient exhibited by the short circuited plate. This phenomenon would be clearly observed in a large transducer composed of a series of plate transducers connected acoustically in series, electrically in parallel and fed from a constant voltage source. A wave generated by any individual transducer would, some time later, be received by some other transducer and transmitted electrically to all individual transducers in the composite structure and reradiated as elastic waves. The effect of this would be to give the composite transducer an infinite impulse response and also to produce a skewing of the output power/frequency characteristic.

A complementary effect exists in the bar transducer. Inspection of Fig. 2.11c shows that a short circuited bar has zero reflection coefficient, and an open circuited bar has nonzero reflection coefficient. Hence if the preceding composite transducer was made from bar transducers it would show no interaction effects. However if this composite bar transducer was fed electrically in series from a constant current source, interactions would again be observed.

This phenomenon of interaction and its appearance in large interdigital transducers is discussed in more detail later. In the field analysis in Section 2.1 this effect appears as a distortion of the surface charge on the electrodes as shown in Fig. 2.3.

Piezoelectric Sources of Sound in Models. The equations governing the Mason equivalent circuit, Fig. 2.11c, are

$$F_2 + \phi V(1-\alpha) - \frac{jI\alpha\phi}{\omega C_0} = \left[F_1 + \phi V(1-\alpha) - \frac{jI\alpha\phi}{\omega C_0} \right] \cos\theta + j\dot{\xi}_1 Z_c \sin\theta$$

$$\dot{\xi}_2 = \dot{\xi}_1 \cos\theta + j\left[F_1 + \phi V(1-\alpha) - \frac{jI\alpha\phi}{\omega C_0} \right] \frac{\sin\theta}{Z_c} \qquad (2.42)$$

$$j\omega C_0 V = -\phi(\dot{\xi}_2 - \dot{\xi}_1) + I$$

where

$$\theta = \omega L/v.$$

To calculate the effective sources we consider the simplest case, a bar fed from a constant voltage source and terminated in its characteristic impedance Z_c at its acoustic ports. Putting $\alpha = 0$ as required to represent a bar we may rewrite (2.42) in the form

$$F_2 + \phi V = (F_1 + \phi V) \cos\theta + j\dot{\xi}_1 Z_c \sin\theta$$

$$\dot{\xi}_2 = \dot{\xi}_1 \cos\theta + j(F_1 + \phi V) \frac{\sin\theta}{Z_c} \qquad (2.43)$$

$$j\omega C_0 V = -\phi(\dot{\xi}_2 - \dot{\xi}_1) + I$$

Also, for the terminations at ports 1 and 2 we have $\dot{\xi}_1 = F_1/Z_c$ and $\dot{\xi}_2 = -F_2/Z_c$. Substitution yields the two equations

$$F_2 + \phi V = (F_1 + \phi V) \cos\theta + jF_1 \sin\theta$$

$$-F_2 = F_1 \cos\theta + j(F_1 + \phi V) \sin\theta$$

which may be solved for F_1 and F_2, yielding

$$F_1 = F_2 = -\tfrac{1}{2}\phi V[1 - \exp(-j\theta)] \qquad (2.44)$$

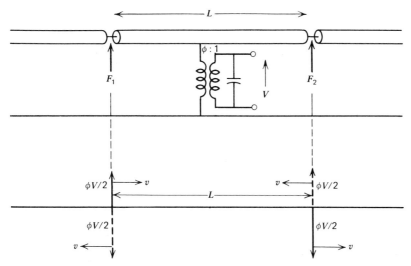

Figure 2.13 Schematic depicting the delta function (amplitude $\varphi V/2$) sources of sound in a voltage-driven piezoelectric bar terminated with its characteristic impedance.

Equation (2.44) shows either force F_1 or F_2 can be identified as the sum of two sources of δ function force placed at the ends of the equivalent circuit transmission line shown in Fig. 2.11c. A δ function source at port 1 having amplitude $\frac{1}{2}\phi V$ will propagate with velocity v to port 2 where its amplitude is $\frac{1}{2}\phi V \exp(-j\theta)$ where $\theta = \omega L/v$. Adding this to a source at port 2 of amplitude $-\frac{1}{2}\phi V$ yields (2.44). Propagation from port 2 to port 1 is identical because both L and v then have negative signs. Thus it follows that a piezoelectric bar feeding its own characteristic impedance can be replaced by a pair of δ function sources placed at the ends of the bar, as shown in Fig. 2.13. It is important to note that this simplification is only valid if there is zero reflection coefficient at ports 1 and 2 (i.e. the bar is terminated in its characteristic impedance), otherwise the wave from port 1 will affect the source at port 2. The case of a non-zero reflection coefficient at ports 1 and 2 has been discussed by Redwood[15] for transient conditions. Although, in principle, this method could be applied to continuous wave operation, the complexity is such that it is simpler to solve the equivalent circuit equations directly.

Parameters of Equivalent Circuits for Interdigital Transducers. The equivalent circuits discussed in the previous section are only strictly valid for simple bulk wave transducers. In this section we consider how these equivalent circuits can be modified to represent surface wave interdigital transducers.

The simplest extrapolation of the equivalent circuit was presented by Smith et al.[10] Each finger pair is replaced by a bulk wave transducer as shown in Fig. 2.14a. The complete interdigital surface wave transducer is then considered equivalent to a series of cascaded bulk wave transducers. Whether these bulk wave transducers should be of the "bar" or "plate" type has been a source of some controversy and we discuss the matter thoroughly, but first we digress a little to consider the much simpler delta function model discussed by Tancrell and Holland.[17]

Consider the surface wave transducer composed of bar transducers, so that in the equivalent circuit the transmission lines may be replaced by delta function sources of force placed at the center of each finger. The amplitude of each source was shown to be given by $\frac{1}{2}\phi V$, but because the sources due to consecutive lengths of line occur in the same place the total source at the center of each finger is ϕV, except for the end fingers, where the source is still $\frac{1}{2}\phi V$. This situation is shown in Fig. 2.14b. If we

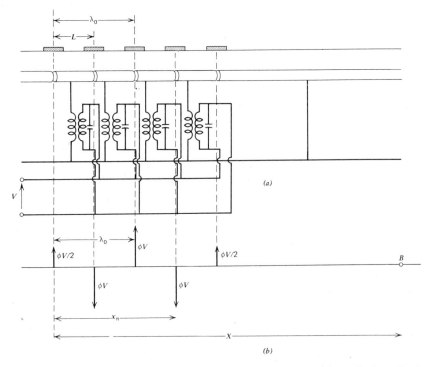

Figure 2.14 Two representations of an interdigital transducer. (a) Equivalent circuit model. (b) Delta function model.

wish to compute the amplitude at the point B distance X from the arbitrary origin, we have merely to add the contribution from each source of strength A_n at position x_n. Thus

$$\text{Amplitude} = \sum_{n=1}^{N} A_n \exp\left[\frac{-j\omega(X-x_n)}{v}\right]$$

$$= \exp\left(\frac{-j\omega X}{v}\right) \sum_{n=1}^{N} A_n \exp\left(\frac{j\omega x_n}{v}\right) \quad (2.45)$$

In particular, the power P at point B is proportional to $|\text{amplitude}|^2$, which in turn is proportional to the real part of the electrical input admittance of the transducer. Input admittance is a relatively easy quantity to measure, so it is an important parameter. Finally we can write

$$\text{Re}\,(Y_{\text{in}}) \propto \left| \sum_{n=1}^{N} A_n \exp\left(\frac{j\omega x_n}{v}\right) \right|^2 \quad (2.46)$$

Equation (2.46) is equivalent to the last two terms of (2.23) when the charge density σ is represented by discrete line sources of charge at the points x_n. Comparison between the two expressions for conductance shows that the proportionality constant omitted from (2.46) contains a factor ω.

Inspection of (2.46) shows that the term inside the modulus bars is the Fourier transform of the set of delta functions, hence (2.46) can be rewritten in the form

$$\text{Re}\,(Y_{\text{in}}) \propto \left| \int_{-\infty}^{\infty} \sum_{n=1}^{N} A(x)\delta(x-x_n) \exp\,(j\omega x/v)\,dx \right|^2 \quad (2.47)$$

Where $A(x)$ is a continuous function of x that takes on the value A_n at $x = x_n$ for $0 < n \leqslant N$. However, because A_n alternates in sign, as shown in Fig. 2.14b, we must define a transducer *weighting function* $W(x)$ such that

$$W(x) = 0, \qquad x < x_1, x > x_{N-1}$$
$$W(x) = |A(x)|, \qquad x_1 \leqslant x \leqslant x_{N-1}$$

where N is assumed even. We further define another weighting function $W^1(x) = -W(x-L)$, where L is the interdigital spacing. Making the assumption that the distribution of negative sources is the distribution of positive sources shifted by the interdigital spacing L, we can completely specify the source distribution by W and W^1. This is shown in Fig. 2.15a.

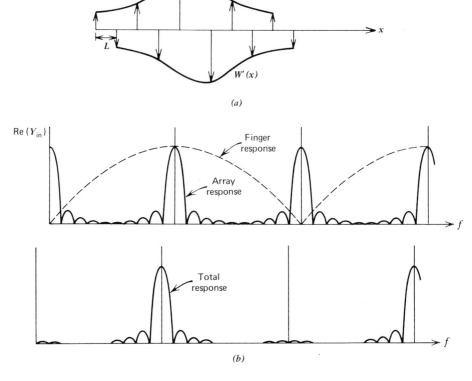

(a)

(b)

Figure 2.15 The effect of weighting functions on interdigital array response. (a) Weighting function. (b) Array response, finger response, and total response.

Equation (2.47) can now be expressed

$$\mathrm{Re}\,(Y_{\mathrm{in}}) \propto \left| \int_{x_1}^{x_{N-1}} \sum_{n=1,3,5}^{N-1} W(x)\delta(x-x_n)\exp\left(\frac{j\omega x}{v}\right)dx \right.$$
$$\left. + \int_{x_2}^{x_N} \sum_{n=2,4}^{N} W^1(x)\delta(x-x_n)\exp\left(\frac{j\omega x}{v}\right)dx \right|^2 \quad (2.48)$$

To proceed further we must invoke the sampling theorem, which can be stated as follows: The Fourier transform of a function $f(t)$ sampled at equal intervals T is the Fourier transform of $f(t)$ repeated at harmonic intervals $2\pi/T$.

In the present case the sampling interval is 2L; hence

$$\text{Re} (Y_{\text{in}}) \propto \left| \int_{x_1}^{x_{N-1}} W(x) \exp\left(\frac{j\omega x}{v}\right) dx - \int_{x_2}^{x_N} W(x-L) \exp\left(\frac{j\omega x}{v}\right) dx \right|^2$$

(2.49)

repeated at harmonic intervals $\omega = \pi v/L$.

Making the substitution $x' = x - L$, it is easily shown that the second integral in (2.49) is

$$\exp\left(\frac{j\omega L}{v}\right) \int_{x_1}^{x_{N-1}} W(x') \exp\left(\frac{j\omega x'}{v}\right) dx'$$

Hence

$$\text{Re} (Y_{\text{in}}) \propto \left| \left[1 - \exp\left(\frac{j\omega L}{v}\right) \right] \int_{x_1}^{x_{N-1}} W(x) \exp\left(\frac{j\omega x}{v}\right) dx \right|^2 \qquad (2.50)$$

repeated at harmonic intervals.

The expression $|[1 - \exp (j\omega L/v)]|^2$ is easily identified as the response of a single finger pair. This has been termed the *finger response* and the square of the Fourier transform of the weighting function

$$\left| \int_{x_1}^{x_{N-1}} W(x) \exp \frac{j\omega x}{v} dx \right|^2$$

has been termed the *array response*. The significance of these two functions is now discussed.

Consider the simplest case of an array with uniform weighting $W(x) = 1$, $x_1 \leqslant x \leqslant x_{N-1}$. The sampled Fourier transform of this is $\sin \omega/\omega$ repeated at harmonic intervals $\omega_m = m\pi v/L$. This must be multiplied by the finger response, which is zero for $\omega = 0$, $2\pi v/L$, $4\pi v/L \ldots$. Hence a uniform interdigital transducer should show a $(\sin \omega/\omega)^2$ input-admittance frequency response repeated at harmonic intervals $\omega = \pi v/L$, $3\pi v/L \ldots$. This situation is shown in Fig. 2.15b, with the overall factor of ω omitted. This response is observed in practice at the fundamental frequency $\omega = \pi v/L$, but it is also observed that a uniform transducer with a 1:1 mark-to-space ratio has no third harmonic response, indicating that some modification of the source distribution is required. This is discussed in the next section. However, if we limit the frequency to be near the fundamental frequency, this form of the delta function model gives satisfactory results.

This argument can be extended to calculate the voltage transfer function of two transducers by the following method. Suppose instead of the single point B we have a receiving array having delta function receiving points of strength B_m placed at position X_m from the origin. Further we must assume that the output from the array is equal to the sum of the outputs at each point (this is only valid for short circuit current with this model). Using these assumptions (2.45) can be modified to yield the voltage across the array V_{out} as

$$V_{out} = \sum_{m=1}^{M} B_m \exp\left(-\frac{j\omega X_m}{v}\right) \sum_{n=1}^{N} A_n \exp\left(\frac{j\omega x_n}{v}\right) \qquad (2.51)$$

We conclude that the frequency response of a surface wave filter is given by the product of the Fourier transform of the input transducer and the inverse transform of the output transducer.

It can be seen from (2.51) that the delta function model yields a very simple formula for the *relative* transfer function of a surface wave filter. (We use the word *relative* here since the absolute value of output voltage is unknown.) It also gives a very reasonable picture of the device action since the delta function model essentially places a delta function source at the center of each finger, the sign of the delta function depends on the sign of the voltage applied to that finger.

The preceding delta function model is derived from the $\lambda_0/2$ form of the equivalent circuit, so called because each section of transmission line is a half wavelength long at the fundamental frequency. A more realistic physical picture is obtained if each finger is represented by two sources placed near the finger edges. The physical justification is that, as shown in Fig. 2.3, the charge density, and hence acoustic source strength, is highest at the finger edges. This redistribution of source positions leads to the $\lambda_0/3$ *model* and *variable model*, to be discussed in more detail later.

We can say that the delta function model is an excellent first approximation. However it is only valid for a filter with short circuit terminations, which is not realized in practice. Resistive termination on a filter produces a frequency response different from the response predicted by the delta function model. This can be seen by reference to Fig. 2.11c. A termination at port 3 other than a short circuit results in a nonzero reflection coefficient at port 1 when port 2 is terminated in Z_c and leads to acoustic interactions among the transducer sections.

A further limitation on the delta function model is that acoustic interactions are observed experimentally even with short circuit terminations. Consider an experiment in which the input admittance Y_{in} of a transducer is measured as a function of the number of fingers N. Reference to (2.46) shows that the real part of Y_{in} is proportional to N^2, whereas it has been observed that for $Nk^2 > 1$ the curve of $\text{Re}(Y_{in})$ against N^2 shows a marked flattening due to acoustic interactions among the transducer sections. A more sophisticated model is required to account for these interactions.

Although, in principle, any equivalent circuit model based on transmission lines could be solved by a delta function model, suitably modified to include acoustic reflections and regeneration, that approach is so complex it is simpler to solve the equivalent circuit equations directly, so we now resume our discussion of equivalent circuit parameters.

In order to demonstrate the validity of an equivalent circuit of the type described here it is necessary to compare its predictions with the results of experimental measurements. By measuring the transient response of uniform interdigital transducers, Krairojananan and Redwood[18,19] found that the simple $\lambda_0/2$ model was unable to predict the experimental results adequately. In the preceding discussion of the delta function model we mentioned that a better physical model could result if each finger is represented by two sources of elastic waves. This separation of sources is achieved in the equivalent circuit if sections of piezoelectrically inactive line are introduced between the sections of piezoelectrically active line. For arrays with a $1:1$ mark-to-space ratio the best correlation with experimental results is obtained with lengths of active and inactive line $\lambda_0/3$ and $\lambda_0/6$, respectively. This model, called the $\lambda_0/3$ *model*, is shown in Fig. 2.16 along with its delta function source distribution. Further confirmation of the validity of the $\lambda_0/3$ model is that it predicts zero third

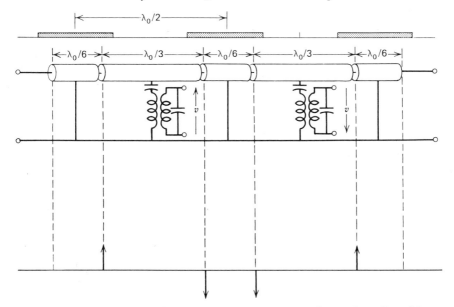

Figure 2.16 Representation of an interdigital transducer according to the $\lambda_0/3$ model.

harmonic response, which is observed in practice for a $1:1$ mark-to-space ratio array.

Since not all surface devices use a $1:1$ mark-to-space ratio the obvious next step is to see how the $\lambda_0/3$ model should be modified to account for other values of mark-to-space ratio. This can be done by comparing a prototype *variable model*, shown in Fig. 2.17, with the accurately computed response of an infinite uniform array, described in Section 2.1.[13] The method of images shows that one section of Fig. 2.17 with shortcircuited acoustic ports has the same input admittance as one section of an infinite array; hence a direct comparison can be made. This fact can be derived from general circuit theory, the physical reason being that in both cases a standing wave is set up in the section.

The equivalent circuit parameters to be determined are the relative lengths of active and inactive line via γ, the value of the negative capacitor via α, the wave velocity v, the static capacitance C_0, and the effective coupling coefficient k. The transformer ratio ϕ is again defined as $\phi^2 = 2k^2 C_0 Z_c v / \gamma \lambda_0$.

The physical significance of the parameters γ and α is as follows: γ specifies the positions of the equivalent delta function sources; α specifies the amount of acoustic mismatch between active and inactive lines, and thus is an acoustic interaction parameter.

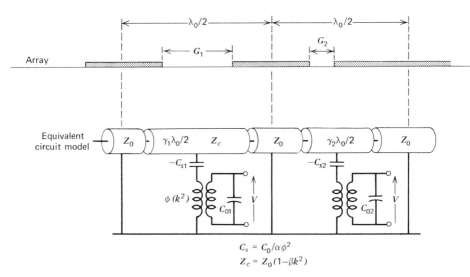

Figure 2.17 Representation of an interdigital transducer according to the variable model. Parameters scaled for PZT 4. Reprinted, with permission, from *Electrom. Lett.* **7,** 1971. *pp.* 217, 218.

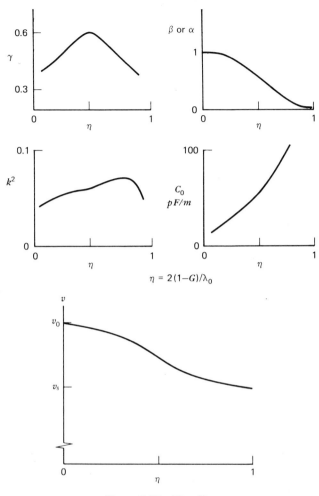

Figure 2.17 (*Contd.*)

Since there are five unknown parameters, five frequencies are chosen to compute them. These are zero frequency and the resonant and antiresonant frequencies of the fundamental and third harmonic.

At this point the value of $Z_c = \rho v A$ is not defined, because neither the effective density ρ nor the wave area A is known. However it is unnecessary to have a value for Z_c, provided we only look into the electrical port (the only one accessible in practice), because measurable quantities always appear in terms of ϕ^2/Z_c, which is a known quantity.

Graphs of the variation of the parameters of this equivalent circuit with mark-to-space ratio are shown in Fig. 2.17 for the specific case of Rayleigh waves on PZT 4. It is interesting to note that for 1:1 mark-to-space ratio γ has a value of almost 2/3, that is, a $\lambda_0/3$ model. It is also noteworthy that at $\alpha = 0.5$ the value of k^2 is almost exactly equal to that derived from (2.28). These two results are not specific to PZT 4 and appear to be equally applicable to all materials.

By referring to the graphs of α and v it can be seen that the interaction parameter α varies from 1 (plate model) at $\eta = 0$ to 0 at $\eta = 1$ (bar model), whereas v varies from the unplated velocity v_o at $\eta = 0$ to the plated velocity v_s at $\eta = 1$. This is exactly what one would expect intuitively, because for very small electrodes the surface is essentially unplated, and the electric field is approximately parallel to the surface. For very large electrodes the surface is essentially plated, and the electric field is predominantly normal to the surface.

The extension of this theory to other materials may, to some extent, be carried out without solving the infinite array problem for each new material. In view of the intuitive correctness of the graphs of α, v, and γ against η, it is expected these will have the same general shape for all materials. The graph of v would, of course, require scaling to give the correct Δv for the material in question. C_0, being static capacitance and thus proportional to dielectric permittivity, should require only the appropriate scale factor. The variation of k^2 with η does not so obviously lend itself to generalization. However, in view of its small variation over a fairly large range of η one could do a lot worse than assume it constant at the value $2\Delta v/v$. This is not such a serious restriction as it might appear, because such a sophisticated equivalent circuit is only likely to be needed for assessing specific filter designs on one given material, which will have been experimentally characterized before progressing to this stage.

So far we have not discussed the parameter β (Fig. 2.17). The reason is that α and β are alternative interaction parameters and are not used together. The circuit of Fig. 2.17 can be used with $\alpha = 0$ and β nonzero or with $\beta = 0$ and α nonzero. Because α and β both affect the acoustic reflection coefficient between transmission line sections, it is obviously unnecessary to use both in the same circuit. It is shown in Section 2.5 that both forms of the equivalent circuit yield the same result over a narrow bandwidth.

2.3 Analysis by Chain Matrices

We have discussed various possible equivalent circuits in some detail without comparing their theoretical predictions. Before proceeding to this comparison, we discuss in general terms the method of analyzing equivalent circuits of interdigital arrays independently of the particular representation of one section.

Development of the Admittance Matrix. In view of the many possible variations in the basic equivalent circuit the most convenient method of analysis is to express each section of transmission line in terms of its three port admittance matrix. The total interdigital transducer may then be represented as a series of cascaded matrices, as shown in Fig. 2.18a. The series is then reduced to the simple three port form of Fig. 2.18b, and represented by an admittance matrix of the form

$$\begin{bmatrix} \dot{\xi}_1 \\ \dot{\xi}_{N+1} \\ I \end{bmatrix} = \begin{bmatrix} Y_{11} & Y_{12} & Y_{13} \\ Y_{21} & Y_{22} & Y_{23} \\ Y_{31} & Y_{32} & Y_{33} \end{bmatrix} \begin{bmatrix} F_1 \\ F_{N+1} \\ V \end{bmatrix} \qquad (2.52)$$

The algorithms necessary to compute this admittance matrix can be written without reference to the basic equivalent circuit. We first write the equations governing each of the elements in the cascaded series in the

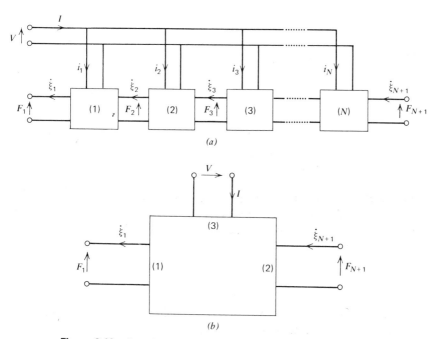

Figure 2.18 Cascaded matrix representation of an interdigital array.

form of chain matrices

$$\begin{bmatrix} F_p \\ \dot{\xi}_p \end{bmatrix} = \begin{bmatrix} h_{11}^{(p)} & h_{12}^{(p)} \\ h_{21}^{(p)} & h_{22}^{(p)} \end{bmatrix} \begin{bmatrix} F_{p+1} \\ \dot{\xi}_{p+1} \end{bmatrix} + \begin{bmatrix} d_1^{(p)} \\ d_2^{(p)} \end{bmatrix} V \qquad (2.53)$$

Further, we require an expression for the input current to each basic section. For this we use the admittance matrix representation of each section:

$$i_p = y_{31}^{(p)} F_p + y_{32}^{(p)} F_{p+1} + y_{33}^{(p)} V \qquad (2.54)$$

The advantage of the chain matrix formulation is that a whole array may be expressed in the form of a single chain matrix simply by multiplication.

Thus we may write

$$\begin{bmatrix} F_1 \\ \dot{\xi}_1 \end{bmatrix} = \begin{bmatrix} H_{11} & H_{12} \\ H_{21} & H_{22} \end{bmatrix} \begin{bmatrix} F_{N+1} \\ \dot{\xi}_{N+1} \end{bmatrix} + \begin{bmatrix} D_1 \\ D_2 \end{bmatrix} V \qquad (2.55)$$

where

$$[H] = [h^{(1)}][h^{(2)}] \dots [h^{(N)}]$$

$$[D] = [d^{(1)}] + [h^{(1)}][d^{(2)}] + [h^{(1)}][h^{(2)}][d^{(3)}] + \dots [h^{(1)}][h^{(2)}] \dots [h^{(N-1)}][d^{(N)}]$$

The first six elements of the admittance matrix $[Y]$ can be obtained from $[H]$ and $[D]$ by use of the following expressions:

$$Y_{11} = \frac{H_{22}}{H_{12}} \qquad\qquad Y_{21} = \frac{1}{H_{12}}$$

$$Y_{12} = H_{21} - \frac{H_{11} H_{22}}{H_{12}} \qquad Y_{22} = -\frac{H_{11}}{H_{12}} \qquad (2.56)$$

$$Y_{13} = D_2 - \frac{H_{22} D_1}{H_{12}} \qquad Y_{23} = -\frac{D_1}{H_{12}}$$

In order to compute the final three elements of the $[Y]$ matrix we must express the total input current I in terms of F_1, F_{N+1}, and V. This is most conveniently done by invoking reciprocity, from which it can be shown that, for the sign convention of Fig. 2.11,

$$Y_{31} = -Y_{13}$$
$$Y_{32} = Y_{23}$$

Finally, we must compute Y_{33}. This can be done by letting F_1 and F_{N+1} be zero and $V = 1$. Under these conditions $Y_{33} = I$, which can be computed by back substitution.

Having obtained the admittance matrix representation of the complete transducer, it is a relatively simple task to compute the characteristics of transmitting and detecting transducers and the transfer function of filter structures. We now consider these computations in a little more detail.

Matrix Equations for the Equivalent Circuit. The equations governing each basic section of the equivalent circuit were stated in (2.42). These may be rearranged into the chain matrix form just described. We now state these equations in their chain matrix form:

$$h_{11} = h_{12} = \frac{\cos \theta - \psi \sin \theta}{1 - \psi \sin \theta}$$

$$h_{12} = -jZc\frac{[\sin \theta + 2\psi(\cos \theta - 1)]}{1 - \psi \sin \theta}$$

$$h_{21} = -\frac{j}{Z_c}\frac{\sin \theta}{1 - \psi \sin \theta}$$

$$d_1 = -\phi\frac{1 - \cos \theta}{1 - \psi \sin \theta}$$

$$d_2 = -j\frac{\phi}{Z_c}\frac{\sin \theta}{1 - \psi \sin \theta}$$

$$y_{31} = y_{32} = j\frac{\phi}{Z_c}\frac{1 - \cos \theta}{\sin \theta + 2\psi(\cos \theta - 1)}$$

$$y_{33} = j\omega C_0\left[1 + \frac{2k^2}{\theta}\frac{1 - \cos \theta}{\sin \theta + 2\psi(\cos \theta - 1)}\right]$$

where $\theta = \omega\gamma\lambda_0/2v$ and $\psi = \alpha k^2/\theta$.

To take care of the alternate phasing of consecutive sections of active transmission line the signs of $[d]$ and y_{31}, y_{32} are reversed on alternate active sections. The inactive sections separating the active sections are characterized by $[d] = 0$ and $y_{31} = y_{32} = y_{33} = 0$. Also $\beta = 0$ for the inactive sections so that the $[h]$ matrix takes the much simpler form

$$[h] = \begin{bmatrix} \cos \theta & -jZ_0 \sin \theta \\ -\frac{j \sin \theta}{Z_0} & \cos \theta \end{bmatrix}$$

Finally we point out that the chain matrix formulation presented here is not the only possible one; an alternative is the more general but computationally less efficient method using four port chain matrices.

Having computed the admittance matrix of a single interdigital transducer, we can use it to compute several important parameters of transducers and filters.

Input Admittance and Output Power. An easily measured parameter of a single interdigital transducer is its electrical input admittance. It can be computed from the admittance matrix when the acoustic ports 1 and 2 in Fig. 2.18b are terminated in their characteristic impedance Z_0. With these terminations we have

$$\dot{\xi}_1 = \frac{F_1}{Z_0}$$

$$\dot{\xi}_2 = -\frac{F_2}{Z_0}$$

where the particle velocity and force at port 2 have been relabeled $\dot{\xi}_2$ and F_2, and the admittance matrix

$$\begin{bmatrix} \dfrac{F_1}{Z_0} \\ -\dfrac{F_2}{Z_0} \end{bmatrix} = \begin{bmatrix} Y_{11} & Y_{12} \\ Y_{21} & Y_{22} \end{bmatrix} \begin{bmatrix} F_1 \\ F_2 \end{bmatrix} + \begin{bmatrix} Y_{13} \\ Y_{23} \end{bmatrix} V \qquad (2.57)$$

Hence we may solve for F_1 and F_2 to yield the acoustic output power P as

$$P = \frac{\frac{1}{2}(F_1 F_1^* + F_2 F_2^*)}{Z_0} \qquad (2.58)$$

and the electrical input admittance Y_{in} as

$$Y_{\text{in}} = \frac{I}{V} = \frac{Y_{31} F_1 + Y_{32} F_2 + Y_{33} V}{V} \qquad (2.59)$$

By conservation of energy the real part of Y_{in} must equal $2P$, which is a useful check on any numerical computations.

The preceding theory can, of course, be useful to compute the acoustic reflection coefficient of a transducer. Consider a transducer with port 2 terminated in Z_0 and port 3 terminated in Z_L; we now have

$$\dot{\xi}_2 = -\frac{F_2}{Z_0}$$

$$I = -\frac{V}{Z_L}.$$

hence

$$
\begin{bmatrix} -\dfrac{F_2}{Z_0} \\[2ex] -\dfrac{V}{Z_L} \end{bmatrix} = \begin{bmatrix} Y_{22} & Y_{23} \\ Y_{32} & Y_{33} \end{bmatrix} \begin{bmatrix} F_2 \\ V \end{bmatrix} + \begin{bmatrix} Y_{21} \\ Y_{31} \end{bmatrix} F_1 \tag{2.60}
$$

which may be solved for F_2/F_1 and V/F_1 to yield

$$
(Y_{\text{in}})_{\text{port 1}} = \frac{-\dot{\xi}_1}{F_1}
$$

as in (2.59).

Detection and Generation. The response of an interdigital array terminated in any electrical load Z_L to an incoming acoustic signal of amplitude A can be computed as follows. Using a standard technique fully described in books on transmission line theory, the incoming wave is represented by a voltage source $2A$ in series with the characteristic impedance Z_0 at port 1. Ports 2 and 3 in Fig. 2.18b are terminated by impedances Z_0 and Z_L, respectively. In this case we have

$$
\dot{\xi}_1 = \frac{(F_1 - 2A)}{Z_0}
$$

$$
\dot{\xi}_2 = \frac{-F_2}{Z_0} \tag{2.61}
$$

$$
I = \frac{-V}{Z_L}
$$

Substitution in (2.52) yields

$$
\begin{bmatrix} Y_{11} - \dfrac{1}{Z_0} & Y_{12} & Y_{13} \\[2ex] Y_{21} & \dfrac{Y_{22}+1}{Z_0} & Y_{23} \\[2ex] Y_{31} & Y_{32} & \dfrac{Y_{33}+1}{Z_L} \end{bmatrix} \begin{bmatrix} F_1 \\[2ex] F_2 \\[2ex] V \end{bmatrix} = \begin{bmatrix} \dfrac{-2A}{Z_0} \\[2ex] 0 \\[2ex] 0 \end{bmatrix} \tag{2.62}
$$

which may be solved for the output voltage V.

Similarly, the output force at the acoustic ports due to a voltage source V with source impedance Z_L can be computed from the similar matrix equation

$$
\begin{bmatrix}
\dfrac{Y_{11}-1}{Z_0} & Y_{12} & Y_{13} \\[2ex]
Y_{21} & \dfrac{Y_{22}+1}{Z_0} & Y_{23} \\[2ex]
Y_{31} & Y_{32} & \dfrac{Y_{33}+1}{Z_L}
\end{bmatrix}
\begin{bmatrix}
F_1 \\ F_2 \\ V
\end{bmatrix}
=
\begin{bmatrix}
0 \\ 0 \\ -\dfrac{V}{Z_L}
\end{bmatrix}
\qquad (2.63)
$$

Filter Transfer Function. A surface wave filter consisting of an input and an output transducer separated by a finite distance can be treated as three separate admittance matrices, as shown in Fig. 2.19.

The admittance matrix $Y^{(2)}$ merely represents a length of piezoelectrically inactive line, and because the electrical terms are all zero it has the particularly simple form

$$
\begin{bmatrix}
Y_{11} & Y_{12} & 0 \\
Y_{21} & Y_{22} & 0 \\
0 & 0 & 0
\end{bmatrix}
$$

In practice the simplest way to solve this circuit is to absorb $Y^{(2)}$ into $Y^{(1)}$ at the chain matrix multiplication stage. If we then wish to solve the circuit approximately and thus neglect the triple transit echo signal, we may do so by assuming the input impedance of $Y^{(3)}$ is Z_0. We can solve (2.63) for F_2 and put $F_2 = A$ in (2.62) to compute the output voltage V_{out}. The triple transit echo referred to here is due to the fact that an electrically loaded transducer has a nonzero acoustic reflection coefficient. Hence, a wave incident on the output transducer is partially reflected

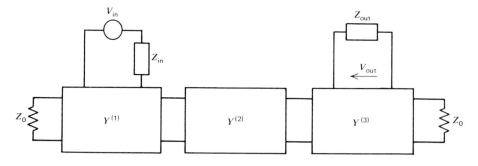

Figure 2.19 Matrix representation of a filter.

back to the input transducer. It is again reflected, and it arrives at the output transducer after making three transits of the intertransducer gap. The effect of this triple transit echo is to produce a small amplitude ripple on the insertion loss frequency response.

If we wish to include the triple transit echo we must first compute the acoustic input impedance of the electrically loaded output transducer and substitute this value for Z_0 in (2.63). This introduces a nonzero reflection coefficient at the output transducer and the triple transit ripple appears in the insertion loss response.

Finally, for purely resistive terminations we may define the insertion loss (in decibels) of the filter via the equation

$$ IL = 20 \log_{10} \left(\frac{V_{in}}{2 V_{out}} \frac{Z_{out}}{Z_{in}} \right) \tag{2.64} $$

and the group delay T by

$$ T = -\frac{d}{d\omega} \left[\arg \left(\frac{V_{out}}{V_{in}} \right) \right] \tag{2.65} $$

2.4 Nonuniform Arrays

So far we have not discussed nonuniform arrays in any detail. In (2.51) we developed the relationship between the frequency response of an array and the Fourier transform of a spatial distribution of assumed delta function sources. This gives us a very useful method of designing interdigital transducers, because the Fourier transform of the desired frequency response yields the required amplitudes of the delta functions. Although, as pointed out, the delta function model is only a first approximation, this design method has proved extremely useful. The main problem lies in getting from the required delta function distribution to the actual array geometry. Three types of weighting are possible, namely, finger-width weighting, finger-overlap weighting, and finger-pitch weighting. Any or all of these types of weighting may be used in the same device; however, because they are to a great extent independent, they are discussed separately. Also, since it is not the purpose of this chapter to deal with device synthesis, we concentrate on aspects of analysis by equivalent circuits.

Finger-Width Weighting. The simplest way of weighting the amplitude of the effective delta functions is by varying the width of successive fingers in the array, as shown in Fig. 2.20. The required values of transmission

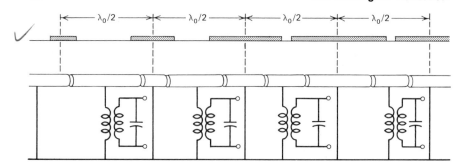

Figure 2.20 Schematic showing relation between equivalent circuit model and metalization for an interdigital transducer with finger-width weighting.

line length, k^2, C_0, and α can then be obtained from the graphs presented in Fig. 2.17. The appropriate value of mark-to-space ratio being taken as the average mark-to-space ratio for the half-finger pair in question. However if one thinks strictly in terms of a plate model, there is a slight ambiguity that must be resolved before this can be done. Because C_0 and $\alpha\lambda_0/2$ are fixed for a given mark-to-space ratio (Fig. 2.17), and, because for a plate model, $C_0 = \epsilon A/(\gamma\lambda_0/2)$ where ϵ is permittivity and A is area, we find that the *wave area* A, and hence the characteristic impedance $Z_c = \rho v A$, is a function of mark-space ratio. This implies a large mechanical reflection coefficient between sections of unequal mark-to-space ratio, a phenomenon that is not observed in practice. This problem may be resolved by assuming that the sections of inactive transmission line act as matching transformers to match the active sections of transmission line. In terms of the equivalent circuit parameters this matching may be included by assuming that the continuous parameters in the chain matrix representation are $F/Z_c^{1/2}$ and $\dot{\xi}Z_c^{1/2}$ instead of F and $\dot{\xi}$. On normalizing the equivalent circuit equations to these new variables we obtain exactly the same result we would have obtained had we assumed $Z_c = 1$ throughout. This is, however, perhaps a slightly more rigorous way of considering the problem.

It is appropriate to mention here that the preceding normalization procedure in no way invalidates the use of the alternative interaction parameter β discussed earlier, because we can make the normalized $Z_0 = 1$ and the normalized $Z_c = (1 - \beta k^2)$.

Finger-Pitch Weighting. An example of a finger-pitch-weighted array is shown in Fig. 2.21. In this case the mark-to-space ratio is (usually) held at 1:1, and the separation between finger centers is varied. The main

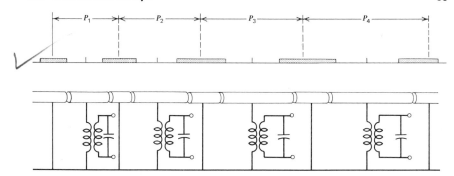

Figure 2.21 Schematic showing relation between equivalent circuit model and metalization for an interdigital transducer with finger-pitch weighting.

reason for pitch weighting is to obtain a specific dispersion characteristic as, for example, in a pulse compression filter.

The application of the equivalent circuit to this geometry is exactly the same as previously described for the finger-width-weighted case, often with the added advantage that the mark-to-space ratio is constant throughout.

Finger-Length Weighting. The third method of weighting transducers is finger-length (or overlap) weighting, also known as apodization. In this case the source strengths are weighted by varying the amount of finger overlap, as shown in Fig. 2.22. This geometry leads to a two dimensional

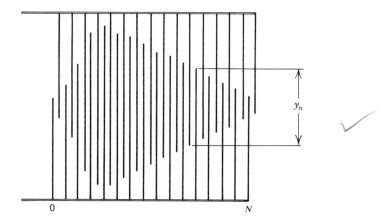

Figure 2.22 Schematic exhibiting the principle of finger-length weighting; also called apodization.

diffraction problem that does not lend itself easily to analysis by equivalent circuits.

The method used, first proposed by Tancrell and Holland,[17] assumes there is no diffraction, and thus waves generated at a particular point along a finger's length propagate directly to the same point on another finger. Thus this wave only affects fingers that lie in its path, so that the finger-length-weighted filter can be divided into a set of parallel unweighted filters, as shown in Fig. 2.23. The virtue of this approach is that the unweighted filter in each strip can be separately analyzed by an equivalent circuit.

However when computing the transfer function of such a filter, it must be remembered that each subfilter is electrically loaded by all the others

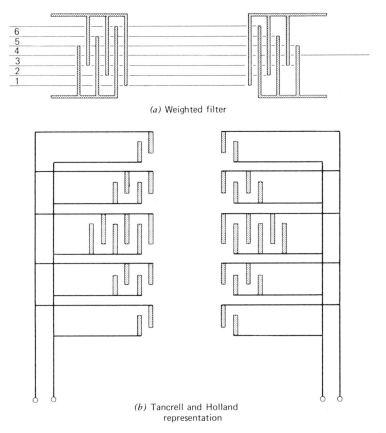

(a) Weighted filter

(b) Tancrell and Holland
representation

Figure 2.23 Schematic showing the principle underlying analysis of a finger-length weighted filter by equivalent circuits.

(except, of course, for short circuit termination). The easiest way of treating this problem is to reduce each subfilter in the network from its four port representation (two acoustic and two electrical ports) to a two port form by including the acoustic terminations in the admittance matrix. This yields a 2×2 complex matrix instead of a 4×4 purely imaginary matrix. Once the two-port admittance matrices for each strip have been computed, the total admittance matrix for the whole network is simply the sum of the matrices for each strip. The stages in this reduction process are shown in Fig. 2.24.

We now consider how the delta function model can be modified to handle finger-length-weighted structures. In order to do this we must first reconsider the meanings of source strength and receiving strength. In (2.44) we identified the amplitude of force generated by a voltage-driven bar as $\frac{1}{2}\phi V$. However, in the present case it is more convenient to define our sources in terms of force per unit finger length. For a finger of length y our new source becomes $\phi V/2y$. This new source is independent of y because both C_0 and Z_c are proportional to y.

Receiving strength was not specifically defined. We now define it as the short circuit current I_s from a bar when a force F_1 is applied to one of its acoustic ports, and the other acoustic port is terminated in Z_c. By use of (2.43) it can be shown, that

$$I_s = \frac{\phi}{Z_c}[1 - \exp(-j\theta)]F_1 \qquad (2.66)$$

which depends only on F_1 and is independent of the finger length y.

Finally, we define a one dimensional stress τ as dF/dy, so that, in terms of this stress, (2.66) can be rewritten in the form

$$I_s = \frac{\phi}{Z_c}[1 - \exp(-j\theta)]\int_0^y \tau\, dy \qquad (2.67)$$

With the preceding definitions we are in a position to apply the delta function model to a finger-length-weighted structure. Let the source strengths of (2.45) be redefined as sources of stress τ, we then have the stress τ_B arriving at point B in Fig. 2.14b given by

$$\tau_B = \exp\left(\frac{-j\omega X}{v}\right)\sum_{n=1}^{N} A_n \exp\left(\frac{j\omega x_n}{v}\right) \qquad (2.68)$$

If the receiving finger at point B is of length Y we have by (2.67)

$$I_s \propto \int_0^Y \exp\left(\frac{-j\omega X}{v}\right)\sum_{n=1}^{N} A_n \exp\left(\frac{j\omega x_n}{v}\right) dy \qquad (2.69)$$

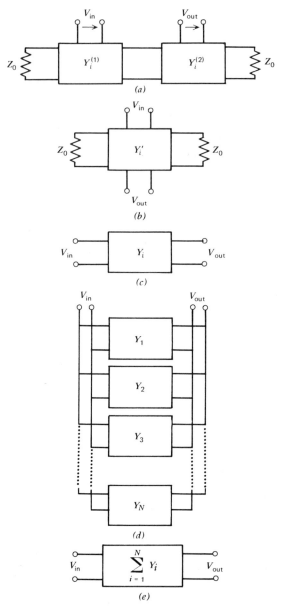

Figure 2.24 Schematic showing the matrix reduction stages used in the analysis of a finger-length weighted transducer. (a), (b), and (c). Reduction of the representation of a single strip from two three-port matrices to one two-port matrix. (d) Representation of the two-port matrices for the several strips. (e) Final two-port matrix representation of the transducer.

Changing the order of summation and integration, we have

$$I_s \propto \exp\left(\frac{-j\omega X}{v}\right) \sum_{n=1}^{N} A_n y_n \exp\left(\frac{j\omega x_n}{v}\right) \tag{2.70}$$

where y_n is the length of the finger at position x_n. *For this to be true Y must be greater than the largest y_n.*

Thus we have shown that in some cases the delta function model can be applied to finger-length weighting simply by making the source strengths proportional to the finger lengths. However some caution must be exercised when doing this, for if both transmitter and receiver are finger-length weighted, it is not correct to apply (2.51) with these modified source strengths, because a very short finger in the receiver does not "see" any weighting on the transmitter. The correct modified form of (2.51) is

$$V_{\text{out}} \propto \sum_{m=1}^{M} \left[B_m \exp\left(\frac{-j\omega X_m}{v}\right) \sum_{n=1}^{N} \int_{0}^{Y_m} A_n \exp\left(\frac{j\omega x_n}{v}\right) dy \right] \tag{2.71}$$

Also, (2.46) is not valid with these modified source strengths, because for the case of an isolated transducer, there is no integration of the amplitudes of stress by a receiving finger. Instead the acoustic output power is worked out as follows. The stress crossing an incremental line δy at point B is $\tau(y)$. The force is thus $\tau(y)\delta y$, and the power is $\|[\tau(y)\delta y]\|^2/Z_c\,\delta y$, where Z_c is the characteristic impedance per unit y. Hence we have the total power given by

$$P = \int_{0}^{y} \frac{|\tau(y)|^2\, dy}{Z_c} \propto \int_{0}^{Y} \left| \sum A_n \exp\left(\frac{j\omega x_n}{v}\right) \right|^2 dy \tag{2.72}$$

which does not give the same results as (2.46).

Finally we point out that although it is tempting to reduce the equivalent circuit to its one dimensional form in an analogous way, by multiplying the transformer ratios by y_n, this is not recommended. The risk of applying it inappropriately is very high. In particular it could give rise to an incorrect value for the input admittance of an isolated transducer, because it would yield a value given by (2.46) (with $A_n \to A_n y_n$) instead of the correct value given by (2.72).

Limitations. The most serious limitation on using the equivalent circuit for analysis of nonuniform arrays is lack of flexibility. This results from the fact that having set up the equivalent circuit, we have essentially represented the interdigital transducer as a series of bulk wave transducers each having an effective wave area (Fig. 2.11) dictated by the geometry of the specific finger pair. For a finger-width or period-weighted filter these wave areas are different for different fingers, so that the abrupt discontinuities in acoustic impedance between fingers must be removed by some artificial means. This is a reasonable approximation providing consecutive fingers do not have vastly different geometries. If they do, it is likely the equivalent circuit will yield an inaccurate result.

The problem is perhaps most severe in the finger-length-weighted case in which diffraction could invalidate the arguments set out in the previous section. However, although it is virtually impossible to apply diffraction corrections to the equivalent circuit representation, it is a relatively simple matter to include diffraction corrections in the delta function model by calculating the modified stress distribution on the receiving finger instead of using (2.69).

Applications of Models to Devices. A number of models have been described and an appropriate choice must be made for the analysis of a specific device. Generally the available computer capacity determines the level of sophistication in the basic model. This level has to be reduced with increasing size and complexity of the device. The active section of the model can take three forms:

1.   Cross-field model without velocity mismatch.
2.   Cross-field model with velocity mismatch.
3.   In-line field model.

Model 1 does not predict acoustic interactions. These are predicted by model 2 only if inactive sections are included to provide acoustic mismatch. Model 3 predicts interactions with or without inactive sections. The delta function model, which can be formulated directly from Green's function theory,[20,21] provides as much information as model 1. This follows from the theory of complex functions, which shows that the imaginary part of the mechanical component of admittance is the Hilbert transform of the real part given by (2.46). Interactions can also be included in the delta function model, but this tends to defeat its simplicity.

The computed radiation conductance of a 78 finger-pair transducer on YZ lithium niobate is shown in Fig. 2.25. Experimental results due to Jones et al.[19] are shown for comparison with three models, model 1 with $\alpha = 0$, $\beta = 0$, $\gamma = 2/3$; model 2 with $\alpha = 0$, $\beta = 0.5$, $\gamma = 2/3$; and model 3 with $\alpha = 0.5$, $\beta = 0$, and $\gamma = 2/3$. Models 2 and 3 are seen to predict the correct distortion caused by interaction. Model 3 also predicts a shift in

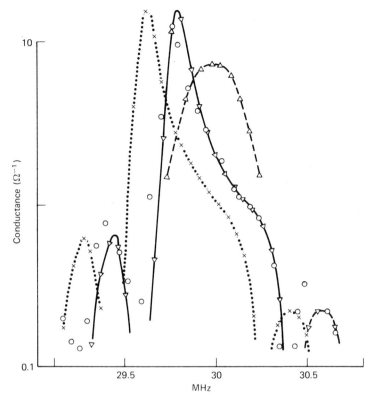

Figure 2.25 Radiation conductance versus frequency characteristic for a 78-finger-pair transducer on YZ lithium niobate. Curve with x from the plate model with $\alpha = 0.05$. Curve with ∇ from the bar model with $\beta = 0.5$. Curve with Δ from the bar model with $\beta = 0$. Curve with $\bigcirc$ experimental data according to reference 20. Copyright 1972 by the Institute of Electrical and Electronic Engineers, Inc. Reprinted, with permission, from *IEEE Trans.* **SU-19,** 1972, p. 376.

frequency, but this can easily be compensated by normalization of velocity.

The equivalent circuit model is normally used for analysis in the second stage of a design routine following synthesis by the delta function model, so that the effect of interactions and loading impedance on passband shape can be studied. Finally, one can use a form of the more rigorous analysis described in Section 2.1 to examine the effects of exact field distribution and bulk waves. Recently more general versions of both the field analysis and the equivalent circuit model have been reported. Finally, we summarize the uses and limitations of the models described here by means of Table 2.1.

Table 2.1 Uses and Limitations of Equivalent Circuit Models

Model		Termination in Arbitrary Z	Triple Transit	Diffraction	Attenuation in Substrate	Bulk Wave Generation	Interactions	Frequency Response	Group Delay	Input Admittance	Impulse Response	Advantages	Disadvantages
		Effects Possible to Include						Predictions					
Bar model without mismatch	$\lambda/2$	✓	✓	×	✓	×	×	✓	✓	✓	✓	Simplicity	Too restricted
	Variable	✓	✓	×	✓	×	×	✓	✓	✓	✓	Simplicity	Does not include interactions
Bar model with mismatch	$\lambda/2$	✓	✓	×	✓	×	×	✓	✓	✓	✓	Simplicity	Does not include interactions
	Variable	✓	✓	×	✓	×	✓	✓	✓	✓	✓	Includes interaction, more versatile	Computing time if finger-length weighted
Plate model	$\lambda/2$	✓	✓	×	✓	×	✓	✓	✓	✓	✓	Includes interaction	Computing time if finger-length weighted
	Variable	✓	✓	×	✓	×	✓	✓	✓	✓	✓	Includes interaction, more versatile	Computing time if finger-length weighted
δ-Function model	$\lambda/2$	×	×	✓	✓	×	×	✓	✓	×[b]	✓	Great simplicity	Restricted
	Variable	×	×	✓	✓	×	×	✓	✓	×[b]	✓	Great simplicity	Restricted
δ-Function model plus Hilbert Transform	$\lambda/2$	✓	✓	×	✓	×	×	✓	✓	✓	✓	Same as bar model without mismatch	
	Variable	✓	✓	×	✓	×	×	✓	✓	✓	✓		
Rigorous analysis		✓	✓	×[a]	×	✓	✓	✓	✓	✓	✓	Accurate	Excessive computer time

[a] Not with two-dimensional analysis.
[b] Real part only.

Acknowledgments. Much of the work reported here was supported financially by the Science Research Council, United Kingdom, and by the Ministry of Defence, United Kingdom, and the authors gratefully acknowledge this assistance.

References

1. S. Ramo, J. R. Whinnery, and T. Van Duzer. *Fields and Waves in Communication Electronics*, Wiley, New York, 1965.

2. C. A. A. J. Greebe et al. "Electric coupling properties of acoustic and electric surface waves." *Phys. Rep.* **1C,** 235 (1971).

3. J. F. Nye. *Physical Properties of Crystals*, Oxford University Press, New York, 1957, pp. 113, 134.

4. J. J. Campbell and W. R. Jones. "A method for estimating optimal crystal cuts and propagation directions for excitation of piezoelectric surface waves." *IEEE Trans.* **SU-15,** 209 (1968).

5. H. Engan. "Excitation of elastic surface waves by spatial harmonics of interdigital transducer." *IEEE Trans.* **ED-16,** 1014 (1969).

6. J. Brown and E. V. D. Glazier. *Telecommunications*, Chapman and Hall, New York, 1964, Appendix A.

7. P. M. Morse and H. Feshbach. *Methods of Theoretical Physics*, Part I, McGraw-Hill, New York, 1953, Chap. 4.

8. K. A. Ingebritsen. "Surface waves in piezoelectrics." *J. Appl. Phys.* **40,** 2681 (1969).

9. R. Holland and E. P. Eer Nisse. *Design of Resonant Piezoelectric Devices*, M.I.T. Press, Cambridge, 1969.

10. W. R. Smith et al. "Analysis of interdigital surface wave transducers by use of an equivalent circuit model." *IEEE Trans.* **MTT-17,** 856 (1969).

11. R. F. Milsom and M. Redwood. "Interdigital piezoelectric Rayleigh wave transducer; an improved equivalent circuit." *Electron. Lett.* **7,** 217 (1971).

12. L. Cairo and T. Kahan. *Variational Techniques in Engineering*, Van Nostrand, New York, 1965, Chap. 7.

13. R. F. Milsom and M. Redwood. "Piezoelectric generation of surface waves by interdigital array; variational method of analysis." *Proc. IEE* **118,** 831 (1971).

14. R. F. Milsom, N. H. C. Reilly, and M. Redwood. "Analysis of generation and detection of surface and bulk acoustic waves by interdigital transducers." To be published in *IEEE Trans., Sonics Ultrasonics*.

15. M. Redwood. "Experiments with the electrical analogy of a piezoelectric transducer." *J. Acoust. Soc. Amer.* **36,** 1872 (1964).

16. W. P. Mason. *Electromechanical Transducers and Wave Filters*, 2nd ed., Van Nostrand, New York, 1948, pp. 200, 399.

17. R. Tancrell and M. Holland. "Acoustic surface wave filters." *Proc. IEEE* **59,** 393 (1971).

18. T. Krairojananan and M. Redwood. "Equivalent electrical circuits of interdigital transducers for the piezoelectric generation and detection of Rayleigh waves." *Proc. IEE* **118,** 305 (1971).

19. T. Krairojananan and M. Redwood. "Piezoelectric generation and detection of ultrasonic surface waves by interdigital electrodes: an electrical equivalent circuit." *Electron. Lett.* **5,** 134 (1969).

20. W. S. Jones, C. S. Hartmann, and T. D. Sturdivant. "Second order effects in surface wave devices." *IEEE Trans.* **SU-19,** 368 (1972).

21. R. F. Mitchell and M. Redwood. "The generation of sound by nonuniform piezoelectric materials." *Ultrasonics* **7,** 123 (1969).

22. R. F. Mitchell and M. Redwood. "Generation and detection of sound by distributed piezoelectric sources." *J. Acoust. Soc. Amer.* **47,** 701 (1970).

THREE

Principles of Surface Wave Filter Design

R. H. TANCRELL

Raytheon Research Division
Waltham, Massachusetts

Surface wave filters belong to the class of filters known as transversal filters. This chapter explains the operation of this class of filters and their implementation by surface wave technology. Methods of synthesis and design are described, and a variety of filter geometries are discussed, each with a particular advantage. The primary second order effects that perturb filter response from the response expected from a simple model are examined, and the effect of external circuits on filter performance is explored.

Most of us view electronic filtering as a frequency selective process, best visualized in the frequency domain, by which one band of frequencies passes through the filter (the passband), and other frequencies are rejected (the stopband). In conventional filter networks, consisting of inductive (L) and capacitive (C) elements, these passbands and stopbands result from resonances in the series and parallel branches of the network, which cause open and short circuited branches and alter the impendance of the network. The resonances occur at particular frequencies determined by the capacitance and inductance of the reactive elements. A desired frequency response is achieved by adjusting the resonant frequencies of these lumped elements.

Frequency filtering can also be accomplished by physical processes viewed in the time domain. The incoming signal is viewed as a propagating wave. Filtering is achieved by passing the signal through a number of delay paths and adding these delayed signals. Under some conditions all the delayed signals add constructively (the passband) and under other conditions they add destructively (the stopband). A schematic diagram of the signal flow through such a filter is shown in Fig. 3.1. The filter consists of N taps separated by delays D_n, and each tap is weighted by a coefficient a_n. As the input signal enters the filter it is first multiplied by a coefficient a_1, and this signal appears at the output. After the signal has passed through a delay D_2 it is multiplied by a coefficient a_2, and this signal is added to that part of the input signal now passing through the first weighted tap. The process continues as the signal passes down the delay line, and the individual outputs from each tap are added together to form the output voltage of the filter.

This type of filter, called a *transversal filter*, was first introduced by Kallman[1] in the 1940s for application to television circuits. Television reproduction, especially color TV, is sensitive to erratic delays in the signal filters. Kallman was seeking filters whose delay response was constant, but whose amplitude response rolled off. Transversal filters can have this type of response. Although conceptually sound and effective in

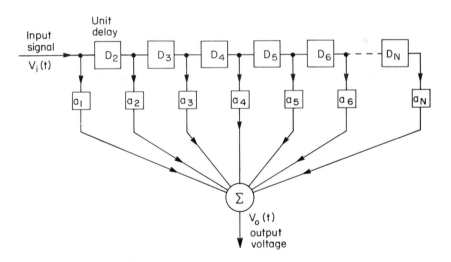

Figure 3.1 Schematic diagram of a transversal filter showing the signal flow from input to output. The delay D_1 is taken as zero delay and is not shown. Copyright 1974 by The Institute of Electrical and Electronic Engineers, Inc. Reprinted, with permission, from *IEEE Trans.* **SU-21**, 1974, p. 13.

the laboratory, transversal filters found only limited use because of difficulty in achieving the necessary time delays. Delays between taps were usually achieved with coaxial cable, which required about 500 cm of cable for each delay when the taps were separated by one wavelength at 40 MHz. The filters were too cumbersome except where no other technique was adequate. With the advent of surface wave transducers, transversal filters became practical. When an electromagnetic signal is converted to an acoustic signal on the surface of a piezoelectric substrate, the wavelength is reduced by a factor of 10^5, which makes the tap separation of the order of 0.01 cm, a dimension compatible with integrated circuit technology.

3.1 Transversal Filters and Their Surface Wave Implementation

Before describing the implementation of a surface wave transversal filter we derive the response of a general transversal filter. The frequency response of a transversal filter can be derived by considering a cw signal of frequency f passing through the delay paths shown in Fig. 3.1. The input signal $V_i(t)$ can be written in the usual complex notation $V_{in}(f)e^{i2\pi ft}$. The quantity $V_{in}(f)$ represents the magnitude and phase of the input voltage, and the exponential represents the time oscillations. The voltage at the filter output is the sum of the signals at each tap. Each signal has been delayed by a time D_n and multiplied by a weighting factor a_n. Mathematically, for a total of N taps, we can write

$$V_{out}(f) = V_{in}(f) \sum_{n=1}^{N} a_n e^{-i2\pi fD_n} \qquad (3.1)$$

The exponent $(2\pi fD_n)$ can be viewed as the phase angle of the cw signal at the nth tap. The time-dependent term $e^{i2\pi ft}$ has been dropped. The frequency response of the filter $H(f)$ is defined as the ratio of the output to input voltages at that frequency:

$$H(f) = \frac{V_{out}(f)}{V_{in}(f)} = \sum_{n=1}^{N} a_n e^{-i2\pi fD_n} \qquad (3.2)$$

As can be seen from (3.2), two sets of variables define the filter: the weighting coefficients a_n and the delay time between taps D_n. The frequency response can be changed by altering one or the other of these variables, or both. The weighting coefficients a_n are pure real numbers in this chapter, except where specifically noted. The delays are also pure real numbers and appear in a complex exponent in (3.2). Each separate term in this equation has an amplitude a_n and a phase $(2\pi fD_n)$.

— sign indicates delay

$z = e^{j\omega t}$

z^{-1} delay : $e^{-j\omega t}$ delay ·

The frequency response $H(f)$ is a vector sum of these terms and hence both amplitude and phase of $H(f)$ are affected by a change in only one of the variables a_n or D_n.

The significance of (3.2) will be illustrated by two examples. For simplicity a uniform delay between the taps is assumed; that is, all D_n's are equal to the same value D. The difference between the two examples is the number of taps in the filter and the tap weighting. The first filter has 15 taps, all with the same weighting coefficient. These coefficients are graphically shown in Fig. 3.2. The total delay length of the filter is designated as T (seconds). The frequency response corresponding to this set of coefficients is computed by using (3.2) and is depicted in Fig. 3.3. As shown, the filter response has a bandpass characteristic with a $|\sin f/f|$ shape. Note that the bandwidth of the filter (at the 4 dB points) is inversely proportional to the total length of the transversal filter T. This illustrates an important property of transversal filters: To obtain a narrow bandwidth, the physical length must be relatively large. In addition to its main central response this filter has smaller responses on either side of the main passband. These *sidelobes* are usually undesirable; in this example these subsidiary responses are only 13 dB less than the main response. Usually the specifications for a filter require sidelobes that are 40 or 50 dB below the main response. The second example has reduced sidelobes. The weighting coefficients are graphically displayed in Fig. 3.4.

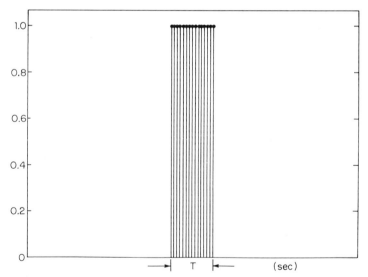

Figure 3.2 Weighting coefficients for a filter with 15 taps, all of them the same magnitude. The taps are uniformly spaced by a time D. The total length of the filter T is equal to $14 \times D$.

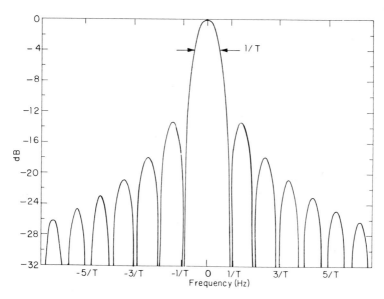

Figure 3.3 Frequency response of a transversal filter having the weighting coefficients shown in Fig. 3.2. Note that the bandwidth is $1/T$.

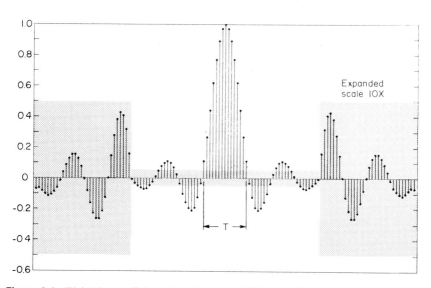

Figure 3.4 Weighting coefficients for a filter with 127 taps uniformly spaced by a time D. The central group of taps has a time duration $T = 14 \times D$. Copyright 1974 by The Institute of Electrical and Electronic Engineers, Inc. Reprinted, with permission, from *IEEE Trans.* **SU-21,** 1974, p. 20.

The corresponding frequency response is shown in Fig. 3.5. Note that the bandpass has a much squarer shape than the $|\sin f/f|$ response and that the sidelobes have been reduced to -60 dB. Both of these desirable properties are a result of the large number of taps, 127 in this second filter, and their varying magnitude.

We now note the important fact that there is a Fourier transform relationship between the filter variables (a_n and D_n) and the frequency response of the filter. Briefly this can be seen from the previous examples. The rectangular envelope of the coefficients in Fig. 3.2 yields a frequency response with a $|\sin f/f|$ shape in Fig. 3.3, and conversely the weighting coefficients with roughly a $\sin t/t$ envelope of Fig. 3.4 yield an almost rectangular frequency response in Fig. 3.5. One method of proving this relationship is to consider the abscissa of Fig. 3.4 as defining a variable t and the lines as defining delta functions with spacing D_n. We can express Fig. 3.4 as an equation in the form

$$v(t) = \sum_{n=1}^{N} a_n \delta(t - D_n) \tag{3.3}$$

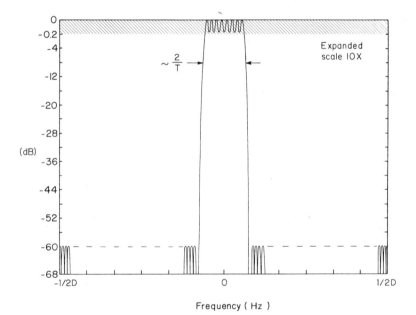

Frequency (Hz)

Figure 3.5 Frequency response of a transversal filter having the weighting coefficients shown in Fig. 3.4. The response is rectangular with small uniform ripples in the passband and stopbands. Copyright 1974 by The Institute of Electrical and Electronic Engineers, Inc. Reprinted, with permission, from *IEEE Trans.* **SU-21**, 1974, p. 19.

where $\delta(t - D_n)$ is the Dirac delta function. Here we have assigned a delta function source with its weighting factor to every tap. Alternatively, (3.3) can be viewed as the output voltage as an electrical impulse travels through the filter; that is, (3.3) is the filter impulse response. The Fourier transform of (3.3) is

$$\int_{-\infty}^{\infty} \sum_{n=1}^{N} a_n \delta(t - D_n) e^{-i2\pi f t}\, dt = \sum_{n=1}^{N} a_n e^{-i2\pi f D_n} \qquad (3.4)$$

Note that the right side of this expression is identical to the frequency response $H(f)$ given by (3.2). Thus we have the important and convenient Fourier transform relationship between the filter variables a_n and D_n of a transversal filter and the filter frequency response $H(f)$. We can proceed backward from a desired frequency response $H(f)$ to the coefficients that produce this response by taking an inverse Fourier transform to obtain the coefficients in the form of (3.3). Because the Fourier transform has a unique inverse transform, we have a powerful tool for synthesizing transversal filters.

Surface Wave Implementation of a Transversal Filter.   Thus far we have described the operation of transversal filters in general with no particular emphasis on their surface wave implementation. In this section we see how an interdigital transducer can approximate an ideal transversal filter. We use a simplified model of the transducer to understand the main features of its operation as a transversal filter.

As shown in Fig. 3.6, the interdigital transducer consists of metal electrodes of alternating polarity on a piezoelectric surface. The electrodes are the taps of the transversal filter, and the bus bars are the summing mechanism.

In the equations of motion for a piezoelectrically coupled surface wave, the electric field gradient can be considered a driving term that generates a surface wave when a voltage is applied across the transducer. The electric field gradient is largest at the edges of the metal electrodes,[2] and we approximate the electric field gradient by delta functions at the edges as sketched in Fig. 3.6. This simple model neglects the fact that an external generator or load resistor will change the behavior of transducers. Such "loading" is usually small and can be neglected in a first approximation. The delta function model is valid for piezoelectric substrates with small coupling constants, and in spite of its simplicity the model is a very good first approximation to the operation of a transducer even on high coupling materials such as lithium niobate.

In the following analysis we assume the transducer is driven by a cw voltage source, so that a cw traveling wave is launched from the transducer at the drive frequency f. Two waves are launched, one to the left

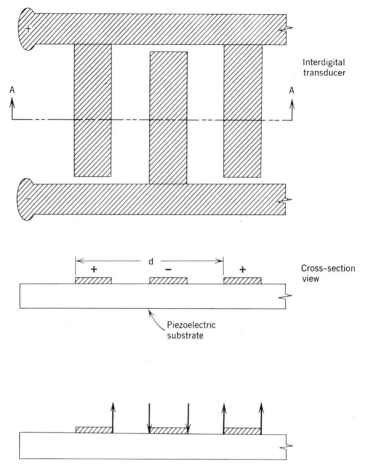

Figure 3.6 At the top is shown an interdigital transducer where the shaded regions represent metal electrodes connected to bus bars, usually made of aluminum. The center figure shows a cross section view of the electrodes. The arrows in the bottom figure represent delta-function sources of acoustic waves at the edges of each electrode.

and one to the right, traveling with a velocity v. The acoustic wave generated by the entire transducer is simply the sum of the contributions from each delta function source. All electrodes attached to a common bus bar are driven by a common voltage and hence generate waves with the same time phase, but since the electrodes have different positions along the transducer, each wave has a different phase factor when it reaches the end of the transducer. If we drive the transducer on the left in Fig. 3.7,

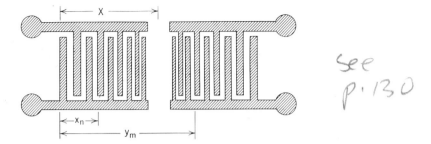

see p. 130

Figure 3.7 Input and output transducers for a surface wave filter. Copyright 1971 by The Institute of Electrical and Electronic Engineers, Inc. Reprinted, with permission, from *Proc. IEEE* **59**, 1971, p. 393.

the total acoustic wave $A(f)$ at the position X is given by

$$A(f) = \sum_{n=1}^{N} I_n \exp i\frac{2\pi f}{v}(X - x_n) \tag{3.5}$$

where I_n has a value of plus or minus one to indicate the sign of the source, as indicated in Fig. 3.6.* The quantity x_n is the position of the nth source, and N is the total number of sources in the transducer. The transducer is most efficient in producing a surface wave [i.e., $A(f)$ is largest] when the spacing of the electrodes is a half wavelength ($\lambda = v/f = d$ in Fig. 3.6). Note the similarity in the form representing the response of one transducer, equation (3.5), to that of the ideal transversal filter, equation (3.2).

The surface wave filter has an output transducer as shown in Fig. 3.7. As an acoustic wave travels under this transducer, each edge detects the wave under it. In other words the output transducer "samples" the traveling acoustic wave at the edge of each electrode. The detected voltage S_1 at the first edge (at y_1) of the output transducer is given by

$$S_1 = \sum_{n=1}^{N} I_n \exp i\frac{2\pi f}{v}(y_1 - x_n) \tag{3.6}$$

The total output voltage is the summation of the detected voltages at each electrode, because they are attached to common bus bars. As with the

* For simplicity the magnitude of the delta function source is approximated as a constant of unity. Physically the delta function represents the electric field gradient at the electrode edge. If all electrodes are equally spaced, then all field gradients are equal, and this approximation is valid. If the spacing is narrower in one part of the transducer, then the gradient is larger for the narrower spacing, and the delta function should increase accordingly. This refinement is considered later in this chapter.

input transducer, each delta function on the output transducer is associated with a sign (of ± 1) indicative of the bus bar to which that electrode is attached. The transfer function $H(f)$ of the total filter is a sum of terms like (3.6) for each edge of the output transducer. When the input transducer has N and the output transducer has M edges,

$$H(f) = \sum_{m=1}^{M} \sum_{n=1}^{N} I_n I_m \exp \left[i \frac{2\pi f}{v} (y_m - x_n) \right] \qquad (3.7)$$

$$H(f) = \sum_{n=1}^{N} I_n \exp \left(-i \frac{2\pi f}{v} x_n \right) \sum_{m=1}^{M} I_m \exp \left(i \frac{2\pi f}{v} y_m \right) \qquad (3.8)$$

$$H(f) = H_i(f) H_o^*(f) \qquad (3.9)$$

Equation (3.9) shows explicitly that the transfer function for the filter is the product of the transfer function of the input transducer $H_i(f)$ multiplied by the complex conjugate of the transfer function of the output transducer $H_o(f)$.

An alternate method of deriving the filter response is to look at the impluse response in the time domain rather than the cw frequency response. When an electrical impulse is applied across the terminals of the input transducer, the piezoelectric surface distorts, and an "image" of the transducer source pattern is formed on the surface. This acoustic distortion propagates away from the transducer, travels under the output transducer and induces an output voltage as each delta-function distortion passes under one of the electrodes of the output transducer. Mathematically we can express the impulse response of the input transducer as $h_i(t)$ and that of the output transducer as $h_o(t)$. Then the total impulse response $v_{\text{imp}}(t)$ is given by the correlation of the two responses

$$v_{\text{imp}}(t) = \int_{-\infty}^{\infty} h_i(\tau + t) h_o(\tau) \, d\tau \qquad (3.10)$$

The impulse response has a finite time duration, because the output voltage is zero after the "image" of the input transducer has traveled beyond the output transducer. For this reason these transversal filters are often called *finite impulse response* filters. The frequency response can be obtained mathematically from (3.10) by taking a Fourier transform of this impulse response. From a well-known theorem in transform theory the Fourier transform of the correlation integral becomes the product $H_i(f) H_o^*(f)$, which is the same result as derived in (3.9).

The equations governing the operation of a surface wave filter are almost identical to those of the general transversal filter described earlier.

The distinctions are small, but worthy of examination. Because of the interdigitated structure of the transducer, the delta functions* reverse sign at each electrode (as in Fig. 3.6) and cannot be of all the same sign, as shown in Fig. 3.2. This means these filters must be bandpass filters rather than low-pass filters centered at zero frequency. The center frequency of the passband is determined by the spacing of the electrodes. At the center frequency one period of the transducer corresponds to one acoustic wavelength ($f_0 = v/d$, where d is one period, as shown in Fig. 3.6). A second distinction between a general transversal filter and the surface wave implementation is that only one array of taps is used in the transversal filter Fig. 3.1, but the surface wave filter uses two arrays of taps, so that the filter response is shared by the two transducers. A designer is at liberty to choose any two factors, $H_i(f)$ and $H_o^*(f)$, to achieve the overall response $H(f)$. Because each factor separately is the Fourier transform of its source distribution, the designer can determine each transducer structure by taking an inverse Fourier transform, in analogy to the procedure described earlier for the ideal transversal filter. The surface wave implementation is effectively two ideal transversal filters in tandem, which gives a great deal of flexibility in design.

In addition to the response at the center frequency f_0, the transducer responds at the odd harmonics of f_0. The first harmonic is the largest and is the response for which the delta function model is à good representation. Evaluation of the higher harmonic responses requires an analysis of the electric fields produced by the electrodes.[3]

Weighted Transducers. Thus far the interdigital structures we have been discussing have only a delay variable x_n. The amplitude I_n has a fixed magnitude. In order to achieve any desired frequency response, the electrodes must be amplitude-weighted also. Conceptually the most straightforward scheme is to place a different voltage on each electrode and in this way "weight" its contribution to the frequency response. The equation for $H(f)$ for each transducer would have the form of (3.2) with the weighting a_n rather than the form of (3.5) where I_n is restricted to ± 1. Physically, implementing this concept is extremely difficult because the small dimensions of each electrode complicate fabrication enormously. Another scheme is to vary the ratio of the electrode width to the gap width in order to change the electric field gradient. This scheme is inadequate because the field strength can only be changed by about a

---

* For simplicity the two delta functions at the edges of each electrode can be approximated by a single delta function at the center of the electrode. This simplification is valid for most purposes. Each electrode then represents a tap of the ideal transversal filter.

factor of 2 and because the exact ratio is difficult to control in photo-lithography. The scheme most commonly used to achieve weighting is to vary the overlap of the electrodes, a technique known as *apodization*.[4]

Apodized Transducers.   Apodized transducers are shown in Figs. 3.8 and 3.9*. In regions without overlap adjacent electrodes have the same polarity and no electric field exists. An acoustic wave is generated only in so called *active regions* where adjacent electrodes of opposite polarity overlap. The amplitude of the acoustic wave generated is the same regardless of the amount of overlap between the electrodes, but the wave has a larger spatial extent where the overlap is large and less where the overlap is small. This difference in the acoustic energy generated at each electrode achieves an indirect weighting of the taps.

Using apodization to achieve weighting has the advantage that fabrication is no more complicated than with unweighted transducers because no additional photolithographic steps are required. Weighting differences of about two orders of magnitude can easily be achieved. A weakness of this weighting technique is related to diffraction of the acoustic beam.[5] The diffraction spreading is larger for waves from electrodes with small overlap than for electrodes with large overlap. This diffraction effect can be compensated during design and is minimal in self-focusing substrates like lithium niobate. Another weakness is that the coefficients of the taps (i.e., the overlap) cannot change by large amounts from one electrode to the next. This restriction arises because each electrode has a neighbor on each side and influences *two* weighting coefficients. In addition, the electric fields extend beyond nearest neighbors tending to smooth out any abrupt changes.

The acoustic beam produced by an apodized transducer is nonuniform in amplitude across the aperture. An example of the acoustic beam is shown in Fig. 3.8 to illustrate the type of wavefront produced. Whereas the beam from an unapodized transducer is uniform and the length of the electrodes does not enter the evaluation of the filter transfer function, the analysis of filters with apodized transducers must incorporate spatial variation. Mathematically we introduce a new variable z along the electrode length. We can *visualize* the transducers as divided into channels, along z, as illustrated by the *imaginary* horizontal lines superimposed on the transducers in Fig. 3.9. For simplicity we neglect diffraction, so that all energy launched in one channel remains in that channel. To evaluate the transfer function mathematically an integral along the electrode

---

* For clarity in illustrating the overlap shape "dummy" electrodes are omitted from these figures. These electrically inactive electrodes are used to complete a uniform array in order to maintain a constant acoustic impedance across the aperture.

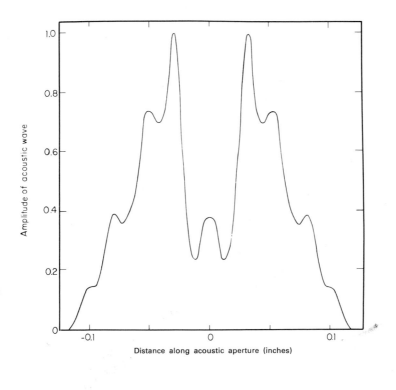

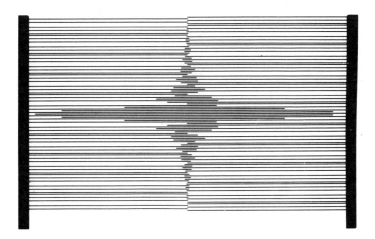

Figure 3.8 Photograph of a transducer apodized with a $(\sin x)/x$ pattern and the amplitude distribution of the acoustic wave launched from this transducer. Amplitude data is obtained by scanning across the aperture with a laser beam.

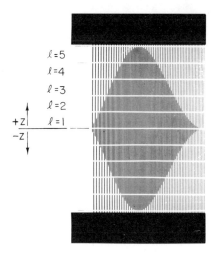
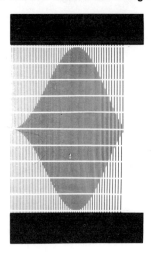

Figure 3.9 Photograph of apodized transducers, shown divided into horizontal strips to illustrate the technique used for analysis. Copyright 1971 by The Institute of Electrical and Electronic Engineers, Inc. Reprinted, with permission, from *Proc. IEEE* **59**, 1971, p. 395.

length must be taken. As one integrates along a receiver edge m, across the beam launched from edge n, the contribution to the transfer function is suppressed where the overlap of either one ends. Therefore, the response caused by an (n, m) pair is weighted by the length of the shorter electrode. If we represent the overlap function for the transmitter as $w(x)$ and that for the reveiver as $g(y)$, this integration leads to

$$H(f) = \sum_n \sum_m C_{nm} I_n I_m \exp\left[i\frac{2\pi f}{v}(y_m - x_n)\right] \qquad (3.11)$$

where C_{nm} is equal to $w(x_n)$ or $g(y_m)$, whichever is *smaller*. This summation does not split into two separate sums, as it did in (3.8) for unapodized transducers, because the term C_{nm} depends on both indices n and m.

An alternative, but mathematically equivalent, expression can be derived by treating each channel (designated by the index l in Fig. 3.9) as a transmitter-receiver pair. Each channel is independent of the other channels, and each channel may have a different number of active electrodes. The total response is the sum of responses for each channel:

$$H(f) = \sum_l \left[\sum_n I_n^l \exp\left(-i\frac{2\pi f}{v}x_n\right) \sum_m I_m^l \exp\left(i\frac{2\pi f}{v}y_m\right)\right] \qquad (3.12)$$

The l index on I_n^l accounts for the apodization, I_n^l has the values ± 1 or 0

according to

$$I_n^l = \pm 1 \qquad \text{if} \quad |w(x_n)| \geq \frac{l}{L} \qquad\qquad (3.13)$$

$$= 0 \qquad \text{if} \quad |w(x_n)| < \frac{l}{L}$$

where L is the total number of channels, and $w(x)$ is the apodization function normalized to unity at its maximum. Similar equations relate I_m^l to the overlap function for the receiver $g(y)$.

Although (3.12) is a simple equation for the response of a pair of apodized transducers, the source distributions for the two transducers cannot be obtained by taking inverse Fourier transforms, as was possible in (3.8) for unapodized transducers. There is no unique inverse transform because (3.12) is a *sum* of Fourier transforms, rather than a single Fourier transform. This fact does not make apodized transducers any less effective for filters, but does make the synthesis procedure more difficult. For this reason, rarely are two apodized transducers used in a filter. Methods for achieving weighting without apodization are not as versatile, but they allow a uniform wavefront and can be used together with an apodized transducer in the same filter. These methods are described below.

The Dogleg Structure. The dogleg structure[6, 7] makes use of the fact that the voltage across adjacent electrodes need not be the same as the voltage on the bus bars. Remember that each electrode pair forms a small capacitor. The dogleg structure "divides" the voltage by segmenting each electrode pair into a group of series-connected capacitors, as shown in Fig. 3.10. The voltage between adjacent electrodes is reduced by the number of sections (J). The name *dogleg* is often given to this technique because of the physical appearance of the jog in the electrodes. It is sometimes called *series weighting* because of the way the voltage reduction is achieved. When a voltage V_a is applied across the bus bars, the voltage between electrodes is V_a/J because there is an equal voltage drop across each of the J sections. Because the amplitude of the acoustic wave launched by the electrodes is proportional to the interelectrode voltage, the acoustic amplitude is proportional to V_a/J and reduced in amplitude by a factor J from that produced by an unsegmented electrode pair.

The manner in which the acoustic amplitude is weighted by the dogleg structure can also be understood from a slightly different viewpoint, namely, in terms of the impedance Z of an electrode pair. First, we note that the impedance of an electrode pair is inversely proportional to the

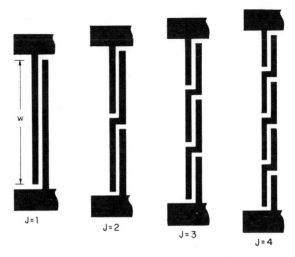

Figure 3.10 Diagrams of the dogleg structure. Each electrode is segmented into J sections to reduce the voltage between the electrodes. Copyright 1974 by The Institute of Electrical and Electronic Engineers, Inc. Reprinted, with permission, from *IEEE Trans.* **MTT-22,** 1974, p. 764.

overlap distance w; see Fig. 3.10, $Z \propto 1/w$. Second, we note that the impedance of *each* section in the dogleg structure is J times larger than an unsegmented electrode pair, because each section is J times shorter. Third, we can compute the total impedance of these J sections in series:

$$Z_{(J \text{ sections})} = J \times (JZ_{(J=1)}) = Z_{(J=1)} \times J^2 \qquad (3.14)$$

We note that the impedance increases as the square of the number of sections in the dogleg. Fourth, we can compute the power in the radiated acoustic wave by evaluating the power dissipated in this impedance. The power is readily shown to be proportional to $1/J^2$. Fifth, since the acoustic amplitude is proportional to the square root of the acoustic power, it is proportional to $1/J$. Thus, we have again shown that the acoustic wave amplitude is proportional to $1/J$, and the beamwidth is the full aperture width.

The advantage of the dogleg structure is that the electrodes can be weighted but their full acoustic aperture still used, thus avoiding diffraction problems and simplifying the design procedure. The dogleg transducer is slightly more difficult to prepare by pattern generation because there are many short electrode sections, but final fabrication involves the same photolithographic steps as for unweighted transducers. The main disadvantage of the configuration is that the weighting coefficients must, be in (integers)$^{-1}$. The values progress in rather crude steps: 1, 0.5, 0.33, 0.25, ... A value of 0.8, for example, cannot be obtained. There are two methods of circumventing this problem. One is to set the maximum weighting to a value other than 1, for example, 5, so that the dogleg for the maximum weighting has five sections. Then the next smaller value is $\frac{5}{6}$ of the maximum rather than $\frac{1}{2}$. The other method is to overlap weight (apodize) each section of the dogleg to obtain intermediate values. This technique leads to nonuniform acoustic wavefronts, as discussed in the section on apodized transducers, but only a small amount of apodization is necessary, since most of the weighting is obtained by the number of sections in the dogleg pattern. Another disadvantage is the limited number (about 50) of sections that the transducer can be divided into before each section becomes so small that the jog in the dogleg (approximately one wavelength long) becomes a significant perturbation. (The size of the jog is exaggerated in Fig. 3.10.)

Withdrawal Weighting. Another method of weighting a transducer without changing the overlap is known as *withdrawal weighting*,[8] Weighting is introduced by selectively withdrawing electrodes to equate the number of electrodes present (averaged over a small section) with the desired weighting function, as illustrated in Fig. 3.11. The basic idea is that the sources in a cluster of electrodes act collectively, so that the acoustic wave amplitude generated by a cluster is proportional to the number of electrodes in it. The resulting weighting is only an approximation to the desired weighting because the changes occur in abrupt steps, and because there are fewer electrodes than in transducers designed according to other weighting schemes. Withdrawal weighting is particularly suited to transducers that have a large number of electrodes and a slowly varying weighting function. For a filter with greater than 20% bandwidth, the number of electrodes is too small to use withdrawal weighting. The withdrawal of any electrode would cause too large a perturbation of the transducer's response. However by gradually changing the electrode spacing along a transducer, for example, by a linear FM "chirp," a large number of electrodes can be used without narrowing the bandwidth, because a large bandwidth is "built into" the transducer by the gradual spacing shange. "Chirped" transducers are particularly suited to weighting by the withdrawal method.

To compute the transfer function of a withdrawal-weighted transducer, we can use (3.5) and carry the sum over only those electrodes that are present. Equation (3.5) treats all electrodes as being equally important. For a more realistic evaluation small corrections should be made, because in fact all electrodes in one cluster do not have equal field strengths.

NOT SO IMP.

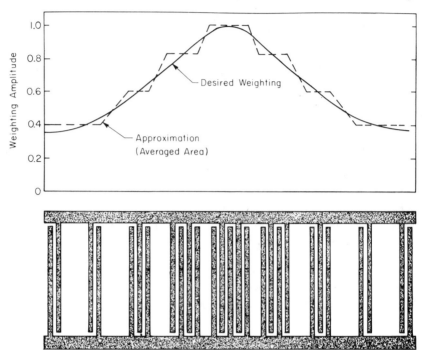

Figure 3.11 Weighting obtained by selective withdrawal of electrodes so that the average electrode density approximates the desired weighting. Copyright 1973 by The Institute of Electrical and Electronic Engineers, Inc. Reprinted, with permission, from *Proc. 1973 IEEE Ultrasonics Symposium*, p. 424.

Electrodes in the center of a cluster have more strength than those on the ends that have no neighboring electrodes to aid them in producing an electric field. Also, the absence of neighboring electrodes tends to shift the effective phase of the waves launched from the remaining electrodes because of a shift in the electric field pattern. The details for these corrections have been computed[8] and are readily included in an iterative computer program for analysis and design.

The advantage of withdrawal weighting is that the acoustic wave is uniform across the aperture, which greatly simplifies the mathematics of analysis and design. Also, the transducer is very simple to draw and fabricate. It is particularly useful in transducers with many electrodes. Its primary disadvantage is that the weighting changes in rather coarse steps.

Phase Reversal Transducers. Another type of transducer, known as a *phase reversal* transducer,[9, 10] contains electrodes of a full acoustic width, but some groups of electrodes are reversed in polarity. The technique is not truly a weighting technique because the electrodes all have equal overlap and voltage. The phase reversals in the transducer, however, change the shape of the frequency response from that of a transducer with continuously alternating polarity. Effectively, the transducer is a "phase coded" rather than an "amplitude weighted" transducer. Not all frequency responses can be achieved by this method, and there is no synthesis procedure whereby the "phase code" can be uniquely selected to achieve a given frequency response. Nevertheless, phase reversal is a particularly useful technique for broadening the response of a uniform transducer that would otherwise have the rounded shape of the $|\sin f/f|$ response. The addition of phase-reversed electrodes on either side of the transducer flattens the response and increases the 3 dB bandwidth. The method is useful when designing broadband filters and is often used in conjunction with an apodized transducer.

Two Theorems on Transducers. It is often helpful when thinking about transducers to have a knowledge of the type of response a transducer will produce without explicitly computing it. The two theorems proved in this section are helpful for quick evaluation of transducers. These general theorems can be proved because the frequency response of a transducer is uniquely related to the position and weighting of the electrodes independently of the technique used for weighting.

First we show that for a transducer symmetric about its center electrode, the group delay is independent of frequency. We prove* this for the case of an odd number of electrodes. The same theorem can also be proved for an even number of electrodes. For a transducer with N electrodes we number the electrode edges from $-N$ to N skipping the number zero. The frequency response is given by

$$H(f) = \sum_{n=-N}^{N} a_n \exp\left(-i\frac{2\pi f}{v}x_n\right) \qquad (3.15)$$

which can be written as two terms for positive and negative n explicitly.

$$H(f) = \sum_{n=-N}^{-1} a_n \exp\left(-i\frac{2\pi f}{v}x_n\right) + \sum_{n=1}^{N} a_n \exp\left(-i\frac{2\pi f}{v}x_n\right) \qquad (3.16)$$

Because the transducer is symmetric, we can impose the relationships that $a_{-n} = a_n$ and that $x_{-n} = U - x_n$, where U is the length of the transducer. Then,

$$H(f) = \sum_{n=N}^{1} a_n \exp\left(i\frac{2\pi f}{v}x_n\right)\exp\left(-i\frac{2\pi f}{v}U\right) + \sum_{n=1}^{N} a_n \exp\left(-i\frac{2\pi f}{v}x_n\right) \qquad (3.17)$$

* Details of the proof may be omitted on a first reading.

which can be rewritten as

$$H(f) = \exp\left(-i\frac{\pi f U}{v}\right) \sum_{n=1}^{N} a_n \left\{ \exp\left[i\frac{2\pi f}{v}\left(x_n - \frac{U}{2}\right) \right] \right.$$

$$\left. + \exp\left[-i\frac{2\pi f}{v}\left(x_n - \frac{U}{2}\right) \right] \right\} \quad (3.18)$$

Note that the term in braces is a real quantity since it is the sum of a complex number plus its complex conjugate. Therefore $H(f)$ has the phase factor $\pi f U/v$, which is linear in frequency. Thus, because group delay is the first derivative of phase with frequency, $H(f)$ has a constant group delay and the frequency response is nondispersive. It should be noted that this nondispersive characteristic holds even if the spacing between the electrodes is nonuniform. The only requirement is that the transducer be symmetric. It also holds for a transducer in which the weighting is achieved by apodization. To prove this we first show that the statement is true for each channel along the aperture (i.e., along z in Fig. 3.9). For any channel l, the frequency response of one transducer is given by

$$H^l(f) = \sum_{n=-N}^{N} I_n^l \exp\left(-i\frac{2\pi f}{v}x_n\right) \quad (3.19)$$

using the same notation as (3.12). Because of the symmetry $I_n^l = I_{-n}^l$ and $x_{-n} = U - x_n$. The remainder of the proof follows exactly as (3.15) to (3.18) for any one channel l. The statement is true for all channels; consequently it is true for the total transducer, because the transducer response is a linear sum of the responses at the individual channels. Thus we have shown that a transducer that is symmetric about its center electrode has a nondispersive frequency response.

Next we show that a transducer with uniform spacing between electrodes has a frequency response whose magnitude is symmetric about the center frequency. This statement is valid regardless of the symmetry of the weighting on the transducer. The frequency response is

$$H(f) = \sum_{n} a_n \exp\left(-i\frac{2\pi f}{v}x_n\right) \quad (3.20)$$

Because we are only interested in the first harmonic response, we can rewrite the equation to explicitly show that response. Equation (3.20) can be written as [similar to (3.3)]

$$H(f) = \int \left[\sum_{n} [a(x)\, \delta(x - x_n)] \exp\left(-i\frac{2\pi f}{v}x\right) dx \right. \quad (3.21)$$

Because the spacing between electrodes is uniform, the term in brackets can be written as the first harmonic component $a(x) \cos [(2\pi f_0 x)/v]$ where the first harmonic frequency f_0 and the spacings satisfy the relationship $(2\pi f_0/v)x_n = (\pi/4)n$. Thus

$$H(f) = \int \left[a(x) \cos \left(\frac{2\pi f_0 x}{v} \right) \right] \exp \left(-i\frac{2\pi f}{v}x \right) dx \qquad (3.22)$$

We are only interested in the response at positive frequencies around f_0. Therefore we can use the complex notation

$$H(f) = \int a(x) \exp \left(i\frac{2\pi f_0}{v}x \right) \exp \left(-i\frac{2\pi f}{v}x \right) dx \qquad (3.23)$$

$$= \int a(x) \exp \left(-i\frac{2\pi(f - f_0)}{v}x \right) dx \qquad (3.24)$$

If we evaluate this expression at frequencies above the center frequency, $f = f_0 + \Delta$,

$$H(f_0 + \Delta) = \int a(x) \exp \left(-i\frac{2\pi\Delta}{v}x \right) dx \qquad (3.25)$$

and at frequencies below the center frequency by the same amount, $f = f_0 - \Delta$

$$H(f_0 - \Delta) = \int a(x) \exp \left(+i\frac{2\pi\Delta}{v}x \right) dx \qquad (3.26)$$

We note that $H(f_0 + \Delta) = H^*(f_0 - \Delta)$. Therefore the magnitude of the frequency response is equal on either side of the center frequency.

$$|H(f_0 + \Delta)| = |H(f_0 - \Delta)| \qquad (3.27)$$

Hence we have proved that the amplitude of the frequency response (first harmonic) is symmetric about the center frequency f_0 for a transducer with uniform spacing between the electrodes whatever the symmetry of the weighting. The corollary can also be proved: A frequency response (first harmonic) whose amplitude is not symmetric about the center frequency can only be produced by a transducer with nonuniform spacing between the electrodes.* Although derived here for unapodized transducers, the proof can be extended to apodized transducers by treating each channel individually.

Transducer Combinations. In this section we develop the response of the whole surface wave filter consisting of two transducers on a

---

* This statement only applies to the first harmonic response. Higher harmonic responses and transducers with more than two electrodes per period may not obey this rule.

piezoelectric substrate. The filter characteristic is due entirely to the combined responses of the transducers. The piezoelectric material itself has no frequency dependent properties. The transducers can be combined in different configurations, and have different kinds of weighting and electrode positioning. In this section various types of configuration are described and compared. The emphasis is on configurations in which both transducers share the burden of shaping the frequency response. The concepts developed here are extended in Chapter 6, where composite *blocks* of transducers combined to formulate a filter are described.

Nondispersive Filters. There are basically two ways to achieve a nondispersive frequency response for a filter. One is to use two nondispersive transducers. The other is to use two identical transducers. As shown previously, a symmetric transducer is nondispersive. Consequently if each transducer is individually symmetric about its center electrode, the total filter is nondispersive. (This statement is true even though the input and output transducers are different, use different weighting techniques, or have nonuniform electrode spacing.)

If the filter has two *identical* transducers the output transducer is a translated version of the input transducer, so that for the mth edge

$$y_m = x_n + S \qquad \text{when } n = m \qquad (3.28)$$

and

$$a_m = a_n \qquad \text{when } n = m \qquad (3.29)$$

(For the notation refer to Fig. 3.7. S is the translation distance.) Thus we can write the transfer function in a form similar to (3.8).

$$H(f) = \sum_n a_n \exp\left(-i\frac{2\pi f}{v}x_n\right) \sum_m a_m \exp\left(i\frac{2\pi f}{v}y_m\right) \qquad (3.30)$$

$$= \sum_n a_n \exp\left(-i\frac{2\pi f}{v}x_n\right) \sum_n a_n \exp\left[i\frac{2\pi f}{v}(x_n + S)\right] \qquad (3.31)$$

$$= \exp\left(i\frac{2\pi f}{v}S\right)\left|\sum_n a_n \exp\left(i\frac{2\pi f}{v}x_n\right)\right|^2 \qquad (3.32)$$

Therefore, $H(f) = \exp(i2\pi fS/v)|H_i(f)|^2$, where $H_i(f)$ is the response of the input transducer. Because the phase $2\pi fS/v$ is linear in frequency, the frequency response of the whole filter is nondispersive. For a pair of identical apodized transducers (3.32) holds for each channel, and therefore the total filter transfer function is nondispersive. Thus the nondispersive property is valid' for apodized and unapodized transducers as long as the transducers are identical. This property is often used to gain the advantages of dispersive transducers when building a nondispersive filter.

One Apodized, One Unweighted Transducer. The first configuration we consider is one transducer overlap weighted and the other with uniform overlap. We will find that the total response $H(f)$ can be factored into the two responses of the individual transducers. Instead of deriving the transfer function directly we note that this filter is a special case of a filter with two apodized transducers, and the transfer function has already been derived and displayed in (3.11). In the present special case the output transducer has constant overlap, and $g(y) = 1$ for all y. Therefore the coefficient C_{nm} in (3.11) is equal to the overlap weighting of the input transducer $w(x_n)$ because it is always smaller than $g(y)$. Hence, (3.11) becomes for this configuration

$$H(f) = \sum_n \sum_m w(x_n) I_n I_m \exp\left[i\frac{2\pi f}{v}(y_m - x_n)\right] \qquad (3.33)$$

$$= \left[\sum_n w(x_n) I_n \exp\left(-i\frac{2\pi f}{v}x_n\right)\right]\left[\sum_m I_m \exp\left(i\frac{2\pi f}{v}y_m\right)\right] \qquad (3.34)$$

$$= H_i(f) H_o^*(f) \qquad (3.35)$$

and the total transfer function is the product of the frequency responses of input and output transducers.

In (3.33) the overlap weighting $w(x_n)$ appears identical to the tap weighting a_n of (3.2), as though $w(x_n)$ were a weighting of the amplitude of the acoustic wave instead of a spatial weighting of the acoustic beam. The fact that the weighting of the wave is contained in the spatial extent of the acoustic beam width is of no consequence, because the output transducer intercepts and integrates this wave independently of its location in the beam. The identity $a_n = w(x_n)$ is a convenient visualization of the operation of this transducer configuration in which one transducer is apodized and the other is unweighted.

Two Apodized Transducers. The transfer function of a filter configuration with two apodized transducers has already been displayed in the two equivalent expressions (3.11) and (3.12). We only mention here the serious disadvantages of this configuration. Diffraction of the acoustic beam causes difficulty because of the variable overlaps and also there is no convenient technique to synthesize the two transducers. Although *analysis* is straightforward once the apodization is specified, the *inverse process* of determining the apodization from a specified frequency response is not possible except by a trial and error procedure. A key point to remember is that the frequency response of a *pair* of *apodized* transducers is *not* the product of the frequency responses of the individual transducers. Because both transducers are apodized, both are sensitive to the spatial position of the acoustic wave.

One Dogleg, One Apodized Transducer.   To derive the transfer function of a filter consisting of one dogleg transducer and one apodized transducer we assume that the nth dogleg electrode is segmented into J_n sections. For the apodized transducer we assume that the mth electrode overlap is proportional to $g(y_m)$. The sum on the channels l can be dropped as in (3.33) because the dogleg transducer performs a uniform integration along the beam width, so that we obtain

$$H(f) = \sum_n \sum_m \frac{I_n}{J_n} g(y_m) I_m \exp\left[-i\frac{2\pi f}{v}(x_n - y_m)\right]$$ (3.36)

This can be easily factored to see that the filter frequency response is the product of the two transducer responses.

Both the dogleg and apodized transducers can be weighted so they contribute equally to the filter response, which is an important advantage. One practical disadvantage is that, because segmenting an electrode pair into a dogleg structure increases its impedance, the impedance of the two transducers may be different, thus making matching more difficult.

Two FM Chirp Transducers.   A nondispersive filter can be built using two identical dispersive transducers. The electrode spacing changes linearly along the input transducer in an FM chirp transducer. The dispersion of the input transducer is removed in the filter by an output transducer which has the same FM chirp so that it has the opposite dispersion. See (3.32). Different frequency responses are obtained by changing the chirp rate. In addition, weighting can be incorporated by electrode withdrawal or by apodization. Transducers with an FM chirp are often used in pulse compression filters[4] in which a net dispersive characteristic is desired. In these filters the chirp transducers are mirror images. A large body of information has been developed on the spectral shapes of chirped waveforms.[11] These results can be used in designing nondispersive filters. Chirped transducers are especially useful for broadband filters, because many electrodes can be used, and the impedance can be altered by changing the chirp rate, as is discussed later in this chapter.

Multistrip Coupler with Two Apodized Transduces.   A multistrip coupler[12] can be placed between two apodized transducers to take advantage of the versatile weighting that can be obtained with overlap-weighting. The multistrip coupler is a group of evenly spaced metal strips much like the electrodes in a transducer but not connected on their ends. Although the operation of a multistrip coupler is interesting in itself, we limit our attention to the salient features important for this application. Refer to Fig. 3.12. When an acoustic wave having unity amplitude and beam width α is incident on the multistrip coupler from the left in track A, the output wave to the right in track B has an amplitude equal to 2α. When a multistrip coupler is inserted between two apodized transducers, as in Fig. 3.13, the spatially-weighted acoustic wavefront generated by the input transducer is converted to a spatially uniform but amplitude weighted acoustic wave for reception by the output transducer. In this way two transducers can be weighted by apodization, and yet the response of the filter is the product $H(f) = H_i(f)H_0^*(f)$. The advantage of this design is that the synthesis procedure can be done easily for each apodized transducer separately. Moreover, the filter response is sharper than when only one transducer is apodized. For instance, when both transducers are identical the stopband ripple is a factor of 2 lower (in dB), the skirt steepness is doubled, and the passband ripples are increased by a factor of 2. The disadvantage is that a larger substrate is required to accommodate the multistrip coupler and the lateral displacement of the transducers into two tracks. The method is limited to high coupling material because the number of strips required for maximum efficiency increases from 110 on lithium niobate to a prohibitively large number on a lower coupling material, like quartz.

Figure 3.13 shows the sharp band edges experimentally achieved[13] by this type of design. Ripple is only 0.4 dB (peak to peak) in the passband,

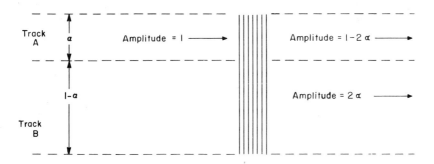

Figure 3.12 Transfer of an acoustic wave in a multistrip coupler from track A to track B for unequal trace widths. Copyright 1973 by The Institute of Electrical and Electronic Engineers, Inc. Reprinted, with permission, from *Proc. 1973 IEEE Ultrasonics Symposium*, p. 421.

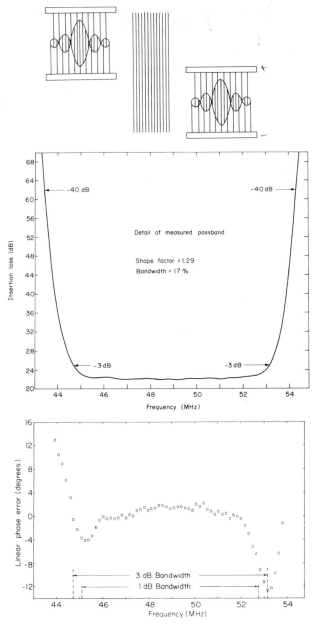

Figure 3.13 Diagram of a filter incorporating a multistrip coupler and the measured amplitude and phase responses for a filter with sharp skirts. The abrupt change in impedance at the band edges causes most of the phase error. Copyright 1973 by the Institute of Electrical and Electronics Engineers, Inc. Reprinted, with permission, from *Proc. 1973 IEEE Ultrasonics Symposium*, p. 421.

and the largest stopband sidelobe is 55 dB below the stopband (offscale in the figure). The skirts are steep: The bandwidth at the -40 dB points is only 1.29 larger than that at the -3 dB points.

3.2 Filter Design and Synthesis

The preceding analysis has developed equations for the transfer functions of surface wave filters. Although the assumed model, a delta function source at the edge of every electrode, is very simple, it is a very good approximation. The same model is the basis for the design procedure to be described here. We show how to take a *desired* transfer function and determine the source positions and weights that will produce that response. We show that the most straightforward approach is to use well-known transform theory to give an initial design, and also show "optimum" filter designs based on more rigorous synthesis procedures.

Network Analysis. Before describing particular methods of filter design, we briefly sketch the relationship of surface wave filters to the more common LC networks from a mathematical viewpoint. There are some fundamental differences in the mathematical formulation of the two types of filters, and consequently the synthesis procedures are different for these two filter technologies. The differences can be seen from the forms of the transfer function for the surface (transversal) filter and an LC ladder network.

The transfer function of a general ladder network is a ratio of two polynomials

$$H(f) = \frac{\sum\limits_{p=0}^{P} a_p f^p}{\sum\limits_{q=0}^{Q} b_q f^q} \tag{3.37}$$

The numerator has P roots and hence $H(f)$ has P zeros. Similarly the denominator has Q roots so that $H(f)$ has Q poles. The poles and zeros are physically the result of resonances of reactive components in the series and parallel branches of the network. When designing an LC filter a designer can distribute the poles and zeros in the complex frequency plane to achieve the best approximation to the desired response. There exists a large literature[14] on the synthesis of LC filters with familiar characteristics, such as Butterworth, Bessel, and Chebyshev.

The transfer function of a surface wave filter has a different form. As can be seen from (3.2), $H(f)$ can be written as a polynomial

$$H(f) = \sum_{n=1}^{N} a_n w^n \tag{3.38}$$

in which $w = \exp(j2\pi fD)$. This function only has zeros. All the poles are combined in an essential singularity at infinity. The absence of poles restricts the degrees of freedom available to the designer. In general, to achieve the same filter shape, a higher order polynomial is required for the transversal filter than for the LC network. Nevertheless a large number of zeros can be easily designed into a surface wave filter because each zero corresponds to one "tap" in the transducer. A hundred zeros are typical in surface wave filters, whereas LC networks are usually constructed with many fewer resonant elements.

The physical reason a surface wave filter has no poles can be readily explained. The response of the filter is essentially a sum of all the acoustic waves launched from each electrode. At some frequencies the waves add destructively. These frequencies are at the zeros of the response. At other frequencies the acoustic waves add constructively, so that they all contribute to the response. Even though waves are adding constructively at a particular frequency, the response has no poles because there is no "resonance." That is, the waves are not reflected back and forth within the transducer to build into a large (ideally infinite) amplitude. Instead waves propagate in only one direction and do not add to themselves by multiple reflections.

Another important feature of surface wave filters can be related to standard network theory. There is a class of filters, known as non-minimum phase filters, in which a desired amplitude characteristic can be achieved while maintaining linear phase in the passband. In contrast, the amplitude and phase responses of minimum phase filters cannot be specified independently but are connected by integral equations derived from the well-known Kramers-Kronig relations.[15] The usual LC ladder network is of the minimum phase type. The designer of LC filters first designs a minimum phase network to the desired amplitude response and then designs an all-pass network (or equalizer) to correct the phase response. Alternatively, the designer can construct a more complicated bridge- or lattice-type network,[16] rather than a ladder network, and eliminate the all-pass network. Lattice networks can have nonminimum phase characteristics, but at the expense of a complicated topology that is difficult to build because there is no common ground connection from input to output. Parasitic effects are also troublesome. Lattice networks have a nonminimum phase capability because there are many paths a signal can take to travel from input to output ports. This multipath feature is a characteristic of surface wave filters. Hence they are ideal for realizing a nonminimum phase response.[15] To understand this point, remember that the wave from any one electrode of the input transducer can reach the output port by the M electrodes of the output transducer. If there are N electrodes on the input transducer the input signal has a total of $N \times M$ paths from input port to output port.

Most textbook synthesis procedures for LC filters are restricted to the minimum phase type.[14] For that reason almost all LC networks are of this type. This fact, combined with the absence of poles in surface wave filters, makes standard LC network theory inapplicable to the design of surface wave filters even though we may desire the usual Butterworth or Chebyshev amplitude characteristics. New design procedures must be formulated.

Related Synthesis Problems. The synthesis of a surface wave filter is very closely allied to synthesis problems encountered in other areas of engineering, in particular for antennas and digital filters.[17] For both these devices the designer must try to design a desired response though restricted to a finite number of elements: radiating antenna dipoles or digital registers. In the surface wave case the restriction is the finite number of electrodes in the transducer. Because all these devices are transversal filters much of the theory developed in one area can be applied to the others.

The synthesis procedure for digital filters is particularly well suited to surface wave filters. There is a class of digital filters known as nonrecursive filters identical in structure to the diagram of Fig. 3.1. These filters are called *nonrecursive* because the output signal is not fed back to the input as in recursive digital filters. The input signal is a sampled version of a real time signal with constant sampling interval. The filter is defined by an array of coefficients a_n used as multiplying factors in the numerical operation. The first sampled value is multiplied by a_1 and this product is the output of the filter for the first interval. The input is then stepped by one sampling interval, so that the first voltage value is multiplied by a_2 and the second voltage value by a_1. The two products are added numerically to give the output for the second interval. This process is repeated as the input signal is stepped through the filter. The similarity of nonrecursive digital filters to surface wave filters is immediately obvious. A great deal of attention has been given to digital filter design within the last few years, and we can draw on the results by analogy. It is possible to design a filter by placing zeros in the complex frequency plane,[18] as in network theory; however most of the design procedures are done in the time domain. Two procedures are outlined here. One is based on a Fourier transform approach, and the other is a numerical procedure that yields "optimum" filter characteristics.

Fourier Transform Approach. In developing a design we first separate the desired total filter response into the two factors that will eventually correspond to the responses of the input and output transducers. See equation (3.35). The designer usually chooses particular factors. For instance, the two factors are made identical; one factor is given a very broad frequency response and the other has the desired response compensated slightly for the small roll-off of the first; one factor is assigned some of the important nulls (or peaks) in the filter response and the second factor is assigned others; or the factors are chosen to resemble responses already known to be easily achieved. Then, one transducer at a time is designed.

To design a transducer we can use Fourier transform theory to deduce the transducer structure. We take the Fourier transform of the desired frequency response centered at a frequency above zero, say f_0. This function is the impulse response of the transducer and is a complex quantity represented by a magnitude and a phase. We determine the location for the edges of the electrodes by noting the times t_n at which the phase has the value $n\pi/4$. We equate t_n to the edge position $x_n = t_n v$. In other words, we sample the impulse response every time the phase changes by 90°. The weighting value a_n for an edge is given by the magnitude of the impulse response at time t_n. This procedure yields the edge positions* and weighting to define the transducer. If the desired frequency response is symmetric, the phase of the impulse response increases linearly with time, and therefore the electrode spacings are uniform. If the desired frequency response is asymmetric, the electrode spacings are not uniform.

Often the transducer structure determined in this way is not practical. To illustrate by a particular case suppose a desired frequency response is the rectangular response shown at the top left of Fig. 3.14. The transform of this frequency response is $\sin t/t$, which is infinite in time duration. It must be terminated in some way to relate it to the impulse response of a transducer with finite length. This termination can lead to a serious difficulty. In practice the overlap shape can be abruptly truncated after a few time sidelobes as shown in the bottom of Fig. 3.14. This truncation is equivalent to multiplying an infinite impulse response by a square window

* Under some conditions fewer electrodes[19] can be used than are indicated here.

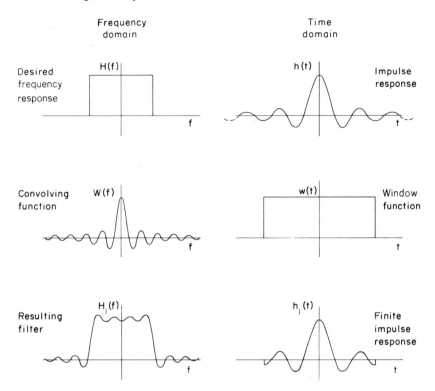

Figure 3.14 Filter design using a Fourier series approach and truncation of the infinite impulse response. Copyright 1974 by The Institute of Electrical and Electronic Engineers, Inc. Reprinted, with permission, from *IEEE Trans.* **Su-21,** 1974, p. 15.

function to obtain a finite impulse response as shown. Because multiplication in the time domain is equivalent to convolution in the frequency domain, if we convolve the desired filter response with the correct convolving function, which for truncation is the Fourier transform of the square window function, we obtain the actual frequency response of the transducer. As shown, the convolving function is oscillatory and hence the resulting frequency response has ripples near the band edges in both passband and stopband. Also the steepness of the skirts is reduced because it is related to the width of the main peak in the convolving function. The skirt falls over a frequency interval called the *transition width* (TW). If the window function time is denoted by τ, the product TW $\times \tau$ is constant, so that the transition width is reduced if the window function is made longer, and vice versa.

Often we wish to reduce the size of the undesirable ripples. They cannot be reduced merely by extending the length of the impulse response by including more lobes in the sin t/t. With a longer impulse response the larger ripples in the frequency response move toward the band edge, but they remain at the same amplitude (9% or 1.4 dB peak to peak). This phenomenon is known as *Gibbs oscillations*.[20] One technique for reducing the ripple amplitude is to use a relatively smooth window function, as shown in Fig. 3.15 to multiply and truncate the impulse response. Now the convolving function has smaller oscillations, but it has a broader width than with the rectangular window function of the same time duration. The smooth window function is characterized by a larger $TW \times \tau$ product than a square window function. Thus the transition width has been increased as a byproduct of reducing the ripple. We would like to have the smallest transition width and the smallest ripple mathematically possible. Several window functions have been proposed; some provide a nearly optimum trade-off. These functions include the Dolph–Chebyshev function,[21] the Kaiser function,[22] and prolate spheroidal functions.[22] All of these reduce the ripple by making the window function fall

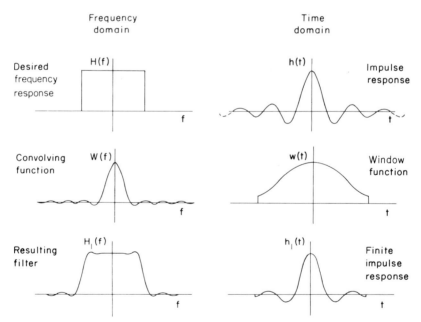

Figure 3.15 Filter design using a weighting function to reduce Gibbs oscillations. Copyright 1974 by The Institute of Electrical and Electronic Engineers, Inc. Reprinted, with permission, from *IEEE Trans.* **SU-21,** 1974, p. 15.

more smoothly; they differ in the exact form of the roll-off. In all these approaches we are confronted with a fundamental dilemma: namely, we want a frequency response that drops to zero in the stopband, but the transducer has finite length. Such a situation is contrary to the uncertainty principle. We must be content with a certain amount of ripple, but we can control the ripple size at the expense of the transition width.

Designs using the window function approach are not totally optimum. First the ripple is largest at the band edges in both the passband and stopband. Although the ripple is smaller away from the edge, the filter is usually specified by its largest ripple. Second, the designer often needs to specify the ripple in the passband separately from that in the stopband. With the window function approach the ripples in the two bands are the same size. These deficiencies can be improved with an equiripple design.

Equiripple Designs. In equiripple filters the ripples are uniform in the passband and in the stopband, as shown in Fig. 3.16. The shape is reminiscent of the Chebyshev response in LC networks. Not only are the ripples evenly distributed, but also the transition width can be smaller

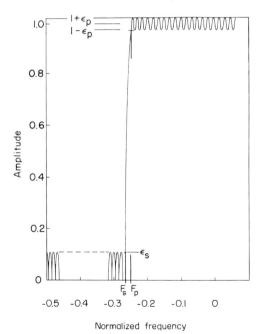

Normalized frequency

Figure 3.16 Notation for the stopband edge (F_s), the passband edge (F_p), and ripples ϵ_p and ϵ_s. Only one-half of the frequency response is shown. Copyright 1974 by The Institute of Electrical and Electronic Engineers, Inc. *IEEE Trans.* **SU-21**, 1974, p. 18.

than in the window function approach. Equiripple designs are also important because the ripple in the passband $\pm\epsilon_p$ and in the stopband ϵ_s can be specified independently in the desired response.

Equiripple filters are "optimum" in the sense that they have the smallest ripple possible for a given transition width. The design procedure[23] uses an iterative method that minimizes the transition width when the maximum ripple sizes are specified. The iterations are carried out automatically by computer. The designer specifies the number of electrodes, the ripple magnitude, and the percentage bandwidth. The computer program uses a Lagrange interpolation scheme varying the weighting values to minimize the transition width. Being a numerical procedure, the method does not yield an analytic relation between the ripple and transition width. But a few rules of thumb have been developed empirically. With the notation given in Fig. 3.16 for a transducer time length τ and ripple $\epsilon_s = \epsilon_p \simeq 0.01$, we have the relationship $TW \times \tau \simeq 2$. A more detailed approximation[24] is given by

$$TW \times \tau \simeq 0.55(1 + \log_{10} \epsilon_p) \log_{10} \epsilon_s + 0.9 \log_{10} \epsilon_p + 2.7 \qquad (3.39)$$

Numerical results (for ϵ_p equal to ϵ_s) are shown in Fig. 3.17.

It is interesting to note that the preceding expressions are independent of the percentage bandwidth of the filter. Mathematically the only important quantities are the transition width and the length of the transducer (τ). Thus there is a time–transition width product associated with a certain ripple size. Two cases are illustrated in Fig. 3.18 for the same number of electrodes, the same transition width, and the same ripple size. The only difference is the percentage bandwidth (22 and 100%). The overlap values for the electrodes are shown in Fig. 3.19 for the two cases. Note that although the number of electrodes is the same, the weighting values are quite different. Implementing these designs with a surface wave transducer is much easier for 22% bandwidth than for 100% bandwidth because the overlap values change more slowly from electrode to electrode in the narrow band filter. In spite of the fact that percentage bandwidth is immaterial from a mathematical viewpoint, it is important for practical implementation. Generally a filter with rectangular frequency response and over 40% bandwidth is difficult to implement with surface waves. Digital filters do not have this limitation because weighting is done numerically by multiplicative constants that can be independent of each other.

Of the design methods outlined here the most straightforward approach is the Fourier transform with a window function. This approach gives the designer the best "physical intuition" on the trade-offs between ripple

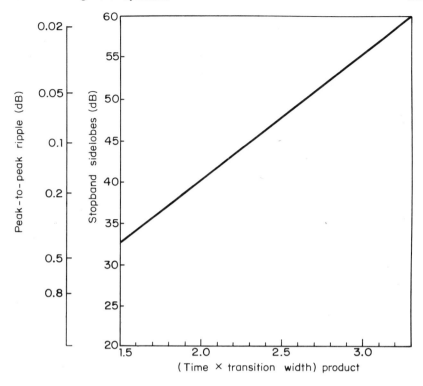

Figure 3.17 Equiripple stopband and passband ripples for one transducer for the particular case of ϵ_p equal to ϵ_s. (The number of electrodes is equal to the time length of the transducer [Time] divided by $2f_0$).

size, transition width, and the number of electrodes. Filters designed by this technique can be almost optimum (to within a few percent). Truly optimum filters can be designed with the more complicated method* that yields equiripple filters. The results of both these synthesis procedures are somewhat idealized because there are second-order effects in surface wave filters that perturb the transducer's response from that of the simple model used here. But these methods provide the first-order design, and further they give the limits of the best possible performance. That is, under no conditions can a desired frequency response be realized with fewer electrodes than determined by these synthesis methods.

---

* Since the design procedure is based on techniques used for digital filters, where there is a constant "clock rate" in the computer, it can be only used for transducers with uniformly spaced electrodes. Optimization techniques have not yet been developed for transducers with nonuniform electrode spacing.

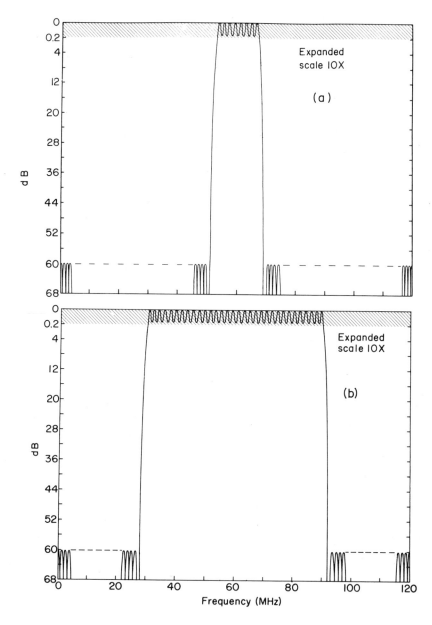

Figure 3.18 Equiripple responses with 22% and 100% bandwidth. The weighting coefficients for these responses are shown in Fig. 3.19. Copyright 1974 by The Institute of Electrical and Electronic Engineers, Inc. Reprinted, with permission, from *IEEE Trans.* **SU-21,** 1974, p. 19.

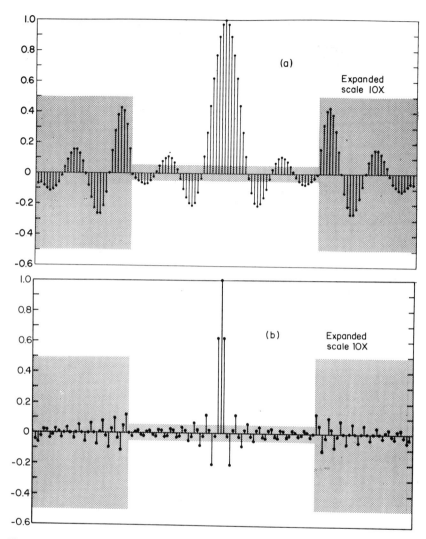

Figure 3.19 Weighting coefficients (127) for the two responses of Fig. 3.18. Small coefficients near the ends of the arrays are plotted on an expanded scale. The alternating polarity of the coefficients has been removed for clarity. Copyright 1974 by The Institute of Electrical and Electronic Engineers, Inc. Reprinted, with permission, from *IEEE Trans.* **SU-21,** 1974, p. 20.

3.3 Input Impedance and Distortion

The preceding discussion of surface wave filter performance is based on a very simple model useful for first-order analysis and synthesis. It neglects, however, interactions between the acoustic wave and the electric currents flowing in the transducer. These interactions are important when the filter is driven by a generator of finite internal impedance and is connected to a load impedance. Neglecting the interactions is valid for weakly coupled transducers if the filter also has a high insertion loss. It is less valid if the impedance of the transducer is matched to that of the generator and load. In this section we evaluate the input impedance and show how it affects filter performance.

Input Impedance.   To evaluate the input impedance of a transducer an equivalent circuit model is often used to describe each electrode pair in the transducer. As discussed in Chapter 2, a Mason model is usually used. Without describing the circuit in detail, we can state that the circuit model depends on certain physical constants of the piezoelectric substrate and the dimensions of the transducer. These quantities are the coupling constant for the substrate k^2, the capacitance per electrode pair C_s, the number of electrode pairs in the transducer P (i.e., the transducer has $2P$ electrodes), and the overlap distance of the electrodes w. Values for the constants are given in Table 3.1 for commonly used piezoelectric materials. For simplicity we consider an unweighted transducer with P electrode pairs, with uniform electrode spacing, and a center frequency f_0. Straightforward circuit analysis[25] shows that the input admittance has the following components for a drive frequency f, as shown in Fig. 3.20

$$G_a(f) = G_0\left(\frac{\sin^2 x}{x^2}\right) \tag{3.40}$$

where

$$x = P\pi\frac{(f-f_0)}{f_0}$$

$$G_0 = 8k^2C_sf_0P^2 \tag{3.41}$$

$$B_a(f) = \frac{G_0(\sin 2x - 2x)}{2x^2} \tag{3.42}$$

$$B_c(f) = 2\pi fC_sP \tag{3.43}$$

The real component of the admittance G_a can be interpreted as the radiation conductance, and represents electric power converted to acoustic power. The imaginary component B_c is the susceptance of the static

Table 3.1 Properties of Piezoelectric Substrates for Surface Waves[a]

Material	Cut	Propagation Direction	Coupling Coefficient k^2(%)	Capacitance/Pair C_s (pF/cm)	Velocity ($\times 10^{-5}$ cm/sec)	Temperature Coefficient of Delay (ppm/°C)
Quartz	Y	X	0.23	0.55	3.159	−24
Quartz (HC)	−20° rotated Y	X	0.25	0.55	3.209	−32
Quartz (ST)	+42.75° rotated Y	X	0.16	0.55	3.157	0
LiNbO$_3$	Y	Z	4.5	4.6	3.488	+90
LiTaO$_3$	Y	Z	0.74	5.7	3.230	+35
Bi$_{12}$GeO$_{20}$	110	001	0.85	—	1.62	+130

[a] From Ref. 26.

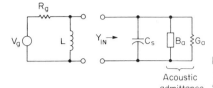

Acoustic
admittance

Figure 3.20 Input admittance of a transducer Y_{in}. The elements B_a and G_a vary rapidly with frequency whereas C_s is a static capacitance.

capacitance (PC_s) of the transducer. The other imaginary term, B_a, is the reactive component of the acoustic admittance and is usually much smaller than B_c. The terms G_a and B_a are related through the Hilbert transform.[20]

Certain features of these impedance values are noteworthy. First, the quantity B_c varies slowly with frequency because it is merely due to a constant capacitance (proportional to the dielectric constant of the material). Usually this reactive term is the largest of all the terms, but because it has no "resonant" properties it does not contribute significantly to the filter characteristics. Second, the conductive term G_a has a strong frequency dependence directly reflecting the frequency response of the filter, which has a bandwidth[25] Δf dependent on the number of electrode pairs $\Delta f/f_0 = 1/P$. Third, the peak value of G_a is proportional to the coupling constant k^2 and the static capacitance C_s. Note that C_s is the capacitance per electrode pair and hence is proportional to the overlap length of the electrodes. Therefore the impedance can be scaled by changing the overlap dimension of the transducers.

The admittance values given earlier were derived from an equivalent circuit model for a simple transducer with uniform spacing between electrodes. For transducers with nonuniform spacing an equivalent circuit can also be used, and the admittance values can be evaluated using standard network analysis. However the analysis may yield very complicated mathematical expressions for G_a, B_a, and so on. An easier procedure has been developed by Hartmann.[26] It is called the *impulse model* because it uses the electrical impulse response of the transducer to derive the impedance values. The equivalent circuit method would require the analysis (usually by computer) of a complicated electrical network, whereas the impulse model only requires the evaluation of an integral and a Fourier transform. Although these operations are also done by computer, the formulation is much simpler and physical interpretation is easier. Hartmann shows that the impulse response $h(t)$ can be derived from arguments based on the conservation of energy and has the form

$$h(t) = 4k\sqrt{C_s} f_i^{3/2}(t) \sin \theta(t) \qquad (3.44)$$

where

$$\theta(t) = 2\pi \int_0^t f_i(x)\, dx$$

and that the conductance is given by

$$G_a(f) = 2\,|H(f)|^2 \tag{3.45}$$

where $H(f)$ is the Fourier transform of $h(t)$. The quantity $f_i(t)$ is the "instantaneous frequency" of the transducer; it is the resonant frequency of the electrode spacing as one moves along the transducer. The form of $h(t)$ is a sine wave with this frequency, weighted by a term $f_i^{3/2}$ to account for the change in acoustic energy with the change in electrode spacing. Using (3.45) we can compute the input admittance for a large variety of transducers with uniform overlap* without resorting to network theory. Other formulations have been developed by Mitchell and Reilly[27] and also by Krimholtz.[28]

A transducer of particular usefulness is the dispersive linear chirp.[11] It is instructive to compare its impedance to the nondispersive transducer described earlier. This transducer's impulse response $h(t)$ is characterized by a linear change in frequency from f_b at the beginning to f_e at the end, with a center frequency f_0. The length of the transducer is designated τ. When the product of τ and the bandwidth $\Delta f = f_e - f_b$ is large ($\tau\Delta f > 50$), the Fourier transform of $h(t)$ is approximately two square spectra[11] of width Δf, one centered at f_0 and the other at $-f_0$. We can equate the energy in the impulse response to that of its spectrum using Parseval's theorem[20]

$$\int_{-\infty}^{\infty} |h(t)|^2\, dt = \int_{-\infty}^{\infty} |H(f)|^2\, df \tag{3.46}$$

The term on the left side is given to a first approximation from (3.44) by

$$\int_{-\infty}^{\infty} |h(t)|^2\, dt = \frac{(4k\sqrt{C_s}\,f_0^{3/2})^2\,\tau}{2} \tag{3.47}$$

Because the spectrum has a constant value over two intervals Δf wide

$$\int_{-\infty}^{\infty} |H(f)|^2\, df = |H(f_0)|^2\, 2\,\Delta f \tag{3.48}$$

---

* Although derived here for unapodized transducers, these equations can be extended to apodized transducers. The equivalent circuit model or the impulse model can be used to evaluate the input admittance provided the transducer is first broken into horizontal channels (Fig. 3.19), and the input admittance for each channel is evaluated by the equations in the text. The admittance for the apodized transducer is found by summing the channel admittances.[4]

Combining (3.46) to (3.48), we obtain

$$|H(f_0)|^2 = \frac{4k^2 C_s f_0^3 \tau}{\Delta f} \qquad (3.49)$$

Substituting into (3.45), we can evaluate the conductance at midband

$$G_a(f_0) \cong 8f_0 k^2 C_s \left(\frac{f_0}{\Delta f}\right)^2 (\tau \, \Delta f) \qquad (3.50)$$

A transducer with P uniformly spaced electrode pairs has a conductance, from (3.41),

$$G_a(f_0) = 8f_0 k^2 C_s P^2 = 8f_0 k^2 C_s \left(\frac{f_0}{\Delta f}\right)^2 \qquad (3.51)$$

where the last equality can be made since a transducer with P electrode pairs has a fractional bandwidth $\Delta f/f_0 = 1/P$. Comparing (3.50) and (3.51), we note that the input impedance of a dispersive transucer is larger by a factor $\tau \, \Delta f$, the *compression ratio*, than a nondispersive transducer with the same fractional bandwidth. This property is particularly useful in the design of transducers with a large fractional bandwidth. Since only a small number of electrodes are used in a wideband nondispersive transducer, the input admittance (3.51) is very small. Parasitic effects, such as the capacitance of the coaxial connectors, are comparable to the transducer capacitance and the transducer is difficult to match. Using a dispersive transducer increases the admittance values by $\tau \, \Delta f$ so that the parasitic admittance can be neglected.

A quantity of particular interest is the radiation Q of the input admittance $Q_r \cong B_d/G_a$. It is an important parameter in designing a matching network and is similar to the "quality factor" of a resonant circuit. For the nondispersive transducer

$$Q_r \cong \frac{2\pi f_0 C_s P}{8k^2 C_s f_0 P^2} = \frac{\pi}{4k^2} \frac{\Delta f}{f_0} \qquad (3.52)$$

and for the dispersive transducer

$$Q_r \cong \frac{2\pi f_0 C_s P_{\text{tot}}}{8k^2 C_s f_0 \left(\frac{f_0}{\Delta f}\right)^2 \tau \, \Delta f} = \frac{\pi}{4k^2} \frac{\Delta f}{f_0} \qquad (3.53)$$

where P_{tot} is the total number of electrode pairs $P_{\text{tot}} \approx f_0 \tau$. Note that the radiation Q is the same for both transducers and is only dependent on the fractional bandwidth and the coupling constant of the piezoelectric material. Thus although the admittance value is scaled by $\tau \, \Delta f$ in going from a nondispersive transducer to a dispersive one, the radiation Q is not affected. It is worth noting also that the radiation Q is not a function of the overlap dimension of the transducer but is an intrinsic property of the substrate material and the transducer bandwidth. A careful discussion of transducer radiation Q, and its use in designing matching structures for surface wave devices is given in Chapter 5.

Once the input impedance is evaluated, the insertion loss due to the impedance of the filter can be determined by analysis of simple networks consisting of the generator connected to the input impedance, and the load connected to the impedance of the output transducer. The details of the transducer structure do not enter the calculation explicitly because they are included in the equation for the transducer impedance. The insertion "loss" is not an energy loss, but rather is due to an impedance mismatch. Knowing the input impedance as a function of frequency, we can compute the insertion loss (i.e., the filter transfer function) in absolute units (dB) rather than the relative units obtained with the simpler model.

In order to minimize insertion loss, the bandwidth of the matching circuit and the acoustic bandwidth should be made approximately equal. Otherwise the matching network narrows the filter bandwidth, so that it is determined by the matching network rather than the acoustic bandwidth of the transducer. By equating the radiation Q to the acoustic Q, we see that a substrate material should be chosen (Table 3.1) such that $k^2 \simeq (\pi/4)(\Delta f/f_0)^2$. If the selected substrate has a coupling constant smaller than this value, the desired bandwidth can only be obtained by increasing the insertion loss of the filter. Usually this is done by broadening the radiation Q with an external resistor, resulting in increased insertion loss,[26] as shown in Fig. 3.21.

Distortion. The primary effect of the transducer impedance is in determining the value of the insertion loss and the ease of matching over the desired bandwidth. There are also important secondary effects that distort the response from that predicted by the delta function model. The distortions originate from three major causes: tight coupling of the transducers to the generator and the load, diffraction of the acoustic wave, and unwanted acoustic waves. A complete model that includes these effects can accurately predict the experimental response of a filter. Although such a model is valuable for analyzing the filter response, it is not convenient for synthesizing a design because it complicates the design procedure to the point that mathematical solution is unwieldy. In design, two alternate procedures are usually employed instead. One procedure is to minimize the sources of the perturbations so that the simple model is valid, and the other is to iterate corrections to a design based on a simple

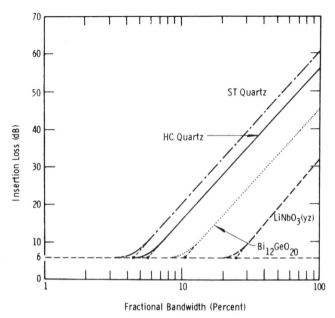

Figure 3.21 Minimum achievable insertion loss for two transducers on various substrates. Copyright 1973 by The Institute of Electrical and Electronic Engineers, Inc. Reprinted, with permission, from *IEEE Trans.* **MTT-21,** 1973, p. 171.

model and analyzed by the more complete model. The latter procedure is particularly useful when correcting for acoustic diffraction.

Tight Coupling Effects. These effects arise because the generator and load are connected not to a constant impedance but to the input and output transducers whose impedances change with frequency. To illustrate, consider a filter with inductively matched transducers. At a frequency in the stopband region of the filter the input impedance is high, because no surface waves are generated and the static reactance is tuned by an inductor. The voltage on the bus bars is equal to the internal voltage of the generator. At a frequency in the passband the input impedance is reduced because surface waves are generated, and the generator must supply more current. The voltage on the bus bars is now less than the generator internal voltage because of the voltage drop across the generator's internal impedance. The amount of the voltage change depends on how well matched the generator is to the transducer. In the extreme case of a perfect match the voltage across the bus bars drops by a factor of 2 (6 dB). Therefore the stopband response is twice as high relative to the passband as that computed by the delta function model, which assumes a constant voltage. In addition to changing in magnitude the voltage on the bus bars can also change in phase because the transducer impedance is changing in both real and imaginary components (G_a and B_a). The phase shift destroys the linear phase response of an otherwise dispersionless filter. The phase shift is most pronounced at the band edges where the impedance changes rapidly with frequency. In typical filters the phase change for both transducers combined is less than $\pm 10°$, and the increase in stopband sidelobes rarely exceeds 8 dB. These values can be reduced by mismatching the generator so that it "sees" a more constant load as a function of frequency.

Triple Transit Echo. In the preceding pages we examined each transducer individually and found that distortions caused by tight coupling with generator and load involved mainly an increase in the size of the stopband side lobes and phase distortions at the band edges. We now note that the two transducers in the filter can interact with each other as well. The interaction arises from the "regeneration" of acoustic waves within a transducer. As an acoustic wave travels under a transducer, it induces a voltage across the bus bars and the external load. This voltage in turn generates another acoustic wave within the transducer. The phase and amplitude of the generated wave depends on the electrical load attached to the bus bars. If the bus bars are short circuited, no voltages can be induced (ideally) and no new wave is generated. If the load is a matched load (i.e., it has a value equal to the complex conjugate of the transducer impedance), a maximum amount of power is absorbed in the resistive part of the load. It can be shown[25] that under these conditions half of the acoustic energy incident on an output transducer is transferred to the resistive load and a quarter is reflected. This wave travels back to the input transducer where a quarter of its energy is similarly reflected. Thus the output transducer receives an "echo" that is 12 dB lower than the original incident wave. Since the first echo has made three trips across the substrate surface, it is referred to as the *triple transit echo* (*TTE*). Echos occur with equal spacing in time, separated by twice the delay time through the filter.

In a cw frequency response measurement the "beating" of the desired wave with the smaller regenerated waves causes ripples in an otherwise smooth frequency response. For a 12 dB triple transit echo the ripple is 4.4 dB peak to peak. Ripple of this size is totally unacceptable for most bandpass filters because ripple values less than ± 0.5 dB are usually desired. The TTE ripple has a period (in frequency) given by the inverse of twice the delay time. For a typical delay time of 1 μsec the period of the ripple is 0.5 MHz. Typically several periods of the TTE ripple appear in a filter's passband. The triple transit echo also causes phase ripple. The size of the amplitude and phase ripple can be directly related to the magnitude of the triple transit echo because the cw output of the filter is a vector sum of the main signal and the smaller triple transit signal. The first column of Table 3.2 lists the magnitude of the triple transit echo relative to the main signal, and the two other columns list the corresponding insertion loss ripple and phase ripple.

The most straightforward technique to reduce the TTE ripple is to mismatch the transducer's load impedance. The improvement in triple transit suppression is twice the increase in insertion loss; that is, for every dB increase in insertion loss, the triple transit echo is reduced by 2 dB. This rule of thumb is valid when the insertion loss is larger than about 10 dB;[6] for a smaller insertion loss the improvement is nonlinear at a slightly higher rate. Expressed mathematically,[6]

$$\frac{\text{TTE power}}{\text{Main signal power}} \, (\text{dB}) = 6 \,(\text{dB}) + 2IL \,(dB) \tag{3.54}$$

where IL is the insertion loss of the filter. Thus to obtain a 1.1° peak to peak phase error, the triple transit echo must be smaller than -40 dB (Table 3.2) and the insertion loss must be greater than 17 dB.

Table 3.2 Relationship Between the Size of a Spurious Signal in a Pulsed Time Domain Test and the Insertion Loss and Phase Ripples in a Frequency Domain Test

Single Spurious Signal Level (dB)	Peak to Peak cw Insertion Loss Ripple (dB)	Peak to Peak Phase Error Ripple (°)
-12	4.459	28.2
-16	2.777	18.0
-20	1.740	11.4
-24	1.097	7.2
-28	0.692	4.6
-32	0.436	2.9
-36	0.276	1.8
-40	0.173	1.1
-44	0.110	0.72
-48	0.070	0.46

The added insertion loss required by this technique to reduce the triple transit echo is often a disadvantage. Usually a designer wishes to obtain low insertion loss simultaneously with low ripple. This can be accomplished by other techniques, but at the expense of increasing the complexity of the filter. Reduction of the triple transit echo is a major design consideration and is discussed thoroughly in Chapter 5.

Perturbations of the Wave Impedance. In addition to the "regenerated" echo, there are other spurious acoustic echos that distort the filter's response. One is due to the transducer itself because it mechanically and piezoelectrically perturbs the substrate surface. These perturbations are a consequence of the mass of the metal, and, more importantly, the conductivity of the metal. The latter "shorts out" the electric field associated with the wave and so "stiffens" the elastic constants of the piezoelectric substrate, changing the wave velocity and characteristic impedance. As an acoustic wave travels from the free surface to the region under an electrode some of the wave is reflected. With the usual electrode spacing of half an acoustic wavelength, the reflections from each successive electrode add constructively in the backward direction so the net reflected wave is large. The percentage of incident power that is reflected depends of course on the coupling constant of the piezoelectric material and its elastic constants. It is greatest for a high coupling material, such as lithium niobate. Roughly the change in wave impedance (Z_0) is proportional to the change in velocity (Δv) due to piezoelectric stiffening,

$$\frac{\Delta Z}{Z_0} \simeq \frac{\Delta v}{v} \simeq \tfrac{1}{2}k^2 \tag{3.55}$$

The mass loading is usually smaller. More exactly,

$$\frac{\Delta v}{v} = \tfrac{1}{2}k^2 \left(\frac{1}{1+(\epsilon_0/\epsilon_p)+(k^2/2)}\right) + F\frac{2\pi}{\lambda}h \tag{3.56}$$

where ϵ_0/ϵ_p is related to the dielectric constant.[29] The second term is the effect of mass loading, where h is the thickness of the metal, λ is the acoustic wavelength, and F is a function of the mass of the metal,[30] (0.037 for lithium niobate, 0.01 for quartz). For 2000 Å thick aluminium at 100 MHz, these values are $\Delta v/v = (0.021)(0.952) + 2.2 \times 10^{-5} = 0.020$ for lithium niobate (YZ) and $\Delta v/v = (0.0012)(0.815) + 4.2 \times 10^{-4} = 0.0014$ for quartz (YX). An approximate plot of the reflected power as a function of the number of electrodes (for piezoelectric stiffening only) is given in Fig. 3.22 based on an equivalent circuit model.[31] It is clear that the reflections are significant with only 10 electrodes on lithium niobate or 100 electrodes on quartz.

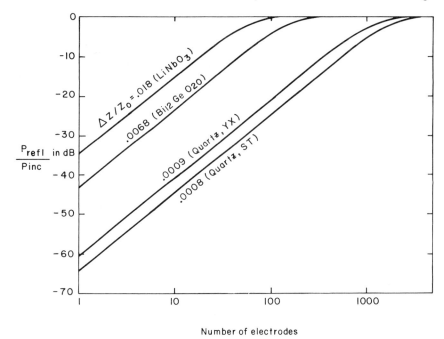

Figure 3.22 Reflected acoustic power from an array of N electrodes at the acoustic resonant frequency for electrodes of $\lambda/2$ spacing. The parameter $\Delta Z/Z_0$ is the change in acoustic impedance due to piezoelectric stiffening for various materials. Reprinted, with permission, from ref. 35, p. 127.

The reflections due to the transducer perturbation of the wave propagation cause two problems. One is similar to the triple transit echo described earlier. The other problem is reflections *within* a given transducer. For a long transducer with many electrodes there may be multiple reflections that cause a complicated distortion of the filter response. Although complicated, the effect of internal reflections can be predicted using equivalent circuit models[32,33] for the transducers.

Internal reflections can be greatly reduced by using the ingenious scheme[34,35] of double (split) electrodes* illustrated in Fig. 3.23. Each electrode is an eighth rather than a quarter wavelength wide. Note that the electrical resonant frequency is half the mechanical resonant frequency. At the filter's electrical center frequency, the mechanical reflections cancel. Somewhat off electrical resonance, but within the band of

---

* Double electrodes require narrower electrode widths and gaps than regular electrodes. This disadvantage can be overcome by operating the transducer at its efficient third harmonic response.[34]

the filter, the mechanical reflections reach a peak value. But even at its peak value the reflected power is much smaller than with quarter wavelength, unsplit electrodes. The mechanical reflections from split electrode transducers have a narrow bandwidth, so that near the electrical resonance the reflected power is *independent* of the number of split electrodes N, although near the mechanical resonance the reflected power is proportional to N^2. Split electrode transducers and the improvement in filter performance obtained by their use are fully discussed in Chapter 6.

Bulk Waves. In addition to regenerated and reflected waves, other unwanted waves can disturb the filter's performance. The transducer is

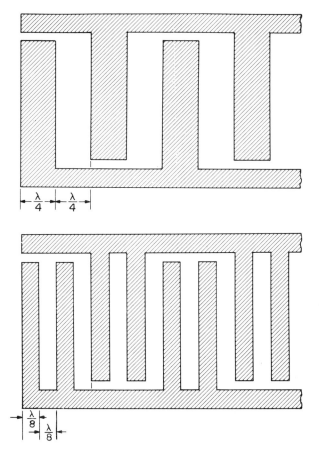

Figure 3.23 Diagrams comparing transducers with single electrode per half-wavelength and the double (split) electrodes.

able to excite acoustic modes in the piezelectric substrate other than the surface wave. Predominantly these are bulk modes[36] that radiate into the crystal, bounce off the bottom of the crystal, and are detected by the output transducer. The bulk wave can undergo several bounces between the bottom and top surface, so that several "plate modes"[37] are possible as the frequency is swept. Roughly, one can say that the velocity of the bulk mode v_b and the angle θ from the surface are related by $v_b/\cos\theta = f_b d$ when a bulk wave at frequency f_b is generated, where d is one period of the electrode spacing. Because the surface wave is slower than any of the bulk waves, all the bulk modes occur at frequencies above the surface wave resonance. This effect is illustrated in Fig. 3.24, where one can see the desired surface wave response at 30 MHz with a distortion at the high frequency end of the peak at about 31 MHz. At higher frequencies there is a collection of undesired responses that prevent the filter from having a large stopband rejection at frequencies above the main surface wave response. In the case illustrated, the stopband rejection is only 35 dB below the main peak because of bulk modes, although the surface wave response by itself would fall to a much smaller value. The case of *ST* quartz is shown in Fig. 3.24. It is particularly prone to bulk waves. Lithium niobate would have a different, and smaller, bulk mode response.

The responses at frequencies far above the resonance, say at 40 MHz in Fig. 3.24, can be reduced by tuning the device with a simple inductor so that the electrical response is small at the higher frequencies. However, distortions close to the resonance must be reduced by reducing the bulk modes themselves. It is impossible to prevent the bulk wave from being generated (for a particular crystal cut). But the bulk wave can be prevented from reaching the output transducer. The bottom surface can be roughened and coated with a soft, conductive material (e.g., silver epoxy) that absorbs and scatters the bulk wave at the bottom of the crystal. Another method is to taper the bottom of the crystal along the overlap length. Bulk waves, reflected from the bottom, have a skewed wavefront when they reach the top surface so different parts of the wave induce canceling voltages in the output transducer. This increases the attenuation of the undesired bulk responses but leaves the surface wave unaffected. Another method uses a metalized region[38] between the input and output transducers in only half the beam width, so that the wave in the metalized portion of the filter has a longer transit time. The corresponding part of the output transducer is displaced slightly toward the input to make the delay times in the two output sections the same for the surface wave. The bulk waves, however, do not experience the delay difference and are canceled at the output transducer by phase interference.

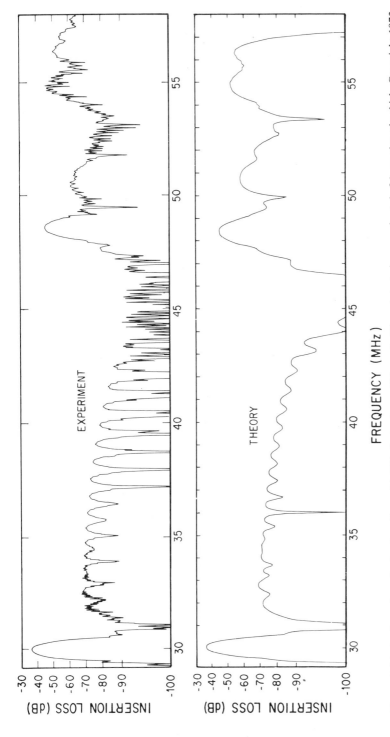

Figure 3.24 Bulk mode excitation in a filter with 250 electrodes on *ST* quartz. The substrate is approximately 24 wavelengths thick. Copyright 1973 by The Institute of Electrical and Electronic Engineers, Inc. Reprinted, with permission, from *Proc. 1973 IEEE Ultrasonics Symposium*, p. 373.

Diffraction. Diffraction of the acoustic wave as it travels between transducers perturbs the measured frequency response from that computed on the basis of the delta function model and in that sense is also a source of distortion. Fortunately, corrections can be made during the design of the filter because diffraction is a well-understood phenomenon. The problem is particularly important in apodized transducers because there are regions of very small overlap. As a rule, diffraction is unimportant on an isotropic material when the overlap w and the acoustic wavelength λ are such that $w^2/\lambda > X$, where X is the distance from the radiating electrode to the receiving electrode. Most single crystal materials are not isotropic; some actually help to collimate the wave. A wave on lithium niobate, for example, travels 10 times farther than a wave on an isotropic material for an equivalent amount of diffraction.

The theory of diffraction has been developed for anisotropic materials by assuming a parabolic approximation[5] for the velocity change with angle that is valid for most surface wave materials. This theory is thoroughly discussed in Chapter 1. Exact numerical methods have also been developed[39] for highly anisotropic materials like lithium niobate. Basically the material has an anisotropy parameter k/k_{iso} that characterizes its diffraction. Values for common materials are given in Table 3.3. Normalized curves,[40] developed from the theory, allow a designer to see if the overlap dimensions cause a diffraction error. A set of these curves is given in Fig. 3.25 plotted as a function of the normalized distance between the receiver and transmitter X. Note that the horizontal axis also depends on the wavelength λ. It should be remembered that diffraction is reciprocal. It does not matter whether the transmitter is wide and the receiver narrow, or vice versa. In order to plot the curves the horizontal axis has been normalized to the overlap of the transmitter a.

Table 3.3 Diffraction Anisotropy Constant[a]

Material	k/k_{iso}
Lithium niobate (YZ)	~ 0.083
Quartz (YX)	1.65
Quartz (ST)	1.38
Lithium tantalate (YZ)	0.79
Bismuth germanium oxide (001–110)	0.70

[a] From Ref. 5.

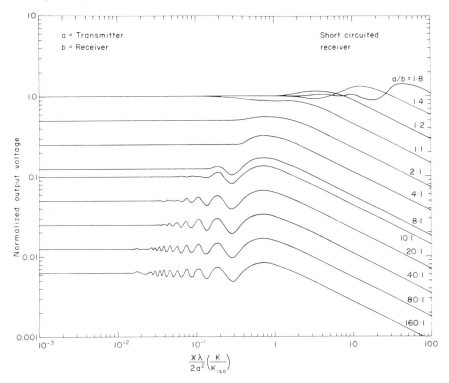

Figure 3.25 Diffraction curves giving the output voltage as a function of (normalized) separation X for a fixed transducer aperture. Curves are normalized to the case of a closely spaced transmitter-receiver pair having equal apertures ($a = b$).

The usual design procedure is to neglect diffraction for the initial synthesis of the desired response; then the overlap values can be checked against Fig. 3.25 to determine whether the values lie in the horizontal portion of the curves. If diffraction is a problem, the overlap values can be adjusted to compensate, as described in ref. 41. Usually these adjustments affect the size of the sidelobes in the stopband. This diffraction correction can be readily incorporated into a computerized automatic design procedure.[42]

Losses and Electromagnetic Feedthrough. There are two other sources of distortion we mention only briefly, losses and electromagnetic feedthrough. Losses within the device can cause some deviation from the desired response. Fortunately these losses are usually small for frequencies below 500 MHz in filters using 2000 Å of aluminum for the electrodes. Acoustic attenuation losses in the propagation path and ohmic losses within the metal of the transducers are the primary sources. Usually they are modeled by a lump resistor (a few ohms) at the terminals of the device. The main distortion is a slight broadening in the response of the filter and an increase in insertion loss. Direct electromagnetic feedthrough between the input and output transducers, a potentially serious source of distortion, can be reduced by the way the device is packaged. The feedthrough signal occurs instantly when the input voltage is applied whereas the desired signal is delayed through the acoustic path. Beating of the two signals causes ripples in the frequency response. Careful electromagnetic shielding can reduce this signal to a value about 60 dB below the desired signal. The filter packaging is very important and for some commercial applications can be as expensive as the surface wave filter itself. Proven packaging techniques are discussed in Chapter 5.

Practical Design Ranges. These distortion effects limit the range of applicability of surface wave filters. The design procedures discussed are best suited for filters with center frequencies in the range of 10 MHz to 1.0 GHz, limited by wavelengths that are too long for practical substrate size or too small for practical electrode fabrication. Bandwidths in the range of 0.1% to 40% are practical. For narrower bandwidths the transducers require so many electrodes that multiple reflections dominate, and for broader bandwidths the transducers require too few electrodes and the response is perturbed by higher harmonic responses. Insertion loss is usually in the range of 6 to 40 dB, determined by the TTE ripple that can be tolerated. Lower insertion loss down to 2 dB can be achieved using unidirectional transducers, but these require sophisticated fabrication techniques. The stopband ripples are limited to about 60 dB by spurious bulk modes and the accuracy of electrode fabrication and of diffraction compensation. Passband ripple of ±0.1 dB is limited by multiple reflections between electrodes and the physical termination of the transducer metalization. Within these bounds there is a large region of useful filter designs, attractive because of the simplicity of the structure and compatibility with integrated circuit technology.

References

1. H. E. Kallman. "Transversal filters." *Proc. IRE* **28,** 302 (1940).
2. I. Cermak, P. Selvester, and G. W. Farnell. "Capacity and field distributions for interdigital surface wave transducers." *IEEE Trans.* **SU-17,** 188 (1970).
3. H. Engan. "Excitation of elastic surface waves by spatial harmonics of interdigital transducers." *IEEE Trans.* **ED-16,** 1014 (1969).

4. R. H. Tancrell and M. G. Holland. "Acoustic surface wave filters." *Proc. IEEE* **59,** 393 (1971).

5. T. L. Szabo and A. J. Slobodnik, Jr. "The effect of diffraction on the design of acoustic surface wave devices." *IEEE Trans.* **SU-20,** 240 (1973).

6. A. Ronnekleiv, H. Skeie, and H. Hanebrekke. "Design problems in surface wave filters," in *Proc. Conf. on Component Performance and Systems Application of Surface Acoustic Wave Devices,* IEE, Stevenage, England, 1973, pp. 141–151.

7. K. M. Lakin, D. W. T. Mih, and R. M. Tarr. "A new interdigital electrode transducer geometry." *IEEE Trans.* **MTT-22,** 763 (1974).

8. C. S. Hartmann. "Weighting interdigital surface wave transducers by selective withdrawal of electrodes," in J. de Klerk, Ed., *Proc. 1973 IEEE Ultrasonics Symposium,* IEEE, New York, 1973, pp. 423–426.

9. T. W. Bristol. "Synthesis of periodic unapodized surface wave transducers," in J. de Klerk, Ed., *Proc. 1972 IEEE Ultrasonics Symposium,* IEEE, New York, 1972, pp. 377–380.

10. M. F. Lewis. "Surface acoustic wave filters employing symmetric phase-weighted transducers." *Electron. Lett.* **9,** 138 (1973).

11. J. R. Klauder et al. "The theory and design of chirp radars." *Bell System Tech. J.* **34,** 745 (1960).

12. F. G. Marshall, C. O. Newton, and E. G. S. Paige. "Theory and design of surface acoustic wave multistrip coupler." *IEEE Trans.* **MTT-21,** 206 (1973).

13. R. H. Tancrell and H. Engan. "Design considerations for surface acoustic wave filters," in J. de Klerk, Ed., *Proc. 1973 IEEE Ultrasonics Symposium,* IEEE, New York, 1973, pp. 419–422.

14. L. Weinberg. *Network Analysis and Synthesis,* McGraw-Hill, New York, 1962, p. 282.

15. N. R. Ogg and D. Healy. "Acoustic surface waves and nonminimum phase shift networks." RRE Memorandum No. 2770, Royal Radar Establishment, Malvern, England, 1972.

16. J. D. Rhodes and M. Z. Ismal. "Cascade synthesis of selective linear phase filters." *IEEE Trans.* **CT-19,** 183 (1972).

17. R. H. Tancrell. "Analytic design of surface wave bandpass filters." *IEEE Trans.* **SU-21,** 12 (1974).

18. G. L. Matthaei and D. Y. Wong. "Some techniques for interdigital acoustic surface wave filter synthesis," in J. de Klerk, Ed., *Proc. 1973 IEEE Ultrasonics Symposium,* IEEE, New York, 1973, pp. 427–436.

19. C. Atzeni and L. Masotti. "Design of interdigital arrays for acoustic surface wave filters," in J. de Klerk, Ed., *Proc. 1972 IEEE Ultrasonics Symposium,* IEEE, New York, 1972, pp. 241–252.

20. R. M. Bracewell. *The Fourier Transform and Its Applications.* McGraw-Hill, New York, 1965, pp. 209–211.

21. H. D. Helms. "Nonrecursive digital filters: design methods for achieving specifications on frequency response." *IEEE Trans.* **AU-16,** 336 (1968).

22. F. F. Kuo and J. F. Kaiser. *System Analysis by Digital Computer,* Wiley, New York, 1966, p. 232.

23. J. H. McClellan and T. W. Parks. "A unified approach to the design of optimum FIR linear phase digital filters." *IEEE Trans.* **CT-20,** 697 (1973).

24. O. Hermann. "Design of nonrecursive digital filters with linear phase." *Electron. Lett.* **6,** 328 (1970).

25. W. R. Smith et al. "Analysis of interdigital surface wave transducers by use of an equivalent circuit model." *IEEE Trans.* **MTT-17,** 856 (1969).

26. C. S. Hartmann, D. T. Bell, Jr., and R. C. Rosenfeld. "Impulse model design of acoustic surface wave filters." *IEEE Trans.* **MTT-21,** 162 (1973).

27. R. F. Mitchell and N. H. C. Reilly. "Equivalence of delta-function and equivalent circuit models for interdigital acoustic surface wave transducers." *Electron. Lett.* **8,** 329 (1972).

28. R. Krimholtz. "Equivalent circuit for transducers having arbitrary asymmetrical piezoelectric excitation." *IEEE Trans.* **SU-19,** 427 (1972).

29. K. A. Ingebrigtsen. "Surface waves in piezoelectrics." *J. Appl. Phys.* **40,** 2681 (1969).

30. M. B. Schulz and J. H. Matsinger. "Rayleigh wave electromechanical coupling constants." *Appl. Phys. Lett.* **20,** 367 (1972).

31. E. H. Sittig and G. A. Coquin. "Filters and dispersive delay lines using repetitively mismatched ultrasonic transmission lines." *IEEE Trans.* **SU-15,** 111 (1968).

32. W. S. Jones, C. S. Hartmann, and T. D. Sturdevant. "Second-order effects in surface wave filters." *IEEE Trans.* **SU-19,** 368 (1972).

33. P. R. Emtage. "Self-consistent theory of interdigital transducers." *J. Acoust. Soc. Amer.* **51,** 1142 (1972).

34. T. W. Bristol et al. "Application of double electrodes in acoustic surface wave device design." in J. de Klerk, Ed., *Proc. 1972 IEEE Ultrasonics Symposium,* IEEE, New York, 1972, pp. 343–345.

35. T. W. Bristol. "Analysis and design of surface acoustic wave transducers," in *Proc. Conf. on Component Performance and Systems Applications of Surface Acoustic Wave Devices,* IEEE, Stevenage, England, 1973, pp. 115–129.

36. V. M. Ristic. "Bulk mode generation in surface wave devices," in J. de Klerk, Ed., *Proc. 1972 IEEE Ultrasonics Symposium,* IEEE, New York, 1972, pp. 424–428.

37. R. S. Wagers. "Analysis of acoustic bulk mode excitation by interdigital transducers." *Appl. Phys. Lett.* **24,** 401 (1974).

38. R. LaRosa and C. F. Vasile. "Broadband bulk-wave cancellation in acoustic surface wave devices." *Electron. Lett.* **8,** 478 (1972).

39. M. S. Kharusi and G. W. Farnell. "Plane ultrasonic transducer diffraction fields in highly anisotropic crystals." *J. Acoust. Soc. Amer.* **48,** 665 (1960).

40. J. D. Maines, G. L. Moule, and N. R. Ogg. "Correction of diffraction errors in acoustic surface wave pulse compression filters." *Electron. Lett.* **8,** 431, (1972).

41. T. L. Szabo and A. J. Slobodnik, Jr. "Diffraction compensation in periodic apodized acoustic surface wave filters." *IEEE Trans.* **SU-21,** 114 (1974).

42. R. F. Mitchell. "Acoustic surface wave transversal filters: their use and limitations," in *Proc. Conf. on Component Performance and Systems Applications of Surface Wave Devices,* IEE, Stevenage, England, 1973, pp. 130–140.

FOUR
Surface Wave Device Fabrication*

HENRY I. SMITH

Lincoln Laboratory, Massachusetts Institute of Technology, Lexington, Massachusetts

Since the invention of the interdigital electrode surface wave transducer, the number of different kinds of ultrasonic devices that have been developed and the variety of electronic functions that can now be performed with surface waves greatly exceed what can be realized using bulk elastic waves alone. The planar fabrication technique is probably the single most important factor in this development, and is the main topic of this chapter.

The basic principles of the planar fabrication technique are illustrated in Fig. 4.1. A substrate surface is coated with a radiation sensitive polymer film and exposed to radiation in some desired pattern. Following exposure, a development step removes either the exposed or unexposed polymer, thereby leaving the pattern in relief on the substrate surface. The substrate itself can then be patterned either by etching a relief structure in it, by chemically doping the patterned areas, or by depositing a material into the interstices of the polymer relief pattern. The substrate can be composed of a single material or it can have one or more thin-film layers on it. The etching can be done by either ion bombardment or chemical means. Both thermal diffusion and ion implantation can

* This work is sponsored by the Department of the Army.

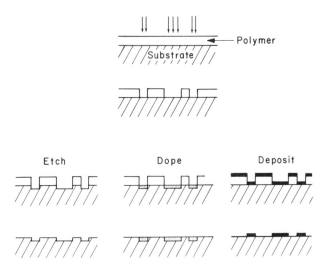

Figure 4.1 Schematic illustration of the principles of the planar fabrication technique. Copyright 1974 by The Institute of Electrical and Electronic Engineers, Inc. Reprinted, with permission, from *Proc. IEEE* **62**, 1974, p. 1361.

be used for chemical doping. In both cases an oxide or metal pattern is usually used as the mask rather than a polymer. The formation of a pattern by deposition, the so-called *lift-off process*, is contingent upon being able subsequently to remove the polymer and its coating of material.[1]

The formation of the pattern in the polymer is fundamental in determining the dimensional aspects of a device and receives the greatest emphasis in this chapter. Light, electrons, and X rays have been used as the exposing radiation, and the processes are called photolithography, electron lithography, and X-ray lithography, respectively. Photolithography is by far the most widely used of the three processes, and is considered in the main body of this chapter. Electron lithography and X-ray lithography are advanced techniques that so far have seen only limited use. They are discussed in separate sections that follow.

Surface wave devices frequently consist of metallic electrode patterns on single crystal substrates. Their fabrication consists of relatively few steps. The metallic pattern can be produced either by etching or lift-off, and we discuss in Section 4.3 the relative merits of these two approaches. Recently, new types of surface wave devices have been developed that involve surface relief gratings in addition to metallic electrodes.[2,3] The ion bombardment etching techniques employed in producing the gratings are discussed in a separate section.

4.1 Substrates and Polymer Film Preparation

The most widely used substrates for surface wave devices are the single crystal piezoelectrics such as $LiNbO_3$, quartz, $Bi_{12}GeO_{20}$, and $LiTaO_3$. A number of other substrates have been used, including silicon, ZnO, CdS, CdSe, GaAs, InSb, Al_2O_3, selenium, TeO_2. On nonpiezoelectric substrates, surface waves can be launched by means of wedge or comb transducers,[4] by interdigital electrode transducers in conjunction with deposited piezoelectric thin films,[5] or by means of piezoelectric blocks bonded onto the nonpiezoelectric.[6-8]

Techniques for depositing piezoelectric thin films and for characterizing their acoustic and piezoelectric properties have been discussed extensively in the literature.[5,9] Most of this work has been directed toward obtaining ZnO film with fine grained structure and a preferred C-axis normal orientation. With proper control of substrate conditions and deposition parameters, high quality films with properties approaching single crystal ZnO can usually be obtained. However propagation loss tends to be high for frequencies above about 200 MHz, and it is generally difficult to reproduce film characteristics consistently. It appears that additional development is required to establish the conditions necessary to obtain consistent quality films, and to expand the number of useful film-substrate combinations. For these reasons and because the techniques for producing piezoelectric films are not yet reduced to routine practice, the subject is not treated further here.

Lardat et al.[6,7] have used bonded blocks of piezoelectrics to launch Love and Rayleigh waves on a variety of substrates. This technique is very effective, but it requires a high degree of skill in handling the blocks. It is not covered here.

Wauk et al.[8] have also used piezoelectric blocks bonded onto nonpiezoelectrics, and have launched surface waves onto the latter from interdigital transducers on the former. This technique is promising, but the interface between the piezoelectric and the nonpiezoelectric presents problems of fabrication. Surface polishing must be done after bonding of the blocks, the bond must be free of discontinuities, and the surface smoothness must be continuous across the boundary. This subject is also outside the scope of the present chapter.

Here we consider only homogeneous, single crystal substrates, since these are the most widely used, are well understood, and can generally be obtained commercially.

The choice of a substrate is dictated by the frequency, insertion loss, and fractional bandwidth required, as well as the delay time and temperature stability needed. For interdigital electrode transducers, minimum

Table 4.1 Surface Wave Substrates

Crystal	Surface Normal and Propagation Direction	Measured $\Delta v/v_\infty(\%)$	$k^2(\%)$	Ideal Fractional Bandwidth (%)	Temperature Coefficient of Delay (ppm)
LiNbO$_3$	Y–Z	2.14	4.5	24	91
Quartz	Y–X	0.095	0.23	5.4	−22
Quartz	ST–X	0.067	0.16	4.5	0
Bi$_{12}$GeO$_{20}$	(100)–(011)	0.718	1.5	14	130
Bi$_{12}$GeO$_{20}$	(111)–(110)	0.823	1.7	15	128
Bi$_{12}$GeO$_{20}$	(110)–(001)	0.413	0.85	10	–
ZnO	Z-cut	0.447	1.0	11	40
LiTaO$_3$	Y–Z	0.364	0.74	10	37

Source: Reprinted, with permission, from *Proc. Conf. on Component Performance and Systems Applications of Surface Wave Devices,* IEE, Stevenage, England, 1973, p. 4.

insertion loss occurs when the fractional bandwidth is given by

$$\frac{\Delta f}{f} \leq \frac{2k}{\sqrt{\pi}} \qquad (4.1)$$

where k is the electromechanical coupling constant. Table 4.1 lists values of the electromechanical coupling constant for a number of useful substrates. For large fractional bandwidths YZ LiNbO$_3$ is the optimum material. Table 4.1 also gives values of the temperature coefficient of delay. This coefficient is zero for ST quartz, and hence it is the preferred substrate where temperature stability is essential. This is true only for straight delay paths. For reflective-array devices in which surface waves propagate in two orthogonal directions on the crystal surface,[2,3] YZ LiNbO$_3$ and (100) or (011) B$_{12}$GeO$_{20}$ are preferred over ST quartz because the anisotropy of the temperature coefficient of delay is smaller for the former two.[10] Beam steering, diffraction loss, and available crystal size must also be taken into account when long delay times are required. Slobodnik[11] has discussed the trade-offs between beam steering and diffraction loss and has provided a review of the various material parameters that must be considered in designing optimum surface wave devices. Extensive data on elastic and piezoelectric properties of surface wave substrates is provided in the *Microwave Acoustics Handbook.*[12]

Substrate Preparation. The preparation of a surface wave substrate includes orientation, cutting, polishing, and cleaning. The commercial suppliers of surface wave substrates are generally able to handle the first two.[13] However they frequently fail to provide an adequate surface polish.[14] Also, among substrates polished by the same source, there are frequently wide variations in surface roughness, in the size and density of scratches, and in the amount of subsurface work damage. One reason is that quantitative measurements of surface microtopography and work damage are difficult to make, especially for a commercial polisher who must also minimize costs. At present, polishing is more an art than a science, and the tendency to keep polishing techniques closely guarded secrets tends to perpetuate this situation. The first step in upgrading the science of polishing is to improve surface measuring techniques and make them more convenient. It is worthwhile at this point to digress for a brief discussion of the topic.

Stylus instruments can map a surface with a vertical resolution of about 25 Å, and a horizontal resolution on the order of a few microns.[15] Submicron cracks and scratches are thus not detected. Tolansky interferometric techniques[16] provide a vertical resolution of about 5 Å, but substrates must be coated with about 700 Å of silver. Horizontal resolution is on the order of 3 μm. Electron microscopy can provide horizontal resolution on the order of 10 Å, but vertical resolution is poor ($\sim$1000 Å), and a number of constraints on the sample and its preparation limit the utility of such microscopy. At the National Bureau of Standards, a topographical measuring instrument is being developed that is based on field emission from a fine tip held in close proximity to a surface.[15] This instrument, the "topografiner," may ultimately be capable of 3 Å vertical resolution and 200 Å horizontal resolution. The substrate must be a conductor or have a conducting film covering it. Nevertheless it appears that this instrument could provide a convenient and accurate means of measuring surface topography. Its further development would be welcome in the surface wave field and a number of other areas.

Surface roughness and work damage can be evaluated by measuring the amount of light scattering.[16] Although this method does not provide a direct measure of topography, it is rapid and convenient, and could serve as a means of quality control in an optical polishing facility. Moreover it may be possible directly to correlate light scattering and surface wave attenuation and dispersion.

Bennett et al.[16–18] have shown that the so-called bowl feed polishing technique produces fewer scratches, a smoother surface, and far less subsurface work damage than conventional fresh-feed techniques. Surfaces with an rms roughness less than 5 Å have been obtained. In the bowl feed technique the substrate being polished and the lap (usually pitch) are immersed in a slurry consisting of a mixture of water and a polishing compound. An agitator at the edge of the bowl stirs the slurry.

No new polishing compound is added during the course of polishing. However there is a natural tendency for the particles of the compound to break down and become finer. In the final stages of the process, agitation is stopped and the slurry is removed or allowed to settle out in the bottom of the bowl. Polishing is continued with water and any abrasive that remains in the lap. The bowl feed process is slower than conventional methods and has not been widely adopted by commercial polishers. It is currently used to produce low scatter optical surfaces,[16,18] and could prove useful in polishing substrates for high frequency or long-path-length surface wave devices.

Chemical-mechanical polishing techniques are widely used in the semiconductor industry to produce surfaces with a minimum of scratches and subsurface damage. Similar techniques have been successful on $LiNbO_3$,[14] but to date are not widely used. The major problem with chemical-mechanical methods is that surface figure is difficult to control. In many surface wave devices surface flatness is not important, and in such cases chemical-mechanical polishing techniques are probably preferred.

Surfaces can also be polished by ion bombardment.[19–22] Usually the ions are incident at an oblique angle to the surface, and the sample is rotated in order to avoid nonuniformities. It has been observed that at normal incidence single crystal surfaces tend to etch more uniformly than amorphous materials, and that their surface flatness is maintained. Although lenses and other optical components have been fabricated by ion bombardment etching, a more important application is probably the removal of the thin damage layer produced by conventional optical polishing. For high frequency devices the removal of several hundred Å from a polished substrate surface by ion beam etching leads to more reproducible device performance.[21] Ion beam etching has been used to increase the threshold for laser damage in Al_2O_3.[23] The optimum energy for ion bombardment polishing using argon ions is around 200 eV. At this energy the sputtering yield is high, yet the depth of any point defect damage produced in the substrate is extremely small, probably on the order of a single atomic layer.[24] The formation of pits has been observed at energies on the order of 10 keV,[25] and alteration of the surface elastic properties may occur.

The procedure for cleaning substrates can be divided into precleaning and final cleaning stages. The details of the precleaning depend on the contaminants likely to be present on the substrate, and also on the chemical reactivity of the substrate. Usually the major contaminants are greases, waxes, fingerprints, lint, and miscellaneous dust particles. The sequence of precleaning steps is usually quite flexible. The final cleaning procedure, on the other hand, should not be varied. It consists of ultrasonic agitation in a hot detergent bath, followed by extensive (one-half to one-hour) rinsing in hot water of the highest practical purity. The principles of substrate cleaning have been discussed elsewhere, usually in reference to glass and ceramic substrates.[26-28] A procedure applicable to $LiNbO_3$ and most other surface wave substrates that has worked well at Lincoln Laboratory is given in Table 4.2.

Steps 1, 2, and 3 are intended to remove the readily soluble organic contaminants. The purpose of step 4 is to remove the more stubborn organic contaminants. Three options are given. The first is probably the optimum approach for all cases where the substrate either is an oxide or is not adversely affected by an ionized oxygen environment. The second is effective, but concentrated sulfuric acid is dangerous to handle, and many substrates of interest are attacked. $LiNbO_3$ is relatively inert, but it has been observed that H_2SO_4 occasionally leaves a pattern of microcracks on its surface. The third option is more gentle and is effective on organics. Studies have shown it to be highly effective in cleaning quartz crystal substrates.[28] It has been observed that the number of small particles clinging to a $LiNbO_3$ substrate is significantly reduced during step 4.

The detergent bath used in step 5 is usually a 1% solution of a technical grade basic detergent. Although the detergent may introduce

Table 4.2 Substrate Cleaning Procedure

Step 1. Immerse in trichlorethylene, ~10 min.

Step 2. Immerse in acetone, ~10 min.

Step 3. Rinse in methanol and water.

Step 4. Remove stubborn organics; three options:
  a. Immerse in an rf plasma of 3% oxygen, 97% helium at 1 torr for ~10 min.
  b. Immerse in concentrated H_2SO_4 at room temperature ~5 min.
  c. Immerse in a mixture of three parts H_2O, one part NH_4OH concentrated, and one part of 30% unstabilized H_2O_2 for 10 min at 75°C.

Step 5. Immerse in a detergent bath at 65°C with ultrasonic agitation, ~10 min.

Step 6. Rinse off detergent in water, of 18 mΩ resistivity at 65°C.

Step 7. Immerse in circulating water bath, of 18 mΩ resistivity, for one half to one hour at 65°C.

Step 8. Remove from water and observe wetting of surface.

Step 9. Reimmerse in water, remove, and blow dry with jet of dry nitrogen.

ionic impurities that would be undesirable for silicon device substrates, such impurities are generally unimportant in surface wave device fabrication. Nonionic detergents are also effective.

Commercially available water filtering and recirculating systems can be used for step 7. Generally ions, organics, and particles down to $\frac{1}{4}\,\mu$m are continuously filtered out of the water, and a constant flow of 10 to 18 mΩ water is passed through one or more cascaded rinsing tanks.

After the preceding steps, the cleanliness of the substrate can be evaluated by observing the way water wets the surface. The contact angle between a water droplet and a surface is a sensitive function of surface contamination.[26,28] To observe the contact angle the substrate is held on the back surface by means of a Teflon suction cup and removed from the pure water bath. Because the substrate and the water are hot, the water evaporates rapidly, and its borders pull inward from the edges of the substrate. If the substrate is free of contamination, the surface of the water at the border generally forms an acute angle with the surface of the substrate, and optical interference fringes are clearly visible in the thin water wedge. On the other hand, if the substrate is contaminated, the water and substrate surfaces form an obtuse angle, and no fringes are visible. Lesser amounts of contamination cause the border of the water to recede unevenly. This water wetting test works only on substrates that water wets, and excludes—for example, silicon.

Substrate cleaning is an important first step in device fabrication, irrespective of the subsequent processing procedure. Failure to clean substrates thoroughly usually results in metal film adhesion failure. In extreme cases surface contamination can adversely affect surface wave propagation.

The phase of substrate processing after substrate cleaning is usually the formation of metal electrode patterns. As discussed previously, two alternative techniques are possible: etching and lift-off. The relative merits of the two are discussed in more detail later. For now, suffice it to say that chemical etching is most appropriate for mass production of large numbers of identical devices whose electrode patterns are simple and of relatively low resolution (minimum linewidth $\gtrsim 5\,\mu$m). Ion bombardment etching is not limited in resolution, but requires the use of expensive capital equipment. Lift-off is preferred where high resolution (minimum linewidth $\lesssim 5\,\mu$m), pattern complexity (hundreds of lines in repetitive arrays), or high yield are required, or where a relatively small number of devices are to be made. If the lift-off technique is used, the substrate is coated with a radiation sensitive polymer immediately after cleaning. If the etching technique is used, the substrate is coated with a thin film of metal after cleaning. Thin film deposition techniques are not discussed little utility in lithography or device fabrication. Similarly, definitions that relate to recording images in photographic emulsions are generally not relevant. Here we use *resolution* as a qualitative term that refers to the minimum dimensions of parts of a pattern. For a quantitative specification of the performance of any pattern generation or replication method, we use the minimum *linewidth* that can be reproducibly created in a grating array of one-to-one line-to-space ratio. *Accuracy* is used to indicate whether the various parts of a pattern have dimensions and spatial relationships consistent with the meter length standard. *Distortion* is used to indicate whether the various parts of a pattern have the desired relative sizes and mutual spatial relations. *Precision* is used to indicate repeatability. As an example, consider the case of a linear grating of one-to-one line-to-space ratio. The distortion of the grating is a measure of the deviations from perfect periodicity. The accuracy of the grating is a measure of whether the average periodicity has the desired dimension. The precision specifies how closely several gratings made by the same technique match one another.*

The most commonly used methods of exposing patterns in photoresist films are projection printing, shadow printing, and holographic recording. These are separately discussed and compared later. The holographic recording technique is an effective method of making gratings of low distortion and is used extensively in the fabrication of thin film optical devices. To date it has not been used in connection with surface wave devices. Nevertheless it is very likely to be used in the future.

Projection Printing. In projection printing an optical system is used to image a reticle mask onto a photoresist-coated substrate. In most cases the reticle pattern is demagnified by the optical system. In designing the optical system, trade-offs are made between pattern resolution and field of view. These trade-offs are well understood and have been discussed extensively elsewhere.[34] The highest resolution lenses are those that have been developed for optical microscopy. A high quality dry objective lens with a numerical aperture of 0.95 can resolve gratings with periodicities of about 0.35 μm. Microscope lenses have been used to expose linewidths less than 1 μm in photoresist.[35,36] However their field of view is severely restricted ($\sim\frac{1}{2}$ mm), diffraction effects are present in the focal plane, pattern distortion is hard to eliminate, and it is difficult to control focus and exposure parameters to achieve linewidths approaching 0.5 μm. If monochromatic light is used, very troublesome problems of optical interference in the thickness of photoresist films are introduced.

*This paragraph is copyrighted by The Institute of Electrical and Electronic Engineers, Inc. Reprinted, with permission, from *Proc. IEEE* **62**, 1974, p. 1362.

here because they are relatively routine and have been extensively reviewed.[26-29]

Polymer Film Preparation and Characteristics. The radiation sensitive polymer films are called photoresists when used to record visible or ultraviolet radiation patterns, and by analogy, electron resists or X-ray resists when used for electron lithography and X-ray lithography, respectively. The term *resist* originally connoted resistance to chemical etchants and is thus somewhat inappropriate when used in conjunction with lift-off, ion beam etching, or ion implantation. Photoresists respond to optical radiation either by cross-linking or by reactions that lead to selective solubility in a developer. The former are called negative photoresists, and the latter positive photoresists. Electron and X-ray resists, on the other hand, either cross-link (negative type) or undergo chain scission (positive type).

A number of photoresists have been developed over the past 20 years. Negative type photoresists are used extensively in semiconductor device fabrication, and information on their performance and characteristics is given in references.[26,27,30] The positive photoresists of the AZ 1350 type[31,32] have proved to be the most useful for surface wave device fabrication. This is due primarily to their high resolution capability and to the fact that vertical sidewalls can be produced. Such vertical sidewalls are important both for the lift-off process and for ion beam etching. Also, the AZ 1350 type photoresists can be dissolved and removed by simple organic solvents such as acetone, whereas the negative-type cross-linking photoresists frequently require rather strong chemical agents for their removal. Such agents may be incompatible with many surface wave substrates. For these reasons the present discussion is restricted to AZ 1350 type photoresists.

The AZ 1350 type photoresists are composed of a base resin plus diazide compounds. The latter are strong absorbers in the ultraviolet, and undergo photochemical decomposition leading to reduced optical absorption (bleaching) and enhanced solubility of the photoresist in aqueous alkaline solutions. The ultraviolet transmission of AZ 1350 is thus a function of an absorber concentration that decreases with exposure. Herrick[33] and Dill and Neureuther[31] pointed out that this behavior is nonlinear and can be mathematically modeled as follows:

$$\frac{\partial I(z, t)}{\partial z} = -I(z, t)[AM(z, t) + B] \tag{4.2}$$

$$\frac{\partial M}{\partial t} = -I(z, t)M(z, t)C \tag{4.3}$$

Surface Wave Device Fabrication

where the coordinate z is normal to the photoresist film, t is the time, $I(z, t)$ is the light intensity, and $M(z, t)$ is the fractional concentration of the diazide compound, also known as the "inhibitor." The constants A, B, and C can be evaluated empirically from a plot of the optical transmission of a photoresist film as a function of time. At a wavelength of 4047 Å, Dill and Neureuther[31] found $A \cong 0.9/\mu m$, $B \cong 0.07/\mu m$, and $C \cong 0.02 \, cm^2/mJ$ for AZ 1350J. Herrick[33] has given solutions to (4.2) and (4.3) that enable one to calculate $M(z, t)$.

The dissolution rate of AZ 1350 type photoresists in an aqueous alkaline solution is negligible when M is unity, but rapidly increases as M is reduced. This is the basis of the development process. For AZ 1350J, Dill and Neureuther[31] have shown that the rate of dissolution in a one-to-one mixture of water and the manufacturer's recommended developer can be modeled by the following equation:

$$R = \exp\left(E_1 + E_2 M + E_3 M^2\right) \tag{4.4}$$

where R is in Å/sec, E_1, E_2, and E_3 are constants, and M is the fractional concentration of inhibitor. At 20°C, $E_1 \cong 5.3$, $E_2 \cong 8.2$, $E_3 \cong -13$.[31] Using (4.4), together with $M(z, t)$, and the assumption that development is a surface limited etching reaction, one can calculate numerically the relief structure obtained in a photoresist film for a given development time.

The usual method of coating a substrate with a photoresist film consists of flooding the surface with the photoresist liquid and then spinning the substrate on a high acceleration whirler. Such whirlers are available commercially. Films of uniform thickness (± 100 Å) are readily obtained on circular substrates. On rectangular substrates, however, thickness nonuniformity occurs at the corners, and this effect becomes more pronounced for large length-to-width ratios. Dip coating can provide extremely uniform films on rectangular substrates.[2] However it is slower and far less convenient than spinning.

Figure 4.2 shows a simple laboratory setup for dip coating. The film thickness is controlled by the speed of withdrawal. For AZ 1350H photoresist, a withdrawal speed of 3 mm/min results in a 4000 Å thick film, whereas a speed of $4\frac{1}{2}$ mm/min yields a 10,000 Å thickness. During operation the inverted plastic box in which the substrate is held fits over the flask containing the photoresist. As a result, photoresist solvent vapors are trapped and saturate the atmosphere above the surface of the liquid. This ensures that the photoresist film formed on a substrate dries slowly and evenly. Thickness uniformity to within 100 Å is readily obtained. The photoresist in the flask must be protected from cumulative exposure by low level stray light and must first be carefully filtered to remove particles. All six surfaces of a substrate must be scrupulously

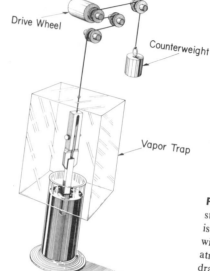

Drive Wheel

Counterweight

Vapor Trap

Figure 4.2 Apparatus for dip-coating substrates to achieve uniform films of photoresist. Thickness is controlled by the speed of withdrawal. The vapor trap ensures that the atmosphere into which the substrate is drawn is saturated with solvent vapors. Also, air currents are eliminated. Thickness uniformity of ± 100 Å is readily obtained.

cleaned to prevent the introduction of particulate contamination. Such particles often float on the surface of the photoresist fluid and becom incorporated in the film as a substrate is withdrawn. In the case of sp coating, on the other hand, only the substrate's top surface needs to cleaned, and only a small amount of photoresist needs to be filtered any one time.

After a photoresist film is formed on a substrate it should be bake accordance with manufacturer's instructions. A temperature of 80° appropriate for AZ 1350, and a duration of 20 to 30 minutes has found satisfactory. Substrates may then be stored in light-tight conta for periods of up to a few months with no adverse effects on exp sensitivity.

4.2 Photolithography

In this section and in later sections on X-ray and electron lith frequent reference is made to the resolution, linewidth, accuracy tion, and precision of patterns exposed in photoresists and ele X-ray sensitive polymers. It is important to clarify the meanings terms, although there is no universal agreement. The classical of resolution (the Rayleigh criterion) as "the distance at which t can be clearly recognized as distinct" is meaningful in microsco

Recently projection systems have been developed specifically for photolithography that provide a demagnification of $10 \times$, and a field of view about 8 mm in diameter. The major application of these projection systems is in the generation of photomasks. A mechanical stage is used to move the photomask in discrete steps under the lens to expose an array of patterns or compose a large area pattern. Areas up to $10 \text{ cm} \times 10 \text{ cm}$ can be covered in this fashion with an absolute accuracy of about 1 μm and a repeatability, or precision, of about 0.25 μm. These systems are capable of exposing gratings of 0.9 μm linewidth in AZ 1350. However to do so, extremely fine control of exposure parameters must be exercised. The depth of focus is only about 1 μm, the photoresist must be about 1000 Å thick, and exposure time must be controlled to within about ±5%. Bell and Mellon[37] have used a commercial projection system to expose high resolution surface wave device patterns directly in photoresist on device substrates. As is discussed later, it is more advantageous to make photomasks and replicate these by conformable-mask contact printing.

In many kinds of surface wave devices, especially high capacity pulse compression filters, a repetitive pattern of electrodes or reflecting grooves extends over areas much larger than can be covered in a single field of view of an optical projection system. Moreover, to achieve a high degree of phase fidelity, each electrode or each groove must be located at its assigned position to within a small fraction of an acoustic wavelength. One way this can be done is by creating a photomask in an optical projection system controlled by a laser interferometer[38] and subsequently transferring this pattern onto a device substrate. A laser interferometer can recognize a distance increment of 100 Å. In making repetitive grating-type masks for surface wave devices, the mask is moved under the lens, and each line is separately exposed when the interferometer indicates that the assigned position has been reached. If the photosensitive material is emulsion, the exposure time is very short, and exposure can usually be done while the mask is in motion. If photoresist is used instead, which is essential for linewidths near and below 1 μm, the mask motion must be stopped in order to expose a line. This puts extreme demands on the mechanical motion system. For low distortion masks environmental conditions must be held stable during fabrication. If the mask involves several thousand lines several hours may be required to expose it. Measurements by Williamson et al.[2] of the phase response of reflective-array pulse compression filters, in which the grating was made by a conformable mask replicated from a master mask produced on a laser interferometer controlled pattern generator, indicated a periodic (1.3 mm period) distortion of ±250 Å.

Some commercial projection instruments do not demagnify and are intended instead to provide a separation between photomasks and substrates, thereby avoiding damage problems associated with conventional shadow printing. Such one-to-one instruments can provide minimum linewidths of about 2 μm over fields 7.5 cm in diameter and are potentially useful in the mass production of large numbers of moderate resolution surface wave devices.

Shadow Printing.   The most widely used photolithographic technique is shadow printing, also commonly called *contact printing*. In this technique a pattern in thin film chromium, Fe_2O_3, silicon, photographic emulsion, or other ultraviolet attenuator on a glass plate is held in close proximity to, or contact with, a photoresist film on a substrate, and the pattern is transferred to the photoresist by passing collimated ultraviolet light through the glass plate. The glass plate with its pattern is called the photomask, and it must be produced by optical projection or some other pattern generation technique. Shadow printing is thus only a replication technique. It is simple, convenient, inexpensive, and the field of view is limited only by the photomask size.

Commercial shadow printing instruments have been developed for the integrated circuits industry. These provide mechanisms for making physical contact between photomasks and substrates, as well as means for superimposing patterns from several masks on the same substrate. Recently, so called off-contact instruments have also been developed. These commercial mask alignment instruments are designed for large-scale production using photomasks 1.5 mm thick. Generally the gap between the photomask and the substrate is highly variable from one area to another, and from substrate to substrate. Diffraction takes place across this gap, and can be very troublesome, especially for the repetitive gratinglike structures that are characteristic of surface wave devices. Diffraction causes a marked rounding of photoresist profiles, which in turn causes failures if the lift-off process is used. The most significant consequence of the failure of commercial mask alignment systems to control mask-sample gap is the inability to replicate high resolution patterns. The experience of the integrated circuits industry with shadow printing has led to a rather widely held rule of thumb that shadow printing can not replicate linewidths below 1 μm. Actually, linewidths well below 1 μm can be replicated with considerable ease if the gap between a photomask and the top surface of a photoresist film is eliminated. In principle this can be done by employing photomasks and substrates that are much flatter than an optical wavelength, by making the thickness of photoresist films uniform to the same tolerance, by excluding all dust and surface asperities, and by bringing the photomask into optical contact with the photoresist. In practice, however, photomasks and many substrates of interest are not so flat, and for substrates of large area, it is generally impossible to exclude all dust completely.

An alternative approach to intimate contact is to use a conformable photomask.[1,2,22,39] A conformable photomask consists of a pattern in thin film chromium (500 to 1000 Å) or Fe_2O_3 (1300 Å) on Corning type 0211 glass, 0.2 mm thick. Such photomasks readily conform to the contours of a substrate, and wherever an occasional dust particle occurs, they deform so as to minimize the area of noncontact (usually <1 mm diameter) as well as the local stress. Figure 4.3 illustrates a vacuum frame that can be used to obtain uniform intimate contact over large areas.

When there is intimate contact between a photomask and a photoresist film, diffraction takes place only in the thickness of the photoresist. The relief structure obtained in the photoresist is determined by the near-field diffraction pattern of the photomask, and the exposure-development characteristics of the photoresist. Figure 4.4 shows a cross-sectional profile of a portion of an 8000 Å periodicity grating exposed in AZ 1350 H photoresist, 9800 Å thick using a mercury arc lamp and a conformable photomask in intimate contact. The photomask was made by scanning electron beam lithography. Such photoresist structures have been used to produce 2000 Å thick aluminum interdigital electrode surface wave transducers having 4000 Å linewidths. In exposing such high resolution patterns it has been found experimentally that the photoresist thickness and exposure time are not critical parameters. For example, using conformable mask photolithography and the metal lift-off technique to produce surface wave transducers with an interline spacing of 8000 Å, a linewidth variation of only 20% is observed when the exposure time is varied by a factor of 3. At an interline spacing of 1.6 μm (1 GHz on YZ LiNbO$_3$), the latitude in exposure time is a factor of 8 for a photoresist thickness of 10,000 Å. For gratings of 7000 Å period, the exposure latitude was a factor of 2 on silicon and chromium substrates. The metal lift-off technique is an especially stringent test of the quality of a photoresist structure because, as is discussed later, it does not work unless the photoresist sidewalls are vertical or undercut and there is complete photoresist development to the substrate surface. The preceding results imply that with careful control of exposure parameters patterns with much higher resolution can probably be obtained.

That shadow printing with conformable photomasks can achieve such high resolution structures over a wide range of exposure time is somewhat surprising, and it is instructive to indicate the factors that make this possible. As mentioned previously, the structure recorded in the photoresist depends on the near-field diffraction pattern of the photomask, and

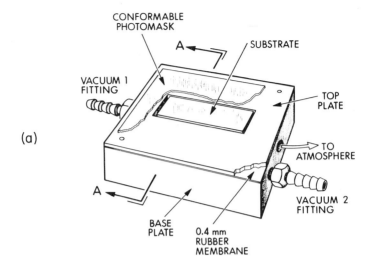

(a)

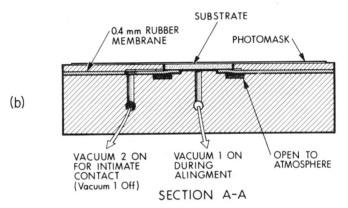

(b)

SECTION A-A

Figure 4.3 (*a*) Vacuum frame that permits a conformable photomask to be algined with respect to a substrate and then pulled into intimate contact. (*b*) Cross section of the vacuum frame. To obtain intimate contact, vacuum 2 is pulled. When vacuum 1 is released, the substrate is free to move up to the conformable photomask. The flexure of the photomask is thus removed and intimate contact can be achieved over the entire substrate surface. (*c*) Exploded view of the vacuum frame. The top plate has a series of grooves milled in its bottom surface and a shallow step milled around the perimeter of the opening so that the space around the substrate can be evacuated by means of vacuum 2. Under the rubber membrane an opening is provided to the atmosphere. During alignment the crystal is held to the base plate by vacuum 1. Copyright 1975 by The Institute of Electrical and Electronic Engineers, Inc. Reprinted, with permission, from *IEEE Trans.* **ED-22,** 1975, p. 496.

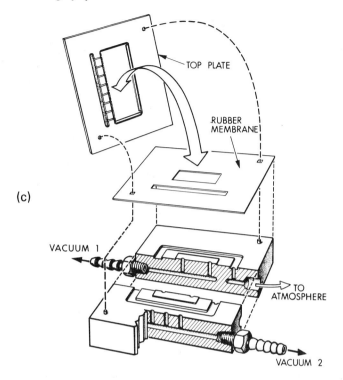

TOP PLATE

RUBBER
MEMBRANE

(c)

VACUUM 1

TO
ATMOSPHERE

VACUUM 2

Figure 4.3 *(Contd).*

the exposure-development characteristics of the photoresist. The near-field diffraction pattern of a photomask is very difficult to calculate exactly for a medium such as photoresist because the light intensity (and perhaps also the phase delay) at a given depth changes with time during the course of exposure, as indicated in (4.2) and (4.3). Moreover, because of diffraction, M and I become functions of the lateral coordinates x and y, and the equations have to be generalized. Equation (4.4) expresses the development characteristics. Obviously it is a difficult and complex problem to calculate the photoresist structure obtained for a given exposure and development, especially when diffraction is significant, as in the case of 4000 Å linewidths.

Even for optically linear media, diffraction calculations are difficult for submicrometer linewidths. Calculations based on the Kirchhoff approximation provide accurate results only at distances of several wavelengths from apertures several wavelengths in diameter. Existing rigorous diffraction theory deals only with apertures in perfectly conducting screens. At

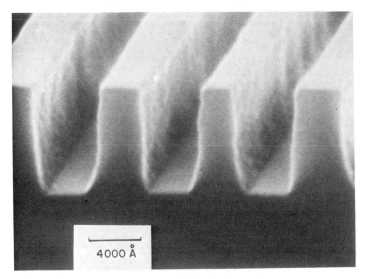

Figure 4.4 Scanning electron micrograph of the cross section of a grating pattern, exposed in AZ 1350 H photoresist using a high-pressure mercury arc lamp and the conformable photomask–intimate contact technique. The photoresist is 9800 Å thick. Because of the angles used in microscopy, vertical dimensions are foreshortened relative to lateral dimensions. The scale refers to lateral dimensions only. The photomask consisted of 5 slits in an 800 Å thick chromium film on 0211 glass. It was made by scanning electron beam lithography and chemical etching of the chromium, which caused irregularities along the edges of the slits. These small, irregular features are replicated in the photoresist. The smaller space between two of the slits was in the original mask, and was caused by an error in the scanning electron beam pattern generator. Micrograph by R. Eager. Reprinted, with permission, from ref. 39, p. 1504.

short-wavelength visible and ultraviolet wavelengths materials used in photomasks, such as chromium and iron oxide, are not perfect conductors. B. J. Lin has developed an approximation method for calculating the very near-field diffraction from narrow apertures in perfectly conducting opaque masks.[40] Some of his results are presented in Fig. 4.5 for the case of a plane wave incident normally on a mask having three slits of width 2λ, with E polarized parallel to the slits. For the E field polarized perpendicular to the slits somewhat more diffraction broadening occurs.

The mercury arc lamp used to expose the structure shown in Fig 4.4 has prominent lines at 4358 Å, 4047 Å, and 3663 Å. Inside the photoresist, which has an index of refraction of 1.6, these become 2700 Å, 2510 Å, and 2270 Å, respectively. The 4000 Å linewidths are thus somewhat less than 2λ. The photoresist thickness in Fig. 4.4 is 9800 Å, or approximately 4λ. For a given exposure time one can construct from Fig.

4.5 surfaces of equal energy density. Although these surfaces clearly cannot be identified with the photoresist profiles of Fig. 4.4, they would have somewhat similar shapes. However their "linewidths" would rapidly widen as a function of exposure time, whereas the observed photoresist profiles change very little with exposure time. Thus the broadening of lines due to diffraction is less in AZ 1350 photoresists than it would be in

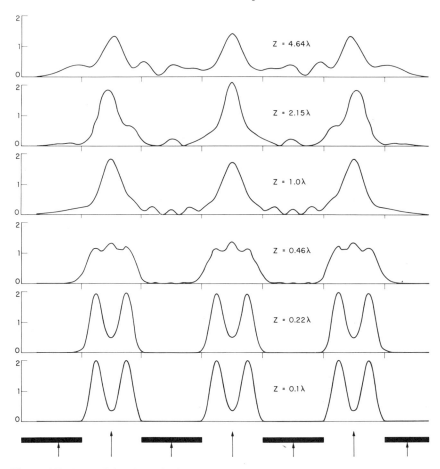

Figure 4.5 Plots of light intensity in the near field of a grating consisting of three slits of width 2λ. The strips between the slits are also 2λ wide. Here Z is the perpendicular distance away from the grating into the near field. The solid bars at the bottom of the figure show the slit positions relative to the intensity patterns. The plots were made from calculations provided through the courtesy of B. J. Lin[41] and are for the case of a normally incident plane wave whose E field is polarized parallel to the slits. Note that at a distance $Z = 2.15\lambda$ there is substantial intensity in between the slits. Reprinted, with permission, from ref. 39, p. 1505.

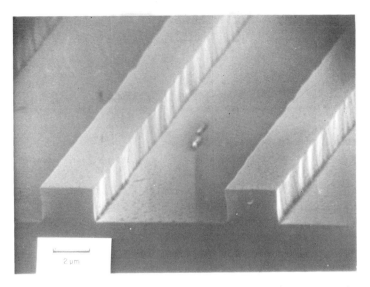

Figure 4.6 Scanning electron micrograph of the cross section of a low-resolution grating pattern exposed in AZ 1350 H photoresist, 18,000 Å thick, using a conformable photomask in intimate contact. Reprinted, with permission, from ref. 1, p. 824.

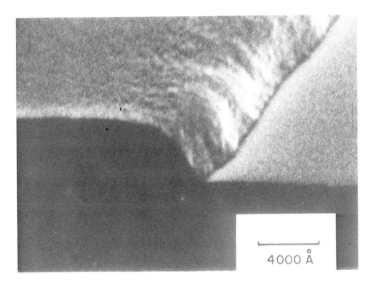

4000 Å

Figure 4.7 Scanning electron micrograph of the cross section of the edge of a pattern exposed in AZ 1350 photoresist, 5000 Å thick, using a photomask that was out of contact by about 2 μm. Diffraction causes the rounding of the sidewall profile. Reprinted, with permission, from ref. 1, p. 824.

184

a medium that recorded the energy dissipation. The optical nonlinearity and the exposure-development characteristics of the photoresist are believed to be the major reasons for this difference.

Intimate-contact shadow printing produces sharp vertical or slightly undercut side walls in a photoresist film. This is illustrated in Fig. 4.4 and also in Fig. 4.6 for the case of a low-resolution grating pattern exposed in 18,000 Å thick AZ 1350 H photoresist. Figure 4.7 shows that when exposure takes place out of contact, diffraction in the air gap causes the photoresist to have a rounded sidewall. As discussed later, such a profile is unsuitable for both metal lift-off and ion beam etching. In the former application there would be continuity between the metal on the substrate and that on top of the photoresist. In the latter application a rapid degradation of the profile etched in the substrate would result.

The fact that conformable photomask shadow printing can produce submicrometer linewidth patterns implies it also permits precise control

Table 4.3   Conformable Photomask–Intimate-Contact Printing

Advantages

1. Minimum linewidths $\leq 0.4\ \mu$m.
2. Pattern area $\sim 100\ \mathrm{cm}^2$ or greater.
3. Linewidth controllable to $\sim 0.1\ \mu$m.
4. Vertical or slightly undercut profiles, ideal for metal lift-off process and ion bombardment etching.
5. Dust defects minimized.
6. Long life of masks.
7. Low distortion (<1 part in 10^5).
8. Wide exposure latitude. Threshold can be exceeded by factor of 3 or more.
9. High index of refraction and nonlinear behavior of photoresist suppress diffraction broadening.
10. Processing independent of pattern resolution.
11. Low cost.

Disadvantages

1. Intimate contact required. Substrates must be smooth.
2. High level of operator skill required, technique not suitable for mass production at present.
3. Multilevel masking precision $\sim 1\ \mu$m.

Source: Copyright 1974 by The Institute of Electrical and Electronic Engineers, Inc. Reprinted, with permission, from *Proc. IEEE* **62,** 1974, p. 1366.

of dimensions. The widths of lines in a mask and the smoothness of the edges of a pattern can probably be replicated with a dimensional control approaching 1000 Å.

Conformable photomask-intimate-contact printing appears to produce very little pattern distortion. Direct measurements of superimposed grating patterns indicated distortions less than or on the order of 1000 Å over a 2 cm distance. Phase measurements of reflective-array surface wave pulse compression filters[2] tend to confirm the direct measurements.

Conformable photomask patterns do not appear to become damaged or wear out even when reused many tens of times. Such degradation is commonly observed with conventional 1.5 mm thick photomasks, presumably because of large stresses at local high points or dust particles. It is believed that the conformable photomask's tendency to deform locally around a high point is responsible for the apparent absence of damage.

The practical advantages and disadvantages of conformable photomask, intimate contact photolithographic printing are summarized in Table 4.3.

The conformable photomask-intimate-contact technique has not yet been used in the mass production of devices. However a mask alignment system has been developed at Lincoln Laboratory that represents a significant increase in convenience and speed over earlier schemes.[39] It permits a mask to be registered relative to the edges of a substrate, or to a previously existing pattern on a substrate, to within about 1 μm in lateral distance and to within about 10^{-4} radians angular orientation in about two minutes.

Holographic Recording.   Patterns can be recorded in photoresist films by holographic means.[42–44] Of special interest is the exposure of periodic gratings. Such gratings have been used as couplers and filters in thin film optical devices and in distributed feedback lasers. To date, holographically produced gratings have not been used in surface wave devices. However it is likely they will be important in the near future. The holographic technique can produce large area gratings rapidly and conveniently with exposure times on the order of seconds. Gratings can be produced either directly on device substrates or on masks. Grating periodicity can be varied over the range from micrometers to a few hundred Å. With reasonable care gratings with less than 1 part in 10^{10} distortion can be easily produced.

The technique for producing holographic gratings consists of interfering two beams from an ultraviolet or short-wavelength visible laser. The beam is first passed through a spatial filter and beam expander, and then split into two plane wave beams of roughly equal intensity. A pair of plane mirrors is arranged to bring the two beams together at a known angle on a photoresist coated substrate. Several other configurations can also be used. The spacing of the system of interference fringes produced in the photoresist film when the two beams have the same angle of incidence on the substrate is given by

$$d = \lambda/2 \sin \alpha \qquad (4.5)$$

where λ is the wavelength and α is half the angle between the two beams. The angle α can conveniently be made as large as about 80°. Special care must be taken to provide sturdy mounts for optical components and to minimize the amplitude of bench vibrations. Holographically produced diffraction gratings are available commercially.

Shank and Schmidt[42] have reported gratings with periodicity as fine as 1108 Å using a He-Cd laser (3250 Å) and a prism with index matching fluid. Tsang and Wang[44] have described an exposure system in which the substrate is immersed in the developer solution during exposure. The refractive index of the developer shortens the wavelength, thereby reducing the grating periodicity. Exposure inside the developer solution permits a relatively steep-walled relief structure to be obtained in the photoresist.

The holographic method provides accurate, precise, low distortion gratings and is rapid, relatively convenient, and even permits blazing.[31] The distortion of a holographically produced grating depends on the flatness of the substrate and the degree to which the two recombined beams are plane waves or have a desired wavefront curvature. Aberrations of the beam expander and the beam splitter, and deviations from flatness or the desired optical figure of the two mirrors cause wavefront distortion. In the Shank-Schmidt technique,[42] the optical quality of the prism and the thickness uniformity of the index matching fluid must also be taken into account. In the Tsang-Wang technique, lack of homogeneity in the developer solution causes pattern distortion.[44] Rudolph and Schmahl[43] have analyzed the deviations from linearity of gratings made by the holographic method for two cases: (1) where both beams are either diverging or converging and (2) where one beam is converging and one is diverging. Applying their results to the case of holographic exposure of a 10^4 line grating using commercially available optical components, and two 4000 Å wavelength beams incident on a substrate at 45°, one finds that the cumulative distortion is about 1 part in 10^{12} for case 1. For case 2 it is less than 1 part in 10^6.[22] Both of these figures are beyond current requirements for surface wave filters. Lack of distortion is a prominent advantage of holographic recording and could prove to be a decisive advantage in future devices demanding extreme phase fidelity.

When holographic gratings are produced directly on device substrates it is difficult to align them with respect to other structures. In a later section on electron beam lithography, techniques for such alignment are discussed, and it is argued that the replication of photo and X-ray lithography masks made by the combined techniques of holographic recording and scanning electron beam lithography is a very promising approach to fabricating high frequency surface wave reflective-array devices. To date, holographic gratings of 7000 Å period and 3600 Å period have been replicated by conformable mask photolithography and X-ray lithography, respectively.

4.3 Etching and Lift-off

Most surface wave devices contain interdigital structures of thin film metal. Sometimes there are hundreds and even thousands of electrodes, and it is generally required that there be no short circuits between them. In the following sections we consider chemical etching, ion bombardment etching, and lift-off techniques for forming such metal electrode structures and try to assess the merits of each technique.

Chemical Etching.   Following exposure and development of the photoresist pattern corresponding to a desired metal pattern, it is generally necessary to bake the photoresist to increase its resistance to chemical etchants. For AZ 1350 a temperature of 120°C and a duration of 30 min is generally adequate. At about 115°C, AZ 1350 begins to flow plastically. During this "post baking" the sidewalls of the photoresist become rounded, and some lateral flowing can take place. Usually this flowing is much less than 1 μm. The rounding of the photoresist profile is unimportant as far as chemical etching is concerned. However, dimensional changes due to plastic flow may be detrimental in some cases.

The metal films most commonly used in surface wave devices are aluminum, double layers of chromium and aluminum, and double layers of chromium and gold. The chromium is usually 50 to 300 Å thick and serves as an adherent interface between the substrate and the primary metalization. The aluminum or gold films are usually 500 to 3000 Å thick. In chemical etching of these or other metal films an etchant must be chosen that attacks the metals but not the substrate or the photoresist. Some surface wave substrates—such as BGO, CdS, ZnO, and sputtered films of the latter two—are chemically reactive and impose limitations on the chemical etchants that can be used. Table 4.4 lists a few etchants useful on chromium, titanium, aluminum, copper, and gold. A more

Table 4.4 Metal Etchants

Metal	Etchant
Chromium	a. 165 g of ceric ammonium nitrate, 43 ml of conc. (70%) $HClO_4$, add water to make 1000 ml.
	b. Bell and Howell HC 300.
	c. 1 part C25 A, 1 part C25 B from Film Microelectronics, Inc., Burlington, Mass.[a]
Titanium	a. 1 part HF, 20 parts water.
Aluminum	a. 80 ml phosphoric acid, 10 ml water, 5 ml nitric acid.
	b. Techni Strip Au 60 g, add water to make 1000 ml; from Technic, Inc., Cranston, Rhode Island.[b,c]
	c. 1 part conc. HCl, 4 parts water.
	d. NaOH in water is an effective etch for aluminum, but is not compatible with AZ 1350 type photoresists.
Copper	a. 100 g of $FeCl_3$ in 1000 ml of water.[b]
	b. Alki etch, 2 parts A, 1 part B, 1 part water, from Philip Hunt Chemical Corp.[d]
Gold	a. Aqua regia; 1 part conc. HCl and 3 parts conc. HNO_3.
	b. 10 g iodine, 6 g potassium iodide, 40 ml water.[d]
	c. C35 from Film Microelectronics, Inc.; Burlington, Mass.[a,d]
	d. Techni Strip Au 60 g, add water to make 1000 ml; from Technic Inc.; Cranston, Rhode Island.[b,c,d]

[a] Compatible with sputtered ZnO.
[b] Solution should be filtered to remove particles.
[c] Compatible with PMMA film (electron or X-ray resist).
[d] Compatible with $Bi_{12}GeO_{20}$.

thorough listing of metal etchants can be found in the physics and chemistry handbooks, and in texts on thin film technology.[26,27]

The rate of chemical etching is a function of etchant concentration, agitation, temperature, and probably a number of more subtle factors, such as surface oxide thickness, crystal grain size and distribution, and the presence of contaminants. Chemical etching usually exhibits fluctuations that are manifested as small-scale roughness along the edges of patterns. The amplitude of this edge roughness depends on the metal and its thickness, and varies as a function of other etching parameters. It is usually less than or on the order of 1 μm. This edge roughness limits the linewidth of patterns that can be etched, and reduces the yield for linewidths near this limit. On surface wave substrates, chemical etching frequently exhibits troublesome local variations that lead to shorts between electrodes. These variations are probably due to scratches and other surface defects. Such defects are prevalent on surface wave substrates because they are mechanically polished. On substrates such as fire-polished glass and silicon that is polished by chemical-mechanical techniques, such scratches and surface defects are less common. As a result the yield of chemical etching is somewhat higher on these substrates. Chemical etchants work in the lateral direction as well as normal to a film, and thus pattern edges shift with time during etching. If the adhesion of the photoresist along an edge is less than perfect, a rapid loss of edge acuity, known as *undercutting*, occurs.

The main advantages and disadvantages of chemical etching are summarized in Table 4.5. Advantage 3 refers to the fact that the adhesion of the metal film can be enhanced by heating of the substrate during deposition, and by use of sputter deposition techniques. Neither heating nor sputter deposition can be readily employed in conjunction with the lift-off process.

Disadvantage 6 refers to the fact that when a complex repetitive pattern is chemically etched, it is common for some areas to remain unetched. In an interdigital structure such as a surface wave transducer, this leads to the least desirable fault, an interelectrode short. With the lift-off technique, on the other hand, shorts are extremely rare. Instead the most common faults are breaks in electrode continuity. Such breaks are usually detrimental but not disastrous to device performance.

Table 4.5 Chemical Etching of Metal Electrode Patterns

Advantages
  1. Simplicity and low cost.
  2. Compatible with mass production.
  3. Metal deposition methods can be used that produce highly adherent films (e.g., sputtering, heating of substrates).

Disadvantages
  1. Difficult to optimize process parameters when a small number of substrates are to be processed.
  2. Chemical etchants must be compatible with substrates.
  3. Postbaking can produce dimensional changes.
  4. Loss of resolution because of ragged edges, lateral etching, and a tendency to undercut.
  5. Low yield for linewidths near 1μm and for repetitive-type patterns.
  6. Shorts are the dominant fault.

In summary, chemical etching is preferred for the fabrication of simple metal patterns on relatively inert substrates such as quartz and $LiNbO_3$ when linewidths are $\gtrsim 5$ μm. The method is particularly suitable if a large number of identical devices are to be made, since this permits optimization of process parameters. Under such circumstances considerable economy can be realized, and thus the method is compatible with mass production of devices.

Ion Bombardment Etching. When ions or neutral atoms bombard a solid surface momentum transfer causes the ejection of atoms from the surface. This phenomenon, which is known as *sputtering*, is utilized both to remove material from a surface and to deposit thin films of the ejected material on substrates placed nearby. In fact, the term *sputtering* has come to mean primarily the latter application. The phenomenon of sputtering was discovered well over a century ago and has been the subject of extensive investigation during the last several decades.[45] In this section we are concerned only with the use of sputtering as a substitute for chemical means of etching metal electrodes through polymer film pattern masks. In a later section we discuss the application of ion bombardment in etching other types of surface relief structures. The main advantages of etching by ion bombardment are higher yield and finer resolution.

The number of surface atoms ejected per incident ion (the yield) depends on the composition and crystallographic orientation of the substrate, the mass and energy of the bombarding ion, and the angle of incidence. The yield starts from zero at a well-defined threshold near about 10 eV. It then increases linearly with energy up to about 500 eV, above which it tends slowly to level off. The yield as well as the sputtering rate increase rapidly for angles of incidence away from the normal, reach maxima, and then fall to zero at glancing incidence. Ion bombardment etching is universal in the sense that any solid material is etchable. However, in etching insulating substrates, provisions must be made to prevent the buildup of charges that would tend to repel bombarding ions. Charge buildup can be avoided by using either radio frequency or neutralized ion beam techniques.

Rf sputtering was introduced around 1966, and soon thereafter instruments designed primarily for deposition of insulator films became commercially available. The use of rf sputter etching to fabricate high frequency surface wave transducers was first reported in 1969.[22] In the usual configuration for rf sputter etching, a substrate with a patterned polymer film coating is placed on the disc-shaped electrode of a conventional rf sputtering system. As the input power is increased a dark space forms around the electrode. Ions are accelerated across this dark space and impinge on the substrate, thereby sputtering the unprotected substrate, as well as the polymer pattern. The dark space is parallel to the disc electrode, and thus ions strike it at normal incidence. In etching patterns in metal films, the progress of the etching is usually monitored visually, and terminated as soon as the unprotected metal is thoroughly removed. In the process there is usually a small amount of etching of the substrate. Although this is generally unimportant, it could be a problem in some cases. It can be avoided by carefully monitoring the etching process and using mass spectrometry or other means to determine the onset of substrate etching.

With rf sputter etching, the disadvantages of chemical etching listed in Table 4.5 are circumvented. Submicrometer linewidth patterns are readily etched with very high yield. However, rf sputter etching has its own disadvantages: (1) Material removed sometimes redeposits on the substrate, leading to contamination problems and somewhat unpredictable etching rates. (2) Excessive substrate heating is commonly observed, although it can be overcome by adequate heat sinking, etching in short bursts followed by long cooling times, or by using metal patterns as the etching mask, in place of a polymer. Relatively expensive equipment and skilled personnel are required for rf sputter etching. Moreover, because substrates must be rigidly mounted on the rf electrode, throughput is relatively low and mass production is probably ruled out.

Neutralized ion beam sputter etching[20,21,46,47] is somewhat more convenient than rf sputter etching, because the substrate is not part of the ion acceleration system and thus can be located in a field-free high vacuum region. Contamination problems are avoided, and etching rates are readily controlled and reproduced. Heating problems are also reduced considerably.

A number of different kinds of sources can be used for ion beam etching. Hollow-anode ion guns, originally developed for thinning samples for electron microscopy, have demonstrated a capability of etching 600 Å linewidths.[42] Duoplasmation-type sources have been used for some time,[47] but do not provide uniform etching of large areas (several cm in diameter). A Kaufmann-type ion source has recently been developed specifically for ion-beam sputter etching of microcircuit patterns.[48] It features a 10 cm diameter beam with a central region of approximately uniform flux about 5 cm in diameter, an accelerating voltage continuously variable from 200 to 2000 V, a hot filament outside the ion source that injects thermal velocity electrons to neutralize the ion beam space charge, and an independently variable current density. Such a system is well suited for ion beam etching of large area, high resolution patterns for surface wave devices. It is illustrated in Fig. 4.18 and is described in more detail later in connection with ion beam etching of surface relief gratings. As in the case of rf systems, ion beam systems are expensive to operate and this is a major deterrent to using them to etch metal electrode patterns. However because substrates are not part of the ion acceleration system, it is relatively straightforward to design fixtures for moving a large number of substrates in sequence under the ion beam. Thus ion beam systems can be adapted to mass production.

Lift-off. The lift-off technique, which is illustrated in Fig. 4.1, consists of depositing a material over a polymer film pattern on a substrate, and then dissolving the polymer. A pattern in the deposited material is left behind on the substrate. Usually the material is deposited by evaporation, in which case some adheres to the polymer, and it is important that there be little or no continuity between the material deposited on the substrate surface and the material deposited on top of the polymer. If such continuity exists, either the "lift-off" does not take place or relatively violent means, such as ultrasonic agitation, must be used to break the continuity. To prevent continuity the polymer film sidewalls must be vertical or slightly undercut, and the deposited material must arrive at the substrate at near normal incidence.[1]

As discussed earlier and illustrated in Figs. 4.4 and 4.6, sharp vertical sidewalls can be obtained in photoresist films only if exposure takes place in the very near field of a photomask. Projection printing and out-of-contact printing produce rounded profiles, as illustrated in Fig. 4.7. It has been found that when the sidewalls are vertical or undercut, the lift-off process is 100% reliable for metal films up to two-thirds as thick as the photoresist, provided the metal arrives at the surface at near normal incidence. Conversely, lift-off fails nearly all the time if the photoresist profile is rounded, or if deposition occurs over a wide range of incidence angles, such as with rf sputter deposition.[1]

Obviously, after exposure and development of a vertical sidewall photoresist pattern, it should not be baked or heated to a temperature near the polymer softening point, as this tends to round the profile and prevent lift-off. This implies that adhesion of the deposited thin film cannot be enhanced by heating the substrate, as is commonly done in deposition for other purposes.

In order to achieve good thin film adhesion in the lift-off technique, it is essential that all traces of contamination be removed from the exposed substrate surface. This can be achieved by brief ion bombardment to etch a small amount of the substrate surface. A more convenient procedure is to immerse the substrate in an oxygen plasma etching apparatus for a time sufficient to remove 100 to 200 Å of photoresist. This generally ensures that any organic contaminants are also removed from the exposed substrate surface and that good thin film adhesion is achieved.

In the case of deposited metal films, such as aluminum and gold, it is common practice first to deposit a film of 50 to 300 Å of chromium or titanium to act as an adherent interface between the substrate and the primary metalization. Deposition of the primary metal should follow immediately after depositing the adherent interface metal to avoid oxidation. A tight vacuum system and a multihearth electron beam evaporator are preferred. Because the deposited material should arrive at the surface at near normal incidence, the evaporation source should subtend a small angle when viewed from the substrate. Typically, the source diameter is about 5 mm and the source-to-substrate distance is about 40 cm. It is unfortunate that rf sputter deposition cannot be used in conjunction with lift-off. However with proper target-to-substrate spacing to ensure normal incidence deposition, there appears no reason not to use ion beam deposition techniques.

There are a number of significant advantages to the lift-off technique for forming metal electrode patterns for surface wave devices, and these are listed in Table 4.6 along with the disadvantages. The features of a polymer pattern appear to be faithfully reproduced to a dimensional tolerance of at least a few hundred angstroms. Advantage 2 refers to the

Table 4.6   Lift-off

Advantages

1. High resolution and precise dimensional control ($\sim$ few hundred Å).
2. Compatible with chemically reactive substrates and substrates with rough surfaces.
3. Compatible with any deposited metal or combination of metals and with nonmetals.
4. Electrical shorts improbable.
5. Processing is the same regardless of whether one or several hundred devices are handled.
6. Photolithographic processing is independent of pattern resolution.
7. Yields approaching 100% are possible.

Disadvantages

1. Special care is required to achieve vertical sidewalls in photoresist (requires intimate-contact photolithography).
2. Substrate cannot be heated during deposition.
3. Deposited material must arrive at normal incidence to the substrate.
4. Substrates must be scrupulously clean in order to ensure good film adhesion.

---

fact that as long as a photoresist pattern can be developed on it, the chemical reactivity and smoothness of a substrate are not problems in lift-off, as they are in chemical etching. For example, interdigital electrode transducers have been produced on sputtered ZnO surfaces that were rather rough and highly reactive to the ordinary metal etchants. Advantage 3 emphasizes a related point that the chemical properties of the metal or other deposited material is immaterial. It has been found that with lift-off, electrical shorts are extremely improbable, and this is especially significant for surface wave devices involving hundreds of electrodes.

4.4 Electron Lithography[*]

Electron lithography is a new technology, and relative to photolithography, only a very few surface wave devices have been made using it. It is likely that in the future electron lithography—in particular, scanning electron beam lithography—will become more important for surface wave devices, and for this reason the technology and its advantages and disadvantages are briefly reviewed. For a more thorough review see ref. 22, 50.

Three types of electron lithography instruments have been developed:

A. Systems similar to a conventional transmission electron microscope in which an electron opaque mask is imaged on a substrate.[51, 52]
B. Systems similar to an image tube, in which a pattern on a photoemitter is projected onto a substrate.[53]
C. Scanning systems in which a pattern is "written" on a substrate by scanning a small diameter electron beam over it.[50, 54, 55]

Types A and B are pattern replicators since they require some sort of mask. With type A there is demagnification of the mask, whereas with type B, the mask is at the same scale as the final image. Type C instruments, on the other hand, are pattern generators and require only the proper electrical signals for beam deflection in order to "write" a pattern.

In the past, type A instruments have produced some very high resolution patterns, but over limited areas and with distortions that can not be tolerated in most surface wave applications. Recently, however, a system has been developed at IBM specifically for electron lithography that seems very promising. Whether it will be useful for fabricating surface wave devices is not known at this time. Problems caused by electron

---

[*] Note added in proof: Recent developments in electron lithography are described in *J. Vacat. Sci. Technol.* **12,** November–December, 1975.

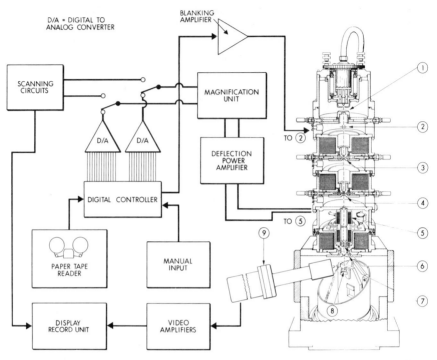

Figure 4.8 A scanning electron microscope modified by the addition of an external digital controller so that scanning electron beam lithography can also be carried out. Items indicated are (1) electron source, (2) electrostatic beam blanking plates, (3) first lens, (4) second lens, (5) double deflection coils, (6) electrostatic astigmatism correctors, (7) final lens, (8) sample mounting platform, (9) photomultiplier. The photomultiplier detects and amplifies the light sent to it through a light pipe from a scintillator located inside the chamber. The deflection coils scan the beam over the sample in a pattern determined by the voltage functions from the digital controller and D/A converters. The physical size of the pattern (the field size) is controlled by the magnification unit, which sets the voltage levels. The rate of scanning is controlled by a clock, which drives the digital controller. Pattern information can be put in either manually or by paper tape. Copyright 1974 by The Institute of Electrical and Electronic Engineers, Inc. Reprinted, with permission, from *Proc. IEEE* **62,** 1974, p. 1369.

backscattering from the substrate, by electrical charging, and by stray fields can be anticipated, as can difficulties in making the required masks.

Recently, Westerberg et al. developed a type A system in which an electrostatic slit lens images an array of apertures to produce a grating.[52] Interdigital electrode surface wave transducers with fundamental frequencies up to 2.8 GHz have been made with this system, which has the virtues of speed, simplicity, and low cost. However in its present form it is applicable only to gratings structures.

Considerable effort has been spent on developing type B image tube systems.[53] The distortion, precision, and orientation of the projected pattern depend upon the uniformity and stability of electric and magnetic fields, and this leads to serious technological and contamination control problems. For example, dust particles charge up and distort the pattern. Fringing fields at the edges of a sample also cause pattern distortion. Development to date has been directed only toward fabricating silicon devices. The fabrication of surface wave devices is a far more difficult task, and it is unlikely that type B systems will be useful in these applications in the near future.

In scanning electron beam lithography a finely focused electron beam is scanned over a substrate coated with a radiation sensitive polymer film in accordance with a desired pattern. Figure 4.8 illustrates a simple system made from a modified scanning electron microscope. More elaborate systems are described in ref. 50, 55, 56. Scanning electron beam lithography has been used both to expose surface wave device patterns directly on substrates[55] and to make masks whose patterns were subsequently transferred onto substrates by photolithography[39] and X-ray lithography.[62–66] The mask-making alternative is preferred for fabricating surface wave devices. This point is emphasized in the following discussion.

It is convenient to discuss scanning electron beam lithography from the perspective of its advantages and disadvantages. These are listed in Table 4.7.

Table 4.7. Scanning Electron Beam Lithography

Advantages
1. Resolution (~ 1000 Å)
2. Registration via electron microscopy
3. Large depth of focus ($\sim 2 \mu$m)
4. Programmability

Disadvantages
1. Limited field of view (~ 1 mm $\times 1$ mm)
2. Electron scattering
3. Slow speed
4. Electrical charging
5. Cost and complexity

Source: Copyright 1974 by The Institute of Electrical and Electronic Engineers, Inc. Reprinted, with permission, from *Proc. IEEE* **62,** 1974, p. 1361.

Resolution. Electron beams can be focused to spot diameters below 100 Å. However linewidths below 1000 Å are extremely difficult to achieve because of the detrimental influence of electron backscattering. The exposure of patterns with linewidths of 3000 Å and wider is relatively straightforward.

Registration via Electron Microscopy. Any scanning electron beam lithography system can be operated in a microscope mode to view relief structures on a substrate surface. This provides a means of focusing the beam and adjusting the size, angular orientation, orthogonality, and position of the scan field. In most systems described in the literature scan field sizing is done by reference to bench marks on the substrate surface. Such bench marks are usually relief patterns in the form of simple crosses or rectangles. They are made by photolithographic means, and this limits the accuracy of scan field sizing. For improved accuracy the use of holographically produced gratings as bench marks has been suggested.[22] When a grating bench mark is viewed by scanning electron microscopy, Moiré fringes between the grating and the scan raster are observed, and the period of the raster can be easily adjusted to be a multiple of the grating period. This Moiré technique also permits a precise adjustment of the angle between the grating and the scan raster.

In some scanning electron beam lithography systems the motion of the substrate is monitored by laser interferometers.[54] In such systems bench marks are not needed for scan field sizing, because the laser interferometers can perform the equivalent function. It is, however, necessary to be able to focus on and view details on the substrate surface. In many cases it is undesirable to place bench marks directly on a surface wave substrate. Bench marks are generally not objectionable on masks, and this is one of many practical reasons for using scanning electron beam lithography as a mask generation technique rather than for direct device fabrication. The mask generation approach also permits gratings made by holographic techniques and structures made by scanning electron beam lithography to be combined on a single photo or X-ray mask. In fact, if the grating is created on the mask first, the Moiré technique can be used to align the scan raster relative to it.

Depth of Focus. The small convergence angle of electrons ($\leq 10^{-2}$ radians) in a typical scanning electron beam system means that substrate surfaces and mounting stages need not be perfectly flat. A variation in height of 1 μm, for example, causes only about 100 Å beam divergence.

Programmability. The deflection of an electron beam is readily programmed by external digital or analog means to create a wide range of pattern geometries. Digital programming systems are preferred for high resolution applications. Many such systems have been described in the literature.[50,54-56] Surface wave devices put extreme demands on the linearity and freedom from distortion of such systems. Wolf et al.[55] designed a system specifically for making multielectrode surface wave transducers. In order to reduce the phase errors introduced by misplaced electrodes, they used a digital voltmeter to monitor the output voltage of their D/A converters and made an analog correction for any deviations.

Digital programming systems depend on one-to-one correspondence between the current to the deflection coils and the actual beam deflection. This assumption is not valid if there is hysteresis induced by coupling of the deflection coil fields to magnetic materials in the optical column.

Limited Field of View. The size of the field that can be scanned by an electron beam is limited by astigmatism and distortions of various kinds. For a beam diameter under $1000\,\text{Å}$, a field $1\,\text{mm} \times 1\,\text{mm}$ is about the practical limit for a modified scanning electron microscope.

A pattern that occupies an area larger than a single field of view must be composed of a montage of several fields, and it is necessary to move the substrate under the beam axis between exposure of each small field. If the large area pattern is a multielectrode surface wave transducer or a reflective array grating, it is easy to appreciate the difficulty of integrating the montage, because positional errors on the order of a few hundred Å can lead to serious phase errors. Obviously, mechanical means alone cannot be used. An array of local bench marks can be used to position and orient the several small fields, but this implies that the accuracy and integrity of the montage depend on the spatial arrangement of the bench marks.

An alternative approach to creating large area patterns has been developed at Thompson-CSF in France. It combines scanning electron beam techniques and laser interferometry.[54] It is illustrated schematically in Fig. 4.9. Two laser interferometers monitor the X and Y positions of a platform on which a substrate is mounted. The platform is moved by stepping motors that can locate it at any desired position to within $10\,\mu\text{m}$. The error in the position is calculated from the readings of the laser interferometers, which can sense distance increments as small as 1/16 of a wavelength. The position error information is fed back to a correction circuit that supplies the appropriate currents to a set of coils that deflect the beam axis to the desired position. This can be done with an absolute accuracy of $1000\,\text{Å}$. The scan field used is $\frac{1}{2}\,\text{mm} \times \frac{1}{2}\,\text{mm}$. One shortcoming

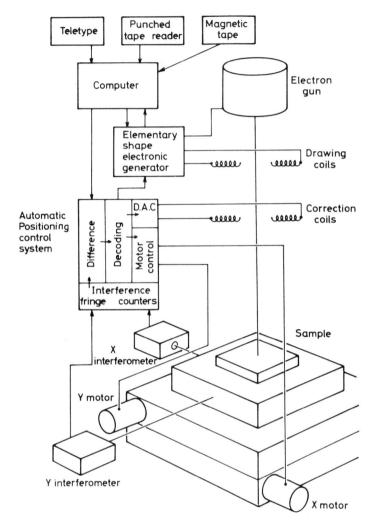

Figure 4.9 Block diagram of the scanning electron beam system developed at Thompson-CSF. Two laser interferometers monitor the X and Y positions of a platform on which a substrate is mounted. The platform is moved by stepping motors that can locate it at any desired position to within 10 μm. The position error is calculated from the readings of the interferometers and corrected by deflecting the beam axis by means of the correction coils. Figure courtesy of J. Trotel.

of the system is that it assumes the beam axis does not wander with time relative to the physical electron optical column. Such wandering can result from contamination charging, stray fields, and so on. In order to correct for this wander it is necessary to return to a bench mark and establish a new coordinate system.

Electron Scattering. The polymer films used in electron lithography react to electron bombardment either by undergoing chain-scission or cross-linking. Chain-scission is a reduction in molecular weight and enhances solubility. Cross-linking is an increase in molecular weight and reduces solubility. The most useful example of a chain-scission electron sensitive polymer is polymethyl methacrylate (PMMA). The solubility of PMMA is close to a cubic function of the electron energy dissipation.[57, 58] Such "high contrast" permits a fairly sharp distinction between exposed and unexposed regions and is the main reason for the widespread usage

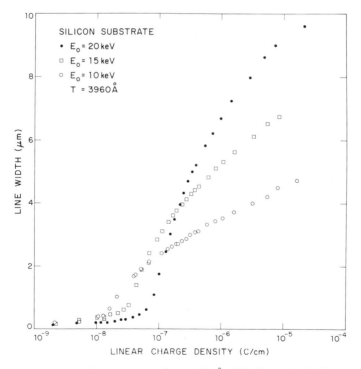

Figure 4.10 The linewidth developed in a 3960 Å thick film of PMMA on a silicon substrate after exposure by 10, 15, and 20 keV electron beams, plotted as a function of the linear charge density. Reprinted, with permission, from R. J. Hawryluk et al., *Appl. Phys.* **46**, 1975, p. 2530.

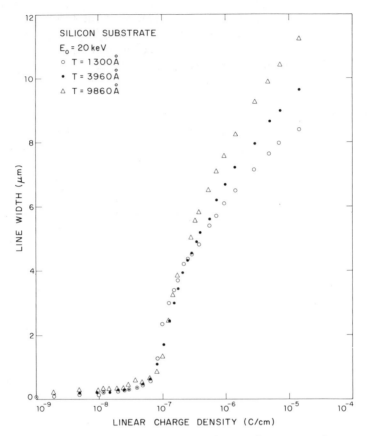

Figure 4.11 The linewidth developed in 1300 Å, 3960 Å, and 9860 Å thick films of PMMA on a silicon substrate after exposure by a 20 keV electron beam, plotted as a function of the linear charge density. Reprinted, with permission, from R. J. Hawryluk et al., *J. Appl. Phys.* **46,** 1975, p. 2531.

of PMMA, despite a relatively low "sensitivity." A large number of cross-linking polymers have been developed.[59] These are usually characterized by much higher sensitivity than PMMA, but lower contrast. As is pointed out later, lower contrast implies that electron backscattering effects are more detrimental, particularly in the repetitive grating structures common to surface wave devices.

When an electron beam enters a polymer film, it immediately begins to broaden and lose energy. Electrons scatter off atoms in the polymer and in the substrate with the result that energy is dissipated in the polymer film at points as far away as several micrometers from the orginal point of entry. It has been widely observed experimentally that when a polymer film is exposed by a scanned electron beam, the linewidth obtained depends on the nature of the polymer, the linear charge density, the polymer film thickness, the substrate atomic number, the accelerating voltage, and the proximity of other exposed regions. These effects are illustrated in Fig. 4.10 to 4.12, taken from the work of Hawryluk *et al.*[57,58,60] for the case of PMMA. Note the rapid increase in linewidth that occurs when linear charge densities about two orders of magnitude larger than threshold are used. This is consistent with Monte Carlo calculations,[60] which predict a broad background of backscattered electrons. The agreement between experiments and Monte Carlo calculations is excellent over a wide range of exposure parameters.[57,60]

Figure 4.13 shows Monte Carlo calculations of the energy dissipation per unit volume in a PMMA film as a function of the interline spacing of

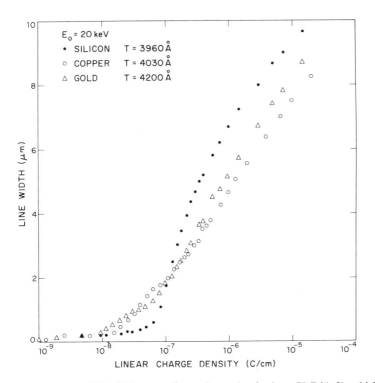

Figure 4.12 Plots of linewidth versus linear charge density for a PMMA film thickness of 3960 Å on Si, 4030 Å on Cu, and 4200 Å on a gold substrate. Exposure was by a 20 keV scanned electron beam. Reprinted, with permission, from R. J. Hawryluk et al., *Appl. Phys.* **46,** 1975, p. 2531.

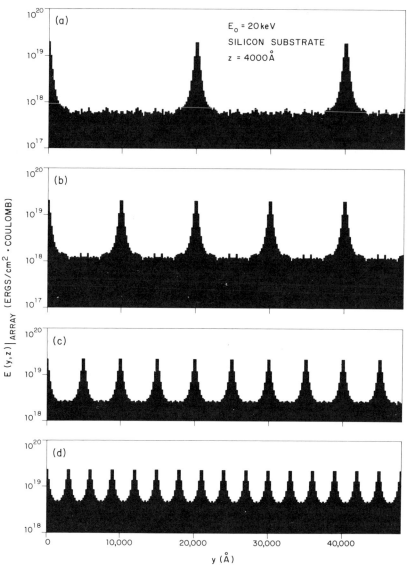

Figure 4.13 Plots of Monte Carlo calculations of the energy dissipated per unit volume in a 4000 Å thick PMMA film on a silicon substrate for an array of parallel line scans. The electron beam is 250 Å in diameter and 20 keV. Each line is exposed with a linear charge density of 1 C/cm. The ordinate is the energy dissipated in ergs/cm^3 divided by the linear charge density. The coordinate y is the distance perpendicular to the line scans and the beam axis. The coordinate z is the depth below the top surface of the PMMA. The interline spacings are (a) 2 μm, (b) 1 μm, (c) 0.5 μm, (d) 0.3 μm. Reprinted, with permission, from ref 58, p. 93.

a grating. The effect of backscattering is clearly evident. From a knowledge of the dependence of development rate on energy dissipation the cross-sectional profile in the polymer can be calculated.[57, 58, 60] For grating structures of submicrometer period, high contrast polymers are necessary. This in turn implies low sensitivity polymers. Thus exposure times are long, and mask making is preferred over direct device fabrication.

Slow Speed. The time required to expose a pattern using a scanning electron beam depends on the pattern resolution and geometry, the substrate backscattering, the polymer sensitivity, and the electron optics. For linewidths of about 4000 Å using PMMA, a writing speed of about 1 mm per sec appears reasonable. Although such times are not prohibitive for fabricating experimental devices they lead to high device costs, and for patterns involving several hundreds of lines, stringent demands are put on the various electronic power supplies of an electron beam system, many of which must be stable to 1 part in 10^5. The slow speed of scanning electron beam lithography is another point in favor of mask making rather than direct device fabrication.

Electrical Charging. In both scanning electron beam microscopy and scanning electron beam lithography, a low resistance path to ground must be provided for the beam current; otherwise the sample charges up. Most surface wave substrates are insulators, and a thin metal film (e.g., 400 Å of aluminum) must be evaporated on top of the polymer film prior to exposure. The metal film must be removed before development, and for thin polymers this often leads to adhesion problems. Isolated dust particles and contamination films can charge up under electron bombardment. That this can lead to distortion in electron microscopy is well-known, but its influence on electron lithography has not been reported.

Cost and Complexity. An electron beam lithography system is a complex installation and represents a capital investment well in excess of $100,000. Commercial systems are now available,[61] but the development of techniques is still in the experimental stage.

4.5 X-Ray Lithography[*]

X-ray lithography[62-66] is a shadow printing technique, similar in principle to photolithographic shadow printing. The wavelengths used range from ~4 to 44 Å, and as a result diffraction effects are reduced considerably.

[*] Note added in proof: Recent developments in X-ray lithography are described in *J. Vacat. Sci. Technol.*, **12**, November–December 1975, and in H. I. Smith and D. C. Flanders," X-ray Lithography," *Jap. J. Appl. Phys.*, January 1977.

Figure 4.14 illustrates the technique. The mask consists of an absorber pattern on a thin membrane that is semitransparent to X-rays. Since X-rays cannot be efficiently collimated, there is penumbral blurring, as illustrated in the inset. Since the X-rays travel in straight lines with negligible diffraction, this is a purely geometric effect given by $\delta = s(d/D)$, where the symbols are defined in Fig. 4:14. The exact choice of these parameters is based on trade-offs among desired pattern resolution, desired mask-to-sample gap, and exposure time, which is proportional to $(D/d)^2$.

Figure 4.15 shows the cross section of an X-ray lithography mask used in combination with the Al_k X ray ($\lambda = 8.34\,\text{Å}$). A 3 μm thick silicon membrane absorbs only about 1.5 dB of Al_k X-rays, whereas the gold absorbs about 6 dB. Procedures for fabricating such masks with diameters of 5 cm are well developed.[64] Intuitively one would expect thin silicon membranes to be fragile. This is decidedly not the case. A 3.5 μm thick membrane measuring 2.5 mm × 2.5 mm can withstand a pressure differential of 1 atmosphere without breakage. No difficulty is experienced in cleaning, handling, processing, and carrying out exposures with silicon

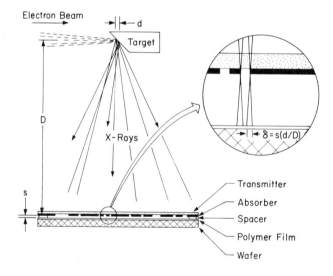

X-RAY LITHOGRAPHIC SCHEME

Figure 4.14 Schematic diagram of a soft X-ray lithography system. The shadow of the mask is recorded in the polymer film. The inset illustrates the penumbral effect that arises because of the finite angular size of the source. The magnitude of δ can be made arbitrarily small either by reducing the mask-sample gap s or the ratio (d/D). Reprinted, with permission, from ref. 62, p. 103.

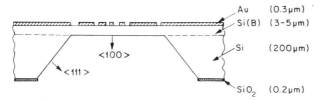

Figure 4.15 Cross section of a silicon membrane X-ray lithography mask. The silicon membrane is 3 to 5 μm thick, and, by virtue of its boron doping, is stretched taut across the window in the 200 μm thick silicon substrate. The 0.2 μm thick SiO$_2$ on the back side serves as a mask for the selective etching of the undoped silicon. Reprinted, with permission, from ref. 64, p. 43.

membrane X-ray masks. Figure 4.16 shows a large area silicon membrane X-ray lithography mask. Other types of X-ray masks have also been made. Large area mylar films, 10 μm thick having patterns in 8000 Å thick gold have been used successfully in combination with the Rh$_L$ X-ray at 4.6 Å.[66]

Absorber patterns for X-ray masks have been produced by scanning electron beam lithography, photolithography, holography, and X-ray lithography, in conjunction with both metal lift-off and ion beam etching. As mentioned previously, one could make masks by a combination of scanning electron beam lithography and holography, and thereby achieve surface wave device patterns not realizable by other means.

Surface wave delay lines[63] and silicon diodes and transistors[64] have been made by X-ray lithography. Gratings of 3600 Å periodicity, produced by holographic means on X-ray masks, have been replicated on other substrates using both Al$_k$ (8.34 Å) and Cu$_L$ (13.3 Å) X-ray sources.[64]

Table 4.8 summarizes the advantages and disadvantages of X-ray lithography. These have been discussed in more detail elsewhere.[22] Here we call attention only to advantages 3, 4, and disadvantage 1.

Most dust and contamination encountered in practice is composed of low atomic number elements, and must be on the order of 1 μm thick to absorb any significant amount of X-rays. X-rays travel in straight lines from their source to their point of absorption and, unlike electrons, are unaffected by stray fields and contamination. Thus, except for purely geometric effects, X-rays produce a faithful replica of the mask.

Cooperative exposure effects due to backscattering, such as those observed in electron lithography, are not observed in X-ray lithography. This is illustrated in Fig. 4.17, which shows 5 polymer stripes standing alone in an otherwise completely exposed field.

The major disadvantage of X-ray lithography is exposure time. The actual value depends on the X-ray source, the polymer, the mask, and the

Figure 4.16 Photograph of a large area X-ray mask taken from the back (etched) side showing the silhouette of the gold absorber pattern on the front side. The circular membrane is 3 cm in diameter and 4 μm thick, and is supported by a ring of unetched silicon 5 mm wide and 200 μm thick.

geometry of the exposure apparatus. For example, using an aluminum source operated at 8 kV with 50 mA of electron current delivered into a 1 mm diameter spot, the exposure time at a 3 cm source-to-substrate distance is 20 min for PMMA and 7 min for KMNR.[67] This can be reduced by increasing the angle subtended by the source, by increasing the source brightness, or by increasing polymer sensitivity. Surface wave substrates are generally flat, and as a result the mask-to-substrate gaps s can be reduced to zero. In this way the angular size of the source can then be increased without suffering a large penumbral blurring δ.

Table 4.8 X-Ray Lithography

Advantages
1. Resolution (~ 500 Å).
2. Finite mask-sample gap (0 to 10 μm).
3. Insensitivity to dust and contamination.
4. Absence of scattering problems.
5. Both cross-linking and chain-scission type polymers can be used.
6. Exposure in nonvacuum environments.
7. Simplicity and low cost.
8. Alignment.

Disadvantages
1. Exposure time.
2. Possible distortion of mask.

Source: Copyright 1974 by The Institute of Electrical and Electronic Engineers, Inc. Reprinted, with permission, from *Proc. IEEE* **62**, 1974, p. 1377.

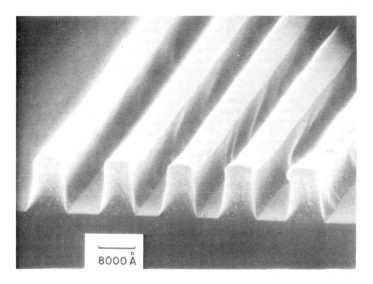

Figure 4.17 Scanning electron micrograph of the cross section of a grating pattern exposed in PMMA by X-ray lithography. The scale refers to lateral dimensions only. The PMMA is 11,000 Å thick. Small irregularities along the edges of the lines in the mask are replicated in the PMMA. Note that the thickness of the polymer stripes is greater than the widths, and that the stripes stand alone in an otherwise completely exposed field, indicating that backscattering effects are negligible. Micrograph by R. Eager. Reprinted, with permission, from ref. 64, p. 44. Note added in proof: For recent results see H. I. Smith, D. C. Flanders Japan. J. Appl. Phys. Jan 1977.

The limitation on source brightness is dissipation of the heat generated by electron bombardment. Water cooled rotating anodes are capable of dissipating about 20 times more heat than nonrotating anodes. Exposure time is inversely proportional to source brightness.

Considerable progress has been made in developing high sensitivity X-ray resists. Reasonable contrast polymers with sensitivities exceeding PMMA by a factor of 150 have been reported.[68]

X-ray lithography is a very simple replication technique. It is readily adapted to the fabrication of high resolution surface wave devices and will probably be widely used in the near future.

4.6. Ion Beam Etching of Surface Relief Gratings*

The subject of ion beam etching was introduced in a previous section. Here we briefly discuss the procedures for etching gratings for reflective-array surface wave devices.

Figure 4.18 illustrates a Kaufmann ion beam source and the fixturing that has been developed for variable depth etching of surface gratings.[2, 21, 46] The grating pattern is first produced in photoresist on the substrate surface, using intimate-contact photolithography to ensure that the photoresist sidewalls are vertical. Failure to provide vertical sidewalls leads to rapid facet formation and degradation of the grating profile, as is discussed later. The substrate (8) is then placed on the water cooled sample-mounting platform (9); a thin film of apeizon grease under the substrate ensures a good thermal contact. The stationary aperture (7) is located in the center of the ion beam, and only those ions that pass through the aperture bombard the substrate. The depth to which any given part of a grating is etched depends on the time it spends under the aperture. This dwell time is controlled by adjusting the velocity at which the substrate is driven by the stepping motor and micrometer slide assembly. A simple numerical control system for driving the stepping motor is described in refs. 2, 46, and 69. The ion current density and the accelerating voltage are held constant during etching. It is estimated that the etching rate is stable to about $\pm 3\%$.

A disadvantage of the fixed-aperture technique is that the edges of the aperture sputter in the forward direction, thereby depositing a thin film of

* Note added in proof: Recent developments in ion beam etching, in particular, investigations of resolution limitations caused by redeposition of sputtered material, are described in H. I. Smith, "Ion Beam Etching," in H. G. Hughes and M. S. Rand, Eds., Proc. Symposium on Etching for Pattern Definition, The Electrochemical Society, Inc., Princeton, N.J., 1976, pp 133–144.

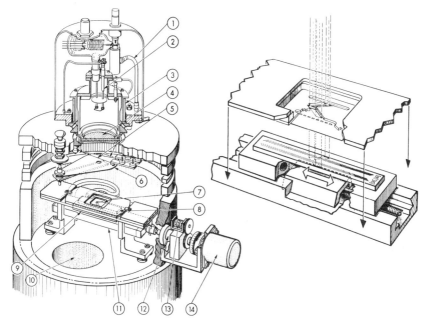

Figure 4.18 Ion beam etching system utilizing a Kaufmann-type source. A substrate (8) with a grating pattern in photoresist is shown mounted on a water-cooled platform (9). This configuration is used to produce a variable depth ("weighted") grating by controlling the amount of time a portion of the grating spends under the chevron aperture (7), which defines the area of etching. Other items indicated are (1) argon gas inlet, (2) arc filament, (3) magnet, (4) ion beam extraction grids, (5) neutralizing filament, (6) shutter, (10) pumping port, (11) micrometer-slide assembly, (12) rotary-motion high vacuum feedthrough, (13) position indicator, (14) stepping motor. The ion beam source was developed at Thompson-CSF. Copyright 1972 by The Institute of Electrical and Electronic Engineers, Inc. Reprinted, with permission, from *Proc. 1972 IEEE Ultrasonics Symposium*, p. 200.

metal on the substrate. For this reason apertures made of titanium or other low-sputtering-rate materials are used. The metal film can be removed by a mild acid etch, or by a uniform ion etching after the weighted etching. Forward sputtering of the source electrodes is not observed.[21]

The weighting of gratings has also been accomplished using a small diameter beam and programming the motion of the substrate in the beam. This technique avoids the problem of aperture forward sputtering. However, small-diameter beams usually imply high voltage and this in turn leads to undesirable surface damage.

The depth-weighting technique described previously has been applied to the fabrication of reflective-array compressors and bandpass filters. Recently filters having 16 separate channels on a single substrate have been fabricated.[69] In this case the metal aperture mask used in the ion beam etching had 16 separate slits, each $\sim\frac{1}{4}$ mm wide.

The rate at which material is removed from a substrate surface by ion bombardment is not a monotonic function of the angle of incidence of the ions. For simple amorphous solids, the removal rate is a minimum at normal incidence, reaches a maximum near 45°, and goes to zero at grazing incidence. Because of this the topography of a surface changes during ion bombardment, and well-defined facets are observed.[20, 21, 46] Theories on the evolution of surface topographies under ion bombardment predict that with sufficient etching time, any surface contour becomes a horizontal plane, and that prior to the occurrence of this final steady state, facets that are parallel to, perpendicular to, or inclined at the angle of maximum sputtering rate to the ion beam are stable planes and are the dominant topographical features.[19–22]

The phenomenon of faceting has important implications for ion beam etching of gratings through polymer pattern masks. To prevent changes in linewidth or other dimensions, and to achieve rectangular profiles in the substrate, facets that form in the polymer pattern sidewalls must not be allowed to intersect the substrate surface. Thus the polymer sidewalls must be initially vertical and relatively thick compared to desired etch depths. If a polymer sidewall is initially sloped, as shown, for example, in Fig. 4.7, a facet quickly forms over the entire sidewall and intersects the surface at an early stage in the etching. The phenomenon of faceting also implies that low energy ion bombardment should have the effect of polishing surfaces, and indeed this has been observed, as discussed previously.

Aluminum and titanium patterns have been used as etching masks in place of polymers. These materials have the advantage of durability, insensitivity to heat, very low sputtering rates, and in the case of titanium, an etching rate that varies very little with angle of incidence. The etching rate of certain metals is significantly reduced in a partial pressure of oxygen, and this can be utilized to increase differential etch rates.[70] When metal masks are used, however, an extra processing step is required. The problem of sidewall faceting has not been studied for metal films.

After argon ion bombardment at an energy of 500 eV, a $LiNbO_3$ surface becomes conducting. This is attributed to a change in stoichiometry through preferential loss of oxygen. The conductivity can be removed by prolonged exposure to humid air, by immersion in an oxygen plasma, or by acid etching. The stoichiometry, however, is probably not restored. A better approach is to conduct the ion beam etching in a partial pressure of oxygen, in which case no conductivity is observed, and presumably there is no change in stoichiometry.

Table 4.9 Ion Beam Etching Rates of Various Materials Using 500 eV Ar⁺ Ions at a Current Density of 0.65 mA/cm² at the Substrate Surface

Material	Rate (Å/sec)	Sputtering yield ($\pm 10\%$) (Atoms or Molecules/Incident Ar⁺)
LiNbO$_3$ (y – cut)	4.63 ± 0.1	0.22
	1.35 ± 0.1^a	0.064
Al$_2$O$_3$(c⊥)	1.4 ± 0.2	0.082
Si (111)	4.39 ± 0.1	0.54
GaAs	14 ± 1	0.76
Photoresist AZ 1350	2.5 ± 0.5	
PMMA	7 ± 1	
Bi$_{12}$GeO$_{20}$ (001)	14.5 ± 1	

^{a} Etching rate of LiNbO$_3$ when the composition of the gas in the source is about 20% oxygen, 80% argon.

Source: Copyright by The Institute of Electrical and Electronic Engineers, Inc. Reprinted, with permission, from *Proc. IEEE* **62,** 1974, p. 1381.

Table 4.9 lists ion beam etching rates for a number of useful substrates. Surface conductivity following argon ion bombardment is not observed on Al$_2$O$_3$, quartz, and Bi$_{12}$GeO$_{20}$.

References

1. H. I. Smith, F. J. Bachner, and N. Efremow. "A high yield photolithographic technique for surface wave devices." *J. Electrochem. Soc.* **118,** 821 (1971).

2. R. C. Williamson and H. I. Smith. "The use of surface-elastic-wave reflection gratings in large time-bandwidth pulse compression filters." *IEEE Trans.* **MTT-21,** 195 (1973).

3. R. C. Williamson. Chapter 9 of this book.

4. H. L. Bertoni. "Design considerations for efficient wedge transducers," in G. Hoffman, Ed., *Proc. 1973 European Microwave Conf.*; H. L. Bertoni and T. Tamir, "VHF-UHF Surface Wave Studies." Final Report, Contract DAAB 07-71-c-0328, U.S. Army Electronics Command, Fort Monmouth, N.J., 1974.

5. F. S. Hickernell. "DC triode sputtered zinc oxide surface elastic wave transducers." *J. Appl. Phys.* **44,** 1061 (1973).

6. C. Lardat, C. Maerfeld, and P. Tournois. "Theory and performances of acoustical dispersive surface wave delay lines." *Proc. IEEE* **59,** 355 (1971).

7. C. Lardat and P. Tournois. "Large time-bandwidth product and ultrawide bandwidth Love and dispersive Rayleigh wave delay lines," in J. de Klerk, Ed., *Proc. 1972 IEEE Ultrasonics Symposium*, IEEE, New York, 1972, pp. 280–281.

8. M. T. Wauk and R. L. Zimmerman. "Bonded planar structures for efficient surface wave generation," in J. de Klerk, Ed., *Proc. 1972 IEEE Ultrasonics Symposium*, IEEE, New York, 1972, pp. 365–366.

9. A. J. Bahr et al. "A comparison between the physical structure of zinc oxide films and the measured electromechanical coupling factor for surface acoustic waves generated by such films," in J. de Klerk, Ed. *Proc. 1972 IEEE Ultrasonics Symposium*, IEEE, New York, 1972, pp. 202–205.

10. P. C. Meyer and M. B. Schulz. "Reflective surface acoustic wave delay line material parameters," in J. de Klerk, Ed., *Proc. 1973 IEEE Ultrasonics Symposium*, IEEE, New York, 1973, pp. 500–502.

11. A. J. Slobodnik. "A review of material tradeoffs in the design of acoustic surface wave devices at VHF and microwave frequencies." *IEEE Trans.* **SU-20**, 315 (1973).

12. A. J. Slobodnik, E. D. Conway, and R. T. Delmonico, *Microwave Acoustics Handbook*, Vol. 2, Air Force Cambridge Research Laboratories, Bedford, Mass., 1974.

13. D. T. Bell, Jr. "Growth, orientation, and surface preparation of quartz," in J. de Klerk, Ed., *Proc. 1972 IEEE Ultrasonics Symposium*, IEEE, New York, 1973, pp. 206–210.

14. A. J. Slobodnik, Jr. "The effect of surface quality on acoustic surface wave attenuation on YZ LiNbO$_3$," in J. de Klerk, Ed., *Proc. 1973 IEEE Ultrasonics Symposium*, IEEE, New York, 1973, pp. 369–371.

15. R. D. Young, "Surface Microtopography," Phys. Today **24**(*11*), 42 (1971); R. Young, J. Ward, and F. Scire. "The topografiner: an instrument for measuring surface microtopography." *Rev. Sci. Instrum.* **43**, 999 (1972).

16. H. E. Bennett and Jean M. Bennett. "Precision measurements in thin film optics," in G. Hass and R. E. Thun, Eds., *Physics of Thin Films*, Vol. 4, Academic, New York, 1967.

17. R. W. Dietz and J. M. Bennett. "Bowl feed technique for producing supersmooth optical surfaces," *Appl. Opt.* **5,** 881 (1966).

18. J. M. Bennett and R. J. King. "Effect of polishing technique on the roughness and residual surface film on fused quartz optical flats," *Appl. Opt.* **9,** 236 (1970).

19. I. S. T. Tsang and D. J. Barber. "Development of the surface topography on silica glass due to ion bombardment." *J. Mater. Sci.* **7,** 687 (1972).

20. J. P. Ducommun, M. Contagrel, and M. Marchal. "Development of a general surface contour by ion erosion theory and computer simulation," *J. Mater. Sci.* **9,** 725 (1974).

21. H. I. Smith et al. "Ion beam etching of surface gratings," in J. de Klerk, Ed., *Proc. 1973 IEEE Ultrasonics Symposium*, IEEE, New York, 1973, pp. 558–563.

22. H. I. Smith. "Fabrication techniques for surface acoustic wave and thin film optical devices." *Proc. IEEE* **62,** 1361 (1974).

23. C. R. Giulano. "Laser induced damage in transparent dielectrics: ion beam polishing as a means of increasing surface damage thresholds." *Appl. Phys. Lett.* **21,** 39 (1972).

24. R. J. MacDonald and D. Haneman. "Depths of low energy ion bombardment damage in germanium." *J. Appl. Phys.* **37,** 1609 (1966).

25. H. Yasuda and K. Nagai. "Growth of craters on LiNbO$_3$ and ion etching without craters." Jap. *J. Appl. Phys.* **11,** 1713 (1972).

26. R. W. Berry, P. M. Hall, and M. T. Harris. *Thin Film Technology*, Van Nostrand, Princeton, N.J., 1968.

27. L. I. Maissel and R. Glang. *Handbook of Thin Film Technology*, McGraw-Hill, New York, 1970.

28. M. L. White. "Clean surface technology," in *Proc. 27th Annual Symposium on Frequency Control*, Electronic Industries Association, Washington, D.C., 1973, pp. 79–88.

29. D. M. Mattox. "Thin film metalization of oxides in microelectronics." *Thin Solid Films* **18,** 173 (1973).

30. K. G. Clark. "Properties and processes for photoresists in semiconductor manufacture, Part I," *Solid State Technol.* **14**(6), 52 (1971), "Properties and processes for photoresists in semiconductor manufacture, Part II," *Solid State Technol.* **14**(9), 48 (1971).

31. A. R. Neureuther and F. H. Dill. "Photoresist modeling and device fabrication applications," in *Proc. Microwave Research Institute Symposium XXIII*, New York, 1974.

32. Shipley Company, Inc. 2304 Washington St., Newton, Mass. 02162.

33. C. E. Herrick. "Solutions of the partial differential equations describing photodecomposition in a light absorbing matrix having light absorbing photoproducts." *IBM.* **10,** 2 (1966).

34. R. Glang and L. V. Gregor. "Generation of patterns in thin films," in L. I. Maissel and R. Glang, Eds., *Handbook of Thin Film Technology*, McGraw-Hill, New York, 1970, Chapter 7.

35. H. J. Schuetze and K. E. Hennings. "Large area masking with patterns of micron and submicron element size." *Semiconductor Products and Solid State Technol.* **9**(7), 31 (1966).

36. S. Middelhoek. "Projection masking, thin photoresist layers and interference effects." *IBM J. Res. Dev.* **14,** 117 (1970).

37. D. T. Bell, Jr., and D. W. Mellon. "Development of an L-band pulse compressor using surface waves," in J. de Klerk, Ed., *Proc. 1973 IEEE Ultrasonics Symposium*, IEEE, New York, 1973, pp. 486–489.

38. D. W. Mann Co., Middlesex Turnpike, Burlington, Mass. 01803; Electromask Co., Inc., 15013 Califa St., Van Nuys, Calif. 91401; Metrigraphics Div., Dynamics Research Corp., Wilmington, Mass. 01887; Thomson-CSF, Corbeville, France.

39. H. I. Smith, N. Efremow, and P. L. Kelly. "Photolithographic contact printing of 4000 Å linewidth patterns." *J. Electrochem. Soc.* **121,** 1503 (1974). J. Melngailis, H. I. Smith, and N. Efremow, "Instrumentation for conformable photomask lithography." *IEEE Trans.* **ED-22,** 496 (1975).

40. B. J. Lin. Electromagnetic near-field diffraction of a medium slit." *J. Opt. Soc. Amer.* **62,** 976 (1972).

41. B. J. Lin. "Deep-UV Lithography," *J. Vac. Sci. Technol.* **12,** 1317 (1975).

42. C. V. Shank and R. V. Schmidt. "Optical technique for producing 0.1μ periodic surface structures." *Appl. Phys. Lett.* **23,** 154 (1973).

43. G. Rudolph and G. Schmahl. "Spektroskopische begugsgitter hoher teilungsgenauigkeit erzeugt mit hilfe von laserlicht und photoresistschichten." *Optik* **30,** 475 (1970). Available as Translation No. 72–14082 from the National Translations Center, John Crerar Library, Chicago, IL 60616.

44. W. T. Tsang and S. Wang. "Simultaneous exposure and development technique for making gratings on positive photoresist." *Appl. Phys. Lett.* **24,** 196 (1974).

45. G. K. Wehner and G. S. Anderson. "The nature of physical sputtering," in L. I. Maissel and R. Glang, Eds., *Handbook of Thin Film Technology*, McGraw-Hill, New York, 1970, Chapter 3.

46. H. I. Smith, R. C. Williamson, and W. T. Brogan. "Ion beam etching of reflective array filters," in J. de Klerk, Ed., *Proc. 1972 IEEE Ultrasonics Symposium*, IEEE, New York, 1972, pp. 198–201.

47. H. L. Garvin. "High resolution fabrication by ion beam sputtering." *Solid State Technol.* **16**(11), 31 (1973).

48. The ion source was developed at Thomson-CSF, Corbeville, France.

49. C. A. Balthrop, R. N. Claytor, and R. B. Hemphill. "Fabrication techniques for $Bi_{12}GeO_{20}$ devices." *1971 IEEE Ultrasonics Symposium*, Miami Beach, December, 1971.

50. A. N. Broers and M. Hatzakis. "Microcircuits by electron beam." *Sci. Amer.* **227**(11), 34 (1972).

51. H. Koops. "On electron projection systems." *J. Vac. Sci. Technol.* **10**, 909 (1973).

52. R. E. Lee, E. R. Westerberg, and A. J. Bahr. "Fabrication of microwave-frequency surface acoustic wave transducer using a novel electron beam projection system," in J. de Klerk, Ed., *Proc. 1973 IEEE Ultrasonics Symposium*, IEEE, New York, 1973, pp. 517–521.

53. W. R. Livesay, "Integrated circuit production with electron beams." *J. Vac. Sci. Technol.* **10**, 1028 (1973).

54. O. Cahen, R. Sigelle, and J. Trotel. "Automatic control of an electron beam pattern generator," in R. Bakish, Ed., *Fifth International Conference Electron and Ion Beam Science and Technology*, The Electrochemical Society, Princeton, N.J., 1972, pp. 92–101.

55. E. D. Wolf, F. S. Ozdemir, and R. D. Weglein. "Precision electron beam microfabrication of acoustic surface wave devices," in J. de Klerk, Ed., *Proc. 1973 IEEE Ultrasonics Symposium*, IEEE, New York, 1973, pp. 510–516.

56. See, for example, the special issue *J. Vac. Sci. Technol.* **10**, November–December, 1973.

57. R. J. Hawryluk. "Energy dissipation by electron beam scattering in thin polymer films," Ph. D. thesis, Massachusetts Institute of Technology, May 1974; also Technical Report 511, MIT Lincoln Laboratory, Lexington, Mass., November 1974.

58. R. J. Hawryluk et al. "Experimental utilization of Monte Carlo models for electron beam lithography," in R. Bakish, Ed., *Proc. VI International Conference on Electron and Ion Beam Science and Technology*, The Electrochemical Society, Princeton, N.J., 1974, pp. 87–94.

59. R. D. Heidenreich et al. "Fundamental aspects of electron beam lithography. I, Depth-dose response of polymeric electron beam resists." *J. Appl. Phys.* **44**, 4039 (1973); and L. F. Thompson et al. "Fundamental aspects of electron beam lithography. II, Low voltage exposure of negative resists." *J. Appl. Phys.* **44**, 4048 (1973).

60. R. J. Hawryluk, A. M. Hawryluk, and H. I. Smith. "Energy dissipation in a thin polymer film by electron beam scattering." *J. Appl. Phys.* **45**, 2551 (1974), and *J. Appl. Phys.* **46**, 2528 (1975).

61. Commercial sources include Advanced Metals Research, Burlington, Mass.; Cambridge Scientific Instruments, Ltd., Cambridge, England; Etec Corp., Hayward, Calif.; Thomson-CSF, Corbeville, France.

62. D. L. Spears and J. I. Smith. "High-resolution pattern replication using soft x-rays." *Electron. Lett.* **8,** 102 (1972).

63. H. I. Smith, D. L. Spears, and S. E. Bernacki. "X-ray lithography: a complimentary technique to electron beam lithography." *J. Vac. Sci. Technol.* **10,** 913 (1973).

64. S. E. Bernacki and H. I. Smith. "X-ray lithography applied to silicon device fabrication," in R. Bakish, Ed., *Proc. VI International Conference on Electron and Ion Beam Science and Technology,* The Electrochemical Society, Princeton, N.J., 1974, pp. 34–46.

65. J. H. McCoy and P. A. Sullivan. "Progress in X-ray lithography," in R. Bakish, Ed., *Proc. VI International Conference on Electron and Ion Beam Science and Technology,* The Electrochemical Society, Princeton, N.J., 1974.

66. D. Maydan et al. "Generation of high resolution, large area patterns by x-ray lithography." Device Research Conference, Santa Barbara, Calif., June, 1974, and *IEEE Trans.* **ED-22,** 429 (1975).

67. Kodak Micronegative Resist, Eastman Kodak Co., Rochester, New York.

68. L. F. Thompson et al. "Polymeric resists for x-ray lithography." *J. Electrochem. Soc.* **121,** 1500 (1974).

69. V. Dolat and J. Melngailis. "16-channel surface acoustic wave filter bank," in J. de Klerk, Ed., *Proc. 1974 IEEE Ultrasonics Symposium,* IEEE, New York, 1974, pp. 756–759.

70. M. Cantagrel and M. Marchal. "Argon ion etching in a reactive gas." *J. Mater. Sci.* **8,** 1711 (1973).

FIVE

Matching Networks and Packaging Structures

PHILIP B. SNOW

Tektronix, Incorporated
Beaverton, Oregon

A complete surface wave filter consists of (1) its primary element, the tapped delay line; (2) the networks that connect the delay line to external circuits; and (3) the package that supports and protects the delay line. The filter design must account for the effects of connecting networks and packaging on performance. This chapter presents the principles governing design of matching networks and the practical options available. The principles underlying packaging design for surface wave filters and solutions to packaging problems are also discussed.

5.1 Criteria for Matching Network Design

The objective of the first three topics in this section is to establish criteria for designing matching networks by relating each pertinent parameter to *transducer* insertion loss. The pertinent parameters are triple transit suppression, maximum fractional bandwidth, and maximum time-bandwidth product, discussed in typical order of importance.

Transducer Insertion Loss and Triple Transit Suppression. A matching network is an important buffer between an interdigital transducer and the generator or load to which it must be connected. The source or load shunt conductance G_L, or series resistance R_L presented to each transducer determines not only the primary insertion loss of a surface wave filter, but also the amplitude of multiple acoustic reflections between the two transducers, and if one is reduced the other is increased. To reduce system amplification requirements and prevent degradation in the signal-to-noise ratio, insertion loss should be minimized. To achieve signal fidelity and low spurious signal levels, multiple acoustic reflections should be suppressed. Achieving low insertion loss while maintaining high spurious response rejection has historically been one of the most difficult problems in surface wave technology because of the three-port nature of the interdigital transducer. For simple filters using bidirectional input and output transducers, the triple transit echo is directly related to the insertion loss of the device, and a sacrifice in the insertion loss must be made to realize a low spurious level. A matching network is the means by which a satisfactory compromise can be achieved.

An appropriate trade-off between insertion loss and multiple acoustic reflections can be determined when their relationship to transducer radiation resistance is understood. These relationships are derived with the aid of transducer equivalent circuits. The transducer can be represented electrically as a shunt circuit consisting of a capacitor C_T and a radiation conductance G_a in parallel, or as a series circuit consisting of a capacitor C_T and a radiation resistance R_a in series. Although both shunt and series circuits are equivalent representations of the electrical port of a transducer, it should be mentioned that R_a is *not* equal to $1/G_a$ because of the reactive (or susceptive) value of C_T associated with each circuit. R_a can be related to G_a by means of a simple series-parallel transformation using vector algebra. The interelectrode capacitance C_T in the shunt circuit is equal to the interelectrode capacitance C_T in the series circuit because the following relationships dominate most transducer designs: $(\omega_0 C_T)^2 \gg (G_a)^2$ or $(1/\omega_0 C_T)^2 \gg (R_a)^2$. To complete the definition of terms it should be stated that G_L denotes the shunt source or load conductance presented to a transducer when it is represented by a *shunt* equivalent circuit, whereas R_L denotes the series source or load resistance presented to a transducer represented by a *series* equivalent circuit.

Figure 5.1[1] shows a plot of reflection loss L_{11} and transmission loss L_{31} as a function of b; b is the normalized shunt conductance G_L/G_a, or the normalized series resistance R_L/R_a, or simply the transducer mismatch ratio. The reflection loss $(L_{11})_{dB} = 10 \log [(1+b)^2]$ is related to the fractional power reflected from a transducer at an acoustic port and is therefore related to the triple transit echo power. The triple transit echo is generally the largest of the many acoustic multiple reflections between transducers that result in spurious time sidelobes. It occurs between

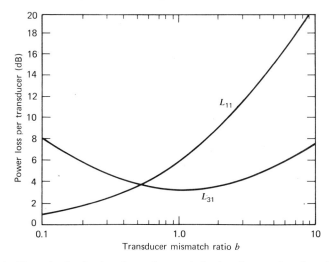

Figure 5.1 Plots of reflection loss L_{11} and transmission loss L_{31} as a function of transducer mismatch ratio b. Copyright 1969 by The Institute of Electrical and Electronic Engineers, Inc. Reprinted, with permission, from *IEEE Trans.* **MTT-17,** 1969, p. 861.

transducers because of the three port nature of interdigital arrays and the consequent inability to match all ports simultaneously. The triple transit echo is that portion of the main acoustic signal that is reflected from the output transducer back to the input transducer and returned again by reflection from the input transducer to the output transducer (see Fig. 5.2). The triple transit echo, therefore, lags the main acoustic signal by twice the delay time between transducers, and it vectorially adds with the output signal to create distortion. In the frequency domain the triple transit echo manifests itself as a periodic ripple in the passband whose

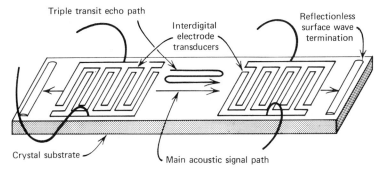

Figure 5.2 Essential elements of a surface wave device.

frequency f_r is a function of transducer spacing T_s; $f_r = 1/(2T_s)$. The power level of triple transit echo is generally measured with respect to the power level of the main delayed signal. The relative power difference between the main delayed signal and the triple transit echo is defined as the triple transit suppression. The transmission loss L_{31} is related to the fractional power transferred from a transducer acoustic port to a load across its electric port. The value of transmission loss is the same regardless of the direction of power flow (i.e., electric to acoustic or acoustic to electric); $(L_{31})_{dB} = 10 \log [(1+b)^2/2b]$.

For ease of further discussion it is assumed that both transducers of a surface wave filter are identical and are identically loaded. Under these conditions *transducer* insertion loss (IL) is equal to twice the transmission loss in dB ($IL = 2L_{31}$), and the value of triple transit suppression is equal to twice the reflection loss in dB ($TTS = 2L_{11}$). From Fig. 5.1 it can be seen that b must be equal to or greater than 1 to achieve some compromise in maximizing L_{11} and minimizing L_{31}. When $b = 1$, L_{31} is at its lowest value, 3 dB. It is 3 dB because most surface wave transducers are bidirectional so that half the acoustic power is radiated away from a desired output transducer. Operation with the load conductance equal to the radiation conductance ($b = 1$) is not generally desirable because L_{11} is only 6 dB ($TTS = 12$ dB). The peak-to-peak passband ripple R_{pp} associated with this level of triple transit suppression is equal to approximately 4 dB. The relationship between the peak-to-peak ripple and triple transit suppression is $(TTS)_{dB} = 24$ dB $- 20 \log (R_{pp})_{dB}$. In practice, the value of b should generally be not less than 20 for adequate triple transit suppression nor greater than 630 for maximum insertion loss. These values of b correspond to $L_{11} = 23$ dB, $L_{31} = 10$ dB, and $L_{11} = 53$ dB, $L_{31} = 25$ dB, respectively. For values of b much greater than 1, $(L_{11})_{dB} = 2(L_{31})_{dB}$. Or, for the assumed conditions of transducer and load uniformity,

$$(TTS)_{dB} = 2(IL)_{dB} + 6 \text{ dB} \qquad (5.1)$$

For simplicity at this point, acoustic loss is neglected in (5.1). The large interdependence of triple transit suppression on insertion loss is a characteristic of the "classical" surface wave filter that uses only a single bidirectional input transducer and a single bidirectional output transducer. A number of designs have been developed that substantially reduce triple transit echo by use of multiple transducers and phase feed schemes,[2,3] and consequently reduce the interdependence of triple transit echo and insertion loss. Because of the unique nature of many of the triple transit suppression schemes, and for the sake of continuity, only the matching of "classical" surface wave filters is discussed in this section.

Transducer Insertion Loss and Maximum Fractional Bandwidth. We have established the relation between transducer insertion loss and triple transit suppression. The following analyisis is presented to show the relationship between transducer insertion loss and maximum fractional bandwidth as a function of the material coupling constant k^2 of a surface wave substrate. Figure 5.3 shows a schematic representation of an interface between a transducer and an arbitrary external source or load resistance R_s. The transducer equivalent circuit also contains a shunt susceptance B_a that is usually negligible within the design passband and has therefore been omitted in Fig. 5.3 and in the following analysis.

The equivalent circuit conductance and capacitance for a uniform periodic transducer are given by

$$G_a = \left(\frac{4}{\pi}\right) k^2 (\omega_0 C_s) N^2 W_{\max} \tag{5.2}$$

and

$$C_T = C_s N W_{\max} \tag{5.3}$$

in which $W_{\max}$ denotes the maximum transducer aperture width, k the electromechanical coupling constant, C_s the interelectrode capacitance per section per unit electrode length, N the number of sections in the transducer, $\omega_0 = 2\pi f_0$ and f_0 denotes the center frequency of the transducer. G_a is the value of the radiation conductance at the transducers fundamental resonant frequency f_0. In this analysis it is assumed constant

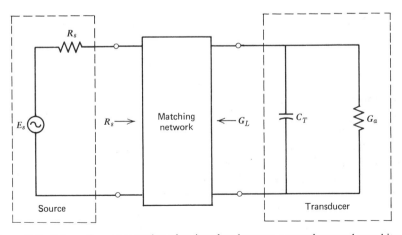

Figure 5.3 Schematic representation of an interface between a transducer and an arbitrary external source or load resistance R_s.

over the frequency band of interest. Equating C_s in (5.2) and (5.3) gives

$$G_a = \left(\frac{4}{\pi}\right) k^2 (\omega_0 C_T) N \qquad (5.4)$$

From (5.4), the radiation $Q_r \equiv \omega_0 C_T / G_a$ is

$$Q_r = \left(\frac{\pi}{4k^2}\right)\left(\frac{1}{N}\right) \qquad (5.5)$$

From the theory relating the geometrical properties of the transducer and the surface wave velocity

$$N = f_0 T \qquad (5.6)$$

in which T denotes the time required for a surface wave to traverse the transducer. The spectral response of a transducer can be shown to have a 4 dB bandwidth

$$\Delta f = \frac{1}{T} \qquad (5.7)$$

Equating T in (5.6) and (5.7),

$$N = \frac{f_0}{\Delta f} \qquad (5.8)$$

where Δf represents the acoustic bandwidth.

Equating N in (5.5) and (5.8),

$$Q_r = \frac{\omega_0 C_T}{G_a} = \left(\frac{\pi}{4k^2}\right)\left(\frac{\Delta f}{f_0}\right) \qquad (5.9)$$

Equation (5.9), although derived for an unapodized periodic transducer, has been found empirically to be approximately correct for all other types of transducer arrays.

For practical calculation it is necessary to account for resistive losses in the electrodes, in the matching network, or in the conductance often added to optimize mismatch. These losses can be accounted for by adding a shunt conductance G to the circuit. Thus a modified radiation conductance $(G + G_a)$ results, and a *modified* radiation Q may be defined as

$$Q_r' \equiv \frac{\omega_0 C_T}{G + G_a} \qquad (5.10)$$

Because $Q_r' = [G_a/(G+G_a)]Q_r$

$$Q_r' = \frac{\left(\dfrac{\pi}{4k^2}\right)\left(\dfrac{\Delta f}{f_0}\right)}{\left(\dfrac{G}{G_a}\right)+1} \qquad (5.11)$$

If in particular the matching network in Fig. 5.3 consists of an ideal transformer and a shunt inductor resonant with C_T at the center frequency of the transducer, then the network Q is

$$Q_n = \frac{f_0}{\Delta f_n} = \frac{\omega_0 C_T}{G_L + G_a} \qquad (5.12)$$

Δf_n denotes the bandwidth of the network, and $G_L = 2G + G_a$ (because of the conjugate match). Inductor tuning, resistive loading (G), and conjugate matching with a transformer in this manner allows maximum power transfer, at the center frequency f_0, between transducer and source or load resistance R_s without mismatch at its terminal interface.

The maximum fractional bandwidth $(\Delta f/f_0)_{max}'$, obtainable without significantly affecting the acoustic response of a surface wave filter with uniform periodic transducers, occurs when the network bandwidth is twice the acoustic bandwidth ($\Delta f_n = 2\,\Delta f$). If this condition is imposed, then from (5.10), (5.11), and (5.12)

$$\left(\frac{\Delta f}{f_0}\right)_{max}' = 2\left[\left(\frac{k^2}{\pi}\right)\left(\frac{G}{G_a}\right)+1\right]^{1/2} \qquad \text{for} \qquad G \geq 0 \qquad (5.13)$$

Equation (5.13) predicts maximum fractional bandwidth as a function of both electromechanical coupling k^2 and normalized loss conductance G/G_a.

The maximum *intrinsic* fractional bandwidth for each acoustic substrate material is obtained by assuming network losses are zero, that is, $G = 0$, then

$$\left(\frac{\Delta f}{f_0}\right)_{max} = 2\left(\frac{k^2}{\pi}\right)^{1/2} \qquad (5.14)$$

Table 5.1 shows the intrinsic fractional bandwidth for three commonly used substrate materials.

Having established the relationship between maximum fractional bandwidth and the ratio G/G_a we are prepared to derive an equation relating the maximum fractional bandwidth and minimum transducer insertion loss.

The efficiency of a single transducer, defined as the fractional power

Table 5.1   Maximum Intrinsic Fractional Bandwidth for Various Crystal Substrate Materials

Material	k^2	$\left(\dfrac{\Delta f}{f_0}\right)_{max}$
ST quartz	0.0016	0.045
Bismuth germanium oxide (001, 110)	0.0136	0.132
YZ Lithium niobate	0.044	0.236

transmitted from its acoustic to electric port divided by the power available at the acoustic port, is given by

$$P_{31} = \frac{2\left(\dfrac{G_L}{G_a}\right)}{\left(1 + \dfrac{G_L}{G_a}\right)^2} \tag{5.15}$$

If p equals the fractional power transmitted to R_s divided by the available power, then by virtue of the ideal transformer

$$p = \frac{G + G_a}{G_L} \tag{5.16}$$

If p'_{31} equals the fractional power transmitted from the acoustic port to R_s divided by the available power, then

$$p'_{31} = p_{31} \cdot p \tag{5.17}$$

Thus, assuming a resonant shunt inductor is used so that $G_L = 2G + G_a$,

$$p'_{31} = \frac{1}{2\left(\dfrac{G}{G_a} + 1\right)} \tag{5.18}$$

Because p'_{31} is only the fractional power transmitted per transducer the total fractional power transmitted through a surface wave filter (excluding acoustic losses) is

$$\frac{1}{IL} = (p'_{31})^2 = \frac{1}{4\left(\dfrac{G}{G_a} + 1\right)^2} \tag{5.19}$$

or

$$IL = 4\left(\frac{G}{G_a} + 1\right)^2 \qquad \text{for} \qquad G \geq 0 \tag{5.20}$$

The combination of (5.13) and (5.20) using the common ratio G/G_a produces an important relation between transducer insertion loss and maximum fractional bandwidth.

$$IL = \left(\frac{\pi^2}{4k^4}\right)\left(\frac{\Delta f}{f_0}\right)^{\prime 4}_{max} \tag{5.21}$$

for $(\Delta f/f_0)'_{max} \geq (\Delta f/f_0)_{max}$.

Equation (5.21) is shown graphically in Fig. 5.4 for three commonly used substrate materials. These curves define the maximum acoustic fractional bandwidth for minimum transducer insertion loss when both transducers are tuned and conjugately matched. The acoustic amplitude degradation at the band edges created by matching networks designed from the relationships used to derive the curves in Fig. 5.4 is usually acceptable for surface wave filters that utilize uniform periodic transducers whose frequency response is $\sin x/x$. When the desired acoustic frequency response of a filter or transducer is nearly rectangular, as is the case for a pulse compression filter, then a shunt conductance G or series resistance R must be chosen so that Δf_n is much larger than $2\Delta f$ (for

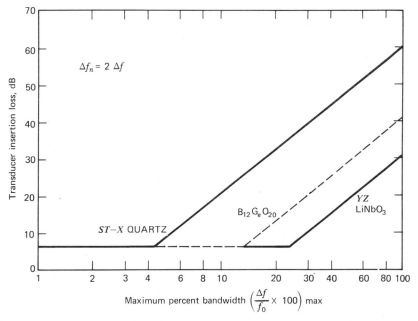

Figure 5.4 Curves that define, for a given crystal substrate, the maximum acoustic fractional bandwidth for minimum *transducer* insertion loss of a surface wave device. Assumes bidirectional transducers tuned and conjugately matched. See (5.21).

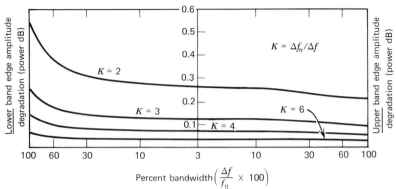

Figure 5.5 A composite family of curves that predicts the upper and lower band edge degradation due to a single tuned matching network.

instance, $6\,\Delta f$) to preserve the desired acoustic amplitude and phase characteristics across the entire bandwidth. The larger the ratio $\Delta f_n/\Delta f$ the higher the insertion loss but with less band edge degradation. Equation (5.21) can be modified appropriately with an additional independent variable K to predict the minimum insertion loss. The modified equation is

$$IL = \left(\frac{K^2\pi^2}{16k^4}\right)\left(\frac{\Delta f}{f_0}\right)^{'4}_{max} \qquad (5.22)$$

in which $K = (\Delta f_n/\Delta f) \geq 2$. Substitution of $K = 2$ into (5.22) yields (5.21).

A composite family of curves has been derived and plotted in Fig. 5.5 to show the relationship between upper and lower band edge degradation, and percent bandwidth as a function of K. The two sets of curves in Fig. 5.5 were plotted from two equations. One defines the *lower* band edge amplitude degradation (left side) and the other defines the *upper* band edge amplitude degradation (right side). The adjacent placement of the two sets of curves in Fig. 5.5 graphically emphasizes the asymmetric amplitude degradation that occurs when low Q (high percent bandwidth), single tuned (nonstaggered) resonant elements are used in transducer matching networks. When the percent bandwidth is small, less than 3%, amplitude degradation is essentially equal at both band edges. When the percent bandwidth is large, greater than 10%, the amplitude degradation is higher at the lower band edge than at the upper band edge.

The curves in Fig. 5.5 show the amplitude degradation for a *single* inductor in shunt or series with a transducer. To determine the overall amplitude degradation in a surface wave filter created by a single inductor at the input transducer and a single inductor at the output transducer, the value read in decibels from the curves is doubled.

The equations used to plot the curves in Fig. 5.5 assumed the radiation resistance of each surface wave transducer to be constant from lower band edge to upper band edge.

Transducer Insertion Loss and Maximum Time-Bandwidth Product. Figure 5.6 depicts equivalent series and parallel circuits for a typical interdigital transducer. These synonymous circuits are the basis for the matching techniques to be described later in this section. Each element in the equivalent circuits in Fig. 5.6 is defined as follows:

$$R_e = \text{series electrode resistance} = \frac{4\rho W_{max}}{(N\lambda_0)} \qquad (5.23)$$

$C_T = \text{interelectrode capacitance}$

$$R_a = \text{series radiation resistance} = \frac{G_a}{(\omega_0 C_T)^2} \qquad (5.24)$$

$G_a = \text{shunt radiation conductance}$

$$G_e = \text{shunt electrode conductance} = R_e(\omega_0 C_T)^2 \qquad (5.25)$$

Here ρ represents the sheet restivity of transducer metal (Ω/sq), and λ_0 the acoustic wavelength.

A series reactance X_a in Fig. 5.6a and a shunt susceptance G_a in Fig. 5.6b have been purposely omitted. This omission is valid because the matching circuitry is specifically designed at the center frequency where this reactance and susceptance are equal to zero. The shunt equivalent circuit shown in Fig. 5.6b was used in the previous analysis to derive (5.21). Identical results can be obtained using the series equivalent circuit

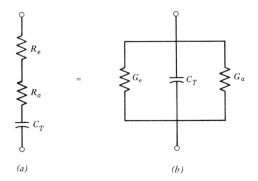

(a)   (b)

Figure 5.6 Equivalent series and parallel circuits for a typical interdigital transducer, and the basis for the matching techniques described in this section.

shown in Fig. 5.6a. Thus (5.13) can be rewritten as

$$\left(\frac{\Delta f}{f_0}\right)'_{\max} = 2\left[\left(\frac{k^2}{\pi}\right)\left(\frac{R}{R_a}+1\right)\right]^{1/2} \qquad \text{for} \qquad R \geq 0 \qquad (5.26)$$

Also (5.20) can be rewritten as

$$IL = 4\left(\frac{R}{R_a}+1\right)^2 \qquad \text{for} \qquad R \geq 0 \qquad (5.27)$$

Where R is the counterpart to G, as R_a is the counterpart to G_a, in Fig. 5.6. G_e or R_e represent various losses that occur in parts of the transducer that cannot be physically separated from the array. The presence of this loss was included by use of an external conductance G in the derivation of the curves for $(\Delta f/f_0)'_{\max} \geq (\Delta f/f_0)_{\max}$ shown in Fig. 5.4. However, for values of $(\Delta f/f_0)'_{\max} < (\Delta f/f_0)_{\max}$, G_e or R_e was assumed equal to zero, and a constant 6 dB transducer insertion loss was plotted. This accounts only for the bidirectional nature of both transducers. The following analysis is presented to give some insight into the relationship of G_e/G_a, or R_e/R_a with regard to transducer lengths (bandwidth), and separation (time delay), and also validate the 6 dB minimum value plotted in Fig. 5.4.

Combining (5.3), (5.23), and (5.25),

$$G_e = \frac{4\rho N(W_{\max})^3(\omega_0 C_s)^2}{\lambda_0} \qquad (5.28)$$

and dividing (5.28) by (5.2) leads to

$$\frac{G_e}{G_a} = \frac{\rho\pi(W_{\max})^2(\omega_0 C_s)}{k^2 N\lambda_0} \qquad (5.29)$$

It is now appropriate to introduce an approximate diffraction equation[4]

$$D_{\max} \doteq \frac{(W_{\max})^2}{(2\lambda_0)} \qquad (5.30)$$

In (5.30), $D_{\max}$ is the maximum distance over which an acoustic beam remains collimated when excited by a transducer of aperture width $W_{\max}$. For simplicity of presentation the anisotropy parameter was set equal to zero, and it is therefore deleted from (5.30). This is a good assumption for ST-X quartz and bismuth germanium oxide (001, 110), but *not* for YZ Lithium niobate. Equating $(W_{\max})^2$ in (5.29) and (5.30), and applying (5.6),

$$\frac{G_e}{G_a} = \left(\frac{4\pi^2 C_s}{k^2}\right)\left(\frac{D_{\max}}{T}\right) \qquad (5.31)$$

Because $D_{max} = V_p T_{max}$, where V_p = acoustic propagation velocity and T_{max} = maximum delay time between transducers, (5.31) can be rewritten as

$$\frac{G_e}{G_a} = \left(\frac{4\pi^2 \rho C_s V_p}{k^2}\right)\left(\frac{T_{max}}{T}\right) \tag{5.32}$$

Equation (5.32) states that for a given substrate material and transducer transit time T, the ratio G_e/G_a, which contributes to transducer insertion loss, is primarily a function of transducer metalization (ρ) and maximum time delay T_{max}. There is a fabrication limitation on transducer metalization thickness, therefore the time delay between transducers is a parameter worth considering when determining transducer insertion loss, with all due regard for center frequency, bandwidth, and substrate material.

If it is assumed that the minimum spacing between two long identical transducers is small compared to twice the array lengths, then $T_{max} \doteq 2T$, and (5.32) becomes

$$\frac{G_e}{G_a} = \frac{8\pi^2 \rho C_s V_p}{k^2} \tag{5.33}$$

For ST-X quartz (QZ), bismuth germanium oxide (BGO), and YZ lithium niobate (LN) with electrodes whose sheet resistivity is 0.7 Ω/sq.

$$\left(\frac{G_e}{G_a}\right)_{QZ} = 0.0062; \qquad \left(\frac{G_e}{G_a}\right)_{BGO} = 0.0026; \qquad \left(\frac{G_e}{G_a}\right)_{LN} = 0.00184$$

Long transducer arrays, as was assumed in (5.33), generally correspond to small fractional bandwidths. See (5.8). It is therefore apparent from the small values (compared to 1) calculated for G_e/G_a that the 6 dB insertion loss for $(\Delta f/f_0)'_{max} < (\Delta f/f_0)_{max}$ is a good minimum value for the curves in Fig. 5.4.

Using $\Delta f = 1/T$ in (5.32) yields

$$\frac{G_e}{G_a} = \left(\frac{4\pi^2 \rho C_s V_p}{k^2}\right)(\Delta f T_{max}) \tag{5.34}$$

If G_e is assumed the only resistive loss associated with the transducers so that G_e/G_a is equal to G/G_a and (5.34) is used in (5.20), the following relation results:

$$IL = 4\left[(\Delta f T_{max})\left(\frac{4\pi^2 \rho C_s V_p}{k^2}\right) + 1\right]^2 \tag{5.35}$$

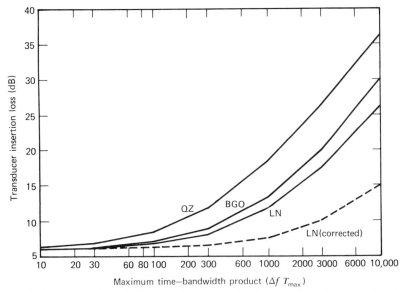

Figure 5.7   Transducer insertion loss as a function of time-bandwidth product and substrate material. See (5.35).

Figure 5.7 is a plot of (5.35). It shows the dependence of transducer insertion loss on maximum time-bandwidth product ($\Delta f T_{max}$) instead of maximum percent bandwidth as plotted in Fig. 5.4. The dashed curve for YZ lithium niobate in Fig. 5.7 has been plotted to show the effects of the anisotropy parameter for this highly focusing material.

Evaluation of Criteria for Determining Transducer Insertion Loss. All requirements for surface wave filters must specify triple transit suppression, bandwidth, center frequency, and time delay. Using the appropriate curves in Figs. 5.4 and 5.7, along with the relationship $(TTS)_{dB.} = 2(IL)_{dB} + 6 \text{ dB} + 2(L_a)_{dB}$, the *total* insertion loss of any surface wave filter can be determined from the specified requirements before actual design or fabrication.

The acoustic propagation loss $(L_a)_{dB}$ is added to the *transducer* insertion loss $(IL)_{dB}$ to give the *total* insertion loss $[(IL)_{dB} + (L_a)_{dB}]$ of a surface wave filter. For frequency applications below 100 MHz an approximate empirical rule for calculating acoustic loss is 0.1 dB per microsecond of delay between transducers. The transducer insertion loss relations developed in each of the previous sections were derived independently of the other parameters involved. The transducer insertion loss determined from the curves in Fig. 5.4 is a minimum value, and can be greater as determined from the curves in Fig. 5.7. If the transducer insertion loss determined from Figs. 5.4 or 5.7 *is not greater than* the value $[(TTS)_{dB}/2 - 3\,dB - (L_a)_{dB}]$, then the *transducer insertion loss* for the device *must be made equal to the previously stated value* to meet the triple transit suppression requirement. This can be done by increasing the shunt conductance G or series resistance R. Once the transducer insertion loss has been determined as just outlined the value of b can be obtained using Fig. 5.1 and an appropriate matching scheme can be devised. Implementation of these networks is discussed in the remaining section on matching.

5.2 Passive Matching Networks

The transducer interelectrode capacitance C_T is a series reactance, or shunt susceptance generally much larger than the respective series radiation resistance R_a, or shunt radiation conductance G_a. If a surface wave transducer is interfaced directly with a resistive source or load, the interelectrode capacitance superimposes a frequency dependent mismatch on the desired acoustic response, and transducer insertion loss is excessive. Because it is important to keep transducer insertion loss at a reasonable and predictable level and also to minimize phase and amplitude distortion across the acoustic passband, it is desirable in most cases to introduce a series or parallel inductor L_T to tune out the effects of interelectrode capacitance C_T.

A commonly used and very simple interface is a series resistor and inductor tuning network. This network can be effectively used if the transducer radiation resistance is considerably smaller than the source (load) resistance, and if the radiation resistance, electrode resistance, intrinsic inductor resistance, and possibly an added resistor R can be summed to meet VSWR, insertion loss, triple transit suppression, and bandwidth requirements. The advantages of a series R/L tuning network are that it allows the least number of components for good temperature stability, simplicity of packaging, and ease of analysis. Its disadvantages are its usually higher insertion loss compared with slightly more complex networks and the few variables available. The latter disadvantage leads to stringent device requirements that are generally difficult to meet. The network Q of each series tuned transducer is $1/(2\pi f_0 C_T R_T)$ where $R_T = (R_a + R_e + R_s + R)$ is the total series resistance and the transfer phase is $\tan^{-1}(X_T/R_a)$, where X_T is the total network reactance at the frequency of interest.

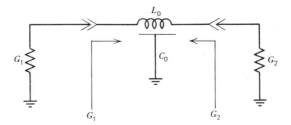

Figure 5.8 Lumped equivalent circuit of a quarter-wave transformer.

A *not* as common passive interface is the shunt resistor and inductor tuning network. Shunt tuning is generally not very useful for passive interfacing *directly* with a generator or load because transducer radiation conductance is extremely small compared to the typical $20\,\text{m}\Omega^{-1}$ load conductance. To achieve reasonable VSWR the network conductance must be very large compared to the transducer radiation conductance, and consequently very little incident power is converted to acoustic power. However, properly coupled with an appropriate transformer, a shunt inductor is an effective method of tuning out transducer capacitance. The network Q of each shunt tuned transducer is equal to $2\pi f_0 C_T/G_T$ where $G_T = (G_a + G_e + G_s + G)$ equals the total shunt conductance, and the transfer phase is $\tan^{-1}(B_T/G_a)$, where B_T is the total network susceptance at the frequency of interest.

Transformers are impedance matching devices readily utilized in interfacing transducers with other electronic components. However, because they are lumped elements they have an upper frequency limit and are also usually restricted to rather low transformer ratios. The quarter-wave transformer is a more flexible and desirable type of matching network because it can be implemented with either lumped or distributed elements. Thus it has no inherent frequency limitation and is a general method for interfacing any two resistive ports. The lumped equivalent circuit of the quarter-wave transformer is shown in Fig. 5.8, where $L_0 = 1/(\omega_0 G_0)$ and $C_0 = G_0/\omega_0$. G_0 is the characteristic admittance of a quarter-wave transmission line that can conjugately couple a conductance G_1 with a conductance G_2 at f_0, $G_0 = \sqrt{G_1 G_2}$.

Impedance Matching Networks. Implementation of an impedance matching network for a surface wave transducer must be based on a good understanding of the relations between triple transit suppression, insertion loss, percent bandwidth, and time delay, all of which are discussed earlier in this chapter. Like any electrical network, the implementation achieved can be as varied as the number of designers making them. Two generalized passive solutions to the impedance matching problem, successfully used by the author, are presented here, but they should not be interpreted as the only or the ultimate approaches. The impedance matching networks can be viewed as a series or shunt circuit having a single tuned response.

The series design starts with a transducer represented by a series equivalent circuit (see Fig. 5.6a), and a series inductor resonant with the interelectrode capacitance C_T at the transducer center frequency f_0. These elements, in conjunction with a quarter-wave transformer provide a *match* with a source, or load resistance R_s, and a series resistance R provides sufficient *mismatch* with the radiation resistance R_a. The mismatch is calculated from an appropriately determined value of b. Figure 5.9 illustrates this in a more graphic manner. At f_0, $L_T = 1/(4\pi^2 f_0^2 C_T)$. Therefore $Z = R + R_a$, where R equals the series electrode resistance (R_e) plus the series resistance in L_T plus any added series resistor for mismatch or bandwidth requirements. From the quarter-wave transformer equation

$$Z_0^2 = Z \cdot Z_{in} \qquad at \qquad f_0 \qquad (5.36)$$

Substituting appropriately

$$Z_0^2 = R_s(R + R_a) \qquad at \qquad f_0 \qquad (5.37)$$

Because R_s is reflected through the quarter-wave transformer as Z, then

$$R_L = 2R + R_a \qquad at \qquad f_0 \qquad (5.38)$$

Equations (5.37) and (5.38) are the basic equations required to design an appropriate *series* matching network. When using this design and a *lumped-element* quarter-wave transformer (see Fig. 5.8), the series L_T

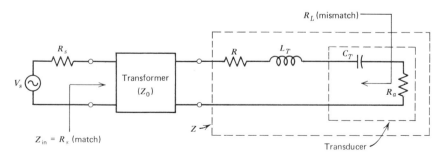

Figure 5.9 Schematic representation of series matching network. See (5.37) and (5.38).

can be combined with the series L_0 to reduce the number of physical inductors. Also, $Z_0 = \omega_0 L_0 = 1/(\omega_0 C_0)$.

The shunt design starts with a transducer represented by a parallel circuit (see Fig. 5.6b) and a shunt inductor resonant with C_T at f_0. These elements together with a quarter-wave transformer provide a *match* with a source or load resistance R_s and a shunt G to provide adequate *mismatch* with G_a. Again the mismatch is calculated from an appropriately determined value of b. Figure 5.10 depicts this format. At f_0, $L_T = 1/(4\pi^2 f_0 C_T)$. Therefore $Y = G + G_a$; where G equals shunt electrode resistance plus the shunt conductance in L_T plus any added shunt conductance for mismatch or bandwidth requirements. Rewriting the quarter-wave transformer equation in admittance form,

$$Y_0^2 = Y \cdot Y_{in} \qquad \text{at} \qquad f_0 \qquad (5.39)$$

Substituting appropriately,

$$Y_0^2 = \frac{G + G_a}{R_s} \qquad \text{at} \qquad f_0 \qquad (5.40)$$

Because R_s is reflected through the quarter-wave transformer as Y, then

$$G_L = 2G + G_a \qquad \text{at} \qquad f_0 \qquad (5.41)$$

Equations (5.40) and (5.41) are the basic equations required to design an appropriate *shunt* matching network. When using this design and a *lumped-element* quarter-wave transformer (see Fig. 5.8), the shunt L_T can be combined with the shunt C_0 to reduce the number of physical components. Also, $Y_0 = \omega_0 C_0 = 1/(\omega_0 L_0)$.

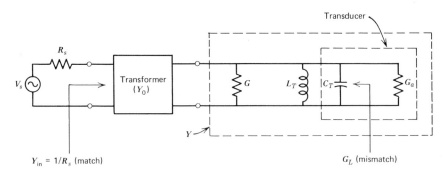

Figure 5.10 Schematic representation of shunt matching network. Refer to (5.40) and (5.41).

Comparison of Series and Shunt Designs Using Quarter-Wave Transformers. For a given transducer, whether it be series modeled and series tuned, or shunt modeled and shunt tuned, the resultant Q's will be equal. This is also true when an equivalent R in the series case or G in the shunt case are introduced to produce a *given* mismatch with R_a and G_a, respectively. An analysis of the network Q's is presented to compare the effects of the quarter-wave transformer designed for each scheme.

Assume that the source (load) is resistive and is a *conjugate match* to the transducer plus external resistor (*with no transformer*) in both series and shunt mode. The network Q in each case is

$$Q_n = \frac{(\omega_0 C_T)^{-1}}{2(R + R_a)} = \frac{\omega_0 C_T}{2(G + G_a)} \tag{5.42}$$

The left expression refers to the series mode and the right to the shunt mode, $R_L = R + R_a$ and $G_L = G + G_a$.

From (5.42) another relationship can be stated

$$(G + G_a) = (\omega_0 C_T)^2 (R + R_a) \tag{5.43}$$

If a quarter-wave transformer is added to transform an arbitrary generator (load) resistance R_s to a conjugate match as already described, see Figs. 5.9 and 5.10, then the *total series network* Q is

$$Q_{ns} = \frac{Z_0 + (1/(\omega_0 C_T))}{2(R + R_a)} \tag{5.44}$$

or

$$Q_{ns} = Q_n + Q_s \tag{5.45}$$

also

$$Q_s = \frac{Z_0}{2(R + R_a)} \tag{5.46}$$

And the corresponding *total shunt network* Q is

$$Q_{np} = \frac{Y_0 + \omega_0 C_T}{2(G + G_a)} \tag{5.47}$$

or

$$Q_{np} = Q_n + Q_p \tag{5.48}$$

in which

$$Q_p = \frac{Y_0}{2(G + G_a)} \tag{5.49}$$

Note: $Z_0 \neq 1/Y_0$. See (5.37) and (5.40).

Because Q_n appears in both (5.45) and (5.48), an appropriate comparison between quarter-wave transformer designs can be best made by relating only Q_p with Q_s. Equating $(G + G_a)$ in (5.43) and (5.49),

$$Q_p = \frac{Y_0}{2(\omega_0 C_T)^2(R + R_a)} \tag{5.50}$$

Equating $1/(2(R + R_a))$ in (5.46) and (5.50),

$$Q_p = \left(\frac{Y_0}{(\omega_0 C_T)^2}\right)\left(\frac{Q_s}{Z_0}\right) \tag{5.51}$$

Equating $(G + G_a)$ in (5.40) and (5.43),

$$Y_0 = (\omega_0 C_T)\left(\frac{R + R_a}{R_s}\right)^{1/2} \tag{5.52}$$

Rewriting (5.37),

$$Z_0 = [R_s(R + R_a)]^{1/2} \tag{5.53}$$

Substituting (5.52) and (5.53) appropriately into (5.51) yields

$$Q_p = \frac{Q_s}{\omega_0 C_T R_s} \tag{5.54}$$

Equations (5.54) shows that the Q's of the quarter-wave transformers (Q_s and Q_p) are related by a factor $\omega_0 C_T R_s$. If this factor is equal to 1, then the total network Q's (Q_{ns} and Q_{np}) are equal. From (5.45) and (5.48) it is also apparent that if Q_s and Q_p are insignificant with respect to Q_n, then Q_{ns} is approximately equal to Q_{np}. If the factor $\omega_0 C_T R_s$ is other than 1, and Q_s and/or Q_p are appreciable, then the total network Q's are *not* equal for an *equivalent* amount of mismatch. The significance of the total network Q is that it directly affects the fractional bandwidth–insertion loss relationship of the surface wave device. See (5.12). Thus for a given mismatch ratio ($b = R_L/R_a = G_L/G_a$) one matching approach may be more desirable than another from bandwidth and insertion loss considerations. It is apparent from (5.54) that if R_s is large, Q_s may become larger than Q_p, and the shunt approach would be preferable. Also if R_s is small, Q_p may become larger than Q_s, and the series approach would be less lossy for a given fractional bandwidth. Selection of the scheme that is best does not necessarily rest solely with the relationships just presented, but must account for practical needs as well. Sometimes the components whose values calculated from the equations presented in each design approach cannot be purchased or fabricated. This type of consideration then dominates the choice of scheme to be used.

Some Unique Feed Schemes for Continuous Comb Filters. A single
channel broadband radar or communications receiver can be fed into a
contiguous filter bank to frequency-split incoming signals into numerous
channels. A surface wave device is well suited to this application. Feeding
a contiguous comb filter efficiently is exceptionally difficult if there are
many outputs. Surface wave comb filter banks are no exception, because
each channel requires a separate input transducer. Each surface wave
filter in the bank must be designed to operate at a different frequency and
over a specified bandwidth that depends on the required resolution.
Accordingly, the series radiation resistance (or shunt radiation conductance) in *each* input transducer is effective only over a limited portion of
the *overall* bandwidth of the filter bank. This can be used to advantage in
designing and evaluating candidate feed schemes. If the series radiation
resistance (or shunt radiation conductance) can be assumed equal and
continuous from input transducer to input transducer over the entire
bandwidth of the filter bank, then the following schemes or *combination
thereof* can be useful to a designer faced with this complex interface
problem.

The constant-k feed network illustrated in Fig. 5.11 is a lumped
parameter approximation to an electromagnetic transmission line and is
derived by interconnecting the filter input transducers with small inductors. Outside the passband of a given filter its input transducer radiation
admittance is negligibly small, and the transducer can be modeled by its
interelectrode capacitance C_T. Within its passband the radiation conductance G_a increases and acts as a light load on the "transmission line."

The unique feature of the constant-k feed network is its low-pass
amplitude versus frequency characteristic. Therefore if the upper cutoff
frequency is greater than the maximum operating frequency of the filter
array and if the respective radiation conductances do not excessively load
the network, the transducer driving voltages are equal and independent of

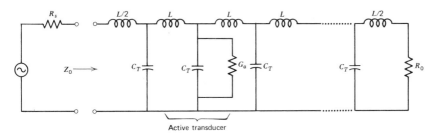

Figure 5.11 Constant-k feed network for driving contiguous comb surface wave filters
from single source.

frequency. Another desirable attribute of this type of network is that only one inductor per transducer is required. These inductors can be readily fabricated in a planar fashion in multiple groups and easily integrated adjacent to the transducers. Inductors can also be produced by meandering a wire-bond pattern on a planar surface with appropriate pad landings.

In principle the loss of a constant-k manifold is independent of the number of filters, but in practice the maximum number is primarily determined by the inductor losses. This type of constraint can be minimized, however, by appropriate design of the transducer and constant-k network.

In such a manifold, the radiation conductance of each transducer is required to be less than the reciprocal of the characteristic impedance Z_0 of the network. Z_0, R_0, and R_s must all be equal where $Z_0 = (L/C_T)^{1/2}$. This accounts for an inherent 3 dB loss in R_s. The cutoff frequency of the network is equal to $1/(2\pi L C_T)$.

A composite transducer feed scheme has been used quite effectively by other investigators.[5] It consists of multiple transducers interconnected into a complex series-parallel or parallel-series network, thus creating a single input port. The following simple comparative analysis of the equivalent radiation quality factor, Q_r'' of an *array* of interconnected transducers with the radiation quality factor, Q_r of a *single* transducer in that array is presented to give insight into its usefulness as an effective feed scheme for narrow-band filter application.

Restating (5.9),

$$Q_r \equiv \left(\frac{1}{\omega_0 C_T R_a}\right)_{\text{Series}} = \left(\frac{\omega_0 C_T}{G_a}\right)_{\text{Shunt}} = \left(\frac{\pi}{4k^2}\right)\left(\frac{\Delta f}{f_0}\right) \qquad (5.55)$$

As before Δf denotes the bandwidth of a single transducer f_0, its center frequency C_T, its interelectrode capacitance G_a, its shunt radiation conductance, and its series radiation resistance $R_a = G_a/(\omega_0 C_T)^2$, which restates (5.24), and $\omega_0 = 2\pi f_0$.

Let n denote the number of transducers or transducer groups in series and m the number of transducers or transducer groups in parallel.

CASE 1. n transducers in series. Using the equivalent circuit in Fig. 5.12,

$$Q_{r1}'' = \frac{n}{\omega_0 C_T R_a} \qquad (5.56)$$

Combining (5.55) and (5.56),

$$Q_{r1}'' = nQ_r \qquad (5.57)$$

Figure 5.12 Equivalent circuit of n transducers connected in series. See (5.56).

CASE 2. m transducers in parallel. Using the equivalent circuit in Fig. 5.13,

$$Q_{r2}'' = m\left(\frac{\omega_0 C_T}{G_a}\right) \tag{5.58}$$

Combining (5.55) and (5.58),

$$Q_{r2}'' = mQ_r \tag{5.59}$$

CASE 3. m parallel groups of n transducers in series.

Using (5.24) to transform the composite series transducer of Fig. 5.12 to the equivalent shunt transducer of Fig. 5.14,

$$G_a' = R_a\left(\frac{\omega_0 C_T}{n}\right)^2 = \frac{R_a}{(m\omega_0 C_T)^2} \tag{5.60}$$

Using the equivalent circuit of Fig. 5.14,

$$Q_{r3}'' = \frac{\omega_0 mC_T}{nG_a'} = \frac{mn}{\omega_0 C_T R_a} \tag{5.61}$$

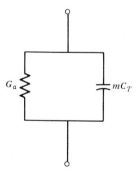

Figure 5.13 Equivalent circuit of m transducers connected in parallel. See (5.58).

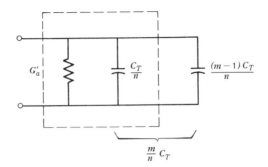

Figure 5.14 Equivalent circuit of m parallel groups of n transducers in series. See (5.61).

Combining (5.55) and (5.61),

$$Q_{r3}'' = mnQ_r \qquad (5.62)$$

CASE 4. n series groups of m transducers in parallel. Using (5.24) to transform the composite parallel transducer of Fig. 5.13 to the equivalent series transducer of Fig. 5.15,

$$R_a' = \frac{G_a}{(\omega_0 m C_T)^2} = \frac{G_a}{(m\omega_0 C_T)^2} \qquad (5.63)$$

Using the equivalent circuit in Fig. 5.15,

$$Q_{r4}'' = \frac{1}{R_a'(\omega_0 m C_T/n)} = mn\left(\frac{\omega_0 C_T}{G}\right) \qquad (5.64)$$

Combining (5.55) and (5.64),

$$Q_{r4}'' = mnQ_r \qquad (5.65)$$

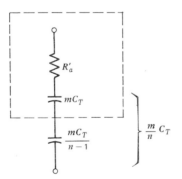

Figure 5.15 Equivalent circuit of n series groups of m transducers in parallel. See (5.64).

From (5.57), (5.59), (5.62), and (5.65) it can be stated that the equivalent radiation Q for all applicable combinations of series-parallel or parallel-series connected transducers is equal to a single transducer radiation Q multiplied by the total number of individual transducers involved. From (5.55) it can be seen that the radiation Q of a *single transducer* is primarily a function of the bandwidth Δf for a given frequency f_0 and substrate material (k^2). Thus if a *group of transducers* is interconnected in a complex or composite manner, such as in a feed scheme, and if the center frequency of each transducer is assumed approximately equal to the average center frequency of all transducers, then the following relation can be stated

$$\frac{Q_r''}{Q_r} = \frac{\Delta f''}{\Delta f} \tag{5.66}$$

where $\Delta f''$ is an equivalent bandwidth for a composite transducer. Combining (5.66) with (5.62) or (5.65) yields

$$\Delta f'' = mn\,\Delta f \tag{5.67}$$

Using the equivalent bandwidth prescribed in (5.67), a matching network for a composite transducer can be designed and the insertion loss predicted using the equations and curves presented and discussed in previous sections for a single transducer. To predict the insertion loss for a composite transducer *input* feed scheme with single transducer outputs, first determine the total insertion loss from the appropriate curve in Fig. 5.4 using $\Delta f''$. In like manner determine the total insertion loss a second time using Δf. The sum of the two results divided by 2 is the actual total insertion loss for such a transducer interconnect scheme.

5.3 The Packaging Structure and the Crystal Substrate

In designing a package to house a surface wave filter primary consideration should be given to the crystal substrate. The important factors are mechanical, environmental, and electrical.

Surface wave filters are fragile because the crystal substrate is fragile. The crystal must not be too thin, and therefore difficult to handle and process, nor too thick because this leads to excessive electromagnetic feedthrough and is economically unsound. The thickness is primarily determined by the surface area of the substrate and the physical properties of the crystal material. Crystal thicknesses range from $\frac{1}{2}$ mm to 3 mm. Packages for surface wave filters are as varied as those used for any other type of electronic component or circuitry. A package can be a simple

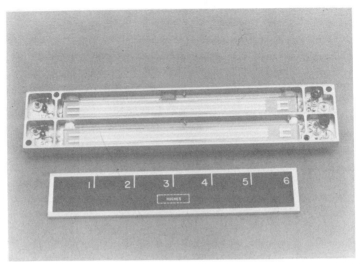

Figure 5.16 Dual 30 MHz dispersive surface wave filters mounted in a machined aluminum package. Courtesy Hughes Aircraft Company.

metal box with a milled (or stamped) cavity (Fig. 5.16), a machined and processed stripline configuration (Figs. 5.17a, b, c), or even a microstrip and box combination (Fig. 5.18). The design is only limited by the designer's imagination and the total requirements of the specific application.

Analysis, confirmed by experiment, shows a rigid metal I-beam frame minimizes mechanical stresses on the substrate. This frame in conjunction with a soft foam shroud protects the crystal from damage when subjected to shock and vibration. Figures 5.19a, b, and c illustrate a typical example of such a package. This package has an I-shaped cross section with the crystal in one cavity and the matching networks in the other. The transducers on the crystal substrate are connected to the matching networks via insulated mechanical feedthroughs in the common wall.

It is important to mount and attach the crystal substrate appropriately in its housing. It must be securely fastened to the package yet not constrained by hard (nonelastic) mounting techniques or bonding materials. RTV is a suitable adhesive for attaching a substrate to a package frame. It bonds to nearly anything, cures at room temperature to a soft plastic state, and is acceptable for most applications. There are numerous RTV compounds. There are three the author recommends for mounting substrate crystals and these are listed in Table 5.2.

A technique for mounting a crystal in a package is to coat the back side of the crystal with an even layer of adhesive approximately 40 mils thick,

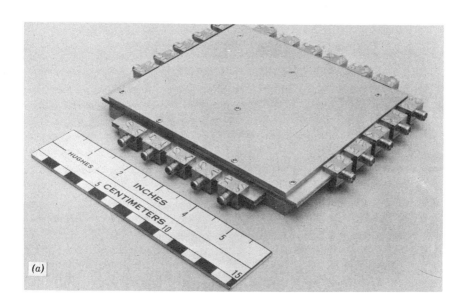

Figure 5.17 A 150 MHz velocity correlator stripline package with 16 inputs and 5 outputs. (a) Completely assembled package. (b) Top view of partially opened package showing the crystal substrates, mounting cavities, and strip-feed lines. (c) Bottom view of partially opened package showing isolated stripline outputs and series tuning inductors for the inputs. Courtesy Hughes Aircraft Company.

245

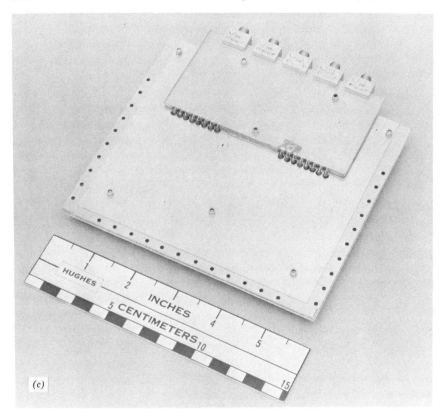

Figure 5.17 (*Contd*).

and then to place the crystal in position and gently apply distributed pressure on the crystal until it seats itself well into the package leaving about a 25 mil cushion between the bottom of the crystal and the package surface. This technique permanently fastens the crystal yet allows it to "float" on a layer of RTV. An alternate method is to use a $\frac{1}{32}$ to $\frac{1}{16}$ in. thick strip of sheet silicone rubber that is first bonded to the package with RTV. The crystal is then bonded firmly to the silicone rubber with additional RTV. The silicone rubber is a good support and has cushioning characteristics similar to those of the molded RTV adhesive layer. Silver loaded RTV (see Table 5.2) and silver loaded silicone rubber are often used to improve electromagnetic feedthrough suppression in a surface wave filter package. The rationale for this is explained later.

Removal of a crystal substrate mounted with RTV (and cured) is difficult, but not impossible. A thin, stiff wire (i.e., tungsten or spring steel) pulled between the substrate and the package will free the crystal.

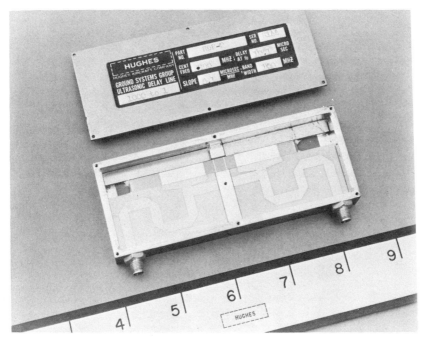

Figure 5.18 Machined aluminum box with ceramic microstrip substrates used to house and match a single 1000:1, 300 MHz highly dispersive surface wave filter. Courtesy Hughes Aircraft Company.

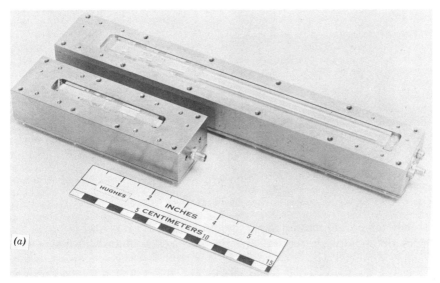

Figure 5.19 *I*-beam-type metal package, ideal for stringent shock and vibration requirements. (*a*) Crystal cavity side of package with silver loaded silicon rubber cushion and electrically insulated metal feed strips. (*b*) Foam filled shroud for shock and vibration damping as well as thermal insulation. (*c*) Bottom view of package with printed circuit boards to support components for matching networks. Also, the package lid for the crystal side with heater, controller, and sensors. Courtesy Hughes Aircraft Company.

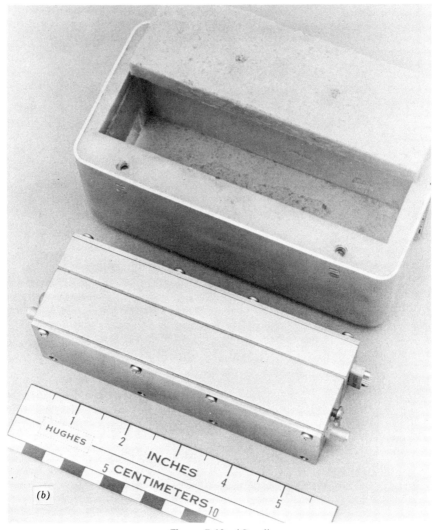

(b)

Figure 5.19 (*Contd*).

If only temporary mounting is required, a little RTV placed between the sides or ends of the crystal and the package is quite sufficient and is readily removed with a sharp knife.

There are better mechanical energy absorbers than RTV and silicone rubber, and foam shrouds around the entire package are bulky and expensive. An alternative is to use a highly effective absorber material bonded directly between the substrate and its package. One such material

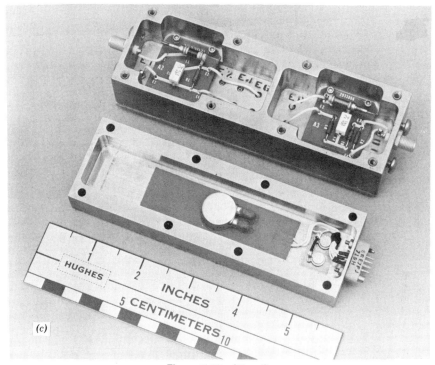

(c)

Figure 5.19 (*Contd*).

has been used for years to eliminate undesirable vibration within gasoline tanks of engine-powered model airplanes. It consists of a thin layer of foam sandwiched between two ultrathin mylar sheets. This technique, and customer acceptance of the absorbing material, is presently being investigated by the author.

The crystal substrate has a smooth, optically flat surface to minimize

Table 5.2 RTV-Type Adhesives for Mounting Surface Wave Crystals

Type	Manufacturer	Comments
RTV-102	General Electric	Room temperature curing (fast rate). For temporary attachment. Corrosive.
RTV-3145	Dow Corning	Room temperature curing (slow rate). For permanent attachment. Noncorrosive.
190-3	Ablestik	Room temperature curing (moderate rate). Reduce electromagnetic feedthrough. Silver loaded.

acoustic wave dispersion and reflections and acoustic energy dissipation. Any contamination deposited on the surface due to inadequate protection of the crystal surface alters the characteristics of a well-designed and well-fabricated device. Moisture and particulate matter such as dirt and dust are all undesirable elements on the surface. Aluminum transducers used on quartz and lithium niobate and the copper transducers used on BGO oxidize unless gold is used as a protective metal layer, especially in the presence of moisture. Oxidation changes the sheet resistivity of the electrodes or creates opens that alter the transducer impedance and transfer characteristics of any surface wave filter.

The best protection for a processed crystal is to seal it hermetically into a package much like monolithic or hybrid microcircuits. Airtight packages for large arrays and long crystals (4 to 9 in.) are not readily available as yet, and much time and money must be spent to make hermetically sealed large packages a practical and economical reality. For small surface wave devices like bandpass filters, microcircuit packages such as those shown in Fig. 5.20 are already in use. At present large packages such as those

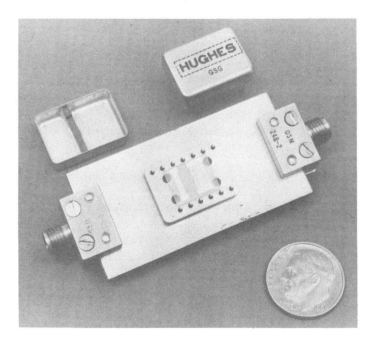

Figure 5.20 Hermetically sealable microcircuit package to house small surface wave devices such as bandpass filters. Package is mounted on stripline test fixture. Courtesy Hughes Aircraft Company.

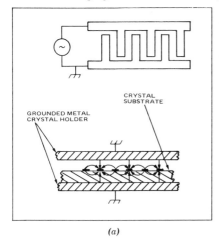 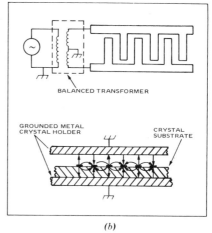

(a)   (b)

Figure 5.21 Unbalanced and balanced electrical feed and detection of transducers with corresponding electric field distribution diagram. (a) Unbalanced electrical connection to transducer. (b) Balanced electrical connection to transducer. Courtesy Hughes Aircraft Company.

shown in Figs. 5.16 through 5.19 are made air-, dust-, and moisture-tight with silicone rubber gaskets, screws, and/or appropriate epoxies and adhesives. To date, such techniques have proved quite successful in both laboratory and field tested units.

Electromagnetic feedthrough in surface wave filters is defined as the energy that is electrically coupled or radiated from one transducer to another. The amount of electromagnetic feedthrough is specified relative to the output acoustic response level and is generally referred to as the electromagnetic suppression. Specifically, electromagnetic suppression is equal to the delayed signal power divided by the *un*delayed signal power, where the power is that dissipated in the load across the output transducer. The dynamic range and overall response of an acoustic surface wave filter could but should not be constrained by insufficient electromagnetic suppression. It is difficult to predict accurately its exact value because the boundary conditions are different for each type of device. Experimental data and a good understanding of the electromagnetic fields involved are important in designing an appropriate package.

The most common method of electromagnetically feeding an interdigital array is to connect the two sum bars of the transducer to an unbalanced transmission line with gold wires. In this arrangement one side of the transducer is grounded to the metallic box housing the crystal. The resulting field distribution is shown in Fig. 5.21*a*. The electromagnetic feedthrough observed using an unbalanced feed arrangement can be viewed as the result of a guided wave phenomena wherein the interdigital electrode arrays generate and detect cutoff waveguide modes propagating in a dielectric filled waveguide. As shown in Fig. 5.21a, this type of feed results in a distribution of normal E-field components that tend to excite cutoff modes in the dielectric loaded waveguide. These modes give rise to significant electromagnetic feedthrough when the distance between the transducers is small.

Assuming the predominant electromagnetic excitation is a TE_{10} dielectric-filled waveguide mode, the amount of *relative* attenuation (isolation) between any two points within the crystal cavity can be determined using the following equation:

$$\alpha = \frac{54.5d}{\lambda_c}\left[1 - \left(\frac{\lambda_c}{\lambda}\right)^2\right] \qquad (5.68)$$

In (5.68) α denotes the isolation between transducers in dB, d the distance between the transducers, λ the operating wavelength in the cavity, and λ_c the cavity cutoff wavelength. The cutoff wavelength is twice the cavity width a ($\lambda_c = 2a$). The operating wavelength is calculated from the operating frequency f and the velocity of electromagnetic propagation V in the cavity: $V = V_c/\epsilon_r^{1/2}$. The velocity of electromagnetic propagation in free space V_c is 1.18×10^{10} in./sec, and the relative dielectric constant ϵ_r is that of the crystal substrate.

If the cavity width of the crystal package is very small compared with the wavelength at the operating frequency, then $(\lambda_c/\lambda) \ll 1$ and (5.68) reduces to a simpler equation relating isolation between transducers to the ratio of transducer spacing and cavity width.

$$\alpha = 27.25\left(\frac{d}{a}\right) \qquad (5.69)$$

Thus the greater the spacing and the narrower the cavity, the lower the electromagnetic feedthrough.

Equation (5.69) is valid for surface wave filters fabricated on quartz, BGO, and lithium niobate crystal substrates operated below 500 MHz and mounted in cavities 1 in. or less in width. Generally the acoustic energy and the radiated electrical energy are not of equal strength at the input transducer. Short transducers with few electrodes do not radiate electromagnetically as strongly as long transducers. To minimize further the coupling effects between transducers as just described, the effective height of the cavity should be made as nearly equal to the crystal thickness as possible. The added transducer capacitance thus created is usually minimal and generally offset by the improvement in isolation. Silver loaded gasket material and adhesives can be used on the sides of and beneath the crystal and on the lid to reduce the cross-sectional area of a crystal cavity. A good example of this is shown in the photographed package Fig. 5.20. When assembled the lid insert, molded from silver loaded RTV, creates an electromagnetic barrier between the transducers without touching the upper surface of the crystal. This technique works well but there is still electromagnetic coupling between transducers *within* the crystal material.

Providing sufficient electromagnetic isolation between closely spaced transducers can be a significant problem in the design of minimum delay acoustic filters or tapped delay lines whose transducer spacings are only fractions of a microsecond. A solution to this problem is to suppress the TE-mode excitation by modifying the field distribution shown in Fig. 5.21*a*. By feeding the transducer in a balanced fashion, as shown in Fig. 5.21*b*, with a balanced transformer there is *no* net normal E field. Thus the excitation or detection of TE modes is suppressed, and it can be expected that the feedthrough and the associated electromagnetic interaction of the transducers will be nearly eliminated. The effectiveness of this method is demonstrated by an experiment using two four-period, 90 MHz transducers on $LiNbO_3$ separated by 0.1 μsec. The input and output transducers are connected to electromagnetic transmission lines with unbalanced feed to both transducers and then with balanced transformers. The time domain response at the output transducer to a 33 nsec input pulse was measured for both cases. The electromagnetic feedthrough for unbalanced feed was only 16 dB down from the desired *delayed* pulse. With balanced feed the feedthrough was approximately 33 dB below the desired *delayed* pulse.

From this experiment it may be concluded that the use of a balanced feed to excite and/or load surface wave transducers is very desirable. However, balanced transformers are not very small and require additional volume to package with a crystal. Since most systems and test equipment have unbalanced feeds for convenience and shielding, the implementation of balanced feedstructures for surface wave filters is further constrained to unbalanced-to-balanced networks for proper interfacing with other electronic components.

5.4 Other Packaging Design Considerations

A change of the temperature of a surface wave filter causes a change in time delay and transducer center frequency. Thermal stress alters both the velocity of propagation and the substrate dimensions. The change in time delay and shift in frequency as a function of temperature are due to both effects. For BGO (001, 110) the velocity of propagation shifts at a rate of -134 ppm/°C, whereas for YZ lithium niobate it changes only -88 ppm/°C. ST-X quartz[6] is a specially cut substrate that has a zero temperature coefficient at about 25°C. ST-X quartz is an extremely useful substrate when ovens are impractical; however it has low electrochemical coupling and its use is limited to applications in which high insertion loss or narrow bandwidths can be tolerated.

Some surface wave filters fabricated from the same mask at the same time and on substrates cut from the same crystal plate have intolerable parameter differences even when measured at the same temperature. This is particularly true for highly dispersive filters. Ovens can be used to heat differentially two such nominally identical devices when phase and amplitude characteristics must be held within exceptionally close tolerance. Heating is one of the few practical ways of varying the operating characteristics of surface wave filters after they have been designed and fabricated.

The thermal environment of a crystal substrate can be controlled by an oven or heater that heats the entire filter package. An alternate method is a heater that only elevates the crystal temperature. Package ovens and heaters are generally used because they are readily available and easy to use, but they have two major disadvantages. Package ovens are large and it is difficult to put semiconductor electronics in the same package because of the high operating temperature. As with any heating method, the oven must be operated at or above the maximum expected temperature of the environment. This could be, in some instances, a temperature of 70°C. When package heaters are used (as shown in Fig. 5.19c) considerable insulation is required around the package. Also, when the package is large and the package material has a large specific heat, long warm-up time and thermal lag can be a problem. Placement of the package heater (and sensor) should be as close to the crystal substrate as possible.

Most of the heating required for surface wave filters delivered for installation in systems has been obtained from *package ovens or heaters.* However the author has investigated mounting and insulation techniques so that a strip or film heater can be effectively attached or deposited *directly* to the crystal substrate without appreciable heat loss into the entire package. Experiments were performed to determine the feasibility of *direct crystal heating.*

The first experiment determined the power required to heat continuously a crystal to various temperatures above a 22°C ambient temperature and demonstrated that a shock absorbing foam material can provide adequate thermal insulation between heater and case. A 100 Ω resistive heater strip 3 in. long, $\frac{7}{8}$ in. wide, and $\frac{1}{16}$ in. thick was laminated with RTV onto a sheet of $\frac{1}{8}$ in. thick shock absorbing foam. A lithium niobate substrate *approximately the same area as the heater* was bonded to the heater strip with silver loaded RTV. The foam side of this assembly was mounted with RTV into the channel of a U-shaped aluminum extrusion 7 in. long with a $1\frac{1}{4}$ in. channel and $\frac{3}{8}$ in. wall thickness. A thermal probe wedged between the crystal and the heater strip and another on the case (aluminum extrusion) measured the heater and case temperatures for various dc voltages applied to the heater strip. Each voltage was maintained for several hours to establish thermal equilibrium and temperature data were taken.

Heater power per square inch is plotted versus heater and case temperatures in Fig. 5.22. The large divergence between the two curves with increasing temperature indicates the foam to be a good thermal insulating material as well as a good substrate mount as previously discussed. The

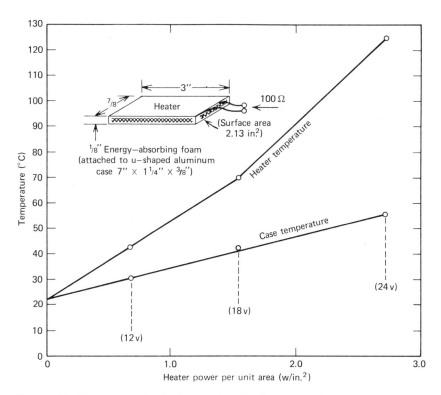

Figure 5.22 Design curves for implementation of a direct crystal heater for a surface wave device thermally insulated from its package.

curves in Fig. 5.22 can be used as a guide for heater strip requirements for various size surface wave crystals operated over a given range of ambient temperatures. The curves in Fig. 5.22 can be shifted up or down to correspond to the lowest operating ambient temperature, and the power required to maintain the heater and crystal at a desired temperature can be found. The ambient temperature for the curves in Fig. 5.22 is 22°C. The two curves intersect at 22°C and zero power. If the lowest ambient temperature is 0°C, the curves should be shifted down so they intersect at 0°C and zero power. The *highest* ambient temperature at which the device is to operate should be about 10°C below the desired operating temperature. It should be remembered these curves are for *continuous* power input, and at least twice the predicted power would be needed for a heater controller that usually operates below its maximum capacity. When the required power per unit area of crystal substrate is determined, the heater resistance can be calculated. If a metal film heater is to be deposited on the back side of the crystal, its sheet resistivity can be similarly determined.

The *surface* temperature of the crystal substrate is the important parameter to measure for controlling the temperature of a surface wave filter. Therefore the temperature sensor should be mounted on the polished surface of the crystal. Also, the sensor should be considerably smaller than the crystal so that it can react quickly to temperature changes and does not thermally load the crystal. These requirements are probably best met with a transistor chip that can be readily mounted, biased, and connected to close a feedback loop between the crystal heater and a proportional controller. This technique was explored in a second experiment. Suitable aluminum pads were fabricated on a lithium niobate crystal along with two transducers. A 2N222A transistor chip was mounted with conductive epoxy on the appropriate aluminum pad. The collector, emitter, and base of the transistor were wire bonded to other pads that were connected to small terminals mounted to the package. The transistor chip was biased with external resistors to form a simple dc amplifier. The surface temperature can be determined for various heater power inputs from the base to emitter voltage versus temperature curve and the gain of the transistor. It was found that the *lithium niobate surface* temperature differed by less than 2°C from the *heater* temperatures previously measured and plotted in Fig. 5.22. Thus the thermal resistance of a 0.070 in. thick lithium niobate crystal substrate is relatively small, and a transistor chip is an acceptable temperature sensor.

The feedstructure can be defined as the physical network or point from which the electrical signal is launched to a transducer on a crystal substrate, and its format depends on the frequency of operation and the type of interdigital array to which it is connected. Short transducers with few electrodes have relatively small interelectrode capacitance. When feeding short transducers it is of paramount importance to minimize the parasitic capacitance associated with the feedstructure, because the larger the parasitic capacitance, the greater the insertion loss required to preserve the acoustic response of the device. Since the interconnections between transducer pads and electrical feedstructures are usually made with thermocompression bonded gold wires, one of the best tie points, for short transducers, is nothing more than a low capacitance package feedthrough or stand-off terminal (see Fig. 5.16). Such terminals are readily available, can be easily secured to a package housing, and can be placed conveniently near the ends or adjacent to a crystal substrate. Particularly at high frequencies, these terminal points should be mounted as close to the transducer as possible to minimize the series inductance associated with a thin gold wire.

Long transducers are best fed with the current flow perpendicular to the crystal propagation axis and parallel to the propagating surface to reduce inherent electromagnetic distributed effects. At frequencies less than 50 MHz, distributed resistance is the predominant factor to be considered. If an extended array is fed at only one point, resistive losses associated with the thin metal transducer pads increase with distance from the feed point. The effect amplitude weights the electrode response, and influences the transfer characteristics of the surface wave device. Figure 5.19a shows two low frequency dispersive delay lines that use a low resistance *distributed* feedstructure. These feedstructures are gold plated copper strips insulated from the package that run parallel to the crystal axis and extend the length of the transducer pads. The transducer pads are connected to the metal strips by numerous gold wires bonded along the full length of the transducer. The metal strips are electrically fed through to the matching networks located in compartments on the opposite side of the package (see Fig. 5.19c). Thus the highly conductive metal feed strips shunt the lossy transducer pads and allow the array to be excited by a potential with spatially uniform amplitude and phase. If the transducers are not too long, a side feedstructure utilizing microstrip matching networks (see Fig. 5.18) can be used effectively at higher frequencies (300 MHz) to overcome distributed resistance and reactance.[7] When the transducer length and frequency are too great to circumvent distributed effects with side feedstructures, it is necessary to consider the total electromagnetic distributed circuit consisting of the array, feedstructure, and respective matching network.[8]

Transducers have metal thicknesses that typically range from 500 to 5000 Å. Therefore conventional wire soldering or gap welding are not feasible methods of connecting transducers with feedstructures. To date, the only practical interconnect techniques known to the author and used by most surface wave fabricators are ultrasonic and thermocompression wire bonding. These techniques are widely used in the semiconductor and microcircuit industries and have been adapted to surface wave filter fabrication. Whether ultrasonic or thermocompression, these wire bonding methods can interconnect silver, copper, gold, and aluminum pads with 0.7 to 2.0 mil diameter gold or aluminum wire. The ultrasonic wire bonder attaches aluminum or gold wires using pressure and ultrasonic energy that converts to heat. The thermocompression wire bonder attaches only gold wire using heat and pressure. With a thermocompression wire bonder, heat can be delivered to the work through a bonding capillary, a heated stage, or both. Although both ultrasonic and thermocompression bonding can be readily used to attach wires between transducers and electromagnetic feedstructures, thermocompression bonding is preferred by the author. An ultrasonic wire bonder requires no direct heat, but the ultrasonic forces can easily crack a crystal if it is not properly clamped to the bonding stage or appropriately mounted in its package. The heated stage thermocompression bonder requires the total crystal to be heated. This is difficult for long crystals or when a crystal is already packaged. Also, care must be exercised to avoid thermally shocking the crystal.

The optimum wire bonder is a *pulsed* thermocompression bonder in which electrically controlled heat is applied across the bonding capillary for a controlled period of time. This method can be used directly to bond wire between transducer and feedstructure after the crystal has been mounted in its package. It is also more reliable and efficient than initially bonding wires to the transducers and then mounting the crystal into its package. Usually the latter method requires attaching the wires to the feedstructure with indium solder or noncorrosive conductive epoxy. Solder and flux can splatter when heated, whereas epoxy is time consuming (mixing and curing) and messy to use.

Figures 5.16, 5.17c, and 5.19c show three different techniques for packaging and mounting lumped element components for matching or interface networks. The lumped elements used in Fig. 5.16 are balanced and unbalanced broadband transformers[9] mounted in separate compartments on standoff and feedthrough terminals. This packaging and mounting is easy to implement and can be readily altered. Although somewhat frequency limited it is most desirable for breadboard and prototype devices. Figure 5.19c shows a modular printed circuit board matching network designed to mount with four screws and four solder connections. The crystal can be mounted and wires bonded in the package while the matching networks are being fabricated elsewhere. Also, because the crystal is located in a separately covered cavity on the opposite side of the package, the matching networks can be inserted or removed at any time without exposing the crystal to environmental damage during that operation. Whereas the surface wave devices in Figs. 5.16 and 5.19c operate below 50 MHz, the device in Fig. 5.17 operates at 150 MHz. Because of the planar arrangement of the stripline feeds, the lumped series tuning inductor for each of the 16 inputs was imbedded in separate vertical drilled holes. One inductor lead was flattened and gold plated to allow gold wire bonding *directly* from it to one side of the appropriate input transducer (see Fig. 5.17b). The other lead of each inductor was soldered to ground on the component side of the package (see Fig. 5.17c). By placing the inductor in the ground side of the transducer feedline, the shunt parasitic capacitance essentially paralleled the inductor. This only changes its effective inductance and can be readily compensated. If the inductor is placed in the high side of the transducer feedline, the shunt parasitic capacitance between it and ground makes it a transmission line that transforms the transducer impedance to an unpredicted value.

In each of the preceding examples, the components associated with the input and output matching networks were shielded in individual compartments to prevent unwanted electromagnetic coupling. The 16 inputs in the planar package were also isolated from the five outputs by using separate vertically interconnected stripline boards.

At frequencies greater than 100 MHz, it can be advantageous to design feedstructures and matching networks using distributed elements. In the package shown in Fig. 5.17, the multiple input/output requirement lent itself well to distributed (stripline) design and fabrication techniques. The multiple inputs and outputs could have been made with semirigid coax, but a more complex package structure would have been required. Also, stripline has the added advantage that, within practical limits, the characteristic impedance of the feedlines can be specified over a continuous range of values. Stripline design and fabrication are outside the scope of this book. There are numerous texts available.[10]

The use of microstrip for distributed matching of surface wave transducers has the distinct advantage of maintaining continuity of planar design for optimum packaging. Figure 5.18 is a good example of the unique construction that can be achieved. The microstrip matching substrates (0.025 in. thick alumina) as well as the strip grounds (opposite side and adjacent to the crystal) are clad with copper/gold metal (0.5 mil thick total) on the top surface for gold wire bonding directly to the transducers. The bottom surfaces of the substrates are copper only for compatible soldering into the box. The box is a milled aluminum, nickel plated package with flash tin plating in the interior. The tin plating allows the substrates to be easily soldered into the box using a hot plate and ribbon solder (97% tin and 3% silver). Not only does the soldering make the substrates an integral part of the box, but in conjunction with the thick copper metal it also keeps resistive losses to a minimum. In this device small resistive loss is particularly important because of the extremely low radiation resistance associated with the dispersive transducers. Without matching, this device had a 50 dB insertion loss. With microstrip matching, the insertion loss decreased 15 to 20 dB. A tight fitting cover with an electrostatic shield to separate input from output keeps the electromagnetic suppression of this surface wave device well below 40 dB. The matching networks were based on the shunt design previously discussed. Shunt design and the appropriate microstrip fabrication equations[11] are the key ingredients in designing similar matching circuits for other high frequency surface wave devices requiring distributed elements.

Acknowledgments. The author would like to express his grateful appreciation for specific contributions made to this chapter, both directly and indirectly, by Frank Kandra (packaging), Chuck Stout (crystal substrates), and Lauda Yarber (photo fabrication). Also with regard to pertinent information on acoustic surface wave theory, the author would like to thank Dr. W. R. Smith and Dr. H. M. Gerard. Special appreciation is also appropriate for the time, effort, and invaluable comments contributed by Dr. T. W. Bristol in reviewing this chapter. Further acknowledgment is made to Hughes Aircraft Company and the U.S. Army Electronics Command, Fort Monmouth, New Jersey, for their courtesy in allowing photographs and other contractually generated information to appear in this chapter.

References

1. W. R. Smith et al. "Analysis of interdigital surface wave transducers by use of an equivalent circuit model." *IEEE Trans.* **MTT-17,** 856 (1969).

2. M. D. Adams et al. "Experimental verification of a new surface elastic wave bandpass filter synthesis technique," in J. de Klerk, Ed., *Proc. 1973 IEEE Ultrasonics Symposium,* IEEE, New York, 1973, pp. 433–436.

3. L. T. Claiborne et al. "VHF/UHF bandpass filters using surface acoustic wave technology." *Microwave J.* **17(5),** 35 (1974).

4. R. D. Weglein et al. "Diffraction spreading of surface waves on LiNbO$_3$." *Electron. Lett.* **6,** 654 (1970).

5. A. J. Budreau et al. "Multiple channel VHF frequency synthesizer using acoustic surface wave filters," in J. de Klerk, Ed., *Proc.* 1973 *IEEE Ultrasonics Symposium,* IEEE, New York, 1973, pp. 464–467.

6. M. B. Schultz et al. "Surface acoustic wave delay lines with small temperature coefficient." *Proc. IEEE* **58,** 1361 (1970).

7. H. M. Gerard et al. "Development of a broadband, low loss 1000:1 dispersive filter," in J. de Klerk, Ed., *Proc.* 1972 *IEEE Ultrasonics Symposium,* IEEE, New York, 1972, pp. 253–261.

8. J. Heighway et al. "Simple approach to the design of interface networks for acoustic surface wave filters, *Electron. Lett.* **8,** 642 (12972).

9. C. L. Ruthroff, "Some broad-band transformers." Proc. IRE **47,** 1337 (1957).

10. G. L. Matthaei et al. *Microwave Filters, Impedance Matching Networks and Coupling Structures,* McGraw-Hill, New York, 1964, pp. 168–174.

11. A. Presser. "RF properties of microstrip line." Microwaves **7(3),** 53 (1968).

SIX

Surface Wave Bandpass Filters

ADRIAN J. DEVRIES

Zenith Radio Corporation
Elk Grove Village, Illinois

In electronic systems, filters passing certain frequency bands and rejecting others are of prime importance, and in this chapter the frequency dependence of surface wave bandpass filters is highlighted. Techniques to predict the frequency response are discussed, presently available synthesis procedures are surveyed, and some of the many possible circuit configurations are shown.

Surface wave bandpass filters compete with filtering devices that have been developed over several decades and are firmly intrenched. Lumped-element passive filters using capacitors, inductors and resistors, and active filters using amplifiers can be realized for the broad frequency range from 0.1 Hz to 1 GHz. Filters using distributed electrical networks, transmission lines, or waveguides have a useful frequency range above 100 MHz. Filters using electro-mechanical resonators—quartz crystals, for instance—can be very selective: 0.1% bandwidth. These can be realized in the frequency range from 1 kHz to 100 MHz.

Surface wave filters closely resemble electrical filters using distributed elements, with the difference that the surface wave velocity in solids is about 10^5 times as low as the electromagnetic wave velocity in air. This ratio brings the useful frequency range for surface wave filters to about 1 MHz to 3 GHz, the lower limit being dictated by the size of the substrate, the upper limit by the ability to fabricate the transducers.

In electronic filters the response must often be very accurately controlled. Calculation of the response of *LC* filters (the class most frequently used) is relatively straightforward, and powerful synthesis techniques have been developed over a period of many years.[1,2] The techniques for analysis and synthesis of surface wave filters are not yet mature enough to permit their potential to be fully evaluated for applications where precisely controlled characteristics are required. Compared to an *LC* filter, a surface wave filter will always be a complicated structure, with many side effects complicating its analysis and synthesis.

Surface wave filters have, however, some strong advantages. They belong to the class of non-minimum-phase networks;[3] therefore, in principle, any amplitude and phase response can be realized over a given frequency band by the very powerful Fourier transform design technique that relates the structure of the transducer directly to its frequency response. Furthermore the stability of such a filter is determined by a solid element; once designed and fabricated it cannot be detuned. All critical dimensions are established by photolithographic techniques, and no precise substrate dimensions need be maintained.

6.1 Selectivity of a Surface Wave Transducer

A surface wave filter usually has two transducers, and the frequency response of the filter is the product of the two transducer responses. Analysis of the filter response begins with analysis of the frequency dependence of its transducers. Several methods are used. The vector model, often called the delta function model, is the simplest method. A second method depends on calculating a Fourier transform, and a third method makes use of the transmission line model. Fourier transform and delta function analysis of transducer frequency response are discussed in Chapters 2 and 3. In this chapter the transmission line model is used to determine the selectivity characteristics of surface wave transducers.

Transducer Selectivity by the Transmission Line Model. The starting point for analysis is representation of a periodic section, length *L*, of the line by a pair of Mason equivalent circuits for piezoelectric transducers,[4] each of length *L*/2. This pair of circuits forms a three-port: two acoustic ports and one electrical port. Smith et al.[5] give two models, the so-called *crossed-field* equivalent circuit model and the *in-line* model. In this chapter only the crossed-field model is discussed, because it describes quite accurately the now widely used split-connected transducer to be discussed later.

Figure 6.1b shows the crossed-field model for a transducer with N interdigital periods (Fig. 6.1a). In the model, N three-ports are acoustically in cascade but electrically in parallel. Voltages V_1 and V_2 represent surface waves at the left and right ends of the transducer; V_3 is the voltage across the electrical port of the model. Generator E_1, which has an internal admittance equal to the acoustic characteristic admittance Y_0 of the transducer, represents a surface wave impinging from the left. The model is terminated at the right with an equal admittance Y_0. The external admittance at the electrical port is Y_L. In order to simplify calculations the total clamped capacitance NC_0 of the transducer fingers is regarded as a part of the (external) load (Fig. 6.1c). The internal part of the model is thus made independent of the coupling constant. The quantities C_0 and Y_0 are related as

$$\omega_0 C_0 = \frac{2\pi Y_0}{k_s^2} \tag{6.1}$$

where k_s is the electromechanical coupling constant for surface waves.

In circuit theory a symmetrical transducer is represented by an admittance matrix equation:*

$$\begin{bmatrix} I_1 \\ I_2 \\ I_3 \end{bmatrix} = \begin{bmatrix} Y_{11} & Y_{12} & Y_{13} \\ Y_{12} & Y_{11} & -Y_{13} \\ Y_{13} & -Y_{13} & Y_{33} \end{bmatrix} \begin{bmatrix} V_1 \\ V_2 \\ V_3 \end{bmatrix} \tag{6.2}$$

In Table 6.1 the four admittance parameters Y_{ij} are listed for complex and purely imaginary values of the propagation constant.[5] The expressions for a purely imaginary value of the propagation constant can be used with a substrate material having low acoustic loss, such as lithium niobate. For PZT, in which the transmission loss is as much as a few tenths of a decibel per wavelength, it is often necessary to use expressions with a complex value of the propagation constant in order to obtain reasonable agreement with empirical results. These are obtained from the Mason circuit by replacing trigonometric functions by hyperbolic functions.

The frequency response of an interdigital transducer is obtained from the admittance parameters. The terminal voltages of the equivalent circuit

---

* The notation in ref. 5 is followed here, where y_{ij} is reserved for the elemental transducers and Y_{ij} for the entire transducer. The elemental-transducer parameters y_{ij} are not discussed here.

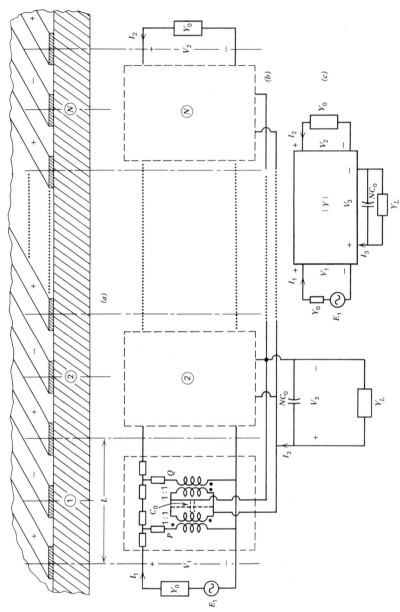

Figure 6.1 Crossed-field transmission line model. (*a*) Substrate with a transducer having N finger pairs. (*b*) Each block represents the equivalent circuit for a pair of elemental transducers. Generator E_1 represents an acoustic wave impinging from the left. A capacitance C_0 is associated with each block. In the approach followed here the total capacitance NC_0 is considered a part of the load. (*c*) Same as (*b*), with the transducer shown as a three-port.

model (see Fig. 6.1c) are

$$V_1 = E_1 - \frac{I_1}{Y_0}$$

$$V_2 = -\frac{I_2}{Y_0} \qquad\qquad\qquad (6.3)$$

$$V_3 = -\frac{I_3}{Y_T}$$

where $Y_T = Y_L + j\omega NC_0$.

Solving (6.3) for I_3 yields

$$\frac{I_3}{E_1} = \frac{Y_0 Y_{13} Y_T}{(Y_T + Y_{33})(Y_0 + Y_{11} - Y_{12}) - 2Y_{13}^2}$$

This can be represented by a Norton equivalent circuit (Fig. 6.2) with a current source

$$I_{3,0} = \frac{Y_0 Y_{13}}{Y_0 + Y_{11} - Y_{12}} E_1 \qquad\qquad (6.4)$$

with the current $I_{3,0}$ flowing through the parallel combination of admittance Y_T and the internal admittance $Y_{3,0}$ given by

$$Y_{3,0} = \frac{Y_{33}(Y_0 + Y_{11} - Y_{12}) - 2Y_{13}^2}{Y_0 + Y_{11} - Y_{12}} \qquad\qquad (6.5)$$

Table 6.1 also shows the admittance parameters Y_{ij} for $\alpha = 0$ in the neighborhood of the synchronous frequency ω_0 (i.e., $\Delta\omega/\omega_0 \ll 1$). At ω_0

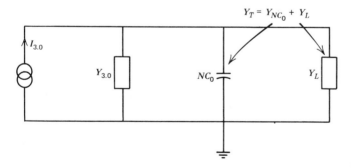

Figure 6.2 Equivalent circuit for a transducer. An impinging wave is represented by a current source $I_{3,0}$. The current flows through the parallel combination of the driving-point admittance of the transducer $Y_{3,0}$, the capacitance NC_0, and the load admittance Y_L.

Table 6.1   Values of the Coefficients Y_{11}, Y_{12}, Y_{13}, and Y_{33} for three cases[a]

	Lossy Substrate $\gamma = \alpha + j\beta$ $\alpha \neq 0$	Lossless Substrate $\omega = \omega_0 + \Delta\omega$ $\alpha = 0, \quad \gamma = j\beta$	Lossless Substrate $\Delta\omega \ll \omega_0$ $\delta = \dfrac{\Delta\omega}{\omega_0} 2\pi$ $\alpha = 0$
Y_{11}	$\dfrac{1}{R_0} \coth\left(N\gamma L\right)$	$\dfrac{-j}{R_0} \cot\left(2\pi N \dfrac{\Delta\omega}{\omega_0}\right)$	$\dfrac{-j}{R_0\,\delta N}$
Y_{12}	$\dfrac{-1}{R_0 \sinh\left(N\gamma L\right)}$	$\dfrac{j}{R_0 \sin\left(2\pi N \dfrac{\Delta\omega}{\omega_0}\right)}$	$\dfrac{j}{R_0\,\delta N}$
Y_{13}	$\dfrac{-1}{R_0} \tanh\left(\dfrac{\gamma L}{4}\right)$	$\dfrac{j}{R_0} \cot\left(\dfrac{\Delta\omega}{\omega_0}\dfrac{\pi}{2}\right)$	$\dfrac{j4}{R_0\,\delta}$
Y_{33}	$\dfrac{4N}{R_0} \tanh\left(\dfrac{\gamma L}{4}\right)$	$\dfrac{-j4N}{R_0} \cot\left(\dfrac{\Delta\omega}{\omega_0}\dfrac{\pi}{2}\right)$	$\dfrac{-j16N}{R_0\,\delta}$

[a] In all cases the capacitance NC_0 is considered to be part of the external circuit.

(6.4) and (6.5) reduce to

$$I_{3,0}\big|_{\omega=\omega_0} = 2E_1 N Y_0$$

and

$$Y_{3,0}\big|_{\omega=\omega_0} = 8N^2 Y_0$$

Normalizing $I_{3,0}$ and $Y_{3,0}$ with respect to their values at ω_0 yields

$$I' = \frac{I_{3,0}}{2E_1 N Y_0}$$

and   (6.6)

$$Y' = \frac{Y_{3,0}}{8N^2 Y_0}$$

This normalization permits a relatively small number of curves to display the selectivity properties of surface wave transducers.

Using (6.4), (6.5), and (6.6), the amplitude of I' and the value of Y' in magnitude and phase can be computed for different values of N. These quantities are plotted in Figs. 6.3 and 6.4; note that the quantity $|I'|$ is plotted on a logarithmic scale. Also note again that for the purpose of obtaining universal curves the clamped capacitance NC_0 is considered part of the external load. A normalized frequency variable $\Delta\omega' = N\Delta\omega/\omega_0$

is used in these plots, so that the main lobe occupies the range $0 \leq \Delta\omega' < 1$ and the first side lobes the range $1 < \Delta\omega' < 2$. The transfer function and the magnitude of the admittance are even functions of $\Delta\omega'$, and the phase of the admittance is an odd function of $\Delta\omega'$. The figures show that for $N \geq 5$, the curves are practically identical. Thus it is possible to construct universal response curves for interdigital transducers—within a limited range, however, because variations in these curves increase at large values of $\Delta\omega'$.

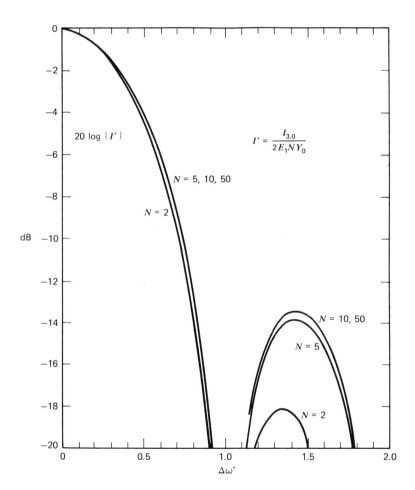

Figure 6.3 The normalized current $I' = I_{3,0}/2E_1NY_0$ is shown as a function of the normalized frequency $\Delta\omega'$ for different values of N. It appears that the curves are nearly identical for large values of N.

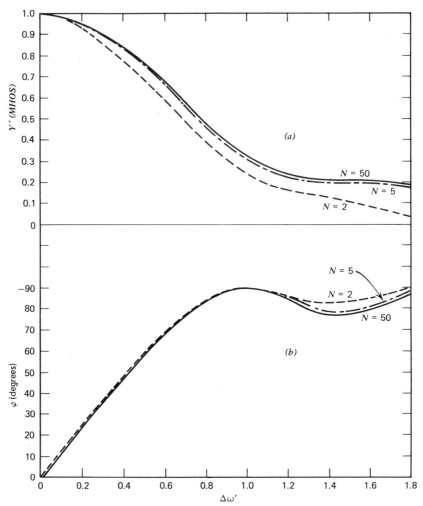

Figure 6.4 (a) Magnitude and (b) phase of the normalized driving-point admittance $Y' = Y_{3,0}/8N^2 Y_0$ (excluding the capacitance NC_0) of a transducer as a function of the normalized frequency $\Delta\omega'$ for several values of N. It appears that the curves are nearly identical for large values of N.

The preceding results are now utilized to calculate the transfer function for two different classes of transducer termination,—resistive and tuned.

Universal Response Curves for Transducers. Suppose a narrow-band transducer ($\Delta\omega/\omega_0 \ll 1$) is terminated with a conductive load admittance $Y_L = 8N^2 Y_0/p$ as shown in Fig. 6.5. This figure is similar to Fig. 6.2; the

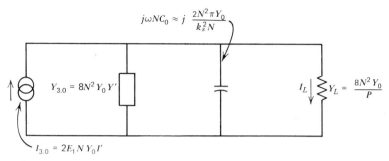

Figure 6.5   Equivalent circuit for calculating the frequency response of a surface wave transducer terminated with a normalized resistive-load admittance $Y_L = 8N^2 Y_0/p$.

quantities $I_{3,0}$, $Y_{3,0}$, and NC_0 are expressed in their normalized values as defined in (6.1) and (6.6). The three admittances in Fig. 6.5 all have the terms $N^2 Y_0$ in common, and for any normalized frequency $\Delta\omega'$ the ratio between the load current and the total source current $I_{3,0}$ is determined by only two exterior parameters, $k_s^2 N$ and p. Therefore a family of universal frequency response curves can be plotted with $k_s^2 N$ and p as parameters. Figure 6.6 shows an example in which the normalized transfer loss $20 \log 4NV_3/E_1$ is plotted as a function of the normalized frequency $\Delta\omega'$ for a value of $k_s^2 N$ of 0.5 and with p as a parameter. (For the meaning of V_3 and E_1 see Fig. 6.1c.) The value $p = 2/\pi$ corresponds to approximately optimum power transfer to the load. Note that for decreasing values of p the response curve approaches a $\sin x/x$ curve. The phase response (not shown) is not linear, the deviation from linearity being greater for larger values of p. Both frequency and phase response are discussed later, where it is shown that for split-connected transducers there is good agreement between theory and experiment.

Very often the clamped capacitance NC_0 is the principal part of the transducer load and causes significant mismatch losses. Tuning this capacitance with a coil (Fig. 6.7) can significantly reduce these losses, but the effect on the overall response is considerable.

As before, universal frequency response curves can be plotted by introducing a normalized resistive load admittance $Y_L = 8N^2 Y_0/p$, where p is again a normalizing parameter. Figure 6.8 shows a family of normalized transfer loss curves as a function of $\Delta\omega'$ for $k_s N = 2.2$, with $p = 0.5, 1, 2, 4$, and 8. Note that the important parameter here is $k_s N$, whereas it was $k_s^2 N$ with a resistive termination.

The frequency response of the transducer is considerably affected by the tuned circuit—especially with a large resistive load (i.e., a high value of Q). If loading approaches the shorted condition, the output voltage

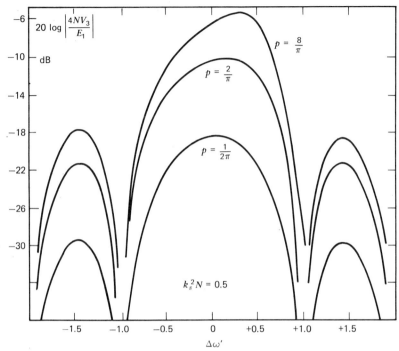

Figure 6.6 Normalized frequency response curves as described by the equivalent circuit of Fig. 6.5, with $k_s^2 N = 0.5$, for three values of an impedance-matching parameter p. The matching is about optimum for $p = 2/\pi$.

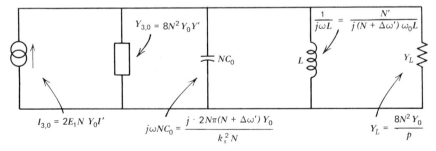

Figure 6.7 Equivalent circuit for calculating the frequency response of a surface wave transducer in which the capacitance NC_0 is tuned with an inductance L to the synchronous frequency ω_0 and is terminated with a normalized resistive-load admittance $Y_L = 8N^2 Y_0/p$. Compare with Fig. 6.5.

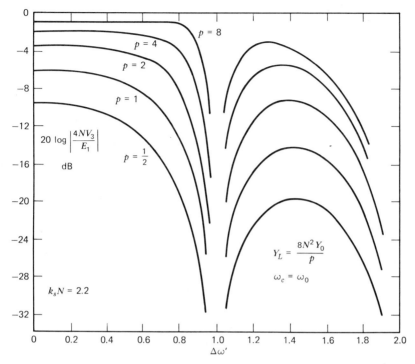

Figure 6.8 Normalized frequency response curves of surface wave transducers described by the equivalent circuit of Fig. 6.7, with $k_s N = 2.2$, for several values of p. The response is symmetrical around ω_0.

and current approach a $\sin x/x$ function. Figure 6.8 shows only the frequency response for positive values of $\Delta\omega'$, because the response is symmetrical if the resonance frequency ω_c of the load equals the synchronous frequency ω_0 of the transducer. Figure 6.9 shows the effect of ω_c not being equal to ω_0. Note that the response at the high end of the main lobe decreases if the electrical circuit is tuned to higher frequencies.

The frequency response of any transducer can be obtained with the aid of the universal response curves if the model parameters can be related to the physical properties of the transducer. The simplest way to relate the model parameters to the physical quantities is first to calculate or measure the clamped capacitance NC_0. For a transducer with N finger pairs of length l meters on an isotropic substrate with dielectric constant ϵ_r it can be approximated by $NC_0 = 2N\epsilon_0\epsilon_r l$ Farad. The quantity Y_0 can be derived from (6.1) if the coupling factor k_s is known. Although an estimate of the coupling factor can be obtained from a measurement of v_s and Δv_s[5] ($k_s^2 = -2\Delta v_s/v_s$), where Δv_s is the change in surface wave velocity due to

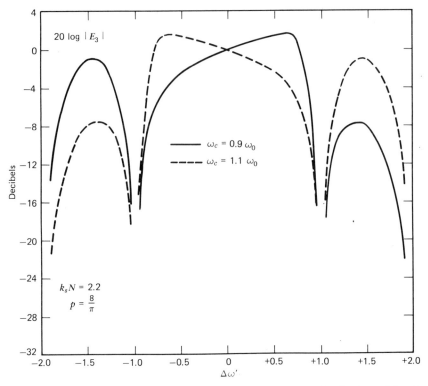

Figure 6.9 As in Fig. 6.8, with tuning frequencies ω_c of the circuit—formed by the capacitance NC_0 and the inductance L—different from the synchronous frequency ω_0.

metalizing the piezoelectric substrate, a more precise figure can be obtained by measuring the particular transducer structure.

Effect of Reflections on the Selectivity of Transducers. At the time the transmission line model was proposed and published it was thought to give a good description of an interdigital transducer with so-called *solid* fingers. Agreement between model and experimental frequency response was only fair, however, and experimental data for reflections from the transducer even contradicted predictions based on the model.

Calculation of reflections based on the transmission line model runs as follows: In Fig. 6.1b an impinging wave is represented by generator E_1 with internal admittance Y_0. By means of (6.2) and (6.3) the acoustic admittance $Y_A = I_1/V_1$ at the left port can be found; the rather lengthy calculation yields

$$Y_A = \frac{Y_0^2 Y_{33} - 2 Y_{12} Y_{13}^2 - 2 Y_{11} Y_{13}^2 - Y_0 Y_{13}^2 + Y_{11} Y_0 Y_{33} + Y_T(Y_{11} Y_0 + Y_0^2)}{Y_0 Y_{33} + Y_{11} Y_{33} - Y_{13}^2 + Y_T(Y_0 + Y_{11})}$$

From this the reflection coefficient ρ, defined as

$$\rho = \frac{Y_A - Y_0}{Y_A + Y_0}$$

can now be calculated. An example is shown in Fig. 6.10 (solid curve) for $Y_L = 0$ (i.e., $R_L = \infty$). Instead of performing the straight forward but tedious computation, certain results can be derived from Fig. 6.1b by inspection. For example, shorting the electrical output terminals (i.e., $Y_L = \infty$ or $R_L = 0$) effectively connects points P and Q of all sections of the transducer, and shorts these points to the base connection. Because the transmission line is then terminated on both sides with its characteristic admittance Y_0, no reflections occur at the input and output; that is,

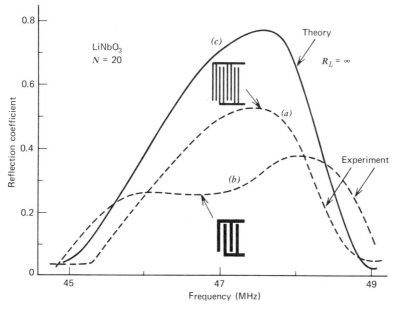

Figure 6.10 Open-circuit reflection coefficient as a function of frequency. (a) Measured values for a split-connected surface wave transducer. (b) Measured values for a transducer with solid fingers. (c) Reflection coefficient for both transducers as predicted by the transmission line model. Copyright 1973 by The Institute of Electrical and Electronic Engineers, Inc. Reprinted, with permission, from *Proc. 1973 Ultrasonics Symposium*, p. 407.

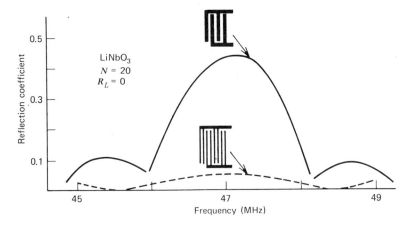

Figure 6.11 Measured short-circuit reflection coefficient as a function of frequency for a split-connected surface wave transducer and for a transducer with solid fingers. The transmission line model predicts zero reflection for the short-circuit condition. Copyright 1973 by The Institute of Electrical and Electronic Engineers, Inc. Reprinted, with permission, from *Proc. 1973 Ultrasonics Symposium*, p. 407.

$\rho = 0$. The same result is obtained from the preceding calculation. Figure 6.11 shows the results of reflection measurements on transducers on lithium niobate[6] for $Y_L = Y_T = \infty$ (i.e., $R_L = 0$). It appears from the solid curve that the reflection coefficient for combs with solid fingers under the shorted condition is not at all zero. The dashed curve is discussed later.

The Split-Connected Transducer.

It is possible to analyze qualitatively the frequency dependence of the reflections from a transducer,[6] and the rather complicated behavior is well understood. The main cause of reflections from a shorted solid finger on LiNbO$_3$ is that the fingers short the electric field component of the wave. The fingers are spaced by $\lambda/2$ and reflections from the fingers reinforce each other at the synchronous frequency. The reflection coefficient for a shorted transducer will be called the *short circuit reflection coefficient*.

The preceding reflections are eliminated in the transducer[6] shown in Fig. 6.12, in which each finger is split into two. The center-to-center distance of two adjoining finger pairs stays $\lambda/2$, the same as the center-to-center spacing of the fingers in the solid comb of Fig. 6.11. Reflections due to adjacent fingers now cancel each other if the transducer is shorted, and a calculation shows that the overall reflection coefficient is very small at the synchronous frequency of the transducer, as shown in Fig. 6.12b.

The measured dashed curve in Fig. 6.11 shows that the short circuit reflections of a split-connected transducer indeed approach zero.

For a nonzero load impedance the reflections can be calculated using circuit theory; no details have to be known about the structure of the transducer. The reflections can be considered caused by the (electrical) voltage across the output transducer, and for noninductive loads they are maximum for the open circuit condition (Fig. 6.10) because the voltage is maximum. The reflection coefficient for this mechanism is called the *voltage-reflection coefficient.*

As mentioned, the measured driving-point impedance and frequency response of a transducer with solid fingers do not agree too well with the behavior predicted by the transmission line model. Differences in these

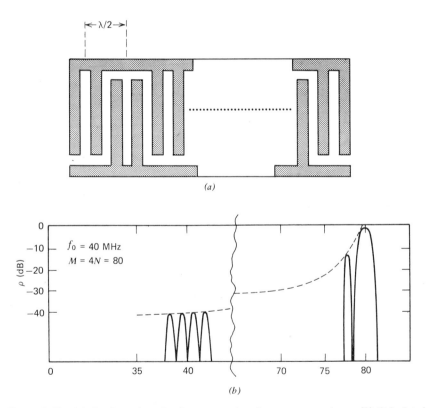

Figure 6.12 (*a*) Configuration of split-connected surface wave transducer. (*b*) Calculated reflection coefficient for a synchronous frequency $f_0 = 40$ MHz. Copyright 1973 by The Institute of Electrical and Electronic Engineers, Inc. Reprinted, with permission, from *Proc. 1972 Ultrasonics Symposium*, p. 357.

quantities are found experimentally also between the solid-finger and the split-connected transducer, as shown in Figs. 6.13 and 6.14. It was postulated[7] that the overall behavior of the split-connected transducer and that predicted by the transmission line model might agree very well with each other; Figs 6.15, 6.16, and 6.17 show that this is indeed the case.

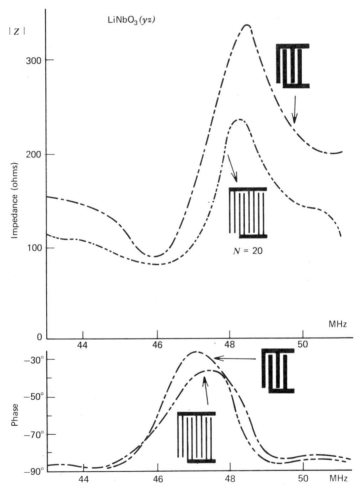

Figure 6.13 Measured phase and magnitude of the driving-point admittances as a function of frequency of a split-connected transducer and of a transducer with solid fingers ($N = 20$). Copyright 1973 by The Institute of Electrical and Electronic Engineers, Inc. Reprinted, with permission, from *Proc. 1973 Ultrasonics Symposium*, p. 408.

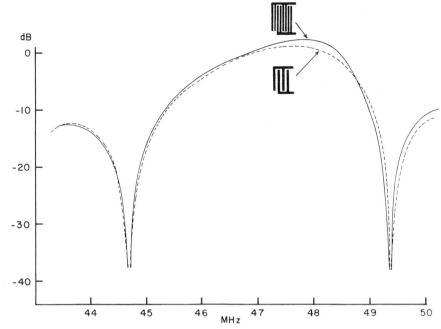

Figure 6.14 Measured open-circuit transfer functions of a split-connected transducer and of a transducer with solid fingers ($N = 20$). A wide-band transducer is used to generate the acoustic wave. Copyright 1973 by The Institute of Electrical and Electronic Engineers, Inc. Reprinted, with permission, from *Proc. 1973 Ultrasonics Symposium*, p. 409.

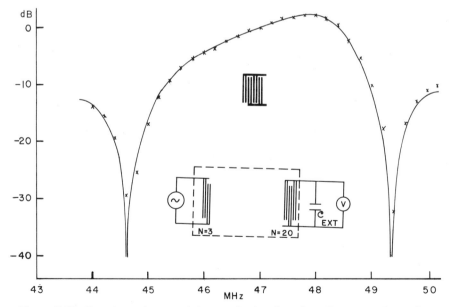

Figure 6.15 Experimental curve of the transfer function of a split-connected transducer compared with calculated values obtained by means of the crossed-field transmission line model. The input transducer is a wide-band transducer. The output transducer has minimum capacitance loading. Copyright 1973 by The Institute of Electrical and Electronic Engineers, Inc. Reprinted, with permission, from *Proc. 1973 Ultrasonics Symposium*, p. 409.

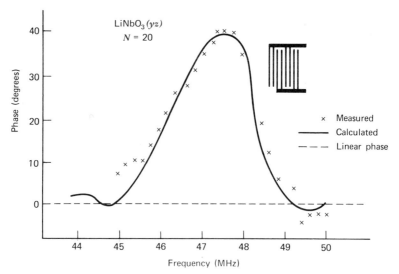

Figure 6.16 Measured deviation from a linear phase response for a split-connected transducer compared with a calculated curve obtained with the crossed-field transmission line model. Copyright 1973 by The Institute of Electrical and Electronic Engineers, Inc. Reprinted, with permission, from *Proc. 1973 Ultrasonics Symposium*, p. 409.

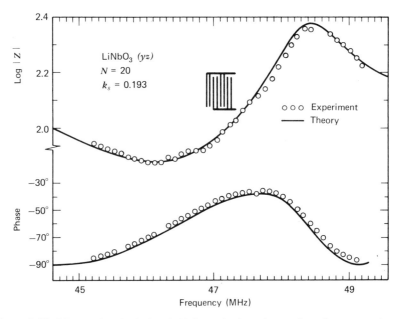

Figure 6.17 Measured and calculated driving-point impedance of a split-connected transducer: (*a*) magnitude, (*b*) phase. The calculated curves were obtained with the crossed-field transmission line model. Copyright 1973 by The Institute of Electrical and Electronic Engineers, Inc. Reprinted, with permission, from *Proc. 1973 Ultrasonics Symposium*, p. 408.

Several modifications to the transmission line model have been suggested in order to make it correspond better to the experimental results for a solid-finger transducer. Milsom and Redwood,[8] for instance, suggested incorporating inactive sections in the transmission line model.

6.2 Filter Response by Means of Admittance Parameters

In this section y parameters are used to obtain the relation between the input and output voltages of a surface wave filter.[9]

A surface wave device containing a number of transducers, reflectors, and directional couplers, but excluding any independent sources or active components, can be treated as a distributed linear network. A voltage source E with internal impedance Z_a is connected to one transducer, and a load impedance Z_b is connected to a second transducer (Fig. 6.18). The pertaining defining equations are

$$I_a = y_{aa} V_a + y_{ab} V_b \qquad (6.7a)$$

$$I_b = y_{ba} V_a + y_{bb} V_b \qquad (6.7b)$$

From these equations follow the short circuit driving-point admittances

$$y_{aa} = \frac{I_a}{V_a}\bigg|_{V_b = 0} \qquad (6.8a)$$

$$y_{bb} = \frac{I_b}{V_b}\bigg|_{V_a = 0} \qquad (6.8b)$$

and the short circuit transfer admittances

$$y_{ab} = \frac{I_a}{V_b}\bigg|_{V_a = 0} \qquad (6.9a)$$

$$y_{ba} = \frac{I_b}{V_a}\bigg|_{V_b = 0} \qquad (6.9b)$$

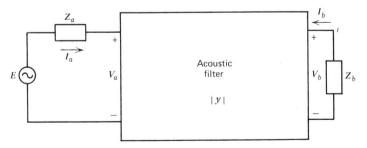

Figure 6.18 Block diagram of an acoustic filter characterized by its short circuit driving-point admittances y_{aa} and y_{bb} and its short circuit transfer admittance y_{ab}.

Because a piezoelectric surface wave device without active elements is a reciprocal network, $y_{ab} = y_{ba}$.

The reason for choosing the short circuit admittance parameters for characterizing a surface wave filter is that the short circuit driving-point admittances y_{aa} and y_{bb} have a simple physical meaning for transducers of the split-connected type. If a split-connected output transducer is shorted, as required by the definition, no waves generated by the input transducer are reflected. The parameter y_{aa} therefore equals the (driving-point) admittance of the input transducer if this were there by itself, provided that no other coherent reflections are caused by any objects on the substrate. A similar reasoning holds for y_{bb}.

The output voltage V_b can now be expressed in E by means of the y parameters, using (6.7a) and (6.7b), together with $E = I_a Z_a + V_a$ and $V_b = -I_b Z_b$:

$$V_b = -\frac{y_{ab} Z_b E}{(1 + y_{aa} Z_a)(1 + y_{bb} Z_b) - y_{ab}^2 Z_a Z_b} \qquad (6.10)$$

The term $y_{ab}^2 Z_a Z_b$ is associated with waves that are reflected from the load and source impedances and is called the *voltage triple transit* contribution (the factor y_{ab}^2 indicates two extra transits of the wave signal), because it is caused by the mechanism responsible for the voltage reflection coefficient defined earlier.

In surface wave acoustics the term *insertion loss* is often loosely used. Because the source and load impedances are often very different, it is better to use the *effective transmission loss*.[10] The effective transmission loss is the difference (in dB) between the power received in the load and the maximum power obtainable from the generator. If in Fig. 6.18 the source and load impedances Z_a and Z_b are assumed to be resistive (i.e., $Z_a = R_a$ and $Z_b = R_b$), the effective transmission loss is defined as

$$20 \log \left| \frac{E}{2 V_b \sqrt{R_b / R_a}} \right| dB$$

It follows, with the aid of (6.10), that the effective transmission loss of a surface wave filter is

$$20 \log \left| \frac{(1 + y_{aa} R_a)(1 + y_{bb} R_b) - y_{ab}^2 R_a R_b}{2 y_{ab} R_2} \sqrt{\frac{R_b}{R_a}} \right| dB \qquad (6.11)$$

The parameters y_{aa}, y_{ab}, and y_{bb} are calculated later. The frequency response and the effective transmission loss can then be calculated.

From (6.10) a voltage triple transit ratio (expressed in dB) can be defined as the ratio between the level of the voltage triple transit and that of the main signal:

$$20 \log \left| \frac{y_{ab}^2 Z_a Z_b}{1 + y_{aa} Z_a + y_{bb} Z_b + y_{aa} y_{bb} Z_a Z_b} \right| \text{dB} \qquad (6.12)$$

In a filter consisting of split-connected transducers, the total triple transit ratio equals the voltage triple transit ratio.

y Parameters of a Filter with Split-Connected Transducers. A surface wave filter with uniform split-connected input and output transducers of equal aperture is shown in Fig. 6.19a. It is schematically represented in Fig. 6.19b by the two pertaining transmission line models (three-port) connected by an acoustic transmission line (two-port) representing the medium in between the transducers. The total resulting electrical two-port is identical to that of Fig. 6.18.

The parameters y_{aa}, y_{bb}, and y_{ab} of the two-port are expressed in the Y parameters of the three-ports. Rather than doing this by a formal matrix calculation, a more instructive step-by-step method is followed.

As explained in the preceding section, the short circuit driving-point admittance of the filter y_{aa} equals the admittance of the input transducer as if it were by itself on the substrate, therefore

$$y_{aa} = Y_{3,0} + j\omega N C_0$$

A similar equation holds for y_{bb}.

The short circuit transfer admittance y_{ab} of the filter is the ratio of the short circuit output current $I_{b,0}$ and the input voltage E_a, as given by (6.9b); see Fig. 6.19c.

The two transducers N and M have, respectively, N and M finger pairs and are separated by a distance d. Both transmission line equivalent circuits are described by matrices like the one in (6.2). The total device can be considered an acoustic transmission line with a characteristic admittance $Y_0 = Y_{0,N} = Y_{0,M}$.

Suppose a voltage generator E is connected to transducer N. From (6.2), with $I_{1,N} = -Y_0 V_{1,N}$ and $I_{2,N} = -Y_0 V_{2,N}$ it follows that

$$V_{2,N} = \left[\frac{Y_{13}}{Y_0 + Y_{11} - Y_{12}} \right]_N V_{3,N} \qquad (6.13)$$

where $V_{3,N} = E$.

Voltage $V_{2,N}$ represents the acoustic wave just to the right of transducer N. The wave impinges on transducer M. Just to the left of this

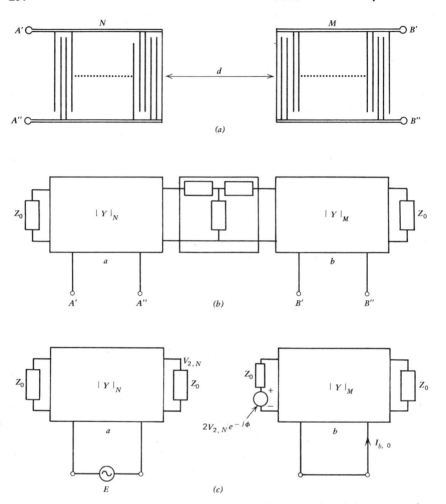

Figure 6.19 Illustrating the calculation of the short circuit transfer admittance y_{ab} of a filter. (a) Two split-connected transducers having N and M elemental transducers. (b) Network with two three-port equivalent circuits representing the transducers, interconnected by a two-port acoustic transmission line. (c) Analysis of the network with notation.

transducer the wave is represented by $V_{2,N}e^{-j\phi}$, where ϕ expresses the delay $\phi = \omega d/v_s$ associated with the distance between the transducers. From (6.4) with $I_{3,0} = I_{b,0}$ and $E_1 = 2V_2e^{-j\phi}$, the following expression can be obtained:

$$\frac{I_{b,0}}{V_{2,N}} = 2\left[\frac{Y_{13}}{Y_0 + Y_{11} - Y_{12}}\right]_M Y_0 e^{-j\phi}$$

The transfer admittance y_{ab} is thus

$$y_{ab} = \frac{I_{b,0}}{E} = 2Y_0 e^{-j\phi} \left[\frac{Y_{13}}{Y_0 + Y_{11} - Y_{12}} \right]_N \cdot \left[\frac{Y_{13}}{Y_0 + Y_{11} - Y_{12}} \right]_M \quad (6.14)$$

It can be remarked that in this formula the terms expressing the selectivity of the N and M transducers are similar. The formula could have been obtained from (6.13) by means of the reciprocity theorem.

To help interpret (6.14) one factor, $(Y_{13})/(Y_0 + Y_{11} - Y_{12})$, is evaluated. Substituting the quantities of the second column of Table 6.1, the following simplification can be made:

$$\left[\frac{Y_{13}}{Y_0 + Y_{11} - Y_{12}} \right]_N = \frac{\cot(\pi/2 \cdot \Delta\omega/\omega_0)}{1 - j[\cot(2\pi N \Delta\omega/\omega_0) + \mathrm{cosec}\,(2\pi N \Delta\omega/\omega_0)]}$$

$$= \frac{\sin(\pi N \Delta\omega/\omega_0)}{\tan(\pi/2 \cdot \Delta\omega/\omega_0)} \cdot e^{j(\pi/2 - \pi N \Delta\omega/\omega_0)}$$

For $\Delta\omega/\omega_0 < 1$ this can be approximated by

$$\left[\frac{Y_{13}}{Y_0 + Y_{11} - Y_{12}} \right]_N \simeq 2N \frac{\sin \pi N \Delta\omega/\omega_0}{\pi N \Delta\omega/\omega_0} \cdot e^{j(\pi/2 - \pi N \Delta\omega/\omega_0)} \quad (6.15)$$

The $\sin x/x$ function in (6.15) gives the frequency selectivity. The right hand factor indicates a linear phase relationship; the associated delay in the N transducer is the time it takes the wave to travel from the middle of the transducer to its right hand edge, and in the M transducer from its left edge to the middle.

Thus for $\Delta\omega/\omega_0 < 1$, (6.14) can be rewritten as

$$y_{ab} = \frac{I_{3,0,M}}{E_{3,N}}$$

$$= 8NMY_0 \frac{\sin \pi N \Delta\omega/\omega_0}{\pi N \Delta\omega/\omega_0} \cdot \frac{\sin \pi M \Delta\omega/\omega_0}{\pi M \Delta\omega/\omega_0} \cdot e^{j[\pi\{1 - (N+M)\Delta\omega/\omega_0\} - \phi]} \quad (6.16)$$

The amplitude and (linear) phase response as given by (6.15) are the same as obtained when using a Fourier transform, because the Fourier transform of a sine burst of N cycles is a $\sin x/x$ function identical to that of (6.15). (See, for instance, Chapter 3.)

In the derivation of the frequency selectivity of a surface wave transducer by means of the Fourier transform the interaction between the electrical and the acoustic circuit is assumed zero. By shorting the receiver and using a voltage source with zero impedance at the transmitter this interaction is zero in the split-connected transducer, and the

Fourier transform method can be used to calculate the frequency dependence of y_{ab} (defined as the ratio between the short circuit output current and the input voltage).

The curves of Figs. 6.15 and 6.16 show that the open circuit response of a transducer can deviate significantly from a sin x/x response and from a linear phase response. For a split-connected transducer this is entirely because of the terms $y_{aa}Z_a$ and $y_{bb}Z_b$ in the denominator of (6.10) that indicate the interaction between the transducer driving-point impedances and the source and load impedances, respectively.

The frequency dependence of the driving-point impedance of bulk wave acoustic transducers is characterized by an alternation of resonance and antiresonance frequencies. The same holds for a surface wave transducer with the modification that the resonances are damped by the emission of surface wave energy. The transducers of Fig. 6.13 both show one resonance and one antiresonance. If a transducer is connected to a voltage generator with a nonzero resistive impedance, the voltage across the transducer is minimum at the resonance frequency (minimum value of the driving-point impedance) and maximum at the antiresonance frequency (maximum value of the driving-point impedance). A similar comment can be made for the effect of a nonzero load impedance. Figure 6.15 shows that, because of these effects, the open circuit response deviates considerably from a sin x/x response.

Exclusive use of split-connected transducers was assumed in the foregoing calculation because their characteristics can easily and accurately be described by the transmission line model. This was not to say, however, that a split-connected transducer always gives the optimum design for all conditions; for certain load conditions reflections from a split-connected transducer are indeed larger than those from a solid-finger transducer, as is apparent from Fig. 6.10.

If a multistrip coupler is used the preceding calculations do not change materially. Terms expressing its loss and selectivity (usually small) have to be added in (6.14).

Response and Impedance of Filters with Weighted Transducers. In this section methods for calculating the network parameters y_{aa}, y_{bb}, and y_{ab} of filters with weighted transducers are indicated. Only filters with one weighted transducer and one uniform transducer facing each other directly and filters with two weighted transducers coupled by means of a multistrip coupler are treated. In both cases the acoustic field of a length-weighted transducer is integrated in the direction of the fingers.

For simplicity it is again assumed that the weighted transducer of Fig. 6.20 has split-connected fingers, and it is further assumed that by means

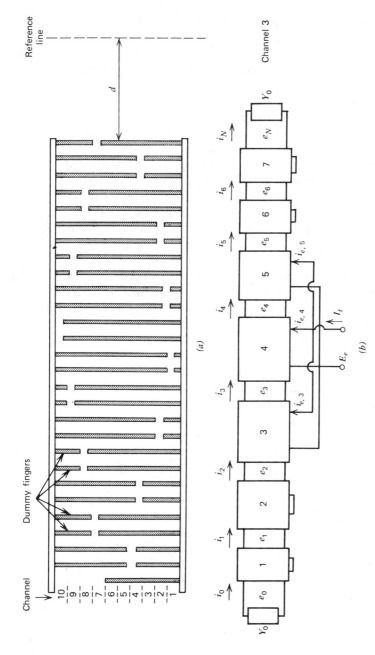

Figure 6.20 Illustration of method for calculating the contribution of a weighted transducer to the short-circuit transfer admittance y_{ab}. (*a*) For the calculation the weighted transducer is divided into 10 uniform channels. (*b*) Block diagram of the third-channel transducer. Note that only elemental transducers 3, 4, and 5 are active. The transducer has split-connected fingers. Dummy fingers are used to keep the wavefronts as parallel as possible.

287

of "dummy fingers"[11] the wavefronts are kept parallel as much as possible. A few of the dummy fingers have been indicated by the arrows in Fig. 6.20a. They have no function in the formation of the active transducer elements, but by maintaining the same pattern of lines and spaces they help to maintain a uniform wavefront.

The driving-point admittance of the transducer and its contribution to the transfer admittance y_{ab} of the filter can be found as follows: If the transducer area is divided into a number of channels, the partial transducers of the different channels (in the following called *channel transducers*) can be represented by generalized transmission line models of which all individual sections may have a different synchronous frequency.

Figure 6.20a shows a transducer with seven different sections divided into 10 channels; Fig. 6.20b shows the transmission line model pertaining to the third channel. The three-port that represents the channel transducer is formed by connecting all sections N in cascade acoustically and in parallel electrically.

If only length weighting is employed, the admittance matrices of all sections are identical. In this case, and if the shape of the transducer is such that no isolated transducers in any one channel are formed, the frequency response can be calculated by means of (6.13), which holds for uniform transducers. If the transducer is also width-weighted the elemental transducers are not identical. In this case, or if—because of the shape of the transducer—parts of some channel transducers are isolated, the calculation is more complicated.

The matrix equation describing the sections is similar to that of (6.2), which was given for an entire (uniform) transducer.

$$\begin{bmatrix} i_{n-1} \\ -i_n \\ i_{e,n} \end{bmatrix} = \begin{bmatrix} y_{11} & y_{12} & y_{13} \\ y_{12} & y_{11} & -y_{13} \\ y_{13} & -y_{13} & y_{33} \end{bmatrix} \cdot \begin{bmatrix} e_{n-1} \\ e_n \\ e_{e,n} \end{bmatrix} \tag{6.17}$$

The values of y_{ij} are given in Table 6.1 for $N = 1$ by (if y_{ij} is substituted for Y_{ij}); $e_{e,n} = E_e$ for all sections. Note that in the third channel of Fig. 6.20 two sections on either side happen to be inactive, because the electrical voltage is zero, thereby reducing (6.17) to

$$\begin{bmatrix} i_{n-1} \\ -i_n \end{bmatrix} = \begin{bmatrix} y_{11} & y_{12} \\ y_{12} & y_{11} \end{bmatrix}_n \cdot \begin{bmatrix} e_{n-1} \\ e_n \end{bmatrix}$$

Instead of expressing the quantities to be calculated in a formal matrix, a recursive calculation is described.

The acoustic output voltage e_n and current i_n of the nth section can be expressed in terms of the electrical voltage E_e and the output voltage e_{n-1}

and current i_{n-1} of the preceding section:

$$e_n = f(e_{n-1}, i_{n-1}, E_e)$$
$$i_n = g(e_{n-1}, i_{n-1}, E_e)$$

Algebraic manipulation of (6.17) yields

$$e_n = \frac{y_{11}}{y_{12}} e_{n-1} + \frac{1}{y_{12}} i_{n-1} - \frac{y_{13}}{y_{12}} E_e$$

$$i_n = \left(\frac{y_{11}^2}{y_{12}} - y_{12}\right) e_{n-1} - \frac{y_{11}}{y_{12}} i_{n-1} + \left(\frac{y_{11}y_{13}}{y_{12}} + y_{13}\right) E_e$$

(6.18)

where the parameters y_{ij} pertain to the nth section. Recursive application of (6.18) allows the acoustic output current i_N and voltage e_N of the channel transducer to be expressed in the input current i_0 and input voltage e_0 and the electrical voltage E_e:

$$e_N = F(e_0, i_0, E_e)$$
$$i_N = G(e_0, i_0, E_e)$$

The boundary conditions yield two additional relations:

$$i_N = Y_0 e_N$$
$$i_0 = -Y_0 e_0$$

so that e_0, and subsequently all voltages e_n, can now be directly expressed in E_e.

The electrical section currents $i_{e,n}$ are given by

$$i_{e,n} = y_{13,n}(e_{n-1} - e_n) + y_{33,n} E_e$$

and can then also be expressed in e_0 and E_e. The total electrical current I_t is found by summing the section currents. By means of this expression and the previously found relations, the total electrical current can now be expressed in the electrical voltage E_e. This yields the contribution of the channel transducer to the driving-point admittance of the entire transducer and thus of the filter. Although the evaluation is straightforward, it is clear that because of the multitude of recursive calculations a computer is required.

The contribution of the transducer to the transfer admittance y_{ab} of a filter can be found by integrating the acoustic intensity, represented by e_N, along a reference line perpendicular to the direction of wave propagation at a place somewhere between the transducers (Fig. 6.20). The contribution of each channel to the integral is given by $e_N e^{-j\phi}$, where $\phi = \omega d/v_s$, in which d is the distance from the last element of the channel to the line that forms the path of integration. The integration yields a relation between the total acoustic voltage E_a and the electrical voltage E_e similar to the relation (6.15) for a uniform transducer. The calculation for the second transducer, if weighted, could be done in the same manner, again giving a relation between the integrated acoustic voltage and the electrical generator voltage E_e. By means of the reciprocity theorem an inverse relation between the short circuit electrical current and the acoustic wave impinging on the second (weighted) transducer can then be calculated. The total short circuit transfer admittance y_{ab} of the filter can be found in a manner similar to that discussed previously for the case of two uniform transducers.

The transfer admittance y_{ab} of a filter with weighted transducers can also be calculated by means of the Fourier transform. For a device consisting of two weighted transducers coupled by a multistrip coupler the transfer admittance can be expressed as

$$y_{ab} = Ce^{-j\phi} \int_{-\infty}^{\infty} F_1(t)e^{-j\omega t}\, dt \cdot \int_{-\infty}^{\infty} F_2(t)e^{-j\omega t}\, dt \qquad (6.19)$$

where the time variable t is related to the space coordinate x as $x = v_s t$. Functions $F_1(t)$ and $F_2(t)$ are obtained from the transducer structures as discussed in Chapter 3. The factor ϕ represents the phase delay of a wave that travels from the coordinate reference of one transducer to that of the other. The frequency dependence of the multistrip coupler is not included in (6.19) but should be if important.

6.3 Bandpass Filter Design

Several methods, of differing degree of sophistication, for realizing bandpass filters are available. Designs based on Fourier transform analysis and the use of window functions are discussed in Chapter 3. Discussion in this chapter is mostly about filters with uniform transducers and designs based on the building block concept.

Filters with Uniform Transducers. It was shown earlier how universal curves—with the number of fingers and the synchronous frequency as parameters—can be made for the response of transducers with specified source and load impedances. By using such curves simple filters can be designed. For a filter with two identical transducers, the response of the first sidelobe is only 26 dB below the maximum response; by using values for N and ω that are different in the two transducers improvements are possible.

Interesting responses can be obtained by combining transducers, as shown in Fig. 6.21. A design suggested by Adler[12] has two transducers

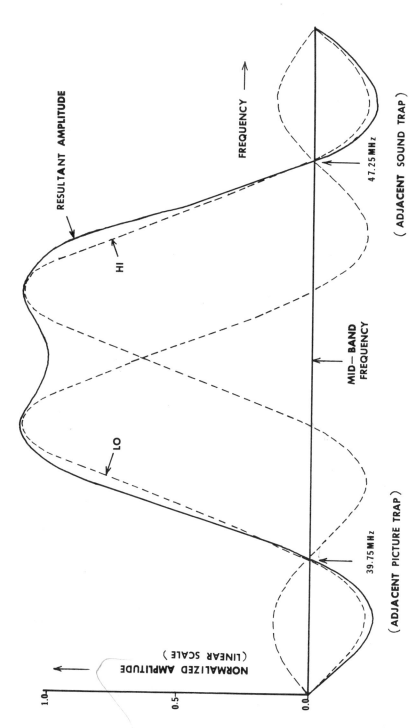

Figure 6.21 By combining the frequency responses of two uniform transducers (marked LO and HI) in phase quadrature, a resultant frequency response with a broad passband (indicated by the solid curve) can be obtained.

291

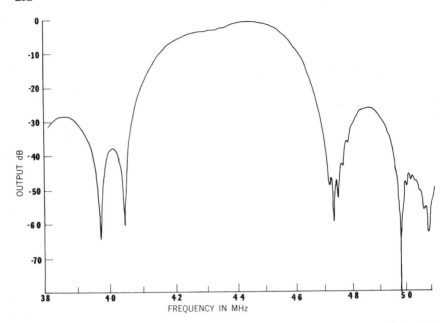

Figure 6.22 Frequency response of a TV IF filter with the transducer system of Fig. 6.21 as receiver, having traps at 39.75 and 47.25 MHz, and a uniform transducer, with traps at 40.60 and 47.25 MHz, as transmitter.

connected electrically in parallel and in quadrature phase, forming a filter characterized by a broad passband and steep slopes. A maximum in the response of one transducer coincides with a zero of the second, and the quadrature phase condition ensures that the sidelobe response of the first transducer does not reduce the maximum response of the second.

The response of a particular filter of this type used as a prototype for a TV IF filter is shown in Fig. 6.22. For this particular application it is very important that deep traps adjoining the passband be maintained. The use of uniform transducers is advantageous here, because the positions of the zeros in the response are well defined.

Design Using Building Block Transducers. It is evident that filter design methods using transducers with uniform fingers are severely limited. Finding the impulse response (transducer configuration) associated with a desired frequency response by straightforward application of the Fourier transform is not possible because of the unavoidable physical truncation of the transducer. (See Chapter 3.)

In the following a practical method is described for approximating a desired frequency response by composing the transducer of a number of "building block" transducers, each of a finite width. In one method[13] the building blocks are uniform transducers. Figure 6.23 shows a filter in which one transducer is composed of two uniform transducers in parallel. Each transducer is characterized by its synchronous frequency ω, number of sections N, and aperture l. Figure 6.24 shows schematically how the upper frequency sidelobe of the sin x/x function of a transducer having a synchronous frequency ω_1 and N_1 sections (Fig. 6.24a) can be compensated by the main lobe of a transducer having a synchronous frequency ω_2 and a number of sections N_2 (Fig. 6.24b). The compensated response is shown in Fig. 6.24c.

In Fig. 6.25 the measured response of a filter in which one of the transducers is replaced by three transducers in parallel is compared with the theoretical response. Of the three building block transducers, the second was used to compensate for the upper sidelobe of the first, and the third to broaden the response of the main lobe.

A system of too many individual transducers becomes inefficient, because the bus bars and the adjoining spaces reduce the effectiveness of the composite transducer. The building block transducers can, however, be replaced by a single length- and width-weighted transducer whose shape

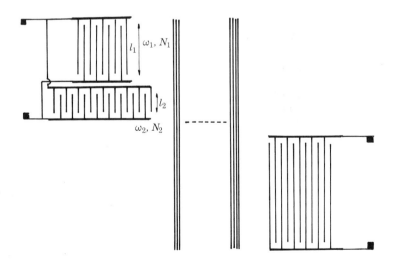

Figure 6.23   The response of a uniform transducer can be modified by connecting a second uniform transducer in parallel. Copyright 1973 by The Institute of Electrical and Electronic Engineers, Inc. Reprinted, with permission, from *Proc. 1973 Ultrasonics Symposium*, p. 441.

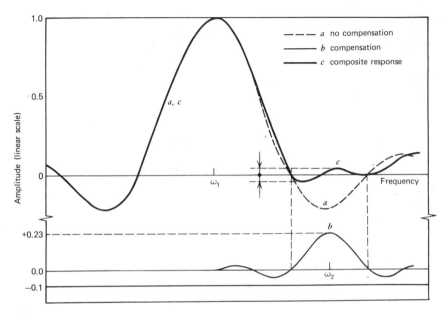

Figure 6.24 Frequency response of transducer system of Fig. 6.23 (*a*) Unmodified response. (*b*) Frequency response of a second transducer to compensate first upper sidelobe. (*c*) Composite response. Copyright 1973 by The Institute of Electrical and Electronic Engineers, Inc. Reprinted, with permission, from *Proc. 1973 Ultrasonics Symposium*, p. 441.

can readily be found. The procedure is based on the property that the inverse Fourier transform of the sum of two functions is equal to the sum of the inverse transforms of the individual functions. Thus if $f_1(t)$ is the impulse response corresponding to a transfer function $H_1(\omega)$, and $f_2(t)$ is the impulse response corresponding to a transfer function $H_2(\omega)$, the impulse response corresponding to the transfer function $\{H_1(\omega)+H_2(\omega)\}$ is $\{f_1(t)+f_2(t)\}$.

The design procedure is demonstrated on the system shown schematically in Fig. 6.23 and yields the frequency response of Fig. 6.24. The desired transfer function is

$$H(\omega) = H_1(\omega) + H_2(\omega) = \frac{\sin N_1 \pi (\Delta \omega)_1}{N_1 \pi (\Delta \omega)_1} + 0.23 \frac{\sin N_2 (\Delta \omega)_2}{N_2 \pi (\Delta \omega)_2}$$

where

$$(\Delta \omega)_1 = \frac{\omega - \omega_1}{\omega_1}$$

and

$$(\Delta\omega)_2 = \frac{\omega - \omega_2}{\omega_2}$$

The inverse Fourier transform of the first term $H_1(\omega)$ of the transfer function, which is centered around ω_1, is a cosine burst of N cycles centered at $x = 0$ with an amplitude that is proportional to ω_1/N_1. Similarly, the inverse Fourier transform of the second term is a cosine burst with N_2 cycles and an amplitude proportional to $0.23\,\omega_2/N_2$ also centered around $x = 0$. The two bursts are shown in Figs. 6.26a and 6.26b. The inverse Fourier transform of the desired transfer function is now equal to the sum of the two bursts (Fig. 6.26c). From this composite waveform the transducer can be constructed. The zero crossings of the waveform correspond to the centers of the fingers, and the interaction length of the fingers is to be proportional to the associated peak values of the curve in Fig. 6.26c. Figure 6.27 shows the calculated and realized frequency response of a TV IF filter[14] designed according to this method.

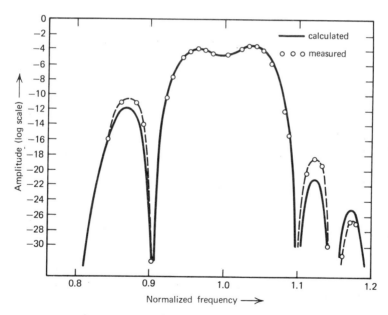

Figure 6.25 Frequency response of a transducer system in which the first upper sidelobe is suppressed and the main passband is widened. Copyright 1973 by The Institute of Electrical and Electronic Engineers, Inc. Reprinted, with permission, from *Proc. 1973 Ultrasonics Symposium*, p. 444.

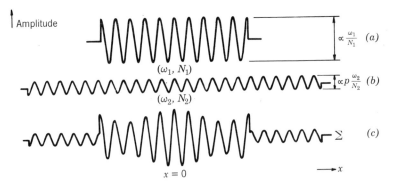

Figure 6.26 Combining the two parallel connected uniform transducers of Fig. 6.23 into a single length- and width-weighted transducer. (*a*) Sine burst representing main uniform transducer. (*b*) Sine burst representing compensating transducer. (*c*) Sum of (*a*) and (*b*) from which the composite transducer can be constructed. Copyright 1973 by The Institute of Electrical and Electronic Engineers, Inc. Reprinted, with permission, from *Proc. 1973 Ultrasonics Symposium*, p. 443.

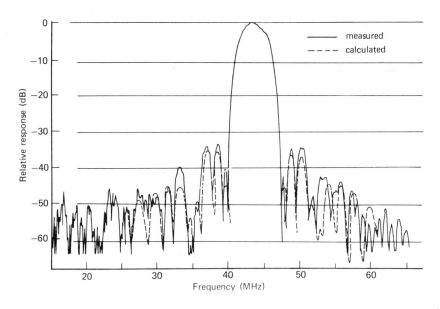

Figure 6.27 Measured and calculated frequency response of TV IF filter obtained by "building-block" approach. Copyright 1973 by The Institute of Electrical and Electronic Engineers, Inc. Reprinted, with permission, from *Proc. 1974 Ultrasonics Symposium*, p. 149.

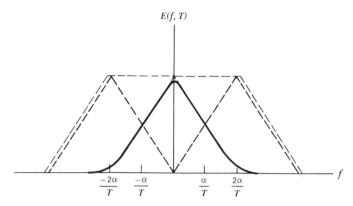

Figure 6.28 An ideal bandpass filter response can be approximated by using "building blocks" with a (nearly) triangular frequency response. The dotted trapezoidal frequency response can be obtained by adding the three triangular frequency responses. Copyright 1974 by The Institute of Electrical and Electronic Engineers, Inc. Reprinted, with permission, from *IEEE Trans.* **SU-21,** 1974, p. 7.

A somewhat similar approach was made by Vasile.[15] His building blocks are length-weighted transducers so that the frequency response is reasonably close to a triangle, as shown in Fig. 6.28. By using several of these building blocks, a response as indicated by the dotted curve in Fig. 6.28 can be obtained. Figure 6.29a shows (on a linear scale) the frequency response of a building block. This response is reasonably close to the required triangular shape. The cosine-squared weighting function (shown in Fig. 6.29b) is given by

$$W(t, T) = \begin{cases} 0.44 + 0.5 \cos \dfrac{2\pi t}{T} + 0.07 \cos \dfrac{4\pi t}{T}, & |t| < \dfrac{T}{2} \\ 0, & |t| > \dfrac{T}{2} \end{cases}$$

Figure 6.29c shows the frequency response (Fourier transform) on a logarithmic scale. Theoretically a stopband rejection of about 80 dB can be obtained; in practice this rejection is difficult to attain because of undesired side effects.

Width, Withdrawal, and Phase Weighting. So far the required strength distribution of the elemental transducers was obtained by length weighting. There are, however, other weighting methods. Length weighting is disadvantageous if it leads to very short fingers, because of

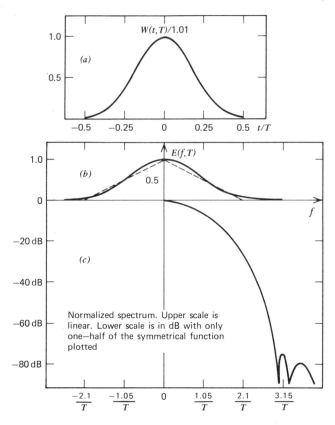

Figure 6.29 (*a*) Cosine-squared weighting function $W(t, T)$ used to approximate triangular frequency response. (*b*) Calculated frequency response (on a linear scale) of a transducer with the weighting function of (*a*). (*c*) As (*b*) on a logarithmic scale. Copyright 1974 by The Institute of Electrical and Electronics Engineers, Inc. Reprinted, with permission, from *IEEE Trans.* **SU-21,** 1974, p. 8.

diffraction problems. Diffraction causes wavefront distortion and leads to extra losses, thereby complicating the design. Width weighting (i.e., varying the metal-to-space ratio of the fingers rather than their length) minimizes diffraction effects.[16] The disadvantage is, however, that width weighting demands a critical photoetching process, especially when very narrow fingers are required.

In another method weighting is obtained by selective withdrawal of electrodes.[17] The design starts with a set of fingers that are evenly spaced. Some fingers are then deleted locally. Weighting is maximum where all electrodes remain, and small in areas where only a few electrodes remain.

Phase weighting

The three weighting methods discussed so far are forms of amplitude weighting. Besides amplitude weighting, phase weighting has been tried. The vector model shows that the contribution of each elemental transducer to the overall frequency response of the transducer depends on the phase angle of the elemental transducers, which is determined by the electrode placement. In one approach[18] a TV IF filter was realized by varying the position of the electrodes through a computer search. By making the filter symmetrical, a linear phase response was obtained. The amplitude response is shown in Fig. 6.30.

A different approach[19] is based on recognizing that the impulse response of a length-weighted transducer with equally spaced fingers can be written as

$$F(t) = a(t) \cdot \cos \omega_0 t = \tfrac{1}{2} \cos \{\omega_0 t + \phi(t)\} + \tfrac{1}{2} \cos \{\omega_0 t - \phi(t)\}$$

where $\phi(t) = \arccos a(t)$. The last expression relates a desired weighting function $a(t)$ to a specific position modulation of fingers with uniform length in order to obtain a desired impulse response. This is realized by a system consisting of an single transmitter transducer and two receiver transducers, one on each side of the transmitter transducer. The left receiver is designed to have an impulse response given by $\cos \{\omega_0 t + \phi(t)\}$ and the right receiver by $\cos \{\omega_0 t - \phi(t)\}$. The two receivers can be electrically connected in parallel.

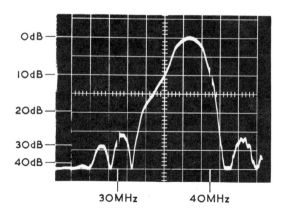

Figure 6.30 Measured response of prototype TV IF filter using phase weighting. The filter was fabricated on *ST* quartz. British Crown copyright. Reprinted, with permission, from ref. 18, p. 138.

Factors That Affect Filter Performance. Once a surface wave filter has been designed and fabricated it cannot be detuned. It cannot be tuned either, however, and therefore it must be designed well and made accurately. The absolute accuracy depends on several factors. The most important are variations in the physical properties of the substrate material and variations caused by temperature changes. Small variations in the physical properties of single crystals result from variations in chemical and crystal structure. Velocity measurements on LiNbO$_3$ done by Williamson[20] indicate that variations of 0.1% occur in the surface wave velocity. Piezoelectric ceramic materials usually exhibit an even larger velocity variation. The center frequency f_0 of a surface wave filter is related to the electrode spacing d and the surface wave velocity v_S by $f_0 = v_S/d$. Through thermal expansion d varies with temperature. In most materials this variation is small compared with the variation of the velocity with temperature. The temperature coefficient of LiNbO$_3$, a material attractive for its high coupling coefficient, is 91 ppm; ST-X cut quartz has a zero temperature coefficient at about 30°C, but the coupling coefficient is very low. Extensive data about the temperature behavior of LiNbO$_3$, LiTaO$_3$, TeO$_2$, and quartz have been published by Slobodnik.[21] Measurements on PZT 6[22] show a temperature coefficient of delay of about 20 ppm. The frequency stability problem of filters on ceramic is compounded by aging.

Diffraction and Beam Steering. In all preceding discussions it was assumed that an elemental transducer generates a parallel acoustic beam with an aperture equal to the interaction length of the fingers of that transducer. Diffraction[23-27] causes the acoustic energy to spread, and the effect is more serious if the aperture (length of the fingers) is a small number of wavelengths, as is frequently the case with length-weighted transducers. Although some papers on the diffraction of surface waves have been published, no studies have appeared in which the effect of diffraction on the frequency response is calculated. Presently diffraction and bulk modes are convenient excuses to explain the difference between calculated and experimentally observed frequency response.

In the configuration shown in Fig. 6.31, which consists of two weighted transducers and a multistrip coupler, some spurious coupling (schematically indicated by the arrow) is probably caused by diffracted wave components.[28] The coupling can be reduced by means of the mechanical barrier (rubber cement) shown in the figure. The calculated response and the experimentally observed response with and without barrier are shown in Fig. 6.32.

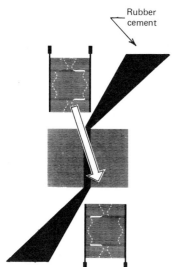

Rubber
cement

Figure 6.31 Rubber cement barrier to prevent surface waves from propagating through the multistrip coupler in the direction of the arrow. Reprinted, with permission, from ref. 28, p. 172.

In anisotropic materials the vector that indicates the power flow does not in general coincide with the transducer normal.[29] One well-known result is that the acoustic energy tends to follow the Z axis in Y–Z lithium niobate. In bandpass filters the distance between the transmitting and receiving transducers is usually not very large and the effect of beam steering is usually not significant.

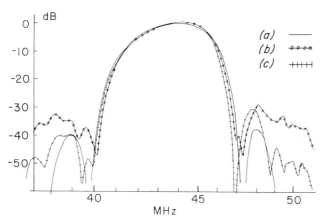

Figure 6.32 Effect of rubber cement barrier of Fig. 6.31 on the frequency response of a filter constructed of two weighted transducers coupled by a multistrip coupler. (a) Calculated response. (b) Measured frequency response without barrier. (c) Same as (b) with barrier. Reprinted, with permission, from ref. 28, p. 172.

Feedthrough and Triple Transit Echo. If in a design of a filter direct
electrical feedthrough and triple transit are not taken into account, the
desired frequency response is not obtained. Both effects cause ripples in
the amplitude and phase response, as shown in Fig. 6.33. The amount of
feedthrough depends on the electrostatic (or sometimes electromagnetic)
coupling of the input and output circuits. To reduce feedthrough, shields
can be employed. A method often used is metalizing and grounding the
bottom of the piezoelectric substrate. This reduces undesired direct
coupling between the transmitting and receiving transducer; it is very
effective if the thickness of the substrate is small compared with the
distance between the transducers. Electrically balancing the signal (e.g.,
by means of a transformer) applied to or obtained from a transducer also
reduces feedthrough. In Fig. 6.34*a* the shown transducer is balanced fed
(by means of a transformer), whereas in Fig. 6.34*b* the transducer is
directly connected to an unbalanced voltage source *V*. The average
potential in the transducer plane in the configuration of Fig. 6.34*a* is
zero, whereas in the transducer of Fig. 6.34*b* it is *V*/2.

In a filter consisting of two split-connected transducers, the triple

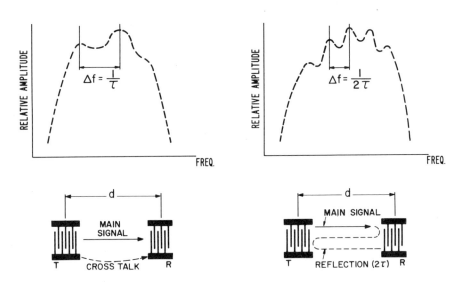

Figure 6.33 (*a*) Effect of crosstalk (direct feedthrough) on the frequency response of the
filter. In the passband ripples are caused with a periodicity $\Delta f = 1/\tau$, where τ is the time for
the surface waves to travel from one transducer to the other. (*b*) Effect of triple transit
reflections—periodicity is $\frac{1}{2}\tau$. Copyright 1971 by The Institute of Electrical and Electronic
Engineers, Inc. Reprinted, with permission, from *IEEE Trans.* **BTR-17**, 1971, p. 21.

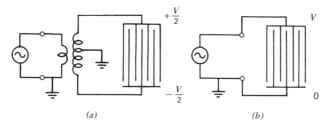

Figure 6.34 (*a*) Transducer connected to the source via a balancing transformer. (*b*) Transducer directly connected to the unbalanced source.

transit ratio is given by (6.12). The triple transit loss is about twice the effective transmission loss in decibels.

Several techniques have been suggested to reduce or to eliminate the triple transit signal. It is beyond the scope of this chapter to go into detail; reference is made to the literature.[30,31]

Effect of Bulk Modes. Under certain conditions surface wave transducers can couple to waves from and into the interior of substrates (bulk waves). Because the velocity of surface waves is usually less than that of shear waves and always less than that of longitudinal waves, wave matching ensures that significant coupling to bulk waves can only be expected at frequencies above the center frequency of a transducer. Thus bulk modes usually reduce the attenuation for frequencies above the center frequency of a bandpass filter. The magnitude of bulk wave interference depends on many factors, such as (1) the thickness of the substrate, (2) parallelism of bottom and top surfaces, (3) acoustic impedance match of the piezoelectric substrate and the supporting base, and (4) the distance between the transducers. For a complete analysis and description we refer to Ristic[32] and Wagers.[33]

One of the most effective ways to reduce bulk wave interference is the use of the multistrip coupler. The bulk waves are mainly confined to one track, whereas the surface waves are switched over to the other track.

Acknowledgments. The work reported in this chapter comes from many sources. The portion I was involved in was all done by a group in the Research Laboratories of Zenith Radio Corporation and I thank all my colleagues for their contributions. Specifically, I thank Mr. A. H. van Asten, with whom I had many discussions about the organization and the presentation of the material in this chapter.

References

1. An early source is "Modern filter design techniques issue." *IRE Trans.* **CT-5** (1958).

2. A more recent source is "Special issue on modern filter design." *IEEE Trans.* **CT-15** (1968).

3. R. H. Tancrell. "Analytical design of surface wave bandpass filters." *IEEE Trans.* **SU-21,** 12 (1974).

4. W. P. Mason. *Electromechanical Transducers and Wave Filters*, 2nd ed., Van Nostrand, New York, 1948, pp. 201–209.

5. W. R. Smith et al. "Analysis of interdigital surface wave transducers by use of an equivalent circuit model." *IEEE Trans.* **MTT-17,** 856 (1969).

6. A. J. DeVries, R. L. Miller, and T. J. Wojcik. "Reflections of a surface wave from three types of I. D. transducers," in J. de Klerk, Ed., *Proc. 1972 IEEE Ultrasonics Symposium*, IEEE, New York, 1972, pp. 353–358.

7. A. J. DeVries and S. Subramanian. "Overall comparison between theoretical predictions using the crossed-field transmission line model and experimental measurements of a split-connected transducer," in J. de Klerk, Ed., *Proc. 1973 IEEE Ultrasonics Symposium*, IEEE, New York, 1973, pp. 407–409.

8. R. F. Milsom and M. Redwood. "Interdigital piezoelectric Rayleigh wave transducer, an improved equivalent circuit." *Electron. Lett.* **7,** 217 (1971).

9. See, for example, S. Seshu and N. Balabanian. *Linear Network Analysis*, Wiley, New York, 1959, Section 8.1.

10. R. Saal and E. Ulbrich. "On the design of filters by synthesis." *IRE Trans.* **CT-5,** 284 (1958).

11. R. H. Tancrell and R. C. Williamson. "Wavefront distortion of acoustic surface waves from apodized interdigital transducers." *Appl. Phys. Lett.* **19,** 456 (1971).

12. R. Adler. U.S. Patent 3,550,045 (1970).

13. A. J. DeVries. "A design method for surface wave filters using simple structures as building blocks," in J. de Klerk, Ed., *Proc. 1973 IEEE Ultrasonics Symposium*, IEEE, New York, 1973, pp. 441–444.

14. A. J. DeVries et al. "Detailed description of a commercial surface wave TV IF filter," in J. de Klerk, Ed., *Proc. 1974 IEEE Ultrasonics Symposium*, IEEE, New York, 1974, pp. 147–152.

15. C. F. Vasile. "A numerical Fourier transform technique and its application to acoustic surface wave bandpass filter synthesis and design." *IEEE Trans.* **SU-21,** 7 (1974).

16. R. F. Mitchell. "Acoustic surface wave filters." *Philips Tech. Rev.* **32,** 179 (1971).

17. C. S. Hartman. "Weighting interdigital surface wave transducers by selective withdrawal of electrodes," in J. de Klerk, Ed., *Proc. 1973 IEEE Ultrasonics Symposium*, IEEE, New York, 1973, pp. 423–426.

18. M. F. Lewis. "Surface acoustic wave filters employing symmetric phase weighted transducers." *Electron. Lett.* **9,** 138 (1973).

19. C. Atzeni, G. Manes, and L. Masotti. "Synthesis of amplitude modulated SAW filters with constant length fingers," in J. de Klerk, Ed., *Proc. 1973 IEEE Ultrasonics Symposium*, IEEE, New York, 1973, pp. 414–418.

20. R. C. Williamson. "Measurements of the propagation characteristics of surface and

bulk waves in LiNbO$_3$," in J. de Klerk, Ed., *Proc. 1972 IEEE Ultrasonics Symposium*, IEEE, New York, 1972, pp. 323–327.

21. A. J. Slobodnik, Jr. "The temperature coefficient of acoustic wave velocity and delay on lithium niobate, lithium tantalate, quartz, and tellurium dioxide." Technical Report AFCRL-72-0082, Air Force Cambridge Research Laboratories, Bedford, Mass., 1971.

22. A. J. DeVries et al. "Characteristics of surface wave integratable filters (SWIF's)," *IEEE Trans.* **BTR-17**, 16 (1971).

23. R. D. Weglein, M. E. Pedinoff, and H. Winston. "Diffraction spreading of surface waves on LiNbO$_3$." *Electron. Lett.* **6**, 654 (1970).

24. F. Y. Cho, R. L. Lawson, and B. J. Huntsinger. "A note on the determination of the diffraction pattern of interdigital surface wave devices." *IEEE Trans.* **SU-17**, 199 (1970).

25. I. M. Mason and E. A. Ash. "Acoustic surface wave beam diffraction on anisotropic substrates." *J. Appl. Phys.* **42**, 5343 (1971).

26. M. S. Kharusi and G. W. Farnell. "Diffraction and beam steering for surface wave comb structures on anisotropic substrates." *IEEE Trans.* **SU-18**, 35 (1971).

27. J. C. Crabb, J. D. Maines, and N. R. Ogg. "Surface wave diffraction on LiNbO$_3$." *Electron. Lett.* **7**, 253 (1971).

28. A. J. DeVries. "Spurious coupling between length weighted transducers acoustically connected by means of a multistrip coupler." *Electron. Lett.* **10**, 172 (1974).

29. A. J. Slobodnik, Jr., and E. D. Conway. *Microwave Acoustics Handbook*, Vol. 1, Air Force Cambridge Research Laboratories, Bedford, Mass., 1970.

30. F. G. Marshall, C. O. Newton, and E. G. S. Paige. "Surface acoustic wave multistrip couplers and their applications." *IEEE Trans.* **SU-20**, 134 (1973).

31. G. L. Matthaei et al. "Non-reflecting acoustic surface wave filters and switching devices," in J. de Klerk, Ed., *Proc. 1972 IEEE Ultrasonics Symposium*, IEEE, New York, 1972, pp. 381–383.

32. V. M. Ristic. "Bulk mode generation in surface wave devices," in J. de Klerk, Ed., *Proc. 1972 IEEE Ultrasonics Symposium*, IEEE, New York, 1972, pp. 424–428.

33. R. S. Wagers. "Plate mode resonances in surface wave delay lines," in J. de Klerk, Ed., *Proc. 1973 IEEE Ultrasonics Symposium*, IEEE, New York, 1973, pp. 372–374.

SEVEN

Phase Code Generators and Correlators

D. T. BELL, JR., AND L. T. CLAIBORNE

Texas Instruments, Incorporated
Dallas, Texas

The general features of surface wave technology have been described in preceding chapters. The devices considered in this chapter have impulse responses derived from discrete codes that modulate the phase of a coherent carrier.

Cook and Bernfeld[1] have described a general waveform for discrete coding by

$$\psi(t) = \sum_{n=1}^{N} a_n p_n(t) \exp\left[j\{(\omega_0 + \omega_n)t + \theta_n\}\right] \qquad (7.1)$$

for the time duration $0 \le t \le N\delta$, where p_n is a unit height pulse of fixed duration δ such that

$$p_n(t) = \begin{cases} 1 & \text{for } (n-1)\delta \le t \le n\delta \\ 0 & \text{elsewhere} \end{cases} \qquad (7.2)$$

For phase shift keyed (PSK) codes, $a_n = 1$ and $\omega_n = 0$. Equation (7.1) becomes

$$\psi(t) = \sum_{n=1}^{N} p_n(t) \exp\left[j(\omega_0 t + \theta_n)\right] \qquad (7.3)$$

Most codes we consider are biphase with θ_n equal to 0 or 180°. However, the flexibility of the surface wave filter can be used to achieve phase

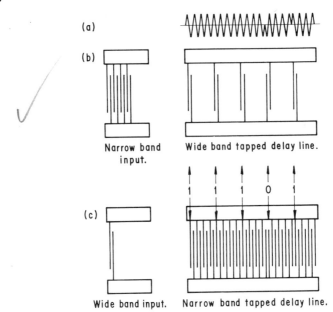

Narrow band
input.

Wide band tapped delay line.

Wide band input.   Narrow band tapped delay line.

Figure 7.1 Realization of phase coding in surface wave matched filters. The waveform (*a*) may be realized by a narrow-band input and wide-band taps (*b*), preferred, or the converse as in (*c*).

coding with arbitrary values of phase as well as arbitrary values of amplitude $a_n(t)$ and frequency ω_n as expressed in (7.1). A simple five chip* biphase sequence waveform and the equivalent surface wave inter-digital transducer pattern are shown in Fig. 7.1. The conventional surface wave device is a linear transversal filter having one electrical input port and one electrical output port. An electrical impulse applied to the coded transducer produces, as a first order approximation, a sinusoidal waveform similar to the schematic waveform shown in Fig. 7.1*a*.

The output of a transversal filter is actually the convolution of the input waveform with the impulse response of the filter.

$$w(\tau) = \int_{-\infty}^{+\infty} u(t)v(\tau - t)^* \, dt \qquad (7.4a)$$

where $u(t)$ is the input waveform and $v(t)$ is the impulse response of the

---

* Note that the term *chip* is used to refer to the pulse $p_n(t)$ of duration δ. A code sequence is made up of a series of N chips. The term *bit* is used to designate a code sequence, code block, or other segment of waveform used to communicate one "bit of information."

filter. Here τ is the time at which the output response is to be measured and includes the time delay required for the filter to be physically realizable. To achieve the function of autocorrelation, as required for a matched filter, it is necessary to realize instead the correlation integral

$$g(\tau) = \int_{-\infty}^{+\infty} u(t)u(t-\tau)^* \, dt \qquad (7.4b)$$

Thus it is necessary to construct a filter with an impulse response $v(t)$ that is the time reverse of the signal $u(t)$ to be correlated or matched, except for an arbitrary time delay. The correlation of a five-chip coded sequence, illustrated in Fig. 7.2, results in a compressed pulse with a width comparable to one chip.

It is the purpose of this chapter to present the component technology for surface wave phase code generators and correlators. Applications in spread spectrum communications systems are discussed in detail in a subsequent chapter. Other applications include position location, identification coding for civil and military aviation, and system synchronization.[2] In the next section, a survey of representative codes includes the key properties for each type and examples of the impulse and correlation responses obtained for several types using surface wave filters. In the following section practical design considerations are discussed for general phase coded filters, with emphasis on the way second order effects and electrical characteristics influence performance. Advanced technology for programmable filters and large time bandwidth product filters are discussed in separate sections. A summary is given in the last section of the range of performance possible in 1974 and improvements to be expected from continued development.

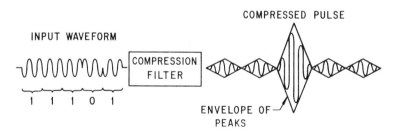

Figure 7.2 Illustration of simple five chip Barker compression filter. Copyright 1971 by The Institute of Electrical and Electronic Engineers, Inc. Reprinted, with permission, from *IEEE Trans.* **SU-18**, 1971, p. 22.

7.1 Code Properties

Biphase, polyphase, and amplitude modulation have all been used, singly and in combination, to produce codes with specialized properties. Historically, biphase codes have had a dominant role, partly because classical transmitters and receivers are easier and cheaper to build when only two phases are involved, but also because one class of biphase codes, the maximal length pseudonoise (PN) codes, can be generated with very long sequences from comparatively short feedback shift registers. Very powerful theorems are available from number theory concerning the existence, construction, and analysis of such codes. Polyphase codes are exactly as easy to generate and correlate as biphase codes when surface wave filters are used for both generation and correlation. The variety of polyphase codes to discuss is more limited, however, because there has been little incentive to study them.

Description of Representative Biphase Codes. The first class of codes to be considered consists of the binary phase codes for which θ_n in (7.3) is either 0 or π. Following Cook and Bernfeld,[1] the term $\exp[j\theta_n]$ is equal to ± 1 and can be replaced by the real coefficient c_n. The magnitude of c_n is unity and can, therefore, be represented by either a $(+)$ or $(-)$. This is the notation to be used here, although the pair $[0, 1]$ is common usage in binary descriptions of the code sequences. The sum $\sum_{n=1}^{N} p_n(t)c_n \exp[j\omega_0 t]$ is simply a burst of CW of time length $T = N\delta$ that is modulated in phase by $180°$ through the coefficients c_n.

In the discussion of the biphase codes that follows, it is convenient to consider first the baseband properties. For example, the baseband impulse response is simply

$$I = \sum_{n=1}^{N} c_n p_n \tag{7.5}$$

The corresponding baseband correlation response for the code with a properly matched filter can be obtained by means of Bernfeld's algorithm,[3] which is a mulitplication operation of the set of (c_n) by the reverse sequence (c_{-n}). A simple example for a three chip sequence is

$$
\begin{array}{ll}
(c_n) & +, +, - \\
(c_{-n}) & \underline{-, +, +} \\
& +, +, - \\
& +, +, - \\
& \underline{-, -, +} \\
& -1,\ 0,\ 3,\ 0,\ -1
\end{array}
$$

As for other matched filter waveforms, it is useful to describe the filter response in terms not only of the time τ measured from the correlation peak, but also in terms of the frequency shift ϕ of the signal from the desired matched filter. If we define this function as the response function[4] $\chi(\tau, \phi)$, then the correlation response of (7.4b) is the special case when $\phi = 0$. For phase coded signals the delay time τ can be expressed in terms of k integral steps of δ, with $k = 0$ for the correlation maximum. Thus the resulting response function for the three chip sequence is

$$\chi(k\delta, 0) = -1, 0, 3, 0, -1 \qquad (7.6)$$

for $k = -2$ to $+2$.

Barker Sequences. Barker sequences [1,5] are a class of binary codes that have correlation functions with maximum sidelobes of unity. In equation form,

$$\chi(k\delta, 0) = \begin{cases} N & k = 0 \\ +1, 0 & k \neq 0 \end{cases} \qquad (7.7)$$

where N is the number of chips in the code. The signal-to-noise ratio of a matched filter is generally equal to the time-bandwidth product, which is N for a PSK waveform ($10 \log N$ in dB). This waveform is one of the rare ones for which the peak-to-sidelobe ratio is also equal to N (but $20 \log N$ in dB). True Barker sequences have only been found up to length 13 and are listed in Table 7.1.

Longer sequences can be constructed from the Barker codes by using an M chip sequence to represent one bit of an N bit sequence. This is

Table 7.1 The Barker Sequences

N	(c_n)	Autocorrelation
2	++	2 +
2	+−	2 −
3	++−	3 0 −
4	++−+	4 + 0 +
4	+++−	4 + 0 −
5	+++−+	5 0 + 0 +
7	+++−−+−	7 0 − 0 − 0 −
11	+++−−−+−−+−	11 0 − 0 − 0 − 0 −
13	+++++−−++−+−+	13 0 + 0 + 0 + 0 + 0 +

accomplished by multiplying the M chip sequence by the (c_n) corresponding to the N bit sequence. The signal-to-noise improvement or pulse
compression ratio becomes the new sequence length of $N \times M$, but the
peak-to-sidelobe ratio remains N.

The Barker codes are well suited to visualizing and investigating the
performance of surface wave PSK code generators and correlators, and
therefore had an important place in early device studies.[6] Their short
length minimizes fabrication difficulties, and the uniformity of the ideal
sidelobes alternating with zeros provides easy recognition of distortions
due to second order effects.[7] For example, Figs. 7.3 and 7.4 show the
impulse and correlation responses of a 13-chip Barker coded device
fabricated on YZ lithium niobate. The correlation response was determined using an electronically generated input signal. Both experimental
and theoretical correlation responses are shown for comparison.

Two of the more important parameters that can be obtained from these
results are the pulse compression ratio and the maximum sidelobe level.
As predicted theoretically, the pulse compression ratio is 13. The maximum experimental sidelobe level is 21 dB below the correlation peak
compared to the theoretical 23.3 dB. It can be seen that the leading
sidelobes closely follow the theoretical performance but that the trailing
sidelobes are distorted. This distortion is due to interelectrode reflections
and can be eliminated, as is discussed in the next section.

Phase errors can be investigated experimentally by shifting the center
frequency of an electronically generated waveform. The amplitude of the
output signal is plotted as a function of both time and frequency to

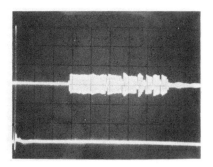

GENERATED
SIGNAL
0.05 VOLTS / DIV

IMPULSE
10 VOLTS / DIV

TIME (0.5 μsec / div)

Figure 7.3 Impulse response of 13-chip 30 MHz matched filter, using 10 nsec, 60 V
impulse. Copyright 1971 by The Institute of Electrical and Electronic Engineers, Inc.
Reprinted, with permission, from *IEEE Trans.* **SU-18,** 1971, p. 23.

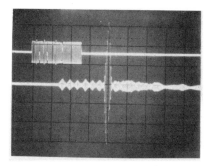

1.0 μ sec/div

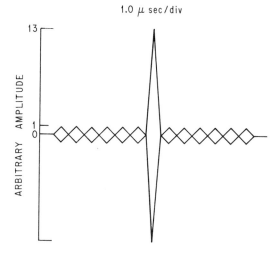

Figure 7.4 Correlation response of 13-chip Barker code, 6 cycles per chip at 29.34 MHz. (a) Experimental, including electronically generated input waveform. (b) Theoretical. Copyright 1971 by The Institute of Electrical and Electronic Engineers, Inc. Reprinted, with permission, from *IEEE Trans.* **SU-18**, 1971, p. 23.

determine the modified response function $\chi'(\tau, \phi)$. Fig 7.5 shows the experimental response function for the 13 chip Barker code. Figure 7.6 is a plot of the correlation peak and one of the next nearest sidelobes as a function of normalized frequency. It was found that the variation of the compressed pulse with frequency closely follows that expected for a long linear filter having 78 pairs of electrodes; that is, there are 6 cycles per chip and 13 chips, therefore the first minima occur at frequencies given by $f_0 \pm f_0/78$. The sidelobe level can be seen to rise to within 5 dB of the correlation maximum.

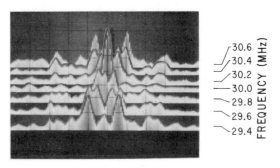

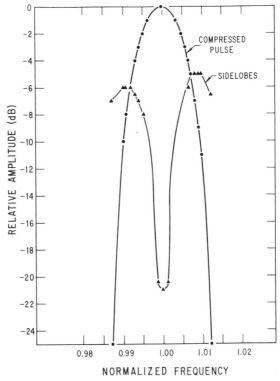

Maximum Length Codes. The extensive use of maximum length or pseudonoise (PN) codes in digital systems is the result of several important properties. The distribution of successive chips satisfies all reasonable randomness criteria. The codes can be efficiently generated using shift registers with feedback taps. They are, in fact, the maximum length codes that can be generated from such a shift register. Finally, when the code is transmitted cyclically (i.e., without any gaps), the correlation response has no sidelobe irregularities.

These codes can be analyzed by means of algebraic coding theory,[8] which is outside the scope of this book. Peterson[8] has listed in his Appendix C the octal representations of all the codes of interest for surface wave filters. The sequence length is $2^n - 1$, where n is the degree of the code and also the number of shift registers required for its generation. Consider the case of $n = 3$. There is one code (and its inverse) with the octal representation of 13, or binary of 1011. Figure 7.7 illustrates the conversion of the octal representation to the generating shift register to the actual code sequence. An n stage shift register is constructed with taps between stages at points corresponding to the 1's in the binary representation, always including the output. The taps are added at each shift of the register and the modulo-2 sum is used to load the first stage. Any sequence of n numbers (except all 0's) can be used to start the shift register. For the case shown the generated sequence is the Barker code of length 7 (1110010) when started with 010 for the direct sequence or 111 for the inverse sequence.

The autocorrelation properties are shown in Fig. 7.8 for two different

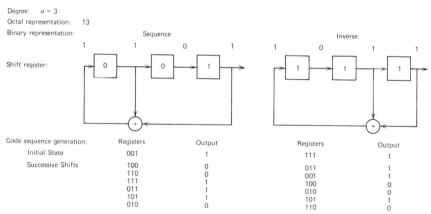

Figure 7.7 Generation of maximum length sequence and its inverse from its irreducible polynomial, for $n = 3$.

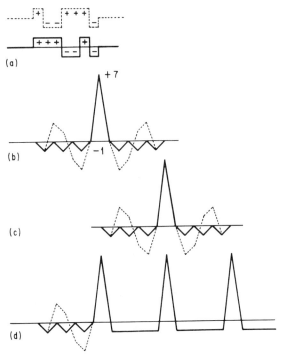

Figure 7.8   Correlation properties of a maximum length sequence. (*a*) Sequence phases for Barker (solid line) and an inverted shifted sequence (dotted line). (*b*) Correlation response (noncyclic, or aperiodic). (*c*) Same, delayed by one sequence length. (*d*) Summation, illustrating cyclic operation.

starting points of this seven chip code. The two codes are shown in Fig. 7.8*a*, with their aperiodic autocorrelation response in Fig. 7.8*b*. Although the sidelobes are quite low for the Barker code, the alternate starting point produces substantial sidelobes. It is not necessarily true, in other words, that PN sequences have low *aperiodic* sidelobes. If the code is generated again immediately following the first sequence, then the second code has the same autocorrelation response displaced in time by the code length, as shown in Fig. 7.8*c*. The sum produces the periodic, or cyclic, response shown in Fig. 7.8*d*. It always occurs for any degee n that the sidelobes are such as to add to -1 everywhere except at the correlation peak, which is $2^n - 1$. If for any reason there is a timing error between the two sequences of one-half cycle at the carrier frequency, then the sidelobes add instead of canceling. Even though all starting chips are equivalent as far as $\chi(\tau, 0)$ is concerned, they are not the same when phase errors are included. The response functions of a variety of these codes are shown in Sakamoto.[9]

Randomly Generated Codes. Many applications require a finite set of coded waveforms that have good cross-correlation properties between all members as well as good autocorrelation properties. The total cross-correlation function must be of the same order of magnitude as the time sidelobes of the autocorrelation function. A set of such codes can be used to construct an alphabet for M-ary transmissions or for identification and ranging applications where communication, position location, and identification information are required from several users, as is the case for air traffic control.

A computer program for the determination of codes entails the generation of random binary sequences, computation of the autocorrelation function of each, selection of a set of codes that pass the autocorrelation test, computation of the cross-correlation functions of all passed codes, and the selection of a subset that has acceptable cross-correlation properties. This process can be carried out in a systematic manner and does not require an excessive amount of computation time if the time sidelobe restrictions are not too severe (e.g., if the ratio of the correlation peak to the maximum auto- or cross-correlation sidelobe is less than $20 \log 2\sqrt{N}$ dB, where N is the number of chips).

An example of a surface wave filter developed as one of a family of randomly coded devices is shown in Fig. 7.9. The code sequence has 100 chips and was selected for its cross-correlation properties with other 100 chip codes. This device was fabricated with aluminum metalization on ST-cut quartz. Figure 7.10 shows the impulse response and correlation response for this device. The time sidelobes are 14.5 dB as compared to a theoretical value of 16.0 dB. Sources of distortion in this device and others are discussed in the next section. The insertion loss from the peak input signal level to the peak of the correlation is only 6 dB. However, the

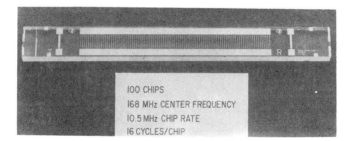

100 CHIPS
168 MHz CENTER FREQUENCY
10.5 MHz CHIP RATE
16 CYCLES/CHIP

Figure 7.9 A 100-chip filter on ST-cut quartz. Copyright 1973 by The Institute of Electrical and Electronic Engineers, Inc. Reprinted, with permission, from *IEEE Trans.* **MTT-21,** 1973, p. 246.

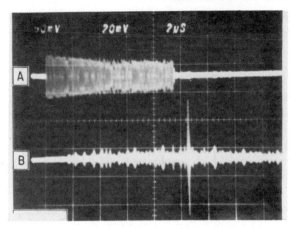

Figure 7.10 A 100-chip filter waveform. (*a*) Impulse response. (*b*) Correlation response. Copyright 1973 by The Institute of Electrical and Electronic Engineers, Inc. Reprinted, with permission, from *IEEE Trans*. **MTT-21**, 1973, p. 246.

true insertion loss for the filter is obtained by subtracting the 20 dB compression gain for a total insertion loss of 26 dB. Insertion loss is discussed in more detail in the next section.

Golay Sequences. Golay codes have two properties with special utility in delay lines. The Golay sequences[10] are a set of binary code pairs such that the correlation functions of codes in a given pair have sidelobes of opposite phase and peaks of equal phase. When the correlation responses are summed in parallel, the sidelobes become identically zero everywhere and the correlation peaks add. Thus long Golay coded transducers can be used on delay lines to reduce the transducer impedance without sacrificing bandwidth or sidelobe and spurious response.[11] The second property is that for any given code pair, it is possible to find a second orthogonal pair[12] (and sometimes more) such that the cross correlation is zero. This allows more than one signal to be transmitted over the same delay line substrate without interference.

Polyphase Codes. The flexibility of tap placement afforded by the surface wave filter permits implementation of a wide range of phase and amplitude coded waveforms that previously were difficult if not impossible to synthesize. The simplest of the polyphase codes are obtained by letting θ_n in (7.3) take on values that are not limited to 0 or 180°. This allows values of c_n that, in general, are complex; and peak-to-sidelobe ratios can be enhanced.[1] Included in this class of codes are the quantized phase codes, such as the Frank polyphase codes[13] and the polyphase Barker sequences.[14] Varying amplitude as well as phase allows even more complex codes, such as the Huffman codes.[15] All these codes can be conveniently achieved using surface wave techniques.[2] Phase code generators and correlators using more complex waveforms have not been fully exploited to date, but the possibilities are intriguing. Random polyphase codes can be generated in the manner described for random biphase codes. Using selection criteria that reject the same number of codes as in the biphase case typically results in sidelobe levels 3 dB lower. For example, 18 quadriphase codes, 127 chips long, were generated for use in the block programmable 1016 chip system described in Section 7.4. The sidelobes for the quadriphase codes were 18 dB below the main peak.

7.2 Design of Devices for Phase-Coded Waveforms

Having chosen a coded waveform based on its signal processing proper-ties, it is necessary to design a device that produces or processes this waveform within some tolerance. The correspondence between finger location and electrical waveform is especially good for the surface wave tapped delay lines used to generate phase coded signals. Consequently the design guides given in the literature[16] for estimating impedances, finger locations, beamspreading, and so on, provide an excellent first order design.

Phase coded devices, however, have special problems because of the large number of cycles encompassed by a typical waveform and the inherently periodic nature of the taps. Phase differences between the desired and actual impulse response result from random and system-atic errors in finger placement. The very long signals involved mean that very small scaling errors due to temperature, orientation, and pattern generation produce significant phase errors. A consequence of the periodic tap locations is that reflections from finger edges tend to add coherently, diverting substantial fractions of the acoustic energy into unwanted parts of the impulse response. The distortions due to these phase errors and acoustic reflections can degrade performance if not controlled properly.

The electrical performance parameters (terminal impedance and inser-tion loss) are also important in determining the effect of the filter on the electronics in which it is embedded.

First-Order Design. First order design consists of first finding the interdigital electrode finger positions required to produce the desired waveform and then evaluating minimum possible insertion loss. The approach discussed here has been covered in detail in Hartmann et al.[16] and cited references. The basis of the method is the correspondence between finger location and individual cycles of the impulse response. Each finger or tap is placed according to the peaks of the desired waveform with a spacing determined by the carrier frequency and surface wave velocity.

To be specific, a 127-chip waveform at 300 MHz with 50 MHz chip rate on ST quartz is used as an example for this and later discussions. The surface wave velocity of 3.157 mm/μsec implies a wavelength of 10.52 μm and a quarter-wavelength finger width and space of 2.631 μm. The basic geometry is similar to that shown in Fig. 7.9 for the 100 chip device. A chip rate of 50 MHz at 300 MHz implies that the input transducers (T and R), which are one chip long, are six wavelengths. The chip separation is 63.139 μm for an overall signal length (127 chips) of 0.8019 cm.

It has been shown[16] that the electrical Q of an interdigital surface wave transducer depends only on the fractional bandwidth of the transducer and the material coupling coefficient. If we assume that parasitics are zero and that a simple one pole matching network is used, then it is possible to construct the generalized insertion loss curves shown in Fig. 7.11. Double ended operation with two identical transducers has been assumed, band edge mismatch loss is 1 dB, and 6 dB bidirectionality loss has been included. The derivation of these curves is covered in more detail in ref. 16 and later in this section. For now we are only interested in using them to estimate insertion loss.

Most phase coded surface wave devices operate in the wideband region, to the right of the breakpoint. In the wideband region the single transducer insertion loss increases 6 dB per octave when the matching network is designed to cover exactly the acoustic signal bandwidth. This is the usual case for bandpass filters and the input transducers of phase coded devices. On the other hand, if either the electrical bandwidth, determined by the transducer electrical Q and matching network, or the acoustic bandwidth is varied without changing the other, then only 3 dB change in insertion loss results from each octave change in bandwidth. This is the usual case for the individual taps of the tapped delay lines used for the coded transducer because the electrical bandwidth is determined by the chip rate or the correlation signal bandwidth. The acoustic bandwidth is much greater to minimize waveform distortion.

Returning to our example, the input transducers have a fractional bandwidth of 16.7%, yielding an insertion loss of 14.3 dB from the curve for ST quartz. The coded transducer has only three pairs per tap for a

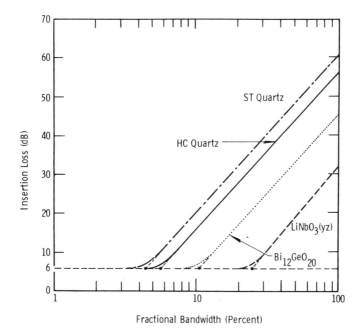

Figure 7.11 Minimum achievable insertion loss for two transducers on various substrates. Copyright 1973 by The Institute of Electrical and Electronic Engineers, Inc. Reprinted, with permission, from *IEEE Trans.* **MTT-21**, 1973, p. 171.

fractional bandwidth of 33%. Doubling the bandwidth results in an additional 6 dB of loss if the matching network is also doubled. If we keep the matched bandwidth at 16.7%, the code tranducer insertion loss is 17.3 dB, for a total device CW insertion loss of 31.6 dB.

These first order calculations can be made quite rapidly to determine if the desired waveform is compatible with system requirements. Other practical considerations—such as parasitic elements, compression gain or loss, losses due to intrinsic code structure, and measurement techniques—are discussed later in this section.

Distortion Effects Due to Phase Errors. Many influences can cause the filter impulse response to be in error in a way that looks like, or is, incorrect finger placement. The easiest to analyze are those that cause a systematic error equivalent to a change in surface wave velocity.[17] Important errors in this class result from incorrect photoreduction of device artwork, temperature variations, substrate orientation errors, and mechanical stress.

Another class of phase errors is due to random or systematic placement errors in the pattern generation process. Most routine devices can be designed so that pattern errors are so small they do not contribute significantly to overall performance. In addition, each type of pattern generator has its own characteristic errors, which must therefore be analyzed separately. For these reasons pattern generation errors are not discussed further.

A discussion of scaling phase errors falls naturally into two parts: (1) determination of the allowable error for a given requirement and (2) the magnitude of error produced by temperature, orientation, and other causes.[17]

The Effect of Phase Errors on Correlation Response. The errors to be analyzed produce a uniform scaling of the signal. To provide some insight, consider a CW signal as illustrated in Fig. 7.12. The perfect device is represented by three interdigital electrode pairs. An acoustic surface wave incident from the left generates a sinusoidal voltage on the transducer as it passes under the electrodes. This signal is maximum when

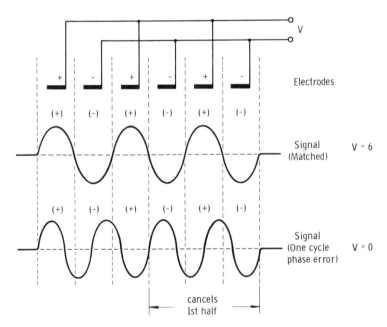

Figure 7.12 Phase errors in pulsed CW signals. Copyright 1972 by The Institute of Electrical and Electronic Engineers, Inc. Reprinted, with permission, from *Proc. 1972 Ultrasonics Symposium*, p. 422.

exactly three cycles of signal match up with the electrodes. As the frequency increases, the voltage on the transducer decreases and disappears completely when a full extra cycle is included under the transducer. This may be seen in the bottom curve, where the signal generated by the right half of the acoustic wave exactly cancels the signal generated by the left half.

Now consider a PSK device in which the electrode geometry is the time inverse of the "exact" signal to be correlated. The correlation response over all time is given by

$$g(\tau) = \int_{-\infty}^{\infty} u(t)u'(t-\tau)^* \, dt \qquad (7.9)$$

where $u(t)$ is the "exact" signal, $u'(t)$ is the reference function represented by the device, and $*$ indicates the complex conjugate.

One can perform a brute force calculation of the correlation response for arbitrary values of the scaling error. However for most cases of practical interest, the phase error is small enough and the bandwidth is narrow enough that changes in the chip locations are of secondary importance compared to phase differences. In other words, for frequency scaling that is not too large, the device function may be represented by the correct function with a small frequency shift ϕ (the Doppler approximation of radar analysis).

$$u' = ue^{i\phi t} \qquad (7.10)$$

Substitution of (7.10) into (7.9) results in the response function given by

$$\chi(\tau, \phi) = \int_{-\infty}^{\infty} u(t)u(t-\tau)^* \, e^{-i\phi t} \, dt \qquad (7.11)$$

where ϕ is the frequency shift between the two otherwise identical functions to be correlated. The effect of this frequency shift was described qualitatively for the CW signal shown in Fig. 7.12.

An additional simplification can be made for PSK signals. Because they are made up of piecewise uniform segments all of the same length, it is necessary to examine (7.11) only for values of t that are multiples of the chip length. Fortunately, it is possible to approximate the integral and get the variation of each sidelobe with phase errors as a simple sinusoidal function of ϕ. The details must be worked out individually for each code and sidelobe of interest. In particular, for the main correlation peak, $\tau = 0$ and the response function reduces to

$$\chi(0, \phi) = \int_{-\infty}^{\infty} |u(t)|^2 \, e^{-i\phi t} \, dt \qquad (7.12)$$

Thus $\chi(0, \phi)$ is the Fourier transform of the squared envelope of the signal, because the carrier frequency drops out. The earlier statement that the frequency scaling not be too large was related to the desirability that (7.12) be true, that is, that

$$\left|u(t)[u'(t)e^{-i\phi t}]*\right| = |u(t)|^2 \tag{7.13}$$

and that the corresponding argument be much less than one radian. This is equivalent to saying that the total phase error in the entire signal should be much less than the carrier phase change occurring in the reciprocal of the bandwidth of the signal (in one chip length).

For the common and important special case where the envelope of the signal is a rectangle of time duration T, the Fourier transform yields

$$\chi(0, \phi) = \frac{\sin \pi\phi T}{\pi\phi T} = \frac{\sin \pi\Delta}{\pi\Delta} \tag{7.14}$$

where Δ is the total phase error in wavelengths. Figure 7.13 is a plot of this function to both linear and logarithmic scales.

The extensive use of class C amplifiers in radar and communication systems justifies some additional analysis of this special case of rectangular envelopes. Equation (7.14) may be written in terms of the number of cycles in the signal and plotted as shown in Fig. 7.14, with sensitivity loss as the parameter. Three typical device specifications are indicated, with allowable phase errors from 27 to 275 ppm.

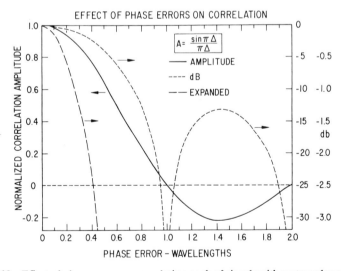

Figure 7.13 Effect of phase errors on correlation peak of signals with rectangular envelope functions.

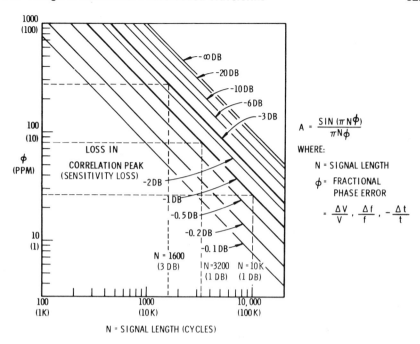

Figure 7.14 Effect of signal length on allowable phase errors. Copyright 1972 by The Institute of Electrical and Electronic Engineers, Inc. Reprinted, with permission, from *Proc. 1972 IEEE Ultrasonics Symposium*, p. 423.

As an example, Fig. 7.10a showed the signal generated by a 100-chip biphase code with 10.5 MHz bandwidth at 168 MHz (1600 cycles). This signal was applied to a second device to produce the correlation response of Fig. 7.10b. The effect of phase errors is to increase the sensitivity loss by reducing the main correlation peak. In special codes with unusually low starting sidelobes, the magnitude of the worst sidelobe may increase substantially, but more generally the most pronounced effect on sidelobes is a change in magnitude relative to each other.

Causes of Phase Errors. Temperature changes produce phase errors through two mechanisms; both the surface wave velocity and the substrate size change with temperature. Normally it is assumed that the devices are all fabricated at the same temperature. Then the velocity and expansion terms can be combined into a single temperature coefficient of delay. Carr et al.[18] have analyzed this situation and tabulated measured values taken from the literature for several common materials and orientations. An extensive set of calculated results is given in Slobodnik.[19]

Quartz is a particularly useful material because it has a zero temperature coefficient cut at room temperature (+42.75° Y cut).[20] The temperature of maximum delay may be varied several degrees either side of room temperature by small changes in the rotation angle.[21] Figure 7.15 shows the calculated phase error based on only the quadratic term given by Schulz et al.[20]

The sensitivity loss of any correlation device can be calculated as a function of temperature by combining Fig. 7.15 with Fig. 7.14, as illustrated in Fig. 7.16 for the 1600 cycle biphase code discussed earlier. Note the close agreement between the theoretical curve and the experimental results for mount B. This mount consisted of a 0.63 mm thick device bonded to an alumina substrate with a thin layer of RTV silicon rubber.

Mechanical stress that causes phase errors is typically introduced either by differential thermal expansion or by forces applied during the mounting process. The effects of thermal expansion are illustrated by mount A of Fig. 7.16, which consisted of the quartz device bonded to PC board with RTV. Comparison of mounts A and B illustrates the advantage of using substrate materials reasonably well matched to quartz in thermal expansion. Similar sensitivity loss results from other mechanical stresses, such as bending during mounting to a curved substrate.

Small alignment errors in cutting and fabricating devices can result in

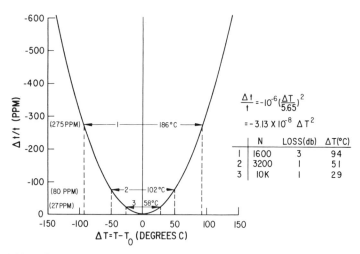

Figure 7.15 Effect of temperature on phase errors (*ST*-cut quartz). Copyright 1972 by The Institute of Electrical and Electronic Engineers, Inc. Reprinted, with permission, from *Proc. 1972 IEEE Ultrasonics Symposium*, p. 423.

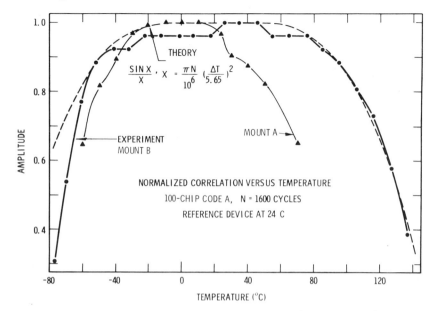

Figure 7.16 Temperature variation of correlation response (100-chip device). Copyright 1972 by The Institute of Electrical and Electronic Engineers, Inc. Reprinted, with permission, from *Proc. 1972 IEEE Ultrasonics Symposium*, p. 423.

velocity errors approaching 0.1%. This exceeds the effect of temperature on *ST* quartz. Alignment errors are also important on lithium niobate when several devices must be matched to each other in the same thermal environment. The angles used for quartz, illustrated in Fig. 7.17, are consistent with the IEEE standards on piezoelectricity.[22] The changes in velocity for errors in each of the angles are shown in Fig. 7.18. Note the strong dependence of velocity on the cutting angle ϕ and the comparatively weak dependence on the propagation angle ψ. In equation form

$$\frac{\Delta V}{V} = [343\delta\phi + 99\theta^2 + 58\psi^2] \times 10^{-6} \qquad (7.15)$$

In a similar way the errors for *Y*-cut, *Z*-propagating lithium niobate may be expressed as[23]

$$\frac{\Delta V}{V} = [13.8\delta\phi^2 + 618\theta + 138\psi^2] \times 10^{-6} \qquad (7.16)$$

where in each case (angles in degrees) $\delta\phi$ equals rotation error of surface about the axis of the desired propagation direction, θ equals angle

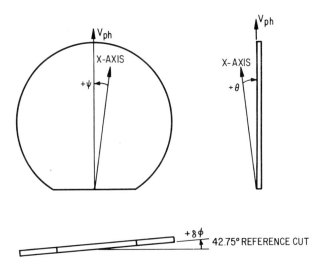

Figure 7.17 Definition of angles for velocity calculations on *ST* quartz. Copyright 1972 by The Institute of Electrical and Electronic Engineers, Inc. Reprinted, with permission, from *Proc. 1972 IEEE Ultrasonics Symposium*, p. 423.

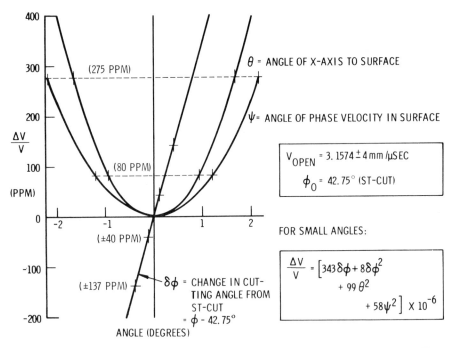

Figure 7.18 Effect of orientation on velocity (*ST*-cut quartz). Copyright 1972 by The Institute of Electrical and Electronic Engineers, Inc. Reprinted, with permission, from *Proc. 1972 IEEE Ultrasonics Symposium*, p. 423.

between the desired propagation direction and the substrate surface, and ψ equals angle between the projection of the desired propagation direction on the surface and the actual direction.

Evaluation Procedure. Evaluation of the effect of phase errors on a surface wave filter starts with the filter specification. From this the number of cycles of signal can be determined (center frequency × time, or time-bandwidth product ÷ fractional bandwidth, etc.). System specifications usually also set a limit on the maximum allowable sensitivity loss or frequency shift. The phase error limit is then determined from (7.14) or from Fig. 7.14.

The allowable temperature range and orientation tolerance are immediate consequences of the allowable phase error, using Figs. 7.15 and 7.18, or the corresponding equations. The wide operating temperature range of devices made on *ST* quartz is its main advantage. For most current devices the temperature range is greater than 100°C.

The most stringent orientation requirement is on the cutting angle. Fortunately, the quartz industry has considerable experience cutting crystal oscillators to nearly the same angle with tolerances of 0.5 to 4 min. Large quantities are required to take advantage of these techniques, however. The propagation angle is the least critical, usually determined in a production environment by photomask alignment accuracy. With proper attention to alignment mark design, the photomask alignment can be held well within requirements. The allowable tolerances on lithium niobate are generally much tighter than those on quartz. In practice, the large, approximately linear temperature dependence of time delay can be used to advantage to compensate for other errors. An oven and additional electronics are required for this or any of several other effective techniques.

Distortion Effects Due to Acoustic Reflections. Of the several second order effects that are important in surface wave filters, the most significant for long PSK devices is acoustic reflection from the electrode edges.[24] The effective acoustic impedance is modified under the electrodes by both the additional mass of the metalization and the reduced velocity caused by electrode shorting of the electric fields. As an impulse of acoustic energy propagates under the electrodes, a small portion is reflected at each edge, with 180° phase difference depending on whether the acoustic impedance change is up or down. These first reflections are spread out in time, but each one generates a second reflection as it passes back under the fingers. The second reflections from each tap are all delayed the same length of time, hence add coherently in a binary-coded device, regardless of the sense of the chip. Therefore an impulse launched by the transmit transducer soon accumulates many bunches of acoustic energy following it down the device at time separations of two chips. This energy can be detected at the receive transducer. This energy is also detected by the last chips of the code, producing considerable amplitude and some phase distortion in the impulse response.

The equivalent circuit model, when modified to include the impedance discontinuities at the electrode edges, allows prediction of the effects due to reflections in excellent agreement with experiment.[24] Figure 7.19 shows both theory and experiment for a 100 chip device on ST quartz. The directly transmitted impulse has been clipped on the theoretical curve to allow the following pulses to show more clearly. The large pulse 2 μsec later is due to reflections from the T^- and R^+ transducers spaced 1 μsec away. The frequency response shows the characteristic notches associated with the 10 MHz tap spacing and also the ripple associated with reflection from the extra sampling transducers.

Prevention of Acoustic Reflections. There are several methods for preventing acoustic reflections from interfering with filter performance. Only three are considered here.

The tilted or slanted design[25] displaces successive chips vertically so that reflections from one chip are not detected by others. Excellent results have been obtained using this technique with only modest additional insertion loss.

The second technique, using split and dummy fingers, prevents reflections rather than avoiding them. Each finger is split in half and the halves separated by $\lambda/8$. Both pieces are connected to the same pad. The reflections from corresponding edges of successive fingers cancel exactly at the synchronous frequency. The spaces between chips must be filled with dummy split fingers to maintain the periodicity and cancellation. Where it can be used, this approach gives the best results of any technique by eliminating the cause of the distortion. The most important limiting factor is the requirement for linewidths equivalent to doubling the device frequency. Also, at very wide bandwidths, the cancellation effect breaks down.[26] The small additional attenuation from the large number of fingers can be compensated by increasing the overlap on successive chips.

The third method minimizes the effect of reflections by modifying the code design, not always an allowable solution. The reason for the large distortion in binary codes is the coherent summation of the reflection amplitudes. If, instead, the reflections from successive chips can be made to cancel, distortion is minimized. Cancellation occurs if successive chips

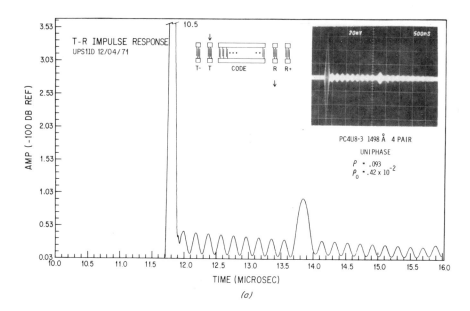

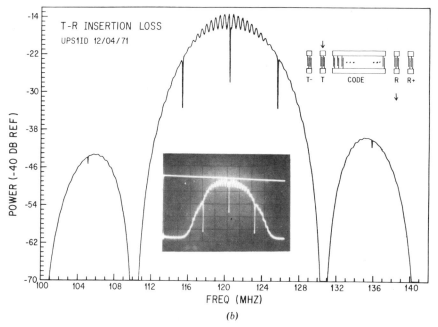

Figure 7.19 Theory and experiment for acoustic transmission through binary PSK devices (100 chips at 10.5 MHz chip rate, four pair taps). (*a*) Impulse response envelope. (*b*) Frequency response (10 dB per division).

331

differ in placement by $\pm 90°$ instead of $\pm 180°$. The resultant minimum-shift keyed waveforms have reduced distortion, but reflections still add from every second chip. Every other pulse shown in Fig. 7.19a will be missing. When the 90° phase shifts are chosen at random, the reflections following the transmitted pulse virtually disappear.[30]

Electrical Terminal Performance. The insertion loss of any device depends on its electrical Q_e compared to the signal Q, as well as the ability to match device terminal impedances to the source and load impedances. Hartmann et al.[16] have shown that a good approximation to surface wave filter impedances (and resultant Q) can be obtained by considering only the fractional bandwidth of the signal that can be generated by the individual transducers and the material constants.

Surface wave filters can be approximately represented by the equivalent circuits shown in Fig. 7.20. The resistance represents power radiated as acoustic energy; hence, it is a strong function of frequency. However, its average value over the operating bandwidth can be readily calculated using formulas derived on the basis of the impulse model.[16] These

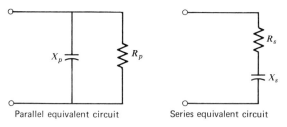

Parallel equivalent circuit   Series equivalent circuit

Figure 7.20   Surface wave transducer equivalent circuits.

$$X_p = \frac{1}{2\pi f_0 C_S N W} = \frac{1}{2\pi f_0 C_p}$$

$$R_p = X_p Q_e \qquad Q_e = \frac{\pi}{4k^2}\frac{\Delta f}{f_0} = \frac{R_p}{X_p} \qquad R_S = \frac{X_p}{Q_e}$$

In the high-Q limit $\left(\text{errors} \approx \frac{1}{Q^2}\right)$: $X_S = X_p \qquad R_S R_p = X_p^2$

C_p = parallel static capacitance of the entire transducer

C_S = static capacitance per pair per unit length

f_0 = transducer center frequency

Δf = desired acoustic bandwidth

k = acoustic coupling coefficient

N = number of finger pairs

Q_e = electrical Q of transducer

R_p = parallel equivalent radiation resistance

R_S = series equivalent radiation resistance

W = interaction width

X_p = parallel equivalent static capacitance

X_S = series equivalent static capacitance

Table 7.2 Data Describing Selected Design

	Interaction Width (in.)	Fractional Bandwidth ($\Delta f/f_0$)	Pairs per Tap	Number of Taps	Total Finger Pairs
Wide-band transducer	0.040	0.167	6	1	6
Coded transducer	0.040	0.333	3	127	381

formulas are collected in Fig. 7.20 with definitions of the symbols used.

As an example, consider the design of a device to produce a 127 chip signal at 300 MHz with 50 MHz chip rate. To minimize phase errors over a useful temperature range, it is to be built on ST-cut quartz and to minimize electrode reflections, thin (800 Å) electrodes of aluminum are used. Then k^2 is 0.0016, C_S is 0.55 pF/cm, the surface wave velocity is 3.157 mm/sec, and the electrode resistivity is 0.34 Ω/square. The selected design is described by the data in Table 7.2.

A typical coded device has two transducers: a wide-band input that is one chip long and a coded output with one tap for each chip. Only the interaction width and pairs per tap are adjustable parameters. Generally parasitics and insertion loss are not strong functions of interaction width, provided the device is wide enough to prevent beamspreading. The width used here is convenient for easy fabrication of many filters on a single 2 in. disc of substrate. The number of finger pairs per tap is a compromise between the maximum possible number (for minimum insertion loss) and minimum number of one pair (for minimum electrode reflection and minimum band narrowing). Each requirement must be evaluated individually with respect to the desired dynamic range, sidelobe degradation, and sensitivity loss.

The filter input impedances can be determined directly from the formulas in Fig. 7.20, with the results shown in Table 7.3. Note in particular the large Q_e, the small C_p for the wide-band transducer, and the small series equivalent resistance of the coded transducer.

Table 7.3 Impedance Parameters for Selected Design

	Q_e	C_p (pF)	X_p (Ω)	R_p (Ω)	R_S (Ω)	R_F (Ω)	C_g (pF)
Wide-band transducer	82	0.336	1.58 K	129 K	19.3	40	1.2
Coded transducer	164	21.4	24.9	41 K	0.152	0.6	2.7

Parasitic Elements. Parasitic elements important to device insertion loss are resistive losses due to the finite resistivity of the interdigital fingers and stray capacitance to ground. See the equivalent circuits in Fig. 7.21. There is also a series inductance due to the input leads. Because this inductance is almost always smaller than that required to tune the reactance due to the static capacitance, it can usually be ignored in estimating insertion loss. Generally speaking, the finger resistance is most important in low impedance devices and stray capacitance in devices with very few fingers.

The bulk resistivity of aluminum gives a rough approximation to thin-film resistance. Approximately doubling the resistance of an 800 Å film to allow for thin-film effects and rough finger edges, and assuming

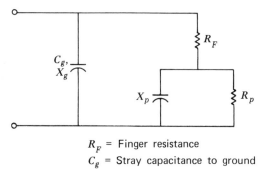

R_F = Finger resistance
C_g = Stray capacitance to ground

(*a*) Added parasitic elements

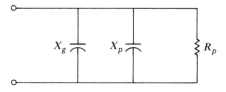

(*b*) Modified parallel equivalent

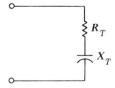

(*c*) Modified series equivalent, total input impedance

Figure 7.21   Equivalent circuit with parasitic resistance and capacitance.

that a complete finger pair is required to generate a conductive path between pads, total series resistance due to fingers (R_F) can be calculated. These numbers were shown previously in Table 7.3.

Parasitic capacitance C_g comes from both connector (or feedthrough) and pad capacitance to ground. Typical connector capacitance is 0.7 pF. Pad capacitance varies greatly, depending on pad size and proximity of the pads to the ground plane. This capacitance can be minimized by mounting a thin substrate on a thicker ceramic strip, which is then mounted to the metal enclosure. Crosstalk is minimized by placing a metal ground plane on the ceramic only in the area between transducers and not under pads or fingers. Resultant pad capacitance was estimated at 0.4 pF for the wideband transducers and at 2 pF for the coded transducer. The total parasitic capacitance is also shown in Table 7.3.

Generalized Matching Technique. A simple matching technique that is effective over most bandwidths of interest (i.e., not too wide a bandwidth) is illustrated in Fig. 7.22. The transducer is represented by X_T, a static capacitance, including parasitic capacitance; R_S, a series-equivalent radiation resistance; and R_F, a parasitic resistance. If this load were connected to the 50 Ω source, there would be insertion loss due to mismatch between the load and source and an additional loss due to the parasitic series resistance R_F.

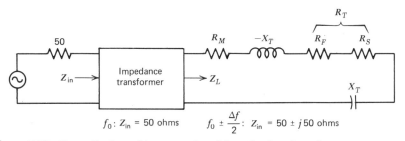

Figure 7.22 Generalized matching network and insertion loss formulas.

$$MM = -10 \log \frac{4R_L Z_0}{(R_L + Z_0)^2 + X_L^2} \qquad R_p' = R_p \frac{R_S}{R_S + R_F} \qquad PS = 10 \log \frac{R_S + R_F}{R_S}$$

MM = mismatch loss
PS = loss due to power splitting between load R_S and parasitic R_F
R_p = parallel equivalent radiation resistance
R_p' = parallel equivalent resistance, including parasitic

R_F = parasitic loss (finger resistance)
R_S = series equivalent radiation resistance
R_L = load resistance
X_L = load reactance
Z_0 = source resistance

Matching consists, first, of tuning out the capacitance. The result is frequently (as here) too narrowband for the signal of interest. Additional matching resistance R_M is added to satisfy the bandwidth requirement. The added resistance depends on the allowable standing wave ratio. A reasonable requirement for many applications is that the total load resistance be the same as the reactance X_T at the band edge. This results in a mismatch loss of 1 dB at band edge and a VSWR of 2.7. Such a criteria is too tolerant for some applications, but has been satisfactory when small solid state amplifiers are placed right at the device. An impedance transformer matches Z_L to the 50 Ω source.

Generalized insertion loss curves can be developed using the procedure described, assuming the parasitic elements are zero. The resultant curves were shown in Fig. 7.11. The addition of parasitic elements requires each case to be evaluated individually, using the additional formulas collected in Fig. 7.22.

Insertion Loss on Correlation. A practical problem arises when it becomes necessary to specify the insertion loss of a particular device. The frequency response of a PSK filter, unlike FM filters or bandpass filters, is a very complicated function of frequency. Figure 7.23a shows the frequency response of the 100-chip code device of Figs. 7.9 and 7.10. The measurements were made on unmatched transducers at a fast scan speed to obtain an "average" insertion loss. The smooth curve shows the response between transmit and receive transducers on opposite sides of the code and has the typical $(\sin x/x)^2$ response of two N-pair transducers in cascade. The more complex response is between one N-pair transducer (16-pair) and the coded transducer. The fine structure is shown in complete detail when a slow sweeper scan rate is used, as in Fig. 7.23b. Both transducers were matched for this figure. The details of the structure are strongly dependent on both the code sequence and any distortion due to matching networks, phase errors, and reflections.

Specification of filter insertion loss is best made on some basis other than frequency response. The most practical and reproducible method is based on the magnitude of the correlated signal compared to the input coded waveform. Generally speaking, there is a relatively clean signal available from an unmatched conjugate filter or from a digital code generator. The question of whether the coded signal and the filter are a properly matched filter pair is much easier to settle than what the proper average value should be of the frequency response. In practice, the actual signal used in the system is the one of interest. Any other method of specifying the insertion loss is less satisfactory because ultimately the level of the correlation peak must still be determined. As illustrated by the

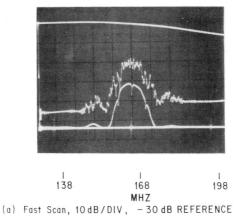

138   168   198
MHZ
(a) Fast Scan, 10 dB / DIV, − 30 dB REFERENCE

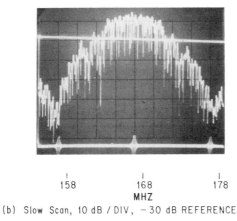

158   168   178
MHZ
(b) Slow Scan, 10 dB / DIV, − 30 dB REFERENCE

Figure 7.23 Insertion loss of PSK devices—frequency response. (*a*) Unmatched 100-chip filters showing *T* to *R* response (smooth) and *T* to code response. (*b*) Matched device, showing *T* to code response.

waveforms of Fig. 7.24, the measurement consists of determining the peak-to-peak correlation signal level, removing the device, inserting an attenuator in its place, and adjusting it until the detected input signal is the same level as the correlation signal. The insertion loss is then the attenuator setting.

Estimation of insertion loss before testing can only be done approximately, but the approximation is good enough for most purposes. Earlier sections described the calculation of CW insertion loss. Some numbers

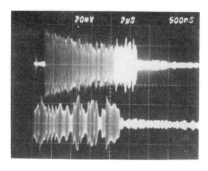

(a) Code generator, 16 interaction device, 20 mV/DIV

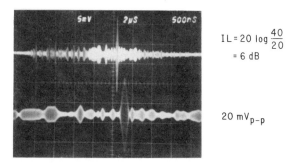

$$IL = 20 \log \frac{40}{20}$$
$$= 6 \text{ dB}$$

20 mV_{p-p}

(b) Correlator, matched 12 interaction device, 5 mV/DIV

Figure 7.24 Insertion loss of PSK devices on correlation. (a) Input waveforms to test device. (b) Correlation response. Intensified portion expanded in second trace of each response.

will have been determined based on the number of fingers per tap, the allowable VSWR, circuit complexity, and parasitic elements. Unless distortion of the signal by the matching network is acceptable, this insertion loss must be the loss to the peaks in the frequency response of Fig. 7.23a. However, a weighted average of this curve more accurately represents the energy transmitted by the device. The peaks are very sensitive to the details of the code and any distortion in its implementation. The difference between the peaks and the weighted average is called the *code loss* and is 6 to 8 dB for many noncyclic random or randomlike codes. On correlation there is a gain of $10 \log N_c$, where N_c is the number of chips in the signal.

The sum of the three losses, (1) minimum CW insertion loss, (2) code loss, and (3) correlation gain, gives a good approximation to the observed insertion loss for a wide variety of devices. To illustrate the calculation the response curves of the 100-chip device of Figs. 7.9 and 7.10 are used. The 16-pair input transducer should contribute 6 dB to the insertion loss (6.25% bandwidth in Fig. 7.1). The six-pair code taps should contribute 4 dB by matching them also to 6.25% bandwidth. The ideal minimum CW insertion loss would be 16 dB. Stray capacitance at the sixteen-pair input transducer adds another 3 dB, for a total of 19 dB. This should be compared to the 16 dB shown in Fig. 7.23b. That filter was actually slightly overmatched, with 18 to 20 dB usually producing better correlation responses. Code loss for this code was almost 7 dB and correlation gain for a 100 chip code is 20 dB, for an insertion loss on correlation of $19 + 7 - 20 = 6$ dB, as measured in Fig. 7.24. Overmatching a small amount reduces the CW insertion loss but also adds distortion, with little effect on the magnitude of the correlation peak.

7.3 Constraints on the Uses of Phase Coded Devices

It is desirable for many applications in identification, system synchronization, and spread spectrum communications to develop surface wave matched filters that can be readily programmed on a chip-by-chip basis. Techniques for performing programmable matched filtering have not been developed to the extent of the conventional fixed code matched filtering. A discussion of programmable filters is of interest here primarily because the techniques have been demonstrated, and programmable filters will be available in the 1976 to 1985 period.

Three basic classes of programmable filters have been demonstrated. The first class, and the earliest to receive extensive study, consists of filters in which the phase of individual taps is switched. Examples are switching with external diodes, the use of MOSFET's as surface wave detectors on silicon, and integration of switches and taps on a common substrate. Such methods were reviewed by Staples and Claiborne,[27] who concluded that long, high-frequency codes are not yet practical with these methods.

A second class of programmable filters employs permutation of blocks of code, as is discussed in the next section. This technique is a usable compromise between complexity and flexibility for codes with a large number of chips.

The third class of programmable filter uses methods of correlating to an arbitrary waveform rather than programming the tap sequence. A recent system had a 50 MHz bandwidth and 10 μsec signal duration.[28] An alternative version transforms the signal and reference to the frequency domain where they are multiplied in a mixer before being transformed back to the time domain.[29] Both these approaches look promising for wideband programmable matched filters.

Large Time-Bandwidth Devices. The most critical problem in producing devices with time-bandwidth products of 1000 or more is controlling the phase errors well enough to realize the advantages of the large time-bandwidth product. Two approaches have been used: the pattern can be made with a high degree of accuracy or it can be made in several pieces, each with much less accuracy, and then assembled electrically.

Accurate pattern generation is limited by the absolute accuracy and error characteristics of photoreduction lenses, step-and-repeat cameras, and other pattern generation equipment, all of which are very sensitive to the equipment supplier, shop procedures, and operator skill. Some approximate limits are discussed in the next section. Care must be taken to avoid periodic errors and to ensure that distortion effects from a large number of fingers do not become excessive. When the waveform is segmented, however, each segment can be made an appropriate length for the frequency and bandwidth required and the equipment available. At least as important, distortion is greatly reduced without restricting system dynamic range. The code segments can be combined into one impulse response by a combination of tapped delay lines and cascading, as shown in Fig. 7.25. The taps on the delay line are not very critical because short lengths of coaxial cable can be used to align the code

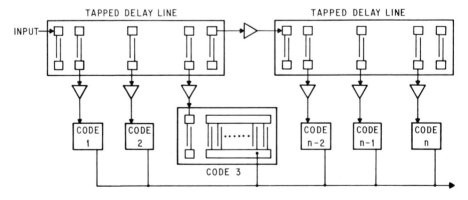

Figure 7.25 Generalized segmented device for large time-bandwidth PSK waveforms.

segments. Cascading must be limited as much as possible to prevent band limiting from the successive transducers and amplifiers.

The segmentation technique was used to implement devices for encoding and decoding a 1016 chip waveform with 50 MHz bandwidth. A single delay line with eight taps was used to feed an 8×8 switching matrix so that not only were eight 127 chip codes assembled into a single 1016 chip code, but the order of the codes could be changed at will. Both quartz and lithium niobate substrates were used with satisfactory results.[30]

The Range of Application of Phase Coded Surface Wave Devices. Waveform design, impedance levels, insertion loss, substrate preparation, and so on, all influence the applicability of phase coded surface wave filters to a given requirement. However the most critical consideration can usually be summed up in one word: lithography. Can the pattern be defined with sufficient fidelity to produce a signal with the required bandwidth, frequency, and time length?

The performance of surface wave filters improved as device designers became familiar with the photolithographic techniques developed for integrated circuits. Progress is expected to continue at a rapid rate because the microelectronics industry is itself on the threshold of a revolution in circuit lithography as electron beam, X-ray, and ion-etching techniques become practical. To keep things in perspective, it should be remembered that we are discussing devices with potential applications in communication systems. Because large numbers of users are usually involved, the choice of technique becomes price sensitive as well as technology sensitive. With this in mind, let us look first at what can be done within the constraints of current mass production techniques.

The most highly automated production lines in the world for photolithography are those used for making integrated circuits. Figure 7.26 shows a set of PSK devices built on a 2 in. quartz slice using such equipment. Both quartz and lithium niobate are readily available in this size. The codes shown are 10 μs on ST quartz. Although it is desirable to make devices for operation below 200 MHz, acceptable results can still be obtained at 300 MHz on ST quartz or 400 MHz on 41.5° Z-cut, X-propagating lithium niobate. For production lines using 3 in. slices, an additional 8 to 10 μsec is available, but at a lower carrier frequency, because of a slightly poorer resolution. Size restrictions are removed by going to custom fabrication, although increases above about 4 in. involve some premium from materials suppliers and increasing difficulty in handling and fabrication. For example, a single code pattern longer than 3.5 in. requires special equipment to generate and use.

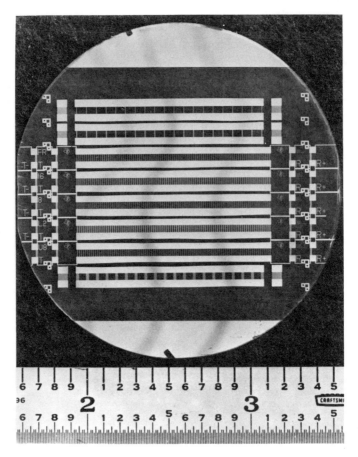

Figure 7.26 PSK devices on 2 in. slice of ST-cut quartz. Copyright 1973 by The Institute of Electrical and Electronic Engineers, Inc. Reprinted, with permission, from *IEEE Trans.* **MTT-21,** 1973, p. 268.

Resolution restrictions can be eased by use of narrow field projection printing. Line widths and space widths of 1 μm (0.7 to 1.0 GHz fundamental) can be obtained over a maximum field of 0.25 in. from a given reticle. Larger patterns require joining several segments with placement errors of a fraction of a linewidth. Addition of a laser interferometer to the translation stage on such a camera increases the effective device size to the maximum material size. Further improvement in resolution can be obtained by using electron beam techniques for producing photomasks and/or devices. The very best resolution (0.14 μm) has been obtained using scanning electron microscopes but over extremely limited fields of view. Several pattern generation and reproduction machines are compared in Table 7.4 in terms of field of view, resolution, and maximum number of line pairs (i.e., cycles of carrier signal) that can be produced without realignment.

For frequencies above 300 MHz and code sequences longer than 1 μsec, intrinsic surface wave attenuation can become important. Small losses can usually be ignored and larger losses can in principle be compensated by weighting the taps. Weighting is not desirable in some applications because the same device cannot be used for both code generation and correlation, thereby making fabrication tolerances more stringent. A reasonable loss allowance for practical filters is 3 dB. Assuming that surface preparation has been properly done, then attenuation increases quadratically with frequency, with 1 dB/μsec at 0.6 and 1.05 GHz for quartz and lithium niobate, respectively.

These restrictions can be summarized graphically as shown in Fig. 7.27. A 25% bandwidth has been assumed for practical reasons (insertion loss, spurious responses from device and electronics, etc.). Devices within the center shaded region are readily obtained in large quantities. Devices in the lightly shaded region are also readily available but require more

Table 7.4 Typical Lithography Limitations (1974)

Technique	Typical Equipment	Full Field Capabilities		
		Field Size (mm)	Linewidth (μm)	Line Pairs
Large-scale photoplotting	Gerber photoplotter	762×1016	50	10,000
Contact printing	Conventional production equipment, 3 in. mask	85 (diagonal)	4	10,000
	Conformal mask	50	0.5	50,000
High-resolution projection	Mann projection printer	6.3×6.3	1	3,100
with laser interferometer		6.3×250	1	120,000
Electron beam	Production oriented	7.6	2.5	1,500
		1.2	0.5	1,200
Electron beam	Scanning electron microscope	0.1	0.1	500

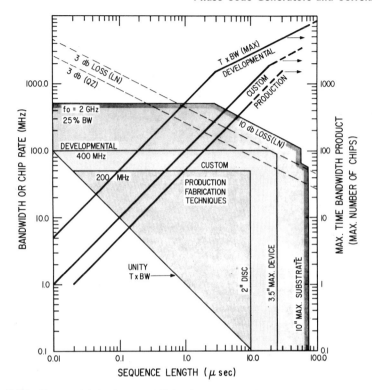

Figure 7.27 Current fabrication capabilities for coded devices. Copyright 1973 by The Institute of Electrical and Electronic Engineers, Inc. Reprinted, with permission, from *IEEE Trans.* **MTT-21,** 1973, p. 269.

custom work. The outer shaded region contains those devices that are technically feasible and potentially producible in quantity but still in the development stage. Extrapolations outside this region entail considerable technical as well as economic risk. The top and right-hand boundaries determine the maximum bandwidth and time lengths that may be obtained using the given level of technology. The product is the maximum chip length obtainable from a single substrate and is shown in the figure for each of the three regions. The boundaries, drawn for 1974 technology, are continually moving outward.

References

1. C. E. Cook and M. Bernfeld. *Radar Signals: An Introduction to Theory and Application*, Academic, New York, 1967, Chapter 8.

2. D. T. Bell, Jr., J. D. Holmes, and R. V. Ridings. "Application of acoustic surface wave technology to spread spectrum communications." *IEEE Trans.* **MTT-21,** 263 (1973).

3. G. J. Simmons. "A factorization technique for binary autocorrelation functions." *Proc. IEEE* **54,** 794 (1966).

4. C. E. Cook and M. Bernfeld. *Radar Signals: An Introduction to Theory and Application,* Academic, New York, 1967, Chapter 4.

5. R. H. Barker. "Group synchronization of binary digital systems," in W. Jackson, Ed., *Communication Theory,* Academic, New York, 1953, pp. 273–287.

6. W. S. Jones, C. S. Hartmann, and L. T. Claiborne. "Evaluation of digitally coded acoustic surface wave matched filters." *IEEE Trans.* **SU-18,** 21 (1971).

7. W. S. Jones, C. S. Hartmann, and T. D. Sturdivant. "Second order effects in surface wave devices." *IEEE Trans.* **SU-19,** 368 (1972).

8. W. W. Peterson. *Error Correcting Codes,* M.I.T. Press, Cambridge, Mass., 1961.

9. T. Sakamoto et al. "Coded pulse radar system," *J. Fac. Eng. Univ. Tokyo* **27,** 119 (1964).

10. M. J. E. Golay. "Complementary series," *IRE Trans.* **IT-7,** 82 (1961).

11. W. D. Squire, H. J. Whitehouse, and J. A. Alsup, "Linear signal processing and ultrasonic transversal filters," *IEEE Trans.* **MTT-17,** 1020 (1969).

12. C. C. Tseng. "Signal multiplexing in surface wave delay lines using orthogonal pairs of Golay's complementary sequences," *IEEE Trans.* **SU-18,** 103 (1971).

13. R. L. Frank. "Polyphase codes with good nonperiodic correlation properties." *IEEE Trans.* **IT-9,** 43, (1963).

14. S. W. Golomb and R. A. Scholtz. "Generalized Barker sequences." *IEEE Trans.* **IT-11,** 533 (1965).

15. D. A. Huffman. "The generation of impulse equivalent pulse trains." *IRE Trans.* **IT-8,** S10 (1962).

16. C. S. Hartmann, D. T. Bell, Jr., and R. C. Rosenfeld. "Impulse model design of acoustic surface wave filters." *IEEE Trans.* **MTT-21,** 162 (1973).

17. D. T. Bell, Jr., "Phase errors in long surface wave devices," in J. de Klerk, Ed., *Proc. 1972 IEEE Ultrasonics Symposium,* IEEE, New York, 1972, pp. 420–423.

18. P. H. Carr, P. A. DeVito, and T. L. Szabo. "The effect of temperature and Doppler shift on the performance of elastic surface wave encoders and decoders." *IEEE Trans.* **SU-19,** 357 (1972).

19. A. J. Slobodnik, Jr., "The temperature coefficients of acoustic surface wave velocity and delay on lithium niobate, lithium tantalate, quartz, and tellurium dioxide." Technical Report AFCRL-72-0082, Air Force Cambridge Research Laboratories, Bedford, Mass., 1971.

20. M. B. Schulz and M. G. Holland, "Surface acoustic wave delay lines with small temperature coefficient," *Proc. IEEE* **58,** 1361 (1970).

21. J. F. Dias et al. "The temperature coefficient of delay time for X-propagating acoustic surface waves on rotated Y cuts of alpha quartz," *IEEE Trans.* **22,** 46 (1975).

22. "Standards on piezoelectric crystals, 1949," *Proc. IRE* **37,** 1378 (1949).

23. G. Judd et al. "Acoustic signal processing devices." Technical Report No. ECOM-0023-F, U.S. Army Electronics Command, Fort Monmouth, N.J., 1973.

24. D. T. Bell, Jr., C. S. Hartmann, and R. C. Smith. "Measuring and modeling electrode reflections." *IEEE Trans.* **SU-19,** 400 (1972).

25. R. H. Tancrell and P. C. Meyer. "Operation of long surface wave interdigital transducers." *IEEE Trans.* **SU-19,** 405 (1972).

26. D. T. Bell, Jr., and D. W. Mellon. "Development of an L-band pulse compressor using surface waves," in *Digest 1973 IEEE-GMTT International Microwave Symposium,* IEEE, New York, 1973, pp. 126–128.

27. E. J. Staples and L. T. Claiborne. "A review of device technology for programmable surface wave filters." *IEEE Trans.* **MTT-21,** 279 (1973).

28. J. H. Cafarella et al. "Programmable matched filtering with acoustoelectric convolvers in spread-spectrum systems," in J. de Klerk, Ed., *Proc. 1975 IEEE Ultrasonics Symposium,* IEEE, New York, 1975, pp. 205–208.

29. R. M. Hays et al. "Surface wave transform adaptable processor system," in J. de Klerk, Ed., *Proc. 1975 IEEE Ultrasonics Symposium,* IEEE, New York, 1975, pp. 363–370.

30. M. Setrin et al. "An IFF system using block programmable surface wave signal expander and compressor," in J. de Klerk, Ed., *Proc. 1973 IEEE Ultrasonics Symposium,* IEEE, New York, 1973, pp. 316–323.

EIGHT
Surface Wave Interdigital Electrode Chirp Filters

H. M. GERARD

Hughes Aircraft Company
Fullerton, California

This chapter describes and explains surface wave techniques for implementing high performance, frequency modulated (FM) chirp filters. The subject enjoys a historical distinction, for chirp filters are one of the first applications[1] to which surface wave techniques were applied, and these techniques solved an important signal processing problem. Chirp filtering is also one of the most thoroughly studied applications, because of the many advantages of surface wave implementation over preexisting FM filter technologies, such as acoustic tape delay line, electromagnetic meander line, and digital filters. The advantages include enhanced signal processing capacity (time-bandwidth product) and design versatility, in addition to reduced design complexity and cost. Moreover, surface wave devices often provide the additional benefits of higher efficiency, improved accuracy, greater stability, and smaller size.

A major asset of surface wave technology is its foundation in photolithographic processing. Mask-making technology has advanced dramatically during recent years to the point that electrode patterns can now be composed automatically on laser interferometer controlled equipment with typical line resolution limits of 1.0 μm (or smaller) and positioning accuracy on the order of 0.25 μm. This capability permits routine fabrication of surface wave filters at frequencies as high as 1.0 GHz with tapping electrodes positioned with a delay accuracy of 70 psec. This inherent

347

photomask accuracy is a keystone for the development of accurate chirp filters.

We begin by comparing surface wave filters with earlier transversal filter implementations. Applications are then briefly discussed to emphasize the immediate practical value of the chirp filters for performing complex signal processing functions. Design principles for interdigital electrode chirp transducers are discussed in Section 8.2, and several design alternatives are explored for spanning a wide range of linear and nonlinear FM waveform requirements. A circuit model for relating design parameters to filter performance is presented in Section 8.3. Included are the effects of material properties, such as piezoelectric coupling constant, surface wave diffraction, and acoustic propagation loss, as well as the effects of electrical tuning circuits and load impedance levels. Design curves are included to aid in the characterization of a wide range of linear FM chirp filters on ST quartz and YZ lithium niobate substrates.

Section 8.4 contains measured data for some typical linear FM filters. The role of fabrication variances is explored with regard to establishing the practical limits within which use of metal electrode interdigital arrays for FM filters is feasible. The impact of developing technologies is then discussed with a view toward extending the range of practicality beyond the limits imposed by metal interdigital structures.

8.1 Surface Wave Transversal Filters and Chirp Filter Applications

Surface wave chirp filters fall broadly into the class of transversal filters because they generally involve the repeated delaying, sampling, weighting, and summing of an input signal. A transversal filter characteristic is achieved by applying specified amplitude and phase weights to individual samples of the input signal, which in nonacoustic implementations are usually taken at uniform time intervals. The weighted samples are then summed to form the filter output.

In a surface wave filter the electrical input signal is converted to a piezoelectric surface wave by the input transducer. The surface wave signal propagates along the crystal surface at constant velocity v_0. It is easily sampled at any position along the propagation path through the use of interdigital metal electrodes (taps) that convert piezoelectric energy back into an electric signal. Tap weighting is built into the tap structures, that is, directly into the electrodes. However, although internal weighting techniques can be successfully employed to control tap amplitudes, they cannot control tap phase. For this reason surface wave filters do not, in general, utilize uniformly spaced tapping electrodes. Instead, sampling times are adjusted to those times that correspond to purely real tap weights. Thus the surface wave transversal filter approach represents a small departure from convention, amounting to sampling at uniform *phase* rather than *time* intervals.[1,2] Aside from this difference, and aside from the fact that surface wave filters having hundreds of taps are readily made, the acoustic implementation is quite similar to that of more conventional transversal filters.

Chirp Filter Applications.   A chirp filter is a filter whose group delay is a nonconstant function of the instantaneous frequency of the input signal. In particular, a linear FM chirp filter manifests a linear delay variation with frequency. Both linear and nonlinear FM filters are widely used in radar pulse compression systems to increase range and target resolution. The chirp filter is the heart of a pulse compression system. Application of an impulse to an expansion filter, or encoder, produces a signal of duration $\Delta\tau$, and bandwidth Δf, coded so that its instantaneous frequency is a specified function of time. This coded signal is then boosted to the saturation level of a transmitter amplifier and radiated. The radar return signal is passed through a compression filter, the decoder, designed to have an impulse response that is the time-reversed replica of the impulse response of the encoder and is therefore the encoder's matched filter. The time-frequency characteristic of the compression filter causes each instantaneous frequency component of the chirp radar return signal to arrive at the output simultaneously, so that it produces a correlation peak. This peak corresponds to a signal processing gain equal to the filter time-bandwidth (TB) product $\Delta\tau\,\Delta f$. A TB product of 100 produces a processing gain of 20 dB. This increases the chirp radar range to equal that of a nonchirp radar having 100 times the power. Pulse compression is therefore quite worthwhile, because it is usually very expensive to increase transmitter power by even a few dB.

A pulse compression system using a linear chirp, constant amplitude waveform has a theoretical correlation peak with a sin x/x shape, whose largest sidelobes on both the leading and trailing edge are 13 dB below the main peak. In most radar applications it is desirable to include special amplitude weighting functions in the decoding filter to reduce these sidelobe levels. When nonlinear chirp filters are used, a particular time-frequency characteristic may be chosen to yield low time sidelobes without requiring amplitude weighting in the decoder. Based on the particular system application, a radar engineer might find either a linear or nonlinear FM waveform most desirable. Surface wave chirp filter design is so versatile that it is straightforward to implement either waveform.

A second application for which linear chirp filters are presently being evaluated is in real-time spectrum analysis using the "continuous-chirp transform."[3] Here the expansion filter is used to generate a precise linear chirp signal that is used as a sweeping local oscillator. The local oscillator signal is mixed with an unknown signal whose properties are to be identified, and the mixer output is injected into the matched compression filter. The result of multiplication by the chirp signal followed by convolution in the compression filter produces an output signal proportional to the Fourier transform of the unknown signal. A broadband receiver based on this principle has been built and tested recently with highly encouraging results.[4] The potential of this real-time signal processing function transcends simple Fourier transformation, because with the availability of inexpensive filters, transformers and inverse transformers may be readily configured to perform more complex processing functions, such as correlation of two signals.

In the pulse compression application, filter bandwidth relates to radar range resolution and filter dispersion to range enhancement. In the spectrum analyzer, chirp filter bandwidth determines the analyzer bandwidth and filter dispersion determines the analyzer frequency resolution. In both applications there is strong motivation to achieve large bandwidths *and* large time dispersion. In short, there is strong motivation to achieve dispersive filters with ever increasing time-bandwidth products. In both applications the insertion loss of the chirp filters restricts the system dynamic range, and filter errors seriously degrade system performance. Thus the goal of surface wave chirp filter design and construction is a filter with large TB product, minimum insertion loss, and maximum accuracy.

8.2 Design of Interdigital Electrode Chirp Filters

The design of chirp filters can be approached from different viewpoints. On the one hand, one could advance the philosophy, based on a prodigious quantity of existing reference material, that all higher order effects that occur in surface wave filters should be analyzed, understood, and incorporated into a general design prescription. This approach, though pedantically gratifying, would certainly relegate surface wave filter design to a small community of experts rather than to the general engineering community. On the other hand, one can be guided, as in this chapter, by the philosophy that surface wave filter design becomes easy when the pitfalls of higher order effects are deliberately avoided. Thus we begin with some words of caution concerning higher order effects, which can be particularly troublesome in strong coupling piezoelectrics. The remainder of this section details a straightforward surface wave filter design procedure whose validity is limited only in extreme cases, for which higher order effects cannot be properly controlled.

Figure 8.1 shows a pair of surface wave transducers configured to form a chirp filter. The input transducer has several constant overlap and periodic electrodes, but apodization (varying electrode overlap) is employed to control the tap amplitude weights in the chirped (nonperiodic) output transducer. Reducing the overlap w_n decreases the tap amplitude in two ways. First, the electrodes sample a smaller fraction of the incident acoustic beam, and second, reducing the overlap reduces the tap efficiency. The proper choice of electrode positions z_n (corresponding to sampling times t_n) and overlaps w_n is the first step in designing the chirp filter.

If we could consider the tapping electrodes to be ideal, noninteractive voltage samplers, the structures in Fig. 8.2 with individual alternating polarity electrodes would be excellent for sampling, weighting, and summing the surface wave voltages. In practice, however, we find that neglecting the real effects of the electrodes leads to two serious problems. The first results from the fact that a surface wave on a piezoelectric surface travels slower under a metalized (shorted) region (i.e., under the electrode) than along a free surface. The difference in velocity is proportional to the strength of the piezoelectric coupling constant, and though it may be only a few percent, it is a cumulative effect that can lead to large acoustic beam wavefront distortions, particularly in long metal electrode arrays. Figure 8.2 shows a modified apodized electrode structure having "dummy" electrodes that in no way affect the sampling strengths of the

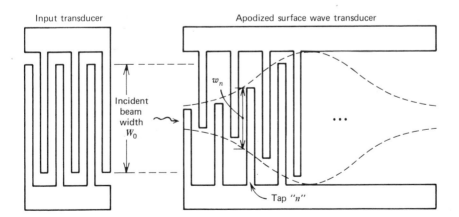

Figure 8.1 Basic transducer configuration of acoustic surface wave chirp filter.

active electrodes. These are included to ensure that the acoustic velocity remains relatively constant across the acoustic beam. Without these "dummy" electrodes the beam would travel more slowly through the center of the apodized array than near the edges, producing undesirable focusing effects. Because it involves no additional mask-making complexity, the use of "dummy" electrodes is *always* advised in apodized transducers, even for relatively short arrays on weakly piezoelectric substrates. The second problem is caused by the small discontinuity that each metal electrode presents to the acoustic beam traveling through the tapping array. These discontinuities arise from two sources, "mass loading" and "piezoelectric shorting." The first is related to the mechanical presence of the electrode material. It may be minimized, in general, by using thin aluminum for the transducer metalization. Therefore mass loading is not usually a serious problem for chirp filters at frequencies below about 500 MHz. The discontinuity caused by piezoelectric shorting, on the other hand, is present at all frequencies. Because it is a piezoelectric effect, the magnitude of the discontinuity is proportional to the piezoelectric coupling constant. For example, the discontinuity is about 1.9% on *YZ* LiNbO$_3$, but less than 0.1% on *ST* quartz. These small discontinuities can lead to severe problems because the tapping electrodes in the chirp filter usually lie on nearly periodic centers. When these centers are spaced close to half an acoustic wavelength apart, the small reflections from successive electrodes add in phase to produce a large acoustic reflection. Indeed we shall see that the surface wave filter design procedure requires the tapping electrodes be located squarely in these

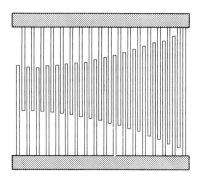
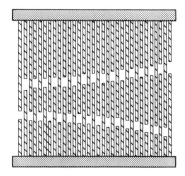

Magnified section, uncompensated design   Magnified section, "dummy" electrode,
                                                         compensated design

Figure 8.2 Comparison of electrode geometry with and without "dummy" electrode wavefront compensation.

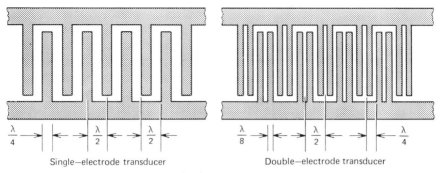

Figure 8.3 Comparison of single ($\frac{1}{4}$ wavelength) and double ($\frac{1}{8}$ wavelength) electrode configurations.

troublesome positions. The prospect of expanding a filter design procedure to include the effects of electrode reflections is quite formidable. It is, rather, more attractive to avoid reflection effects either by utilizing *only* weak piezoelectric substrates or by modifying the electrode structure, as shown in Fig. 8.3. In the latter case the two metal strips, comprising one tapping electrode, are placed on quarter-wavelength centers, causing the reflections from adjacent strips to cancel. The double-electrode solution, being compatible with strong coupling substrates, is therefore highly attractive. But it imposes added difficulty by requiring twice the photomask resolution capability necessary to produce the same frequency filter using conventional electrodes on half-wave centers. Empirically this double-electrode geometry has proved quite valuable, and it is generally mandatory when strong coupling lithium niobate substrates are used.[5]

At high frequencies, when photolithography resolution prevents use of double electrodes on strong coupling substrates, serious reflection problems can be avoided by utilizing only down-chirp designs.* Empirically, down-chirp filters do not exhibit a "stop band" within the filter bandwidth, as is the case with up-chirp filters.[4]

Electrode Positioning Law. As mentioned earlier, a complication arises in the surface wave implementation of a transversal filter because it is impractical to incorporate phase weights into the electrode structure. In practice this problem is bypassed by specifying the electrode positions so as to place the taps at times for which the desired chirp waveform is real,

---

* That is, with minimum delay at the maximum frequency.

that is, at times for which the sample phase is 0 or π, as shown in Fig. 8.4. For a general waveform given, in complex notation, by

$$h(t) = a(t) \, e^{-j\phi(t)} \qquad (8.1)$$

the frequency versus time characteristics are determined by

$$f(t) \equiv \frac{-1}{2\pi} \frac{\partial \phi(t)}{\partial t} \qquad (8.2)$$

The sample times t_n are found by solving the equation

$$\phi(t_n) = n\pi + \text{constant} \qquad (8.3)$$

and the corresponding spatial positions of the electrodes are given by

$$z_n \simeq v_0 t_n \qquad (8.4)$$

where v_0 is the "free surface" surface wave velocity. More accurately, particularly with strong coupling piezoelectrics for which the presence of metal electrodes introduces significant additional delay, the correct positions must be calculated iteratively,[6] from the relation

$$[z_n - z_{n-1}] \simeq v_0[t_n - t_{n-1}] - l_n \left[\frac{\delta v}{v_0}\right] \qquad (8.5)$$

where l_n is the width of the nth electrode, $\delta v / v_0$ is the fractional change in velocity caused by the shorting effect of the metal, and $[t_n - t_{n-1}]$ is found

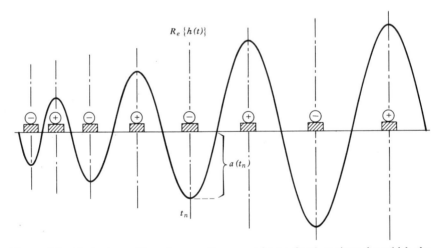

Figure 8.4 Electrode positions for sampling an arbitrary signal at times for which the sample weights are real.

from the solution of (8.3).* If the electrode pattern is designed with the electrodes and adjacent gaps having equal widths, that is, $l_n = (z_n - z_{n-1})/2$, then (8.5) reduces to (8.4) with an effective reduced velocity of

$$v_{eff} = \frac{v_0}{1 + \frac{1}{2}(\delta v/v_0)} \simeq v_0\left(1 - \frac{1}{2}\frac{\delta v}{v_0}\right) \tag{8.6}$$

It is important to mention that when the electrode patterns are composed using a photorepeater the process is least expensive when l_n is held constant at $l_n = l_0$. If positioning is not determined by iterative calculation, the cumulative tap position error amounts to $\Delta z = N_{tot}l_0\,(\delta v/v_0)$, where N_{tot} is the total number of metal electrodes in the array. Thus only if N_{tot} and $(\delta v/v_0)$ are small enough that $N_{tot}(\delta v/v_0) \ll 1$, is the cumulative error in neglecting the shorting effect negligibly small.

As a simple example that is particularly relevant to this chapter, we calculate the electrode positions for a linear downchirp filter of bandwidth Δf and dispersion $\Delta\tau$. If all the dispersion is accomplished in one array, as shown in Fig. 8.1, and the desired time waveform has constant amplitude, then the desired impulse response is

$$h(t) = \begin{cases} \exp\left[j2\pi\left(f_0 t + \frac{\Delta f}{2\Delta\tau}t^2\right)\right] & \text{for } |t| \le \frac{\Delta\tau}{2} \\ 0 & \text{for } |t| > \frac{\Delta\tau}{2} \end{cases} \tag{8.7}$$

Combining (8.3) and (8.7) leads to $2[f_0 t_n + (\Delta f/2\Delta\tau)t_n^2] = n - (N_{tot}/2)$, where the constant, $N_{tot} = (2f_0\Delta\tau + 1)$, which equals the number of electrodes in the chirp array, has been included to make $t_n = 0$ at the center of the array. Solving for t_n and using (8.4) as modified for equal electrode widths and gaps gives

$$z_n = v_{eff}f_0\frac{\Delta\tau}{\Delta f}\left[-1 + \left[1 - \frac{1}{f_0^2}\frac{\Delta f}{\Delta\tau}\left[\frac{N_{tot}}{2} - n\right]\right]^{1/2}\right] \tag{8.8}$$

Thus the sampling times are directly related to the phase of the desired filter response. The actual electrode *positions* corresponding to these *times* are then derived by using the pertinent acoustic wave velocities.

If a periodic input transducer, as shown in Fig. 8.1, is used and the required bandwidth is large, it may be necessary to add an amplitude modulation function $a(t)$ in (8.7) to equalize for the input transducer

---

* The term $(\delta v/v_0)$ is a constant that is approximately equal to half the piezoelectric coupling constant of the substrate, that is, $\delta v/v_0 \simeq \frac{1}{2}k^2$.

roll-off at the edges of the filter passband. It is also possible, as we see later, that in some filter designs the effect of tuning circuits or transducer capacitance can introduce appreciable distortion in the overall filter phase response. In such rather special cases the particular nonlinear FM phase equalization term can be included in (8.7) to offset the anomalous phase behavior anticipated when the transducers are connected to external circuits.[6] Such phase equalization (or predistortion) is usually called for only when the filter has very broad bandwidth and very low loss, and this circumstance is not treated further here.

Electrode Overlap Weighting (Apodization). We have already learned that amplitude weights may be incorporated directly into the tap structure. However in order to relate relative tapping efficiency to the electrode overlap we must have a model that characterizes the physical workings of the tapping electrodes. With due respect to the complexity of the electrode–surface wave interaction, no thorough characterization is attempted here. Rather, we discuss a relatively simple model that has

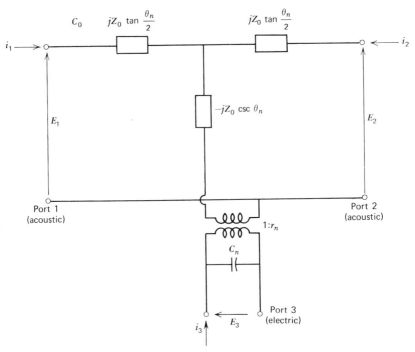

Figure 8.5 Crossed-field equivalent circuit model (Mason model) of one electrode section.

proved remarkably accurate in predicting the essential characteristics of the interdigital transducer.[8] This model, the cross-field model, has its foundation in bulk wave acoustics. It works very well, particularly when electrode reflections are either negligible or canceled by double electrodes.

The cross-field model relates the current and voltage at the electrical terminals of an interdigital transducer to the particle displacements and velocities of the surface wave that is piezoelectrially coupled to the electrode fields. A block diagram of the circuit model for a single electrode section is shown in Fig. 8.5. In essence, the equivalent circuit corresponds to an acoustic transmission line of impedance Z_0 and length θ_n, coupled through a mechanical-to-electric transformer of ratio $1 : r_n$, to the electrode capacitance C_n, and to the external electrical terminals. Using this circuit as a building block, the complete surface wave transducer can be represented as a combination of single electrode sections with acoustic ports in cascade and electrical terminals in parallel. Through lengthy but straightforward development of the crossed-field model it has been shown that, with proper choice of the electrode apodization, the electric-to-acoustic transfer function of an interdigital transducer is roughly proportional to the Fourier transform of the desired filter impulse response.[6] This result forms the foundation of the surface wave chirp filter design procedure.

Periodic/Chirp Filter Configuration. Chirp filters generally use two surface wave transducers to achieve the desired electrical input-to-output filter characteristic. The simplest configuration, shown in Fig. 8.6, employs a single constant aperture, periodic, nondispersive input transducer in combination with an apodized, nonperiodic, dispersive output array. This configuration is easiest to analyze because the acoustic beam width

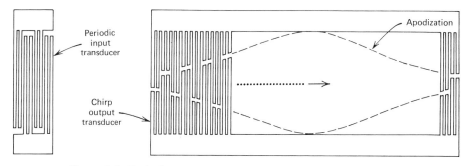

Figure 8.6 Periodic/chirp configuration shown with double electrodes.

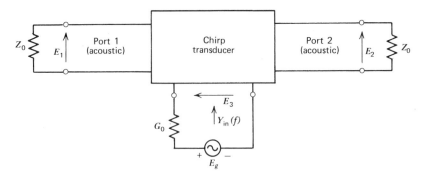

Figure 8.7 Equivalent circuit for electrical excitation of chirp transducer.

(hence power density) entering the output transducer is frequency independent. Thus neglecting the effects of multiple echos between the input and output transducers, the input and output transducers can be designed independently, so that the overall filter transfer function is the *product* of the transfer functions of the individual transducers.

The chirp transducer, driven by an external signal source, has the equivalent circuit depicted in Fig. 8.7, where G_0 is the source conductance and $Y_{in}(f)$, is the input admittance of the transducer.* The electric-to-acoustic transfer function $T_{13}(f)$, for the chirp transducer is given by

$$T_{13}(f) = \frac{j2\pi(2G_0k^2C_0W_0)^{1/2}\{\text{FT}h(t)\}}{G_0 + Y_{in}(f)} \tag{8.9}$$

Where the bracketed term is the Fourier transform of the desired chirp impulse response, k^2 is the piezoelectric coupling constant, C_0 is the capacitance per unit length of one electrode, and W_0 is the width of the incident beam (which equals the maximum aperture in the apodized chirp transducer). Equation (8.9) is valid only if the electrode overlaps w_n are related to the waveform amplitudes $a(t_n)$, by

$$\frac{w_n}{W_0} = \left[\frac{f_n}{F}\right]^{-3/2} \frac{a(t_n)}{A} \tag{8.10}$$

where f_n is the instantaneous frequency of the nth electrode, A is the maximum value of the chirp impulse response, and F is a normalization

---

* The electrical equivalent circuit of the chirp transducer is discussed further in Section 8.3, where $Y_{in}(f)$ is evaluated in terms of an "acoustic" conductance $G_a(f)$, an array susceptance ωC_T, an "acoustic" susceptance $B_a(f)$, and possibly some additional elements from a tuning circuit.

constant, determined so that the maximum value of w_n equals W_0. The instantaneous frequency f_n in (8.10) is evaluated using (8.2), that is,

$$f_n \equiv -\frac{1}{2\pi} \frac{\partial \phi(t)}{\partial t}\bigg|_{t=t_n}$$

In summary, then, we now have sufficient information to design a chirp filter. Equations (8.3) and (8.10) specify the positions and overlaps of the N_{tot} taps, as required to ensure the validity of (8.9). Because the transducer transfer function is proportional to the Fourier transform of the desired chirp impulse response, we can be certain that the transducer impulse response corresponds to the desired output waveform. Furthermore, the transfer function $T_{13}(f)$ in (8.9) is normalized so that $|T_{13}(f)|^2$ equals the transducer efficiency. The considerations relating to transducer efficiency are discussed in depth in Section 8.3.

On closer examination of (8.9) we see that $T_{13}(f)$ and $\{FTh(t)\}$ are not strictly proportional, because the denominator is a function of frequency through the term $Y_{\text{in}}(f)$. Because $Y_{\text{in}}(f)$ is itself related to the desired waveform $h(t)$, the utility of the filter design procedure is critically linked to the condition that $Y_{\text{in}}(f)$ is maintained at a relatively small or a constant level over the filter bandwidth. For most purposes the frequency variation arising from the denominator in (8.9) may be considered an inherent error whose magnitude must be kept small enough that the transducer response complies with the specified chirp waveform. In terms of chirp filter performance, the amplitude and phase errors related to the denominator term lead to a trade-off between filter accuracy and insertion loss. Chirp filter accuracy is critical because, in a pulse compression application, filter errors broaden the compressed pulse (decreasing target resolution) and reduce time sidelobe suppression (i.e., decrease the dynamic range).

Because of the restricted bandwidth of the periodic input transducer, the periodic to chirp configuration is limited to relatively narrow-band chirp waveforms. Periodic transducers have $\sin x/x$ passbands, where $x = [\pi N_p(f - f_0)]/2f_0$ and N_p is the number of electrodes in the periodic transducer. With optimal design and electrical matching circuits, the maximum practical transducer bandwidth increases with piezoelectric coupling constant. Typical values for the fractional bandwidth of the periodic transducers on ST quartz range between 3% and 5% and between 20% and 25% for YZ LiNbO$_3$. Although techniques do exist for modifying the periodic input transducer to achieve moderate increases in bandwidth, a more versatile approach for achieving broadband chirp filters is available.

Chirp-to-Chirp Filter Configuration. A very successful means of achieving broadband chirp filters consists of splitting the filter dispersion in half and using "mirror image" dispersive transducers, as shown in Fig. 8.8, for the input and output. In this configuration chirp filters with up to an octave bandwidth are feasible. The design procedure is, however, more complex, because both arrays are nonperiodic and both are usually apodized.

A subtle problem arises from the use of apodization in both transducers. In the periodic-to-chirp configuration the input acoustic beam is uniform over the aperture W_0, a consideration of fundamental importance when summing the tap voltages from output electrodes of overlap w_n in order to arrive at (8.9). When the chirp-to-chirp configuration is used, the strength of the signal at output electrode n is determined by the electrode overlap w_n and the width of the input electrode that launched the beam w_m. The total filter response thus involves the summation over all pairs of input and output apodized electrodes, m and n, with term-by-term tapping strengths dependent on the relative sizes of w_m and w_n. The overall chirp filter response is therefore determined by a double sum that is not factorable into individual input transducer and output transducer characteristics. This makes a rigorous design procedure extremely complex. To circumvent this problem it is *assumed* that at a given frequency f_n only the small segment of each chirp transducer immediately surrounding frequency f_n is strongly involved in launching or detecting the surface wave signal. It is assumed, further, that at frequency f_n the effective width of the resulting beam equals w_n. This is reasonably accurate when the apodization does not vary abruptly along the array. If the detecting transducer has the identical apodization as the launching transducer, the double summation problem disappears, because the effective launching and detecting regions have equal overlap. For this configuration (8.9) is

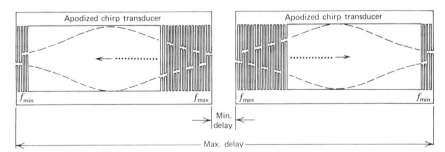

Figure 8.8 Chirp/chirp configuration (down-chirp) with "mirror image" apodization and double electrodes.

valid when the amplitude weights and electrode overlaps are related by*

$$\frac{w_n}{W_0} = \left[\frac{f_n}{F}\right]^{-3} \frac{a^2(t_n)}{A^2} \tag{8.11}$$

Thus we see that the apodization relationship between w_n and $a(t_n)$ is not the same for the chirp-to-chirp and periodic-to-chirp configurations. Two transducers are always required to construct the surface wave chirp filter, therefore it is important to remember that the overall transfer function is the product of the transfer functions T_{13} of the input and output transducers. When two "mirror image" chirp transducers are used, the overall transfer function is $[T_{13}(f)]^2$. Therefore each transducer must be designed so that $T_{13}(f)$ corresponds to the *square root* of the desired chirp function. That is, if $h_0(t)$ is the desired chirp waveform, then each transducer design is based on the auxiliary waveform $h(t)$, where

$$h(t) = FT^{-1} [FT\{h_0(t)\}]^{1/2} \tag{8.12}$$

and where FT^{-1} denotes inverse Fourier transformation. The procedure for determining the auxiliary function $h(t)$ in (8.12) appears straightforward but difficulties sometimes arise when the computed auxiliary function contains singularities. In this circumstance a slight modification in $h_0(t)$ is often sufficient to eliminate the singularities. For moderate to large time-bandwidth product waveforms adding weighted "tails" to the chirp function usually eliminates the singularities without introducing significant error.

The considerations for relating apodization w_n to waveform amplitude $a(t_n)$ are summarized as follows. When a narrow band chirp filter is required, a flat pass band, nondispersive, and periodic input transducer can be used in conjunction with an apodized chirp transducer, with overlaps given by (8.10). For broadband chirp waveforms we use the chirp-to-chirp configuration, with transducers apodized in accordance with (8.11) based on an auxiliary time waveform that is derived from the desired waveform using (8.12).

We end this section on chirp filter design by mentioning the design of matched pulse compression filters having high time sidelobe suppression, but a compression ratio of less than 10 : 1. In this domain passband ripple

---

* The double sum problem also vanishes if one chirp transducer has constant overlap while the other is apodized, in which case the pertinent apodization relationship is

$$\frac{w_n}{W_0} = \left[\frac{f_n}{F}\right]^{-3} \frac{a(t_n)}{A}$$

dominates the chirp filter frequency response and renders the conventional, linear chirp spectral weighting functions virtually useless. In fact, below 10:1 in compression ratio, linear chirp weighting functions give less than 25 dB sidelobe suppression. By taking advantage of the inherent design versatility of surface wave chirp filters, however, we need not be restricted to linear FM waveforms. Indeed we can specify, a priori, a desired low time-sidelobe, compressed pulse spectrum $WT(f)$ and the spectrum of a simple, linear FM expansion pulse $EXPAN(f)$. The problem then reduces to designing a compression filter whose response to input $EXPAN(f)$ is output $WT(f)$. The spectrum of the nonlinear FM compression filter $COMP(f)$ is given therefore by

$$COMP(f) = \frac{WT(f)}{EXPAN(f)} \tag{8.13}$$

An excellent, detailed discussion of this special filter synthesis procedure is contained in ref. 8.

8.3 FM Filter Performance

This section concentrates on the details of surface wave chirp filter performance as characterized by the electrical circuit model. The circuit model is an immensely valuable design aid for three reasons. First, it leads to simple relationships between the relevant substrate material constants and filter performance. Second, it encompasses the effects of tuning circuits, parasitic elements, and electrical loading. Third, the model allows the most important chirp filter properties to be characterized in terms of the familiar concepts of resistance and reactance, rather than a confusing mixture of electrical and elastic variables. This section begins by relating the circuit model elements to the chirp filter properties. The model is then used to explore design trade-offs between insertion loss, bandwidth, and accuracy. Propagation loss and acoustic diffraction effects are discussed and related to design limitations.

Equivalent Circuit of a Chirp Transducer. We have seen that the surface wave transducer is a three port device, including an electric port and two acoustic ports. Although the general scattering characteristics are determined by the specific electric and acoustic conditions on all ports, we can gain much valuable insight by examining the characteristics at the electrical terminals when the acoustic ports are terminated in their characteristic impedance. If we were to measure the impedance of the transducer at the contact pads, neglecting resistive losses in the electrodes, dielectric losses, electromagnetic radiation losses, and, for the moment, acoustic wave generation, the measurement would reveal only the capacitance of the interdigital metal structure. But these losses are not always negligible, and the actual impedance includes resistances corresponding to each power dissipation mechanism. Therefore the generation of propagating surface waves, carrying power from the transducer structure, manifests intself as an apparent resistive loss appearing across the transducer electrical terminals (i.e., the contact pads). In fact, we could measure this "radiation" resistance over the chirp transducer bandwidth. If the measured resistance results entirely from surface wave generation, then the electric-to-acoustic transducer insertion loss is determined directly from the measured VSWR. Consequently we can determine the overall insertion loss spectrum of a chirp filter (or at least the contribution from transducer losses) from independent measurements of the impedance of the input and output transducers over the filter passband.

The crossed-field model for conveniently relating surface wave transducer parameters to an equivalent circuit was mentioned in Section 8.2. The electrical circuit is most concisely described in terms of conductances and susceptances with the electrical admittance of the transducer given, in general, by

$$Y_{in}(f) = G_a(f) + j(\omega C_T + B_a(f))$$

Neglecting the higher order effects of electrode resistance and parasitic reactance the capacitor C_T is the electrostatic capacitance of the entire transducer structure. The frequency dependent conductance $G_a(f)$ corresponds to the surface wave radiation loss over the bandwidth of the transducer. The susceptance $B_a(f)$ is also related to the acoustic radiation and is a natural consequence of the fact that G_a varies with frequency. When the transducer electrical terminals are connected to a signal source, perhaps through a tuning or attenuating network, the completed electrical circuit typically resembles Fig. 8.9.

From the details of the crossed-field transducer model we find that the acoustic conductance of a surface wave transducer is related to the electrode geometry and position by[6]

$$G_a(f) = k^2 \left| \sum_{n=1}^{N_{tot}} (-1)^n \sqrt{f_n C_n} \sin\left(\frac{\pi}{2}\frac{f}{f_n}\right) e^{-j2\pi f t_n} \right|^2 \qquad (8.14)$$

where k^2 is the piezoelectric coupling constant of the substrate; C_n is the capacitance; f_n, the instantaneous frequency; and t_n, the temporal position

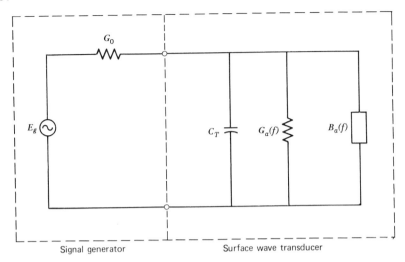

Figure 8.9 Equivalent electrical circuit for electrical excitation of untuned chirp transducer.

of the nth electrode. Similarly, the array capacitance equals the sum of the individual electrode capacitances

$$C_T = \sum_{n=1}^{N_{tot}} C_n = C_0 W_0 \cdot \sum_{n=1}^{N_{tot}} \left(\frac{w_n}{W_0}\right) \qquad (8.15)$$

where w_n is the electrode overlap dimension of the nth electrode. W_0 is the maximum overlap in the transducer, and C_0 is the capacitance per unit length for one electrode, which is a constant proportional to the dielectric constant of the substrate material. For completeness the radiation susceptance $B_a(f)$, which is generally negligible compared to the capacitive susceptance of the transducer, is derived from $G_a(f)$ using the Hilbert transform,

$$B_a(f) = \frac{1}{\pi} \int_{-\infty}^{\infty} \frac{G_a(u)}{u-f} \, du \qquad (8.16)$$

In Section 8.2 we developed the mathematics for designing chirp transducers. With (8.14) to (8.16) we can now evaluate the transducer admittance $Y_{in}(f)$. And from (8.9) we can determine the transfer function of a general surface wave chirp filter. We derived the electrode positions t_n based on the desired filter phase response using (8.3) and the electrode overlaps w_n based on (8.10) or (8.11). Now calculation of the equivalent electrical circuit follows directly. The input admittance in turn permits us to calculate the magnitude of the transfer function and thus determine the power delivered to the acoustic conductance G_a at each frequency, which is equivalent to the transducer insertion loss spectrum.

Approximate Active-Electrode Representation for Linear Chirp Transducers. The equations for evaluating circuit elements are perhaps less than completely satisfying in that the general formalism does obscure some fundamental relationships between design and performance. For example, it is not clear how substrate coupling constant and chirp filter bandwidth relate to insertion loss, or how the maximum electrode overlap dimension W_0 relates to other chirp filter design parameters. To answer these questions we use a technique for approximating the crossed-field circuit elements for linear chirp transducers. Although this "active section" approximation is used for linear FM, the validity of the results seems to extend to more general cases, and therefore the conclusions are quite valuable for understanding and optimizing chirp filter design in general. The approximation is based on viewing a chirp transducer, at a given frequency, as comprised of a section of interdigital electrodes that is actively generating surface waves at this frequency. This "active section" is electrically in parallel with the remainder of the array, assumed acoustically inactive at this frequency. The electrode spacings in the linear chirp transducer are generally slowly graded, being nearly periodic over a substantial region surrounding any point in the array. We consider the "active section" as that group of electrodes for which the electrode spacings are nearly correct to give synchronous surface wave excitation at the driving frequency (i.e., the place where the surface wave propagates one array period in one cycle of the rf field). As is shown in Fig. 8.10, the

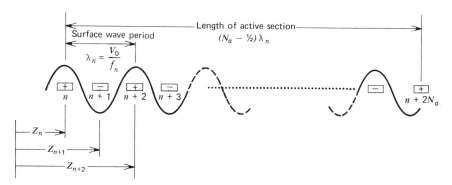

Figure 8.10 Diagram of chirp electrode spacings superimposed on $(N_a - \frac{1}{2})$ periods of wavelength λ_n, representing length of "active" section at frequency f_n.

active section is replaced by a periodic array whose length equals the propagation distance for which an acoustic wave would become 180° out of phase with the excitation fields of the linear FM-spaced electrodes. This criterion corresponds to the condition that, at the excitation frequency f, the contributions of electrodes on either side of the "active section" approximately cancel each other, making them virtually inactive acoustically. Based on the linear FM spacing law, the appropriate length L of this active section is given by

$$\left| k_p(0)L - \int_{-L/2}^{L/2} dz\, k_{\mathrm{FM}}(z) \right| = \pi \tag{8.17}$$

where $k_p(0)$ equals 2π divided by the acoustic wavelength at the center of the active section, and $k_{\mathrm{FM}}(z)$ equals 2π divided by the electrode period of the linear FM transducer as a function of position z along the transducer.* For linear FM, $k_{\mathrm{FM}}(z)$ is given by

$$k_{\mathrm{FM}}(z) = \frac{2\pi}{v_0}\left[f(0) + \frac{\Delta f}{\Delta \tau}\left(\frac{z}{v_0}\right) \right] \tag{8.18}$$

where $f(0)$ is the synchronous frequency at the center of the active section, v_0 is the surface wave velocity, Δf is the filter bandwidth and $\Delta \tau$ is the time dispersion of one chirp transducer. Equations (8.17) and (8.18) lead to the result that

$$L^2 = v_0^2 \frac{\Delta \tau}{\Delta f} \equiv [N_a \lambda(0)]^2 \tag{8.19}$$

where N_a is the number of periods in the active section and $\lambda(0)$ is the electrode period at frequency $f(0)$. Equation (8.19) leads to the result that the number of periods in the active section is given by

$$N_a(f) = \frac{f}{f_0} \cdot \frac{N_{\mathrm{tot}}}{2\Delta \tau\, \Delta f} \tag{8.20}$$

where N_{tot} is the total number of electrodes in the linear FM transducer ($N_{\mathrm{tot}} = 2f_0\, \Delta \tau + 1$) and f_0 is the midband frequency.

Making the approximation that N_a is the number of *periodic* electrode pairs equivalent to the total acoustic generation in a linear chirp transducer, we now replace the "active section" with such a periodic transducer. The acoustic conductance of this periodic transducer (at the synchronous frequency) is given by[8]

$$G_{a_{\mathrm{periodic}}}(f) \simeq G_{a_{\mathrm{LFM}}}(f) \simeq 8fC_0 w(f)k^2 N_a^2(f) \tag{8.21}$$

---

* For simplicity the appropriate summation has been replaced by an integral.

where $w(f)$ is the electrode overlap (apodization) at array frequency f. Thus (8.20) and (8.21) lead to a quick estimate of the acoustic conductance of the linear FM filter. Of course for a more accurate determination we cannot avoid the summation in (8.14).

Based on (8.15) and (8.21) we define the important transducer design parameter, the radiation quality factor (Q_R), as the ratio between midband transducer susceptance and conductance,

$$Q_R \equiv \frac{2\pi f_0 C_T}{G_{a_{LFM}}(f_0)} \tag{8.22}$$

If we express the total capacitance of the linear FM transducer as $C_T = C_0 N_{tot} W_{AV}$ where W_{AV} is the average overlap dimension (8.22) reduces to

$$Q_R = \left(\frac{\pi}{4k^2}\right)\left(\frac{\Delta f}{f_0}\right)\left(\frac{W_{AV}}{W(f_0)}\right) \approx \left(\frac{\pi}{4k^2}\right)\left(\frac{\Delta f}{f_0}\right) \tag{8.23}$$

Thus the quality factor of a general linear FM transducer depends only on the substrate piezoelectric coupling constant and the fractional bandwidth of the filter. As we shall soon see, the value of Q_R is important for comparing the transducer performance for different chirp waveforms on different piezoelectric substrates.

Chirp Design Trade-Offs. Equipped with an electrical circuit model for surface wave chirp filters and a simplified technique for evaluating the circuit parameters, we can formulate some general procedures for optimizing substrate material, transducer width W_0, and the electrical circuit for coupling the chirp transducers to a signal generator or load. Specifically these considerations relate to transducer loss, phase error, and acoustic reflection level, and they are controlled by the design of the electrical coupling circuit and the value of Q_R.

Figure 8.11 depicts the equivalent circuit of a chirp transducer coupled to a signal source of admittance G_0 through a transformer of ratio $1:r$ and tuned by a shunt inductor L. The only dissipative element shown in the transducer circuit is the conductance* G_a; therefore the power delivered from the generator to element G_a corresponds to the surface wave power generated in the transducer and radiated along the substrate.

---

* Parasitic losses, such as electrode conductance loss, have been neglected in this "idealized" treatment. These should be included as appropriate.

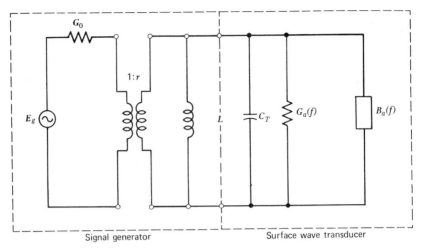

Figure 8.11 Equivalent circuit for chirp transducer, tuned and coupled to source through an electrical transformer.

The power delivered to the acoustic conductance, relative to the maximum power that the generator delivers to a matched load, is given by

$$\bar{p} = |T_{13}(f)|^2 = \frac{2[G_0/r^2] G_a(f)}{[G_0/r^2 + G_a(f)]^2 + [2\pi f C_T - \frac{1}{2}\pi f L + B_a(f)]^2} \quad (8.24)$$

where a factor of $\frac{1}{2}$ has been introduced to account for the bidirectional loss of the surface wave transducer. Equation (8.24) therefore corresponds to the conversion efficiency from electrical input to acoustic output from one end of the transducer. If we choose the value of L to resonate C_T at f_0 and neglect the radiation susceptance $B_a(f)$, (8.24) reduces to

$$\bar{p} \simeq \frac{2[Q_L/Q_R]}{[1 + Q_L/Q_R]^2 + 4Q_L^2[(f - f_0)/f_0]} \quad (8.25)$$

where

$$Q_L \equiv \frac{2\pi f_0 C_T}{G_0/r^2} \quad (8.26)$$

Equation (8.25) demonstrates that the transducer efficiency is controlled by the factor Q_L/Q_R, and likewise, the bandwidth, by the term $4Q_L^2[(f - f_0)/f_0]$. This general characteristic of all surface wave transducers indicates that at resonance maximum transducer efficiency occurs when $Q_L/Q_R = 1$. However, we shall see that it is more practical to restrict the values of Q_L/Q_R to the range of $Q_L/Q_R \ll 1$, with $Q_L/Q_R \simeq 0.1$ representing a common design guideline.

We impose constraint on circuit coupling to suppress two problems that would otherwise degrade the chirp filter performance. The first problem arises from the reflection, or "regeneration," properties of surface wave transducers. It can be shown that the reflection efficiency $|\Gamma|$ of a transducer is related to the transducer efficiency by[8]

$$|\Gamma| \simeq \tfrac{1}{4}\bar{p}^2$$

Therefore if $Q_L/Q_R = 0.1$, the midband transducer efficiency from (8.25) is -7.8 dB and, correspondingly, the reflection efficiency is approximately -21.6 dB. It follows that when two identical transducers are used to form the chirp filter there is a total transducer loss of 15.6 dB and a total reflection loss of 43.2 dB. The acoustic reflection (regeneration) results in an undesirable spurious time signal trailing the main filter impulse response. The second problem occurs when Q_L is large, independent of the size of Q_R. Equation (8.9) demonstrates that the electric-to-acoustic transfer function $T_{13}(f)$ is not *exactly* proportional to the Fourier transform of the desired chirp impulse response. The design procedure is only valid if the denominator of $T_{13}(f)$ is a slow function of frequency, and therefore constraints must be placed on the size of Q_L. For example, the transducer circuit in Fig. 8.11 has input admittance given by

$$Y_{in}(f) = G_a(f) + j\left[2\pi f C_T - \frac{1}{2\pi f L} + B_a(f)\right] \qquad (8.27)$$

For this case the denominator of (8.9), neglecting B_a, contributes a phase variation $\phi_e(f)$ given by

$$\phi_e(f) \simeq \tan^{-1}\left[\frac{2Q_L[(f-f_0)/f_0]}{1 + (Q_L/Q_R)\cdot[G_a(f)/G_a(f_0)]}\right] \qquad (8.28)$$

Thus since $G_a(f)$ is usually less than or equal to $G_a(f_0)$, the condition stated earlier that $Q_L/Q_R \le 0.1$ effects some reduction in the frequency variation of the transducer phase response. However, as seen by expanding (8.28) for small angles,

$$\phi_e(f) \simeq 2Q_L\left[\frac{f-f_0}{f_0}\right] - \tfrac{8}{3}Q_L^3\left[\frac{f-f_0}{f_0}\right]^3 - \cdots \qquad (8.29)$$

the value of Q_L must itself be limited in order to restrict the phase variation over the pass band. Clearly the presence of large transducer phase error is most likely for low loss filters (i.e., with large Q_L) having large fractional bandwidths.

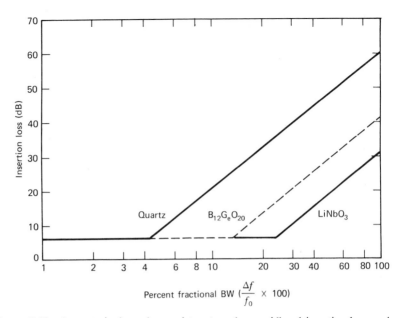

Figure 8.12 Asymptotic dependence of two-transducer midband insertion loss on bandwidth, for substrates of different k^2.

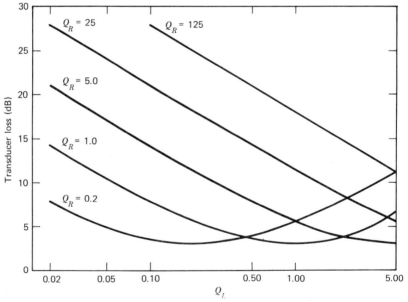

Figure 8.13 Chirp transducer midband conversion loss versus electrical coupling factor Q_L, with Q_R as a parameter—$\bar{p}(f_0) = [(2Q_L/Q_R)/(1 + Q_L/Q_R)^2]$.

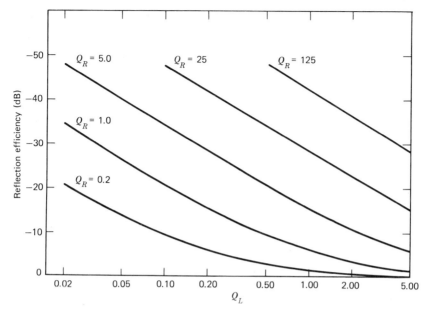

Figure 8.14 Chirp transducer midband acoustic reflection efficiency versus electrical coupling factor Q_L, with Q_R as a parameter—$|\Gamma(f_0)|^2 = [(Q_L/Q_R)^2/(1 + Q_L/Q_R)^2]$.

For $Q_L/Q_R \ll 1$, we see from (8.25) that transducer efficiency increases about proportional to Q_L/Q_R, and transducer bandwidth varies inversely with Q_L. As a general consequence of (8.23), we see, therefore, that transducer efficiency increases with piezoelectric coupling constant k^2, but decreases with fractional bandwidth $\Delta f/f_0$. Figure 8.12 exhibits this point, showing midband transducer loss plotted against filter fractional bandwidth, for several substrate materials of different k^2. Figures 8.13 and 8.14 show two curves that are helpful in determining the optimal drive and load circuit design for a chirp transducer. Midband transducer loss based on (8.25) and acoustic reflection loss are plotted against Q_L. Because Q_R is determined by the fractional bandwidth and piezoelectric coupling constant, the optimal value of Q_L is determined by consideration of the desired transducer loss and acoustic reflection loss. The required value of Q_L may be implemented in several ways, such as by suitable choice of the average aperture (i.e., C_T), by choosing the value of generator or load conductance G_0, or through the use of an electrical transformer of ratio $1 : r$.

Propagation Loss and Diffraction. Up to this point our characterization of the chirp transducer has been idealized in that we have not included the effects of acoustic propagation loss or diffraction. Because the filter design procedure is based on the delayed sampling of an acoustic impulse, it is clearly necessary to compensate for acoustic wave propagation attenuation. Furthermore the effective beam width of the acoustic wave increases with propagation distance as a result of diffraction from the transducer aperture. There is a corresponding decrease in the surface wave power density and a progressive curving of the acoustic wavefronts. Acoustic surface wave propagation loss and diffraction effects have been treated in great detail in the literature.[9,10] Although equalization for propagation loss is quite straightforward, compensation for diffraction effects are considerably more complicated and beyond the scope of this chapter,[11] but some general guidelines are presented for avoiding serious problems.

Surface wave propagation attenuation constants have been precisely measured as a function of frequency for a variety of high quality polished crystal substrates.[9] However when designing chirp filters these loss constants should be considered as minima, rather than as firm design parameters, because the actual attentuation constants always depend on the quality of the substrate polish and on the presence of surface metalization.

Once the appropriate propagation loss characteristics are established for the frequency range of interest, the effect of propagation loss is equalized by predistorting the desired impulse response $a(t)$, so that the amplitude at time t_n is increased by the anticipated loss for the (instantaneous) frequency f_n. Thus the modified amplitude function $a'(t_n)$ is related to the desired response by

$$a'(t_n) = a(t_n)10^{\left[\dfrac{\gamma(f_n) \cdot \tau(f_n)}{20}\right]} \qquad (8.30)$$

where $\gamma(f_n)$ is the frequency dependent propagation loss factor in dB/μsec and $\tau(f_n)$ is the filter time delay function in μsec.

Analytical techniques have been developed for modifying electrode positions and overlaps to compensate for diffraction effects. Though these procedures are reported to be quite successful, they do entail rather extensive computations.[11] Over a wide range of chirp filter requirements these computations can be avoided by restricting the transducer overlaps so that the input and output apertures remain in the near field region where beam spreading and wavefront curvature are negligible. For an electrode overlap w_n the near field condition corresponds to

$$\frac{w_n^2}{[1-2b]\lambda_n D_n} = \frac{w_n^2 f_n}{[1-2b]v_0^2 \tau(f_n)} \gg 1 \qquad (8.31)$$

where D_n is the distance between input and output, and $(1-2b)$ is the velocity anisotropy factor of the substrate, which is $(1-2b) \simeq 0.08$ for YZ $LiNbO_3$, and $(1-2b) \simeq 0.75$ for ST quartz. The near field condition is most easily satisfied for all electrodes when the desired FM amplitude function $a(t)$ does not span a wide range of values. In spectrally weighted designs, such as for a Hamming filter in which the amplitude varies over 22 dB, special care must be taken that the near field condition is satisfied even for the smallest apertures. We can gain an appreciation for the consequences of this near field diffraction constraint with the aid of Fig. 8.15, which shows average electrode aperture plotted against the total number of electrodes N_{tot}. The plot refers to a linear FM filter on YZ $LiNbO_3$ and contains the electrical coupling factor $G_0 Q_L/r^2$ as a parameter. We recall that for a fixed value of Q_R, the value of Q_L controls the transducer conversion loss and acoustic reflection efficiency (see Figs. 8.13 and 8.14). Here we can see how circuit coupling, piezoelectric coupling constant, and surface wave diffraction are related to dispersive delay, bandwidth, insertion loss, and reflection level in the chirp filter.

As described earlier, we first evaluate Q_R based on the transducer bandwidth and k^2. Next we select a value of Q_L that is consistent with the

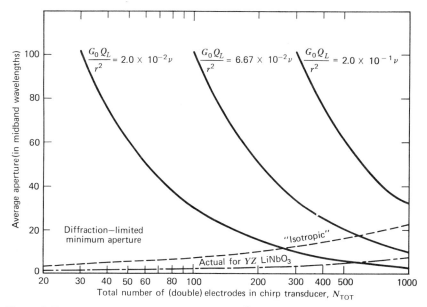

Figure 8.15 Average aperture W_{AV} (with $G_0 Q_L/r^2$ as parameter) versus total number of linear FM (double) electrodes on YZ $LiNbO_3$ substrate—$W_{AV} = [(G_0 Q_r/r^2)/2\pi v_0 C_0 N_{TOT}]$.

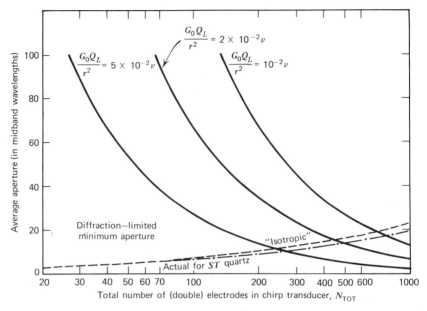

Figure 8.16 Average aperture W_{AV} (with $G_0 Q_L / r^2$ as parameter) versus total number of linear FM (double) electrodes on ST quartz substrate—$W_{\text{AV}} = (G_0 Q_r / r^2)/2\pi v_0 C_0 N_{\text{TOT}}$.

conversion loss and echo suppression requirements.* Figure 8.15 now permits us to determine the range of acceptable apertures, consistent with the required transducer dispersive delay (i.e., N_{tot}), the load impedance level, and the near field diffraction condition. This range of apertures specifies the maximum range of amplitude weighting in a weighted chirp filter design. For example, a filter having 30 MHz center frequency and 10 μsec dispersion has 601 electrodes (or double-electrode pairs). If the filter is driven by a 50 Ω generator with no transformer and we wish to couple with $Q_L = 1$, the average aperture must be only five wavelengths. Similarly, if a 5 Ω generator (or 50 Ω, with a 10 : 1 impedance transformation) were used, then the average aperture increases to 50 wavelengths. The near field diffraction curve in Fig. 8.15 shows that for an *isotropic* substrate the minimum acceptable aperture for the 601 electrode transducer is about 18 wavelengths. For YZ LiNbO$_3$, which is strongly self-collimating, the minimum acceptable aperture drops to about seven wavelengths. Thus the five wavelength average aperture satisfying the

---

* We must be careful here to remember that the design must also satisfy the condition $Q_L/Q_R \ll 1$. If Q_L/Q_R is not much less than unity for a particular design, then a smaller value of Q_L must be selected based on the level of tolerable errors.

condition $Q_L = 1$ for a 50 Ω system with no transformers and on LiNbO$_3$ fails to satisfy the diffraction constraint. If, however, the transducers are coupled to the 50 Ω system through a 10 : 1 transformer, the average aperture grows to 50 wavelengths. Consequently the individual electrode overlaps can now vary over a wide range without violating the diffraction condition that merely constrains the apertures to be at least seven wavelengths. To continue with this example the chirp filter could contain apertures ranging from about 100 to 7 wavelengths while averaging near 50, corresponding thereby to amplitude weights spanning roughly 25 dB. This example demonstrates the close interaction between electrical circuit impedance, acoustic diffraction, and required filter amplitude and dispersion characteristics in arriving at an optimally designed surface wave chirp filter. Figure 8.16 contains a plot similar to Fig. 8.15, for use in designing filters on *ST* quartz substrates.

8.4 The Status of Interdigital Chirp Filters

The design principles and performance expectations presented in the preceding sections provide a fairly comprehensive treatment of chirp filters, covering a wide range of filter parameters. In practice, most chirp filters are constructed on either *ST* quartz or *YZ* lithium niobate. The former is used for narrow band applications (< 5 MHz), at low center frequencies (< 100 MHz), where low insertion loss or long time delays are not required. *ST* quartz has the important quality that the chirp filter characteristics are virtually insensitive to temperature changes. Lithium niobate has found utility primarily where large bandwidths and low insertion loss are required. It has the added qualities of a "self-collimating" surface wave anisotropy and a low acoustic propagation loss. Together these are compelling advantages in high frequency, long delay applications.

In the past the development of filters on quartz has generally proven easier than on lithium niobate. The fact that measured amplitude and phase characteristics have been in closer agreement with theory has resulted in greater time sidelobe suppression. This is not surprising because the designs relegated to LiNbO$_3$ generally require broader bandwidths and hence greater equalization for the frequency dependent effects of acoustic propagation loss and parasitic reactance. Moreover, the performance of a LiNbO$_3$ filter is more sensitive to fabrication variations than a quartz filter. As is discussed later fabrication considerations are of major importance in high frequency, large time-bandwidth product filters. These problems not withstanding, the use of lithium niobate does yield the great advantage of significantly lower conversion loss, which is a principal consideration in most chirp filter applications.

Two lithium niobate filters are discussed in this section. The first, with a compression ratio of 20 : 1, exhibits low insertion loss and high time sidelobe suppression. Although the second, with a compression ratio of 1000 : 1 operates quite well, it mainly serves to demonstrate some practical limits for the interdigital electrode chirp transducer.

This section closes with some comments about new high resolution photolithographic techniques and new chirp filter geometries that promise to improve the performance of very large time-bandwidth product filters.

Moderate Time-Bandwidth LiNbO₃ Chirp Filters.

Moderate Time-Bandwidth LiNbO$_3$ Chirp Filters. Figure 8.17 shows the impulse response of a pair of matched 30 MHz linear FM chirp filters. Figure 8.17*a* shows the impulse response of the expansion filter, designed to have a flat amplitude response, 4.0 μsec dispersion, and 5.0 MHz bandwidth. Figure 8.17*b* shows the impulse response of the internally weighted compression filter. The expansion and compression filters exhibited insertion loss of only 20 dB and 16 dB, respectively. Figure 8.18 shows the measured compressed pulse shape and time sidelobe suppression. Figure 8.18*a* shows the compressed pulse on an expanded time scale, exhibiting its virtually ideal shape. Figure 8.18*b* shows the compressed pulse with vertical scale expanded to demonstrate 35 dB time-sidelobe suppression.

Both filters were implemented with one periodic and one chirp transducer as shown in Fig. 8.6. With a fractional bandwidth of 17%, the LiNbO$_3$ filters are about 25 dB less lossy than if they were built on quartz substrates (see Fig. 8.12).

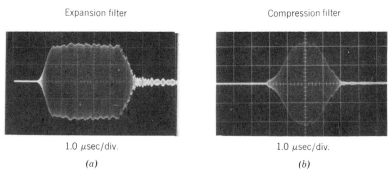

Expansion filter   Compression filter

1.0 μsec/div.   1.0 μsec/div.

(*a*)   (*b*)

Figure 8.17 Measured impulse response of matched 30 MHz linear FM expansion and compression filters having time-bandwidth product of 20.

Expanded vertical scale

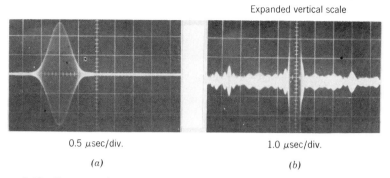

0.5 μsec/div.   1.0 μsec/div.

(a)   (b)

Figure 8.18 Compressed pulse exhibiting excellent shape and 29 dB time sidelobe suppression.

Large Time-Bandwidth LiNbO₃ Chirp Filters.

Large Time-Bandwidth LiNbO$_3$ Chirp Filters. The 20 : 1 chirp filter data illustrate the excellent performance that is characteristic of well-designed surface wave chirp filters. In this section we consider the extreme case of a $1000 : 1$ LiNbO$_3$ filter having 100 MHz bandwidth, 300 MHz center frequency, and 10.0 μsec dispersion. Because of the high frequency, double electrodes could not be employed. To achieve the broad bandwidth two chirp transducers were used (as shown in Fig. 8.8), in the down-chirp configuration. Microstrip impedance matching transformers were required to reduce the 50 Ω generator impedance to a more optimum level of 3 Ω for driving the 3000 electrode transducers. Figure 8.19a shows the measured insertion loss spectrum of the $1000 : 1$ expansion filter, exhibiting only 30 dB insertion loss over the full 100 MHz

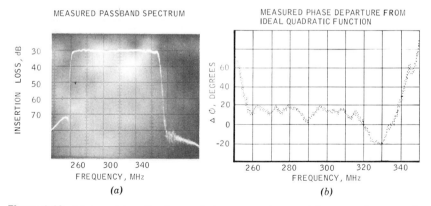

Figure 8.19 Measured insertion loss and phase error characteristics versus frequency for linear FM filter having time-bandwidth product of 1000.

Expanded pulse   Compressed pulse

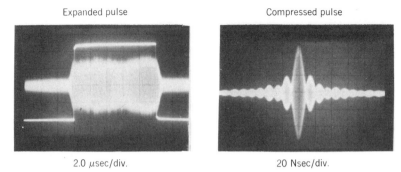

2.0 μsec/div.   20 Nsec/div.

Figure 8.20 Measured expanded pulse and compressed pulse characteristics of unweighted linear FM filter having time-bandwidth product of 1000.

bandwidth. Once again, if implemented on quartz, the loss of this filter would increase by more than 25 dB. Figure 8.19*b* shows the measured departure from ideal quadratic phase (i.e., the phase "error") exhibited by this filter. The 20° peak-to-peak error is rather large for a linear FM chirp filter. Figure 8.20*a* shows the amplitude of the 10 μsec expanded output and Fig. 8.20*b* shows the unweighted compressed pulse. This data looks deceptively encouraging, particularly in view of the 13 dB sidelobes in Fig. 8.20*b*. However manifestation of a 20° phase error becomes apparent when an external spectral weighting filter is used to attempt greater time-sidelobe suppression. With no phase error, 42 dB sidelobes are predicted; however the measured level could not be reduced below about 20 dB. It is perhaps most significant that subsequent copies of this 1000 : 1 filter, fabricated from the same photomask, exhibited similar but *not* identical phase responses. Each device exhibited roughly the same peak error, but the chirp slopes were not equal, and two independently fabricated filters would not match each other. These difficulties were traced to the filter's high sensitivity to fabrication variations. With respect to normal variations in photoresist exposures, this filter was, in effect, not reliably reproducible.

Fabrication Errors. When designing the 1000 : 1 chirp filter, it was recognized that with constant-width electrodes, the electrode positions required iterative correction, as described by (8.5). The error problem with the large TB product filter arose from the fact that the *actual* electrode widths are not necessarily constant throughout the fabricated chirp transducers, even if they are in the original photomask. Thus normal processing variations may produce an electrode metalization pattern that is somewhat random, and the acoustic surface wave, propagating through the long metal grating, may experience sizable phase shifts resulting from the integrated effect of these width variations.

A measure of the severity of the fabrication tolerance problem can be gained by assuming a uniform deviation in electrode width Δl and expanding the resulting frequency dependent phase error about the filter center frequency. The error term that is cubic in frequency is the first one that leads to serious problems. A quadratic term, corresponding to a small difference in chirp slope, can be corrected by adjusting ambient temperature. The cubic error term is given by

$$\Delta\phi^{(3)}(f) = \frac{3\pi}{2}\frac{\tau}{\Delta f f_s}\left[\frac{\Delta l}{l}\left[1 - \frac{\delta v}{v}\right]\right][f - f_0]^3 \text{ radians} \qquad (8.32)$$

where τ is the transducer dispersion, Δf is the bandwidth, and f_s is the frequency at which l is a quarter wavelength. For the $1000:1$ filter with $\tau = 5$ μsec, $B = 100$ MHz, $f_s = 350$ MHz, and $\delta v/v = 2.2 \times 10^{-2}$, (8.32) reduces to

$$\Delta\phi^{(3)}_{1000:1}(f) = 3.86 \times 10^{-2}[f - f_0]^3_{\text{MHz}} \cdot \left[\frac{\Delta l}{l}\right] \text{ degrees} \qquad (8.33)$$

From (8.33) we find that the error at 275 MHz (or 325 MHz) is given by

$$\Delta\phi^{(3)}_{1000:1}\left(f_0 \pm \frac{\Delta f}{4}\right) = \pm 5.9 \times 10^2\left[\frac{\Delta l}{l}\right] \text{ degrees}$$

Therefore even if fabrication tolerances could be held to 5%, the resulting phase errors are intolerably large. By way of comparison, using the $20:1$ filter values in (8.32) gives

$$\Delta\phi^{(3)}_{20:1}(f) = 6.5\left[\frac{\Delta l}{l}\right][f - f_0]^3_{\text{MHz}} \qquad (8.34)$$

which amounts to only 1.3° peak phase error for 10% error in l near the edges of the passband. Thus we see that a very serious problem in achieving high performance, large TB product chirp filters is intimately related to the reliability of high resolution photolithography techniques.

References

1. R. H. Tancrell et al. "Dispersive delay lines using ultrasonic surface waves." *Proc. IEEE* **57**, 1211 (1969).

2. C. Atzeni and L. Masotti. "Linear signal processing by acoustic surface wave transversal filters." *IEEE Trans.* **MTT-21,** 505 (1973); see also, W. D. Squire, H. J. Whitehouse, and J. M. Alsup. "Linear signal processing and ultrasonic transversal filters." *IEEE Trans.* **MTT-17,** 1020 (1969).

3. J. M. Alsup, R. W. Means, and H. J. Whitehouse. "Real time Fourier transforms using surface acoustic wave devices," in *Proc. Conf. on Component Performance and Systems Applications of Surface Wave Devices,* IEE, Stevenage, England, 1973.

4. H. M. Gerard et al. "Design and applications of highly dispersive acoustic surface wave filters." *IEEE Trans.* **MTT-21,** 176 (1973).

5. T. W. Bristol et al. "Applications of double electrodes in acoustic surface wave device design," in J. de Klerk, Ed., *Proc. 1972 IEEE Ultrasonics Symposium,* IEEE, New York, 1972, pp. 343–345.

6. W. R. Smith, H. M. Gerard, and W. R. Jones. "Analysis and design of dispersive interdigital surface wave transducers." *IEEE Trans.* **MTT-20,** 458 (1972).

7. W. R. Smith et al. "Analysis of interdigital surface wave transducers by use of an equivalent circuit model." *IEEE Trans.* **MTT-17,** 856 (1969).

8. G. W. Judd. "Technique for realizing low time sidelobe levels in small compression ratio chirp waveforms," in J. de Klerk, Ed., *Proc. 1973 IEEE Ultrasonics-Symposium,* IEEE, New York, 1973, pp. 478–481.

9. A. J. Slobodnik, Jr. "A review of material tradeoffs in the design of acoustic surface wave devices at VHF and microwave frequencies." *IEEE Trans.* **SU-20,** 315 (1973).

10. A. J. Slobodnik, Jr., E. D. Conway, and R. T. Delmonico. *Microwave Acoustics Handbook,* Vol. 1, Air Force Cambridge Research Laboratories, Bedford, Mass., 1970.

11. J. D. Maines, G. L. Moule, and N. R. Ogg. "Correction of diffraction errors in acoustic surface wave pulse compression filters." *Electron. Lett.* **8,** 431 (1972).

NINE

Reflection Grating Filters

RICHARD C. WILLIAMSON

Lincoln Laboratory, Massachusetts Institute of Technology, Lexington, Massachusetts

Most surface wave filters use spatially distributed transduction in interdigital transducers on piezoelectric substrates to produce analog transversal filters. This chapter describes the use of controlled reflection of surface waves from surface gratings in an alternate type of filter. Reflection grating filters are remarkably free of spurious signals and second order effects; consequently filters of this type have nearly ideal performance for bandwidths, correlation lengths, and time-bandwidth products greater than filters based on distributed tapping by interdigital transducers. The major application of reflection gratings has been in large time-bandwidth product pulse compressors.[1-5] Preliminary results with bandpass filters[7] and filter banks[8] also illustrate the potential advantages of reflection gratings in these applications as well.

An entirely different application of reflection gratings is surface wave resonators.[9-10] Such a device is made possible by the ability of distributed reflectors to provide reflection coefficients close to unity. A pair of reflection gratings form a high Q cavity. A significant advantage of this type of resonator is that the fundamental frequency of operation extends throughout the UHF frequency range. Single-mode, high Q resonators in this range have been difficult to obtain by other means.

The goal in the development of most surface wave devices is to implement a transversal filter that approaches as closely as possible a

This work was sponsored by the Department of the Army.

mathematical ideal in which the output signal is the appropriately weighted sum of a finite number of time delayed samples of an input signal.
The great utility of surface wave filters comes from the fact that in many
cases implementation of the desired sampling scheme is straightforward
and successful. However the use of interdigital electrodes or taps to
sample a surface wave passing through them perturbs the wave and
causes the output signal to deviate from the mathematical ideal. Although
sophisticated techniques have been developed for minimizing or compensating for these effects, the problem becomes increasingly difficult and
devices become more marginal as the magnitude of the samples increases
(i.e., low insertion loss devices and high-coupling substrates) and the
number of samples becomes large (e.g., devices with large center
frequency-time delay products such as narrow-band filters or large time-
bandwidth phase coded or linear FM filters). The use of reflection gratings
to perform the sampling of a surface wave significantly reduces second
order effects and thus allows high performance to be achieved over a
wider range of device parameters. In this type of device a number of
samples are reflected out of a propagating wave and these samples are
summed at an output transducer.

Surface wave reflectors are usually shallow grooves etched in the
substrate or strips of deposited material. The use of grooves instead of
overlays has several advantages. Mechanical properties, and therefore
reflection coefficients, are usually difficult to reproduce when an overlay is
a deposited film. Overlays are inherently dispersive and this can introduce
phase distortions in filter response. Also, the reflectivity of conducting
overlays on high coupling piezoelectrics is usually too large. This fact
greatly restricts the utility of conducting films as reflectors in filters.

An attractive feature of reflection-grating devices is their defect tolerance. Unlike the electrical effect in interdigital arrays, signal processing in
reflection-grating devices is performed by localized mechanical reflections. Defects such as broken or joined reflectors cause only a small
effect. In contrast, such defects in interdigital devices correspond to open
circuiting a finger in the array or short circuiting an entire array. A flaw in
a reflecting edge merely reduces the net reflection from that edge by an
amount proportional to the fraction of the edge that is missing. For this
reason a reflection grating can contain a relatively large number of
defects (particularly if each is small and randomly distributed) without
causing a significant change in the overall response of the grating. This
feature is extremely important for filters with long impulse responses,
many grooves over a large area, or devices that operate at high frequencies. A section of this chapter discusses the relative merit of interdigital
and reflection-grating filters and establishes criteria for identifying the
filter designs best implemented with each approach.

One of the first applications of surface wave reflection gratings as taps in a delay line was proposed by Tseng.[11] The use of acoustic wave reflection gratings to construct bandpass and dispersive filters was analyzed by Sittig and Coquin in 1968.[12] Their prototype devices demonstrated the concept but the quality of filter response was not particularly encouraging. A major advance in reflection-grating devices was achieved by Martin, who conceived and developed a unique chevron or herringbone configuration of acoustic reflection gratings that is particularly good for use in large time-bandwidth dispersive filters.[1,13] The IMCON device[1,13] is not a surface wave filter. It uses the propagation of a nondispersive shear wave (SH plate mode) in a thin steel strip. Oblique grooves etched into the strip act as acoustic reflectors. Because the strip is thin, much of the acoustic energy in the SH plate mode is close to the surface of the strip and thus the IMCON has a basic similarity to surface wave devices. Although IMCON filters have very high performance, they have restricted bandwidth because the strip thickness must be less than half an acoustic wavelength in order to ensure that unwanted propagation modes are cut off.

Williamson and Smith investigated the physics of surface wave reflections and developed the technology for implementing the IMCON configuration in a surface wave device.[2] The resulting dispersive delay line, called a reflective-array compressor (RAC), demonstrated that the excellent phase and amplitude response characteristic of IMCON filters could be achieved in broadband surface wave filters using reflection gratings. Subsequently several laboratories launched efforts to develop pulse compressors in the RAC configuration.[3,5] Because dispersive filters (pulse compressors) are the most advanced and rapidly growing application of reflection gratings, the major emphasis of this chapter is on such devices. However other types of filters are feasible. The use of reflection gratings has been extended to bandpass filters[7] and filter banks.[8] The possibility exists that reflection gratings would be useful for constructing other types of filters, such as phase-coded filters. However the effort to date has been limited to bandpass and dispersive filters. Surface wave resonators have received relatively little development, but the preliminary results obtained by Staples[10] suggests that this application will be an area of major interest. Among other uses, surface wave resonators show promise as the essential building blocks of narrow-band filters at UHF and VHF.

Typical configurations of reflection-grating devices are shown in Fig. 9.1. Interdigital transducers are used to convert electrical signals into acoustic waves and the reflected waves are converted back into a processed electrical signal. Usually the transducers do not play a major role in obtaining the filter function of a reflection-grating device, although future designs may take advantage of the fact that part of the filtering action

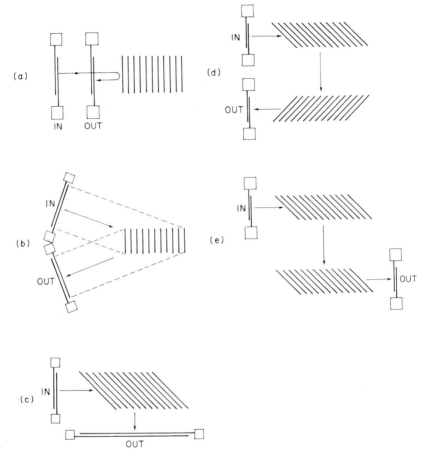

Figure 9.1 Some of the geometries employed in reflection-grating devices. (*a*) Normal-incidence reflections. (*b*) Transducers tilted at a small angle to separate incident and reflected waves. (*c*) Single reflection at 90°. (*d*) Two 90° reflections. (*e*) Two 90° reflections such that the twice-reflected wave is parallel to the incident wave.

may take place in the transducer to obtain a hybrid of a standard interdigital filter and a reflection-grating filter. The overall transfer function for any device is the product of the individual transfer functions of the input transducer, reflection grating, and output transducers. The transducers shown schematically in Fig. 9.1 are of the simplest interdigital type. The labels *IN* and *OUT* in Fig. 9.1 are applied for ease in describing device operation. In fact, all the devices are linear and reciprocal. Almost all reflection-grating devices have been fabricated on piezoelectric substrates, but the piezoelectric effect is only necessary for the operation of the interdigital transducers. Since the reflection process is not usually dependent on a piezoelectric substrate, other types of transducers allow reflection-grating devices to be fabricated on non-piezoelectric substrates, for example, the IMCON on steel.[1]

Figure 9.1a illustrates the simplest type of reflection-grating device in which the reflections are at normal incidence. Most of the early experimental work on the physics of surface wave reflections employed this configuration and an in-line dispersive delay line was fabricated and tested by Sittig and Coquin.[12] A pair of properly spaced normal incidence reflection gratings are the basic elements of a surface wave resonator. A transducer placed in the cavity formed by the gratings couples to the mechanical resonance and thus yields a two-terminal (one-port) resonator. The in-line configuration has several disadvantages for use in two-port filters. It is difficult to separate input and reflected signals, and relatively high levels of spurious signal are experienced.

The configuration of Fig. 9.1b allows separation of incoming and reflected waves by placing the transducers at a slight angle to normal incidence. Both surface wave and shear wave strip dispersive filters have been made in this configuration.[1,12] Limited success was achieved in both cases because of relatively high spurious signal levels.

By placing the transducers at right angles as in Fig. 9.1c, a better rejection of spurious signals is obtained, and for anisotropic substrates it is usually possible to place the transducers along perpendicular crystalline directions that possess attractive surface wave propagation characteristics. Such perpendicular directions occur on lithium niobate, bismuth germanium oxide, and several other materials. Bandpass filters have been constructed in this configuration on LiNbO$_3$.[7,8]

The double-reflection geometry of Fig. 9.1d is employed in IMCON[1,13] and reflective-array-compressor (RAC) devices.[2–6] Narrow-band filters have also been achieved with this configuration.[7] Because of the folded geometry, the effective overall grating length on a substrate of given size is twice that of configuration Fig. 9.1c. Also, for highly dispersive filters, the RAC configuration, Fig. 9.1d, generally has lower insertion loss than Fig. 9.1c.

Figure 9.1e shows a variant of Fig. 9.1d that is potentially useful for obtaining nondispersive bandpass filters with relatively large bandwidth and low shape factor. If the gratings are "chirped"—that is, the spacing in the grating varies in such a manner that high frequencies are reflected at one end of the grating and low frequencies at the other—this configuration is the analog of the nondispersive response achieved by cascading dispersive interdigital transducers.

The various geometries of reflection-grating devices shown in Fig. 9.1 are by no means an exhaustive summary. Among the infinity of possible two dimensional arrangements of transducers and gratings, it is likely that many clever and useful designs will emerge. At any rate, the desired transfer function of a reflection-grating device is tailored by adjusting the position of each reflector in the grating and adjusting the magnitude of its reflection coefficient. The physics of surface wave reflections that underlies this design procedure is the subject of the next section.

9.1 Physics of Surface Wave Reflections

A complete theoretical analysis of the reflection of surface waves for grooves, steps, overlays, and other types of reflectors does not currently exist, largely because of the complexity of the problem. An appreciation of this complexity can be obtained by comparison with reflection of bulk waves from planar boundaries. For a bulk wave, the mechanical motions are uniform in a plane perpendicular to the propagation vector and the propagation and reflection process is essentially a one dimensional problem that can be solved in closed form even for anisotropic materials. However the mechanical motions of a surface wave are not uniform in a plane perpendicular to the propagation vector, but die away as a function of distance from the surface carrying the wave. Surface waves must be described in two dimensions. When such a wave impinges on a reflector, the resulting scattering problem, even for normal incidence, is an extremely complex two dimensional problem, and to date, only numerical solutions for specific cases have been obtained.[14-16] Experimental observations such as Viktorov's measurements of reflection from beveled edges[17] and Dally and Lewis's observations of scattering from a step[18] also illustrate the complexity of surface wave reflections.

Despite the complexity of the general problem of surface wave reflections, relatively simple and useful descriptions of the reflection process can be obtained for the condition usually present in reflection-grating filters, namely, weak reflections. In a typical filter each line in a grating reflects only a small fraction of the surface wave energy. It is the combined reflection from many lines that results in relatively large overall reflection coefficients. Thus surface wave reflections can be discussed in two steps, first the description of weak reflection from a single element in a grating, and second, the analysis of the combined effect of many such weak reflectors.

Weak Reflection from a Single Edge.   A surface or Rayleigh wave is one of a number of waves that can exist in an elastic material. The surface wave solution to the equations of motion for a semi-infinite homogeneous medium, which may be piezoelectric, differs from other modes of propagation (bulk waves) because the surface wave must satisfy a set of boundary conditions on a plane surface. Any change in the boundary that couples to the surface wave reflects the surface wave and possibly scatters some energy into other modes. It is useful to start with a simple description of surface wave reflections to gain an understanding of the physical situations that cause reflections and then discuss the more detailed theory of these reflections.

Of the many possible surface perturbations that can reflect surface waves, three of the most significant are illustrated in Fig. 9.2. A general case is shown in Fig. 9.2a, wherein the region to the right is overlaid with a material that may be different from the substrate. The resulting reflections are commonly referred to as an effect of "mass loading." Figure 9.2b is a special case of Fig. 9.2a in which the "overlay" is the same material as the substrate and the reflection is caused only by a step in the surface. This "topographic" reflection is examined later in some detail

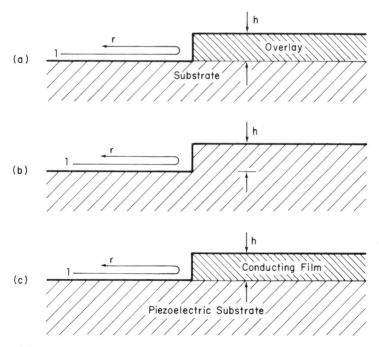

Figure 9.2 Surface perturbations that cause surface wave reflections. (a) General case of a thin overlay. (b) Vertical step. (c) Conducting film on a piezoelectric substrate.

because it is the type of reflection most generally employed in reflection-grating devices. A groove that contains a "down" and an "up" step is a generalization of Fig. 9.2b. Figure 9.2c illustrates another special case in which the overlay is a conducting film on a piezoelectric substrate. The conducting film couples to the surface wave through the piezoelectric effect and causes a reflection commonly referred to as a $\Delta v/v$ reflection.

A simple dimensional argument yields the functional dependence of the reflection coefficient for step and overlay reflections. In these cases only two dimensions are significant, the wavelength of the surface wave λ and the height of the step or overlay h. Thus the reflection coefficient must be a function of h/λ. Assuming that r, the reflection coefficient, can be expanded in a Taylor's series,

$$r\left\{\left(\frac{h}{\lambda}\right)\right\} = r_0 + C \times \left(\frac{h}{\lambda}\right) + \text{higher order terms} \qquad (9.1)$$

Note that here and throughout this chapter reflection coefficients refer to amplitude ratios. Unless the phase is explicitly shown, the coefficients represent magnitude only. The reflection coefficient r is defined such that $|r|^2$ is the ratio of reflected and incident power.

For the case of a conducting overlay on a piezoelectric (Fig. 9.2c), the reflection coefficient remains finite even when h/λ goes to zero; that is, a thin, massless, but conducting film can cause a reflection and such a residual reflection is independent of frequency. For this situation $r_0 \neq 0$. For a step (Fig. 9.2b), a nonconducting layer on any substrate or any layer on a nonpiezoelectric substrate, $r_0 = 0$, and the reflection coefficient is linear in h/λ for small values of h/λ. By varying h for a step or dielectric overlay, the reflection coefficient at any frequency can be varied in a linear fashion. This ability to adjust reflectivity conveniently is an important feature of reflection-grating devices. Dimensional arguments cannot yield the magnitude of the reflection coefficients, and we must resort to more sophisticated theories or experiment to determine the proportionality constant C for each material combination and the range of accuracy of the linear approximation.

The topic of surface wave scattering is an old one and numerous papers on the subject exist, particularly in the geophysics literature.[18–22] Of particular interest here are weak reflections from relatively idealized line reflectors such as those illustrated in Fig. 9.2. Four different approaches to evaluating the reflection coefficient are discussed next.

Oliner, Bertoni, and Li[23–26] have developed certain network techniques for use in the analysis of surface and bulk waves in isotropic media. These techniques have been applied to surface wave reflections for the case of an isotropic layer on an isotropic substrate. The analysis is separated into two parts. First the boundary value problems for a free and a layered surface are solved to yield the corresponding surface wave velocities v_0 and v_1 as well as the fields of the mechanical motions in the two regions. The reflection coefficient is then derived on the basis of an approximate field matching across the step, and this field mismatch is embodied in the network model as a turns ratio n (Fig. 9.3). Whenever there is a field mismatch, $n \neq 1$. Any coupling to bulk waves is neglected. In the context of this model the reflection coefficient is given by

$$r = \frac{n^2 Z_1 - Z_0}{n^2 Z_1 + Z_0} \qquad (9.2)$$

At normal incidence the impedances Z_1 and Z_0 are given by $Z_1 = \rho v_1$ and $Z_0 = \rho v_0$, where ρ is the substrate density. Therefore r at normal incidence is

$$r = \frac{n^2 v_1 / v_0 - 1}{n^2 v_1 / v_0 + 1} \qquad (9.3)$$

Equation (9.3) indicates that reflections occur whenever there is a field mismatch ($n \neq 1$) or when $v_1 \neq v_0$. For h/λ small, both n^2 and v_1/v_0 are equal to 1 plus terms linear in h/λ. Thus in the weak coupling limit (9.3) satisfies the dimensional argument of (9.1).

In many cases a first-order estimate of the reflection coefficient for an overlay can be obtained by making the approximation that $n = 1$ and using the dispersion curves for the overlaid region to obtain v_1 as a function of h/λ. Also, r for a conducting film on a piezoelectric is fairly well predicted by setting $n = 1$.[27-29] In this case $r \approx \Delta v / 2v$ where Δv is the

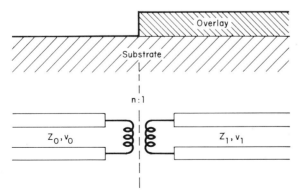

Figure 9.3 Transmission line model of reflections caused by an overlay.

velocity difference between surface waves traveling on the metalized and unmetalized regions. However caution should be exercised in using this approximation. For example, setting $n \approx 1$ is totally wrong for describing a simple step.

The model of Oliner, Bertoni, and Li[23-26] also applies to the more complicated case of oblique incidence and the reader is referred to the cited references for a discussion of this case. One feature is worth noting; the reflection coefficient at oblique incidence is generally an increasing function of angle.

Li has specialized the network techniques to the case of normal-incidence reflection from a step.[30] In this case $v_1 = v_0$ so that the reflection is entirely due to elastic field mismatch. The prediction of Li's calculation has been compared with data on the scattering from steps in LiNbO$_3$, an anisotropic single crystal. However the comparison cannot be exact because the theory applies only to isotropic media. In order to make a semiquantitative comparison, a set of "equivalent" isotropic parameters has been chosen such that the surface wave velocity on the "equivalent" isotropic substrate is equal to the actual velocity for the particular cut of LiNbO$_3$ (Y-cut, Z-propagating wave). The calculated reflection coefficient is a relatively insensitive function of Poisson's ratio and the experimental results of Williamson and Smith[2] (Fig. 9.4) are well fitted by a Poisson's ratio of 0.3, which is a reasonable value for a crystalline material. In this case $r = 0.35\, h/\lambda$.

An entirely different approach has been used by Tuan and Li[31] to analyze surface wave reflections from groove and step discontinuities. A boundary perturbation technique is employed in which the perturbation (step or groove) in an ideal plane surface is replaced by an equivalent stress distribution. Although this analysis includes the effects of bulk waves, the published work does not evaluate the coupling to bulk waves. Tuan and Li[31] show that the reflection coefficient of a small step ($h/\lambda \ll 1$) is independent of the angle of the groove side walls when those walls are very steep. In addition, reflection from an up step is shown to be 180° out of phase relative to reflection from a down step. This is analogous to the situation that occurs in optics and in transmission line analysis wherein the reflection coefficient for a wave incident on one side of a boundary is the negative of the reflection coefficient for a wave incident from the other side. The quantitative predictions of Tuan and Li's perturbation technique have been compared with measurements on LiNbO$_3$. As in Li's analysis,[30] an "equivalent" set of isotropic parameters was assumed. The predicted reflection coefficient is $r = 0.34\, h/\lambda$, which agrees well with experiment.

Sabine[32] has employed a coupled mode theory developed by Auld[23] to

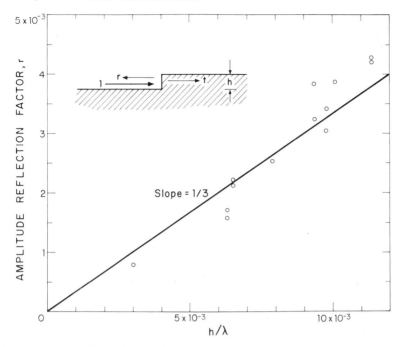

Figure 9.4 Reflectivity of a step in YZ LiNbO$_3$. Copyright 1973 by The Institute of Electrical and Electronic Engineers, Inc. Reprinted, with permission, from *IEEE Trans.* **MTT-21,** 1973, p. 195.

predict the surface wave reflection coefficient of periodic overlay strips for surface waves at arbitrary angles of incidence. Sabine has compared predictions of this coupled mode theory with experimental results achieved in a "crossbar coupler" consisting of gold strips deposited on AT quartz.[32–34] The reflection coefficient for an angle of incidence of 34° was within 20% of the theoretically predicted value.

Yoneyama and Nishida[35] have used a Wiener-Hopf technique to derive a first order approximation for the reflection of surface waves at normal incidence on an overlay (Fig. 9.2a). Their solution specifically includes scattering into bulk waves, a subject that is discussed in more detail later. Numerical examples are calculated for gold, aluminum, nickel, and copper overlays on fused silica. Unfortunately there is a scarcity of data to compare with their calculations and no comparisons are made in ref. 35.

Although little data exist concerning overlay reflections, values of r for steps in the most popular surface wave substrates have been measured. Meyer and Schulz[36] have measured reflection coefficients for steps in

**Table 9.1 Amplitude Reflection Coefficient of a
Step at Normal Incidence ($r = C(h/\lambda)$ where
$h/\lambda \lesssim 0.01$)**

Material	C	Reference
YZ LiNbO$_3$	0.33	2, 37
ST quartz	0.27	37
(100)(011)BGO	0.23 (?)	37

Source: Copyright 1973 by The Institute of Electrical
and Electronic Engineers. Inc. Reprinted, with permission, from *Proc. 1973 IEEE Ultrasonics Symposium,*
1973, p. 500.

quartz and bismuth germanium oxide (BGO). A summary of available
data on normal incidence reflections is given in Table 9.1. The usual
conventions on crystal cut and propagation direction are used in designat-
ing the material. The value of C for BGO is a tentative best estimate
because the accuracy of the measurements were degraded by spurious
loss. Meyer and Schulz have also measured the reflection coefficient for
reflection of Z-directed into X-directed waves on Y-cut LiNbO$_3$, a 90°
reflection.[36] For this important case the value of C is 0.45. As expected
on the basis of network models and analogous situations for optical
reflection, the reflection coefficient at oblique incidence is higher than at
normal incidence.

The Effect of Combined Reflections from Many Reflectors. The
foregoing discussion focused on the reflection coefficient at the boundary
between distinct regions on a surface. This boundary is referred to as a
step, although any of the situations illustrated in Fig. 9.2 could be the
source of the reflection. The question that now must be addressed is,
"What is the overall effect when there are many reflectors or steps in the
path of a surface wave?"

The simplest case of multiple reflectors is a shallow rectangular groove
consisting of a down step and an up step. The reflection coefficient r_g
for a groove can be straightforwardly calculated if we make a number of
simplifying assumptions that are likely to be valid for weak reflections.
The transmission coefficient for a step is assumed to be nearly equal to 1.
The reflection from each step is considered to be independent. There is
no phase shift on transmission or reflection except the phase shifts due to

propagation delay. The reflection at an up step is the negative of the reflection at a down step. Coupling to bulk waves is neglected. For normal-incidence reflections these approximations yield

$$r_g = -r \exp\left[i2k\left(x - \frac{W}{2}\right)\right] + r \exp\left[i2k\left(x - \frac{W}{2}\right)\right] \qquad (9.4)$$

where r is the reflection coefficient of an up step, the wave number $k = \omega/v$, v is the surface wave velocity, x is the distance from a reference point to the center of the groove, and W is the width of the groove. The first term is the contribution from a down step and the second term from an up step. Equation (9.4) can be rewritten as

$$r_g = 2ire^{ikx} \sin kW \qquad (9.5)$$

At normal incidence the reflection coefficient of a groove is a maximum when the groove width is approximately $\lambda/4$.

Tuan and Li[31] have calculated the reflectivity of a shallow groove by a perturbation technique that does not invoke the simplifying assumptions discussed earlier other than a neglect of bulk wave effects. Their result is the same as those of (9.4) and (9.5). Accordingly, this lends credibility to the assumptions of the simplified calculation.

Delta Function Model. If the overall reflection coefficient $R(\omega)$ that summarizes the combined reflections from many steps is small, $R(\omega)$ can be calculated in a simple fashion. The transmitted wave is assumed essentially unattenuated as it passes through a number of grooves and thus the amplitude of the wave reflected by each step is proportional to the reflectivity of the step, and the overall reflectivity of the array of grooves is the sum of these reflections. This model is analogous to the "delta function" model of interdigital transducers.[37] If we ignore multiple reflections the impulse response of the grating is approximately a series of delayed delta functions, each corresponding to a single reflection from a particular step in the grating. The magnitude of each delta function is equal to the reflectivity of the step with which it is identified.

The delta function model is very useful because of several significant features. There is direct correspondence between grating geometry and the impulse response of the grating because the impulse response is simply a weighted sum of delta functions and each step contributes a single delta function. Both design and analysis of gratings are simplified. The model can be easily extended to oblique reflections and complicated two dimensional grating geometries.

A subtle difficulty of the delta function model is that the reflectivity of a step is not a constant, but increases with frequency. This means that the response of a step to an impulse is not a simple delta function. However it is possible to include this fact formally in the analysis in a simple fashion. Let the impulse response of a step be $g(t-\tau)$ where τ is the acoustic transit time from the input to the step and thence to the output. The function $g(t)$ is close to, but not quite, a delta function. The frequency response is

$$G(\omega) = \int_{-\infty}^{\infty} g(t-\tau)e^{-i\omega t}\, dt \tag{9.6}$$

or

$$G(\omega) = e^{-i\omega\tau} \int_{-\infty}^{\infty} g(t')e^{-i\omega t'}\, dt' \tag{9.7}$$

We can then identify the integral

$$r(\omega) = \int_{-\infty}^{\infty} g(t')e^{-i\omega t'}\, dt' \tag{9.8}$$

as the reflectivity of the step. In the delta function approximation the impulse response of a series of steps is

$$h(t) = \sum_{n} g_n(t-\tau_n) \tag{9.9}$$

where the index n enumerates the steps and τ_n is the delay corresponding to each step. The frequency response is

$$R(\omega) = \int_{-\infty}^{\infty} h(t)e^{-i\omega t}\, dt \tag{9.10}$$

or

$$R(\omega) = \sum_{n} r_n(\omega)e^{-i\omega\tau_n} \tag{9.11}$$

where $r_n(\omega)$ is the reflectivity of the nth step. If $g(t-\tau)$ were exactly a delta function in (9.6), r_n would be a constant instead of a function of ω. Thus it is convenient to think of the impulse response of a step as being a reflected delta function, but in computing the frequency response of a grating, we must include the frequency response of the reflectivity, as shown explicitly in (9.11).

A simple example illustrates application of the delta function model. Figure 9.5 shows a periodic array of N constant-depth grooves with

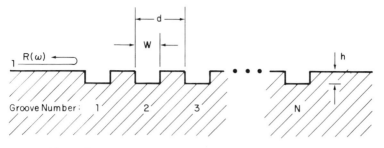

Figure 9.5 Simple periodic grating consisting of grooves.

constant width W. In the delta function approximation the overall reflection coefficient $R(\omega)$ for the array is

$$R(\omega) = (-r) \exp\left[i2k\left(x - \frac{W}{2}\right)\right] + r \exp\left[i2k\left(x + \frac{W}{2}\right)\right] + \cdots$$

$$+ r \exp\left[i2k\left(x + (N-1)d + \frac{W}{2}\right)\right] \quad (9.12)$$

where x is the distance from a reference point to the center of the first groove, k is the wave number, and d is the groove period. For convenience we will set $x = 0$, thus placing the reference point at the center of the first groove. Rewriting (9.12),

$$R(\omega) = \sum_{n=0}^{N-1} (-re^{ikW} + re^{ikW})e^{i2knd} \quad (9.13)$$

or

$$R(\omega) = r_g(\omega) \sum_{n=0}^{N-1} e^{i2knd} \quad (9.14)$$

where the reflectivity of a groove r_g has been introduced, as given by (9.5). Performing the sum, we obtain,

$$R(\omega) = r_g(\omega)e^{i(N-1)kd}\frac{\sin Nkd}{\sin kd} = r_g(\omega)e^{i(N-1)kd}(-1)^N \frac{\sin N\pi(\omega - \omega_0)/\omega_0}{\sin \pi(\omega - \omega_0)/\omega_0} \quad (9.15)$$

where $\omega_0 = \pi d/v$. This is the familiar $\sin Nx/\sin x$ type of response except that r_g also has a frequency dependence. If r_g is expressed in terms of groove depth h and frequency

$$r_g(\omega) = \frac{Ch\omega}{2\pi v} \sin \omega \frac{W}{v} \quad (9.16)$$

where v is the surface wave velocity and C is the reflectivity constant defined by (9.1). If $W = d/2$, both the groove response and overall grating response peak approximately at ω_0. However, the frequency response is skewed toward higher frequencies by a factor proportional to frequency, because r is proportional to frequency.

The accuracy of this calculation depends on whether the transmission coefficient T for the grating is sufficiently close to 1. By energy conservation,

$$|T| = (1 - |R|^2)^{1/2} \tag{9.17}$$

or

$$|T| \approx 1 - \frac{|R|^2}{2} \tag{9.18}$$

At normal incidence the error in calculating R is approximately equal to $\frac{1}{3}R^2$ and the error is maximum at ω_0, in which case $R = Nr_g$. This establishes an essential criterion for the accuracy of delta function calculations: The reflection coefficient per groove times the number of grooves contributing synchronously at any frequency must be much less than 1. For example, if $r_g = 0.01$ and $N = 32$, $|R(\omega_0)|$ is predicted to be 0.32 or 10 dB. $|T|$ is equal to 0.9 or 1 dB and the value of $|R(\omega_0)|$ predicted by this approximation is too large by about 3% or 0.3 dB. For oblique reflections from reflectors of finite length, the condition $|R| \ll 1$ is a necessary but insufficient condition for the validity of the delta function model.

When the overall reflection coefficient R for a grating is not small, it is necessary to account explicitly for the multiple reflections within a grating and the consequent attenuation of the transmitted wave. A qualitative understanding of the effects of multiple reflections can be obtained by an extension of the delta function model to also include the next order of reflections, that is, triply reflected waves. For the array of three grooves shown in Fig. 9.6a, 1–6 are single reflections and, in the impulse response of the grating, each step contributes a time-delayed signal we represent as a delta function, but, as discussed previously, the actual response is only approximately a delta function.

The reflection from a "down" step is arbitrarily assigned a negative value. Reflections 7–9 are examples of waves reflected three times. Note that wave 7 arrives at the same time as wave 3, but wave 7 is never reflected from a down step and consequently has the opposite polarity to wave 3. This illustrates a general conclusion concerning triply reflected waves; all such waves tend to cancel the singly reflected waves and thus lower the reflection coefficient at those frequencies for which the singly reflected waves add coherently.

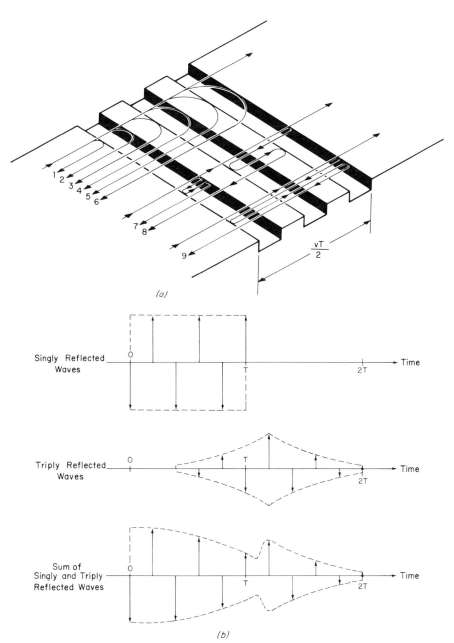

Figure 9.6 (*a*) All of the singly reflected waves and some of the triply reflected waves associated with a simple three-groove grating. (*b*) Impulse response due to singly and triply reflected waves.

There are 55 different waves triply reflected from the three grooves shown in Fig. 9.6a. As many as 15 of these arrive simultaneously and the impulse response shown in Fig. 9.6b is proportional to the number that are simultaneous. First the multiple reflections cause a decay of the impulse response that corresponds to a broadening of the frequency response, and second the multiple reflections put a tail on the impulse response. The triply reflected waves peak at the time that the singly reflected waves cease. If the multiple reflections are large enough, the impulse response suddenly increases after the last of the singly reflected waves has arrived. The envelope of the impulse response shown schematically in Fig. 9.6b is typical of those experimentally measured for periodic gratings for which the condition $Nr \ll 1$ is not satisfied.

Transmission Line Models. For the general case of arbitrarily large reflections where all multiple reflections must be included, it is necessary to resort to a more complete theory in order to calculate the reflection coefficient of a grating. This can be done conveniently for normal-incidence reflections, but is extremely difficult for reflection at oblique incidence from gratings of finite length and width. Also, reflections from conducting strips on piezoelectric substrates are complicated by a number of added electrical effects. However the analysis of the response of a hypothetical device at normal incidence can often be a useful guide to understanding multiple-reflection effects in more complicated geometries. In order to obtain a high Q, surface wave resonators depend on the efficient reflection from normal incidence gratings. Theoretical analysis of the operation of such resonators depends on a complete description of the phase and amplitude of the reflectivity of highly reflecting gratings.

At normal incidence, for reflectors of uniform length, one may use standard one dimensional transmission line analysis. Sittig and Coquin have used such an approach.[12] The tops and bottoms of grooves (or strips and gaps in an overlay) are characterized by different characteristic impedances (Fig. 9.7b). In this model the impedances Z_0 and Z_1 are chosen such that

$$r = \frac{Z_1 - Z_0}{Z_1 + Z_0} \tag{9.19}$$

or

$$r \approx \frac{(Z_1/Z_0 - 1)}{2} \tag{9.20}$$

where r is the reflection coefficient per step. The impedances have no physical meaning and are only a means of characterizing the reflection. Because r varies with frequency, the impedance ratio must also be

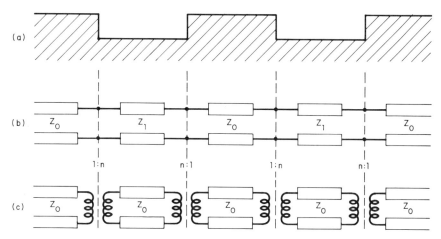

Figure 9.7 (a) Two grooves at normal incidence. (b) Sittig and Coquin model with impedance mismatches. (c) Oliner, Bertoni, and Li model specialized by Li to describe an array of grooves.

frequency dependent. Over a small fractional bandwidth, the variation can usually be neglected, as was done by Sittig and Coquin.

The network technique of Oliner, Bertoni, and Li[23-26] directly yields a transmission line model for a step (Fig. 9.3). A number of steps may be modeled by a cascade of the model for each step, that is, by connecting the transmission lines together (Fig. 9.7c). Recall that (9.3) characterizes the reflectivity of a simple step in terms of turns ratio n^2 such that

$$r = \frac{n^2 - 1}{n^2 + 1} \tag{9.21}$$

For $r \ll 1$,

$$r \approx n - 1 \tag{9.22}$$

In this case the turns ratio n is a function of frequency. The two models reduce to the same physical predictions.

Many examples of calculations of the frequency response of finite periodic arrays are given in references 12 and 30. In such calculations each groove is characterized by a transformation matrix that transforms the mechanical variables, force and velocity, in front of the groove to the corresponding mechanical variables behind the groove. Multiplication of matrices representing successive grooves allows the overall transformation matrix from the first to last groove in the array to be calculated. From this matrix the complex transmission and reflection coefficients can be obtained.

In the context of these transmission line models, the reflection coefficient at center frequency of a periodic array of N grooves with $W = d/2$ can be expressed in the closed form.[12]

$$|R(\omega_0)| = \frac{|(Z_1/Z_0)^{2N} - 1|}{(Z_1/Z_0)^{2N} + 1} \qquad (9.23)$$

where the impedances are those of Fig. 9.7b. As before, these impedances have no physical meaning other than to characterize the reflections. In the limit $N \gg 1$, $2Nr \ll 1$, this expression may be approximated

$$|R(\omega_0)| \approx 2Nr\left(1 - \frac{(2Nr)^2}{3}\right) \qquad (9.24)$$

where terms of order $N^2 r^3$ and r^4 or greater have been neglected. The leading term $2Nr$ is the magnitude of the reflection coefficient predicted by the delta function model. The term $(2Nr)^2/3$ is the deviation from the delta function model caused by triply reflected waves. Equation (9.24) suggests a rule of thumb for periodic or nearly periodic gratings, namely: The overall peak reflection coefficient $R(\omega)$ predicted by a delta function model tends to be too high by about $\frac{1}{3}|R|^2$. Equation (9.24) also illustrates a basic limitation of delta function models. Such models break down whenever the fraction of the energy reflected is large, in this case $(2Nr)^2$.

Reflections at Oblique Incidence.   For waves impinging on a grating at normal incidence, the direction of the reflected wave and frequency of maximum reflection are simply related to geometry. The direction is the reverse of that of incident wave and the frequency at which reflection occurs is determined by the condition that the period of the grating must be equal to one-half wavelength of the surface wave in the grating. However analysis of the reflection of surface waves at oblique incidence on anisotropic substrates is more complex and can best be summarized in terms of scattering-vector diagrams.

When a wave is elastically reflected by a stationary periodic grating, the condition for reflection is

$$\mathbf{K}_{in} + \mathbf{K}_g = \mathbf{K}_{out} \qquad (9.25)$$

where $\mathbf{K}_{in}$ and $\mathbf{K}_{out}$ are the wave vectors of the incident and reflected waves in the grating. Also, $|\mathbf{K}_{in}| = \omega/v_{in}$ and $|\mathbf{K}_{out}| = \omega/v_{out}$, where v_{in} and v_{out} are the velocities of the incoming and outgoing waves within the grating. The effect of the grating is characterized by its scattering vector

$\mathbf{K}_g$,

$$\mathbf{K}_g = \left(\frac{2\pi n}{d}\right)\mathbf{k} \tag{9.26}$$

where n is an integer, d is the spatial period of the grating (measured perpendicular to the grating lines) and $\mathbf{k}$ is a unit vector perpendicular to the grating lines. Only a grating consisting of an infinite number of infinitely long grooves can be characterized by a scattering vector of the form of (9.26). However the peak reflection from a grating, composed of a finite but large number of grooves, whose length is large compared to an acoustic wavelength is well described by (9.25) and (9.26).

Equation (9.25) specifies both the direction of the reflected wave and the frequency of reflection. We focus our attention here on reflections that occur at the first harmonic of the grating that corresponds to $|n| = 1$ in (9.26). It should be emphasized that all quantities in (9.25) are evaluated within the grating. In particular, the direction and velocity of the incoming and outgoing waves are those within the grating. On entering a grating a wave may change velocity or refract, and thus the quantities in (9.25) are not necessarily those of the free surface. A case in point is conducting overlay strips on a piezoelectric wherein velocities in the grating are different from those on the free surface.

The scattering relations (9.25) for 180° and 90° reflections are shown in Fig. 9.8. At normal incidence $v_{in} = v_{out}$ and $f = v/2d$ or $d = \lambda/2$. At oblique incidence on anisotropic substrates v_{out} is not necessarily equal to v_{in}. As illustrated in Fig. 9.8b, the angle of incidence must be given by

$$\tan\theta = \frac{|\mathbf{K}_{out}|}{|\mathbf{K}_{in}|} = \frac{v_{in}}{v_{out}} \tag{9.27}$$

in order to obtain 90° reflections.

For isotropic substrates or materials in which the crystal symmetry is such that v_{in} equals v_{out}, θ is 45°. On anisotropic substrates ($v_{in} \neq v_{out}$) it is necessary to determine the velocity ratio quite precisely in order to establish the correct grating angle and thus assure that the reflected wave lines up with the output transducer. For example, a device with an acoustic beam width of 100 wavelengths and input and output transducers set at 90° suffers a 1 dB misalignment loss if θ fails to satisfy (9.27) by only 0.075°. Equivalently the velocity ratio must be determined to within ±0.26%. If a device uses two reflections, as in Fig. 9.1d, the tolerances are twice as tight. The value of θ for 90° reflections has been determined with a high degree of accuracy for several substrates and these values are summarized in Table 9.2. In general, calculations of surface wave velocities from material constants cannot determine the value of θ for

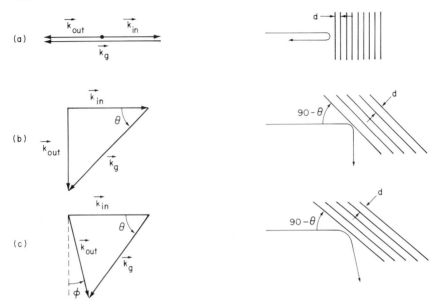

Figure 9.8 Scattering-vector relations. (*a*) Normal-incidence reflections. (*b*) 90° reflections. (*c*) Near 90° reflections.

anisotropic substrates with sufficient accuracy. The angles quoted in Table 9.2 were determined by direct measurement.

On anisotropic substrates the surface wave velocities along perpendicular directions may have unequal temperature variations. As a result, the value of θ that satisfies (9.27) is a function of temperature. Also, the thermal expansion coefficients along perpendicular directions may be

Table 9.2   Grating Angles for 90° Reflection

Crystal	Surface Normal	Direction of Incident Wave	θ (25°C)	Ref.
LiNbO$_3$	Y	Z	43.18°	2
Quartz	ST	X	41.93	37
Quartz	Y	X	39.67	37
Bi$_{12}$GeO$_{20}$	(100)	(011)	45.00	

different, and this in turn causes the angle of a grating to change with temperature. If a grating is fabricated such that at temperature T, $90°$ reflections are obtained, then a temperature change ΔT causes the grating angle at the new temperature to deviate by $\Delta\theta$ from the condition specified in (9.27). Meyer and Schulz[38] have analyzed the combined effects of thermal expansion and velocity changes and have derived the following expression for $\Delta\theta$:

$$\Delta\theta \approx \frac{v_{in} v_{out}}{v_{in}^2 + v_{out}^2} (\gamma_{in} - \gamma_{out}) \Delta T \qquad (9.28)$$

where γ_{in} and γ_{out} are temperature coefficient of delay $(1/\tau)(d\tau/dT)$ along the incident and outgoing directions, respectively. Equation (9.28) allows one to determine the correct angle to be used in designing a photomask for a device that is fabricated at one temperature and operated at another. Table 9.3 lists the anisotropy of temperature coefficient for several materials.[38] The large anistropy for YZ quartz is due to the fact that the temperature coefficients of delay along perpendicular directions are of opposite sign.

In analyzing the effect of grating misalignment it is useful to refer to the general oblique-reflection condition shown in Fig. 9.8c. In this case

$$v_{in} \cos(\theta + \phi) = v_{out} \sin\theta = fd \cos\phi \qquad (9.29)$$

For ϕ small

$$\phi \approx -(\sin\theta_0)^{-2}(\theta - \theta_0) \qquad (9.30)$$

where θ_0 is the angle for $90°$ reflections given by (9.27), that is, $\theta_0 = \arctan(v_{in}/v_{out})$. Note that $\phi = -2(\theta - \theta_0)$ for isotropic substrates but may deviate significantly from this relation for anisotropic substrates.

Table 9.3 Anisotropy of Temperature Coefficients

Crystal	Surface Normal	Direction of Incident Wave	Γ_{in}[a]	Γ_{out}[a]	$(\Gamma_{in} - \Gamma_{out})$[a]
LiNbO$_3$	Y	Z	90	78	12
Quartz	ST	X	0	47	-47
Quartz	Y	X	-24	66	-90
Bi$_{12}$GeO$_{20}$	(100)	(011)	130	130	0

[a] Units are parts per million/degree C.
Source: Reprinted, with permission, from ref. 38, p. 523.

Equation (9.29) is also useful for examining the frequency shifts that occur when v_{in}, v_{out} or θ are changed.

The grating geometry for 90° reflection has a practical advantage for fabricating high frequency devices. When the reflection condition is satisfied, the projection of the grating vector along either the incident or reflected directions is equal to the magnitude of the surface wave vector. Equivalently the periodicity of the grating in the direction of propagation of the surface wave is one wavelength. The period of the grating d measured perpendicular to the grating lines is equal to $\lambda \cos \theta$. For 90° reflections d is approximately $\sqrt{2}$ larger than the grating period required for normal-incidence reflections and also $\sqrt{2}$ larger than the electrode-to-electrode periodicity of an interdigital transducer operating at the same frequency. As a result, lower photomask resolution is required when fabricating oblique-incidence gratings.

Effects of Bulk Waves. The modes of propagation in a semi-infinite substrate include bulk waves (shear and longitudinal waves) in addition to the surface waves that are the main emphasis of this chapter. It has long been recognized that a surface discontinuity can scatter surface waves into bulk waves.[17,19,39] Seismologists investigated such scattering long before the development of surface wave technology. Several experimental and theoretical studies of radiative scattering of surface waves into bulk waves have concentrated on assessing the radiative loss a surface wave experiences in propagating on random or periodically roughened surfaces.[35,39-41] Also, it has been demonstrated that efficient conversion of surface to bulk waves can be obtained in a unique transducer geometry.[42]

Although it is clear that surface waves can scatter into bulk waves in a reflection grating, there exists another more subtle effect of bulk waves, reactive storage of bulk wave energy in the vicinity of a surface discontinuity. This reactance effect does not result in surface wave energy loss but does introduce phase shifts in the transmission and reflection coefficients at a step. Such phase shifts can degrade the response of surface wave signal-processing devices because stringent controls on phase response are usually required. Bulk wave scattering and reactive storage effects are discussed separately in the following sections.

Radiative Scattering into Bulk Waves. It is important to put this problem in perspective by noting that loss to bulk waves has not been a significant problem in most of the reflection-grating devices developed to date. Inclusion of the subject here is stimulated by a desire to assess the reason bulk wave scattering has not been a common problem and to anticipate the possibility of problems if one is forced to use deep grooves, as in, for instance, devices with few grooves and requiring low insertion loss.

Scattering into bulk waves can cause two types of problems. Whenever a significant amount of energy is scattered out of a surface wave by a reflection grating, the grating response is distorted and reduced in amplitude. Such a loss of energy would lower the Q of a surface wave resonator. A second and often more serious problem occurs in filters if the bulk waves propagate to the output transducer where they give rise to spurious signals. In this case spurious signals can be significant even if the total amount of scattered energy is small.

Because the gratings in reflection-grating devices are usually nearly periodic, it is useful to invoke scattering-vector relations to estimate when radiative loss into scattered bulk waves is likely to be a problem. The analysis proceeds in a manner similar to that outlined in Fig. 9.8 except that $\mathbf{K}_{out}$ is interpreted as the projection on the surface plane of the propagation vector of a bulk wave.

Several qualitative conclusions can be drawn from scattering-vector analysis. Because bulk waves generally have higher velocities than surface waves, radiative scattering from a periodic grating into bulk waves can occur only if the frequency exceeds some value f_B that is higher than the frequency f_0 at which scattering into reflected surface wave occurs. In general, the scattering conditions at oblique incidence are more restrictive than at normal incidence, which suggests that scattering losses are likely to be somewhat lower for oblique-incidence gratings.

The fact that significant loss to bulk waves can occur only for frequencies above that for which surface waves are scattered is important in the design of dispersive reflection gratings. In a "down-chirp" grating (i.e., closely spaced grooves close to the input), loss to bulk waves can occur only in those sections of the grating that lie farther from the input than the portion of the grating where surface waves are dominantly reflected. For this configuration, loss to bulk waves is not a problem. In an "up-chirp" grating with large fractional bandwidth, loss to bulk waves might be troublesome, but no such devices have been studied to date.

In oblique-incidence gratings, scattering-vector analysis shows that a scattered bulk wave travels at a significant angle relative to the direction of a reflected surface wave. Because surface wave transducers usually span a wide aperture (typically 100 wavelengths), they reject waves coming in at any except near normal incidence. Thus there exists a mode-filtering action in oblique-incidence gratings that effectively rejects scattered bulk waves. If the surface wave is twice reflected as illustrated in Fig. 9.1d, bulk waves are even further rejected because the scattering-vector relations in the upper and lower gratings cannot be satisfied

simultaneously. Note that in such gratings, bulk waves generated by the input transducer cannot reach the output transducer.

Scattering-vector arguments specify the conditions under which radiative loss to bulk waves can occur: Either the frequency exceeds some minimum value or the grating geometry is significantly nonperiodic and must therefore be described by a spectrum of scattering vectors some of which satisfy the scattering-vector condition. This departure from periodicity is more significant in gratings consisting of a small number of reflectors.

The limited theoretical and experimental work on the subject of bulk wave scattering can serve as qualitative guide to the magnitude of scattering loss. The theoretical analysis of surface-to-bulk wave scattering by Brekhovskikh,[39] Sabine,[41] and Yoneyama and Nishida,[35] as well as the experimental results of Rischbieter,[40] have shown that scattering loss is strongly frequency dependent and that the dominant scattering is into shear waves. For normal incidence, such scattering becomes strong at about $1.3f_0$. Marshall and Paige[43] have observed similar loss well above f_0 in oblique-incidence gratings. A significant feature of the theoretical work is that scattering loss to bulk waves is proportional to the square of the groove depth and thus goes rapidly to zero for shallow grooves. For frequencies close to f_0, the loss from shallow grooves is quite small, typically less than 1 dB for arrays of several thousand grooves. Such small loss can often be compensated for in a filter by a slight adjustment of grating reflectivity as a function of propagation distance.

In summary, bulk wave scattering is usually no problem in reflection-grating devices because such scattering is weak. In addition, oblique incidence gratings have a mode-filtering action that effectively rejects bulk waves. Bulk losses may be important in high-Q resonators, but preliminary results give little evidence of such losses.[10]

Reactive Energy Storage Effects. Bulk waves, surface waves, and waves in elastic waveguides, all of the same material, have successively lower velocities, respectively, because, as one progresses from bulk waves to waveguides, the mechanical motions interact with more surface area which results in lower restoring forces and consequently lower velocity. Similarly a step reveals additional surface area and a surface wave slows down in the vicinity of a step. This effect is reminiscent of the behavior of transmission systems with shunt capacitive loading where capacitive energy storage produces a slowing of the propagated wave. The wave motions in the vicinity of a step cannot be satisfied by a surface wave alone but must also involve bulk wave modes. It is energy stored in the vicinity of the step as nonpropagating bulk waves that slows the wave.

The previous section has shown that radiation into bulk waves is usually small so that energy storage is often a more important effect in shallow grooves. This slowing of a surface wave in a grating has been observed by Rischbieter[40] and by Williamson and Smith[2] (Fig. 9.9).

Because the amplitudes of the stored and scattered fields at a shallow step of height h are linear in the perturbation h, the energies associated with these fields are quadratic in h. Also, the phase shift and loss for a surface wave passing a step are linear in the energy of the stored or radiated waves and consequently the phase shift and loss are quadratic in h. Calculations by Mal and Knopoff[21] and Munasinghe and Farnell[14,16] show also that the phase shift on transmission past a step is approximately quadratic in h/λ for shallow steps or thin overlays. These physical arguments can be included in the transmission line model of a step by introducing a conductance to represent loss and reactance B to represent energy storage at the point on a transmission line corresponding to the step.[44] In this section we neglect the radiative loss represented by the conductance and use the equivalent circuit shown in Fig. 9.10.

Li's analysis of this model shows that the phase shift on transmission

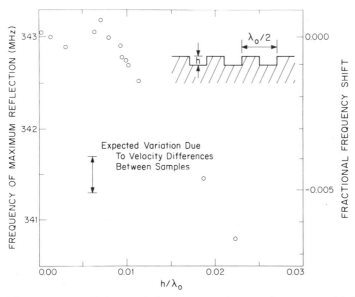

Figure 9.9 Frequency shift in a periodic array caused by reactive storage of bulk wave energy at a step. Normal-incidence reflection on YZ LiNbO$_3$. Copyright 1973 by The Institute of Electrical and Electronic Engineers, Inc. Reprinted, with permission, from *IEEE Trans.* **MTT-21,** 1973, p. 195.

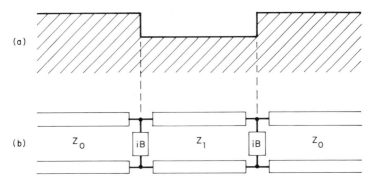

Figure 9.10 (*a*) Groove in homogeneous substrate. (*b*) Modification of the transmission line model of a groove that includes the reactive effect of bulk wave energy storage.

past the step is $-BZ_0/2$ and thus B is quadratic in h/λ. Accordingly the effective velocity of a wave traveling through a periodic grating and the frequency of maximum reflection from a periodic grating are shifted down by an amount that is quadratic in h/λ. In the latter case Li's analysis[44] shows that the downward shift Δf is given by

$$\frac{\Delta f}{f_0} = -\frac{BZ_0}{\pi} \tag{9.31}$$

A quadratic fit to Williamson and Smith's data[2] (Fig. 9.10) for periodic rectangular grooves on YZ LiNbO$_3$ yields

$$BZ_0 \approx 42\left(\frac{h}{\lambda}\right)^2 \tag{9.32}$$

for normal-incidence reflections.

The effective surface wave phase velocity for a surface with periodic grooves is

$$v \approx v_0\left(1 - \frac{Ch^2f}{2\pi dv_0}\right) \tag{9.33}$$

where C is the proportionality coefficient defined by $BZ_0 = C(h/\lambda)^2$, d is the periodicity of the grating, and v_0 is the free-surface velocity. For 90° reflections the number of grooves per length of propagation path is less at the same f_0 than at normal incidence. Accordingly the velocity perturbations are likely to be less for the same value of h in oblique gratings than at normal incidence.

The inclusion of the reactance in the model of a step modifies the reflection coefficient of a step. In this case

$$r' = r - \frac{iBZ_0}{2} \qquad (9.34)$$

and

$$r' = -r - \frac{iBZ_0}{2} \qquad (9.35)$$

for an up step and a down step, respectively. In these expressions r is the reflection coefficient for an up step due to impedance mismatch alone as given by (9.1). For shallow grooves $BZ_0/2 \ll r$ and the magnitude of reflection at the fundamental frequency is essentially unaltered by the reactance. The major effect is a shift in frequency response.

Equations (9.34) and (9.35) indicate that the reflections due to the reactance alone are of the same phase. Thus at the second harmonic of a groove, where groove width $= \lambda/2$, the contributions due to impedance mismatch cancel and one is left with an overall reflection coefficient due to reactance alone. This effect has been measured by Li and Melngailis[44] and the experimental reflection coefficients match the theoretical predictions of the equivalent circuit shown in Fig. 9.10.

The effect of energy storage at a step on the response of a reflection grating is a distortion of the amplitude and phase response of a filter relative to the response that would be obtained if the surface wave velocity were constant in the reflection grating. The magnitude of such distortions must be calculated separately for each filter design and groove depth. For shallow grooves ($h/\lambda < 0.01$), the effects are normally quite small. For such shallow grooves with groove width $= d/2$, the velocity perturbation predicted by (9.33) is less than 1.3×10^{-3}. However, high-Q resonators are very sensitive to velocity shifts and consequent phase and frequency shifts. Accordingly these reactive effects must be included in any resonator design.

Overall Trade-off Between Insertion Loss and Distorted Response. Three types of distortions in reflection grating filters have been examined: multiple reflections, scattering into bulk waves, and velocity perturbations (energy storage) in gratings. It has been shown that the relative amplitude of multiple reflections is proportional to $(Nr)^2$, where N is the effective number of grooves contributing to the reflection at any one frequency. The loss coefficient for scattering into bulk waves in nearly periodic gratings is proportional to $(h/\lambda)^2$ and therefore proportional to r^2. Also, the undesirable phase shift at a step and the corresponding velocity shifts in reflection gratings are proportional to $(h/\lambda)^2$ or r^2. In any given filter design N is usually fixed by the specified frequency response and r is the most important free variable to be chosen. The value of r must be small enough that the distortions in filter response are reduced to a tolerable level. However reducing r also reduces the overall reflection coefficient of a grating and therefore increases the insertion loss of a reflection-grating device. Consequently, the trade-off between insertion loss and distorted response is a major consideration in many device designs. In some cases it is possible to compensate for some of the distortions—for instance, changing groove reflectivities to correct the amplitude response, or changing groove positions to correct for imperfections in phase response. However these techniques can be pushed only so far, and one eventually faces the inevitable trade-off between insertion loss and distortions in filter response.

Reflection gratings are particularly useful for achieving certain types of device response because distortions can be minimized without a major sacrifice in insertion loss. The significant feature of such device responses is that the number of reflectors contributing to the overall reflection is large. In such cases the reflection loss, which is generally proportional to Nr, can be kept at a moderate level even if r is so small that scattering losses and velocity perturbations are at a negligible level. Pertinent examples are dispersive delay lines with small fractional bandwidths or large time-bandwidth products, as well as filters with small fractional bandwidths. The opposite situation arises if N is small. In such cases one may try to obtain a reasonable insertion loss by making r large; however signal distortions increase rapidly and limit the achievable insertion loss.

The undesirable effects of multiple reflections in any device can only be reduced by decreasing the overall reflection coefficient of a grating. Because the relative level of multiple reflections is approximately proportional to $(Nr)^2$, these reflections can usually be minimized at only a small cost in increased insertion loss. For this reason reflection coefficients ranging from 0.3 to 0.5 (10 dB to 6 dB) are often chosen. In such cases the relative level of multiple reflections typically ranges from 0.03 to 0.08, which is usually small enough.

The considerations in designing a reflection grating can be compared with the analogous situation in interdigital transducer arrays. In the analysis of interdigital fingers,[27,37] the piezoelectric coupling coefficient k plays a role analogous to that which the reflectivity r plays in the analysis of reflection gratings. A number of deleterious effects in interdigital arrays, including undesired surface wave reflections,[27-29] velocity dispersion,[45-48] and velocity shifts due to varying line space ratios,[48,49] are proportional to k^2. However the conversion loss of an interdigital transducer is also a function of k. Consequently, when k is decreased to reduce the magnitude of undesirable effects, the insertion loss of the interdigital transducer increases. Thus designers of interdigital arrays face a trade-off analogous to that for reflection-grating devices.

In view of the inevitable trade-off between distortions and insertion loss, how would a filter designer choose between an interdigital array or a reflection grating as a means of implementing a specified filter response? Because the reflection process in reflection-grating devices is a localized mechanical effect, there are only a small number of possible sources of filter distortions. In contrast, the more complicated electrical effects in interdigital arrays give rise to effects such as velocity dispersion, velocity shifts, resistive loss in electrodes, distortions due to circuit coupling and electrical transmission line effects that have no analog in reflection gratings. Interdigital electrodes must be thick enough to have low resistance and this introduces dispersion due to mass loading, an effect that is minimized in grooved reflection gratings. In addition, surface wave reflections are undesirable in interdigital arrays, whereas they are employed to advantage in reflection gratings. Spurious bulk waves are difficult to avoid in in-line interdigital devices but are negligible in oblique-incidence reflection-grating devices. Many of the effects in interdigital transducers remain large even when k is reduced. Distortions in filter response are particularly troublesome for situations in which the number of interdigital electrode pairs is large. It is this type of filter response for which reflection gratings are best suited.

As a practical matter, substrate materials with a continuous range of values for $\Delta v/v$ are not available for designing interdigital arrays. In most cases, either $LiNbO_3$ or quartz is used, depending on whether one desires $\Delta v/v$ to be large or small. In contrast, the depth of a groove or deposited strip is continuously variable and during the development of a filter, it is possible to experiment with various ranges of reflectivity without any basic changes in filter design; that is, the same grating pattern and substrate material can be used. Ease of fabrication and defect tolerance are also desirable features of reflection gratings that become more important when N is large.

If insertion loss is a consideration, it is important to recognize the initial price paid to use reflective arrays is the insertion loss of the input and output transducers. Loss in the reflection grating is added to these losses. Because the input and output transducers need not play an essential role in forming the overall response of a reflection-grating filter, the transducer design and substrate can be optimized for minimum transducer insertion loss. When comparing large time-bandwidth pulse compressors with comparable phase and amplitude distortions, reflection-grating devices generally have lower insertion loss than devices employing interdigital arrays.

9.2.   Grating Geometries and Their Relation to Device Response

The response of a reflection grating is a function of the position, length, and reflectivity of the individual reflectors. In this section the relationship between geometry and device response is derived. It is not possible to derive a general expression for the infinity of possible two-dimensional geometries for reflection grating devices, but the examples discussed here cover several important cases and illustrate the general principles.

Surface Wave Resonators.   The principles of operation and figures of merit for surface wave resonators are quite different from those for surface wave transversal filters. Resonators operate by reflecting a propagating wave on itself many times. It is desirable that the reflectors be efficient (i.e., high reflectivity) in order to obtain a sharp, high-Q resonance. Surface wave reflection gratings have the special property that they can be made efficient and, at the same time, frequency selective. This latter feature allows such devices to operate in the UHF frequency range, where bulk wave resonators would have to be very thin or be operated in an undesirable overtone mode.

The surface wave resonator illustrated in Fig. 9.11 makes use of two reflection gratings to form a surface wave cavity. An interdigital transducer placed inside the cavity couples to the standing surface waves. Unlike a filter, a resonator is a one-port device whose special characteristic is a rapidly varying terminal impedance in the vicinity of the resonant frequency.

The essential features of a resonator are illustrated in Fig. 9.12. For

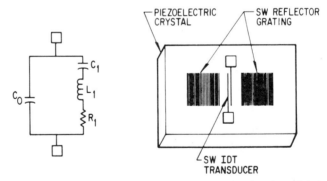

Figure 9.11 Surface wave crystal resonator structure showing interdigital transducer placed inside cavity formed by two surface wave reflectors. The resonator equivalent circuit is identical to that used for conventional bulk wave resonators. Reprinted, with permission, from ref. 10.

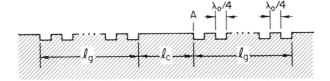

Figure 9.12 Cross-sectional view of a simple resonator with grooves as reflectors.

simplicity the reflectors are shown as identical periodic arrays of simple grooves. Because the reflection gratings are highly reflecting, transmission line models are employed in the analysis of the grating response, and because all the reflectors are the same length, the problem is one-dimensional and the models discussed previously can be used. The amplitude and phase of the overall reflection coefficient of the right hand grating as measured at point A in Fig. 9.12 is shown schematically in Fig. 9.13. At the middle of the reflection band (often referred to as the

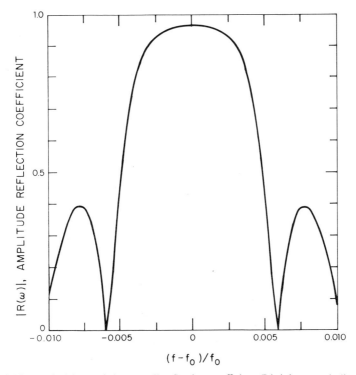

Figure 9.13 Typical form of the overall reflection coefficient $R(\omega)$ for a periodic grating. These results are for a 200-groove grating. Figure courtesy R. C. M. Li.

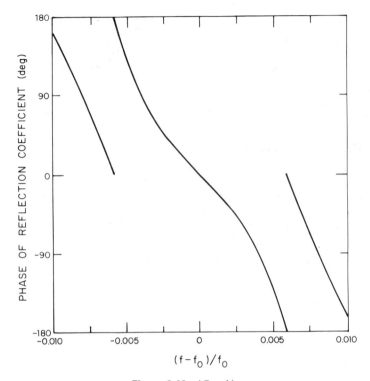

Figure 9.13 (*Contd.*)

"stopband"), the phase of the reflection coefficient is zero. Thus if the cavity length l_c between the inside edges of the two gratings is an integral number of half-wavelengths, waves multiply reflected between the two gratings have the same phase, add coherently, and the cavity resonates at the frequency of maximum reflection. It is possible to obtain this desirable resonance condition even when the surface wave velocity in the grating differs from that on the free surface (e.g., as a result of energy storage or the presence of overlay strips). The center of the stopband is determined by the grating period and the velocity in the grating. As before, resonance occurs at the center of the stopband if l_c is an integral number of free surface wavelengths at the frequency corresponding to the center of the stopband.

If the length l_g of the gratings is comparable to or smaller than the cavity length l_c between gratings, an undesirable situation arises. In this case the stopband becomes so broad that more than one resonance can occur within the stopband. To assure a single resonance the condition

$l_g \gg l_c$ must be satisfied. In the limiting case where $l_c = 0$, a necessary condition for resonance is that the phase of the reflection coefficient be zero. However 9.13 shows that, except at center frequency, the phase passes through zero only at those frequencies for which $R = 0$. Therefore resonance can occur only at f_0 in a resonator for which $l_c = 0$.

For several reasons it is desirable that the number of reflections in a surface wave resonator be large. As discussed in the previous paragraph, a large number of reflectors ensures a single resonance. The use of reflectors with $r \ll 1$ necessitates many reflectors in order to obtain an overall reflection coefficient R close to 1. When the gratings are composed of many weak reflectors, the stopband is narrow and the phase of the reflection coefficient is a rapidly varying function of frequency. This is desirable in order to obtain a high-Q resonance. Also, when r is small, scattering loss to bulk waves is minimized.

Analysis of Reflection-Grating Filters. The overall transfer function of a reflection-grating filter is the product of the frequency response for the input transducer, the output transducer, and the reflection grating. The response of interdigital transducers is well covered in other chapters, and this section concentrates on that portion of the response due to the grating.

In most reflection-grating filters other than those employing normal incidence reflectors of constant length, the reflected acoustic beam is not uniform in amplitude across the beam width, and this fact must be accounted for when calculating the overall transfer function $H(\omega)$. In the analysis of grating response it is assumed the interdigital transducers have uniform electrode overlap l and thus emit an acoustic beam of constant amplitude over a beam width equal to the electrode overlap. The transfer function $H(\omega)$ of such a transducer is related to the total acoustic power P_a emitted in one direction by the transducer.

$$|H(\omega)|^2 = \frac{P_a}{P_e} \qquad (9.36)$$

where $P_a = l|A|^2$, A is the amplitude of the emitted wave and P_e is the maximum available electrical power. In this section amplitudes refer to quantities whose magnitude squared has units of power or power density. The overall transfer function of a device can be defined as

$$H(\omega) = H_{in}(\omega)H_{out}(\omega)R(\omega) \qquad (9.37)$$

where H_{in} and H_{out} are the transfer functions of the input and output transducers as given earlier. All effects of nonuniform beam response and grating reflections are contained in $R(\omega)$, which is defined as the transfer function of the grating.

This definition of $R(\omega)$ has some subtle consequences. In the general case of oblique-incidence reflections from reflectors of varying length, the reflection coefficient of a grating is a function of both frequency and position. The quantity $R(\omega)$ as defined is an *effective* overall reflection coefficient at the output transducer obtained by integrating the actual reflection coefficient over the aperture of the transducer. Only in special cases is the reflection coefficient of a grating independent of position (i.e., uniform reflected beams). The transfer function $R(\omega)$ is equal to the reflection coefficient only in these special cases.

When a transducer is illuminated by a nonuniform acoustic beam, the output signal is given by

$$A_{out} = H_{out}(\omega)\bar{A}l^{1/2} \tag{9.38}$$

where $|A_{out}|^2 = P_e$, the power delivered to the electrical load, $l=$electrode overlap, and $\bar{A}$ is the average of the complex wave amplitude $A(l')$ over the width of the transducer l.

$$\bar{A} = \frac{1}{l}\int_0^l A(l')\,dl' \tag{9.39}$$

The integral is over the width of the transducer. These relations are used explicitly or implicitly in the derivation of many of the transfer functions in this section.

The delta function model is used here because it is relatively simple to apply to both normal and oblique-incidence reflections. The model also allows a grating to be designed in a straightforward way by providing a direct relationship between geometry and impulse response. The procedure for designing a reflection grating is basically the same as that used in designing interdigital arrays. The desired impulse response is either given or obtained by Fourier transform of the frequency response. The task of the designer is then to specify a geometry that yields an adequate approximation to the desired impulse response. This section does not directly address this synthesis problem, but rather concentrates on analysis of the response of gratings with specified geometries. Once this is done, the synthesis procedure is often relatively obvious.

These simple models of grating response do not include effects due to multiple reflection, dispersion, diffraction, or propagation loss. It is necessary to bear in mind these limitations of the model. Often these effects can be included as corrections to the predictions of the simple model.

When assessing the validity of a delta function model, an important consideration is the fraction of incident power reflected by a grating. In the analysis of the transmission line model of normal-incidence reflections, it was shown by (9.17) that the delta-function model breaks down whenever the fraction of power reflected out of the incident acoustic beam becomes large. The power reflection coefficient can be related to the grating transfer function $R(\omega)$ defined by (9.37). To show this relation let us define a reflection coefficient $\Gamma(l')$ that relates the local amplitude of the reflected wave to the uniform amplitude of the wave incident on a grating.

$$\Gamma(l') = \frac{A_{out}(l')}{A_{in}} \tag{9.40}$$

where l' is a position coordinate over the width of an output transducer, A_{in} is the amplitude of a wave incident on the reflection grating, and $A_{out}(l')$ is the amplitude of the reflected wave at the position l'. The total power reflection coefficient is

$$\frac{\text{Total power reflected}}{\text{Total power incident}} = \frac{\int_0^{l_{out}} |A_{out}(l')|^2 \, dl'}{|A_{in}|^2 \, l_{in}} = \frac{1}{l_{in}} \int_0^{l_{out}} |\Gamma(l')|^2 \, dl' \tag{9.41}$$

where l_{in} and l_{out} are the widths of the input and output transducers and the reflected wave is assumed to have no energy outside the width of the output transducer. However $R(\omega)$ is related to $\Gamma(l')$ by

$$|R(\omega)|^2 = \frac{1}{l_{in}l_{out}} \left| \int_0^{l_{out}} \Gamma(l') \, dl' \right|^2 \tag{9.42}$$

A comparison of (9.47) and (9.48) show that

$$|R(\omega)|^2 \le \frac{\text{Power reflected}}{\text{Power incident}} \tag{9.43}$$

The equality holds only when $\Gamma(l')$ is a constant, that is, when the reflected wave is uniform both in phase and amplitude over the width of the output transducer. When the reflected wave is not uniform, an additional fraction of the energy travels under or is reflected by the output transducer. Equation (9.43) indicates that $|R(\omega)|^2 \ll 1$ is a necessary but insufficient condition for the validity of the delta function model. Examples of the application of this criterion are given in the following sections.

Normal-Incidence Reflections, Some General Features. Although normal-incidence reflections are employed in surface wave resonators, 90° reflections are generally used in surface wave filters. However the operation of hypothetical filters employing normal-incidence reflections is analyzed in some detail in order to illustrate some general features of reflection-grating filters (i.e., nonuniform acoustic beams, definition of grating transfer functions, and "length" and "depth" weighting of the impulse response). Figure 9.14 shows the geometry for reflection at normal incidence. In this and the following figures grooves are represented by single lines and coordinates refer to distances to the center of the grooves. Because many of the grooves shown span only a fraction of the incident acoustic beam, the reflected beam has a nonuniform amplitude. The amplitude of the wave reflected from the nth groove is $r_{g,n}A$, where $r_{g,n}$ is the reflectivity of the nth groove and A is the amplitude of the incident wave. The average amplitude of this wave is $l_n r_{g,n} A / l$.

Equations (9.36) to (9.39) yield the transfer function of the grating. Summing the reflected waves originating from each groove, we obtain

$$R(\omega) = \sum_{n=0}^{N} r_{g,n}\left(\frac{l_n}{l}\right)e^{-i\omega 2x_n/v} \tag{9.44}$$

When $l_n = l$, all acoustic beams are uniform and this result is the same as that derived for a one-dimensional transmission line in 9.11.

Equation (9.44) is the form for specifying the response of a transversal filter. An input signal is sampled at successive times, $2x_n/v$, after the signal is applied to the device and these samples are summed with weights $r_{g,n}(l_n/l)$. This correspondence is not totally precise because the reflectivity of a groove $r_{g,n}$ is a function of frequency as given by (9.5).

As (9.44) indicates, the effective reflectivity of a groove can be varied either by changing $r_{g,n}$ or l_n. In other words, there are two means available for "weighting" the impulse response of a grating—varying groove depth or groove length. If "length weighting" is employed, an

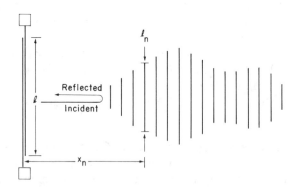

Figure 9.14 Normal-incidence grating consisting of grooves of variable length.

objectionable distortion of the wavefront of the incident wave may occur if the grooves significantly slow the wave. In this case the portions of the incident wave at the outer edges of the incident beams (Fig. 9.14) pass through fewer grooves than the center of the beam and thus the outer portions of the beam are not slowed as much. This effect can be important in long arrays of deep grooves. The slowing effect as given by (9.33) can be used to judge the degree of wavefront distortion and consequent degradation of filter response. Also, small weights may require grooves whose length are so short that significant diffraction occurs. On the other hand, length weighting is often desirable because the weights of successive grooves can be significantly different, the grating can be etched to uniform depth, and the response of the grating can be reliably reproduced because the weighting is specified by the photomask. When depth weighting is employed, the reflectors can span the incident acoustic beam and thus eliminate wavefront distortion and minimize diffraction. Changes in weighting on successive devices do not require a change in the photomask. However it is difficult to etch gratings whose groove depth varies rapidly with position. Etching grooves with varying depths is more complicated and requires more time than etching grooves of uniform depth. Similar statements apply to devices wherein the reflectors are strips of deposited overlay.

Reflections at 90°.   The reflection of a single groove is illustrated in Fig. 9.15a. The reflectivity of the groove is defined such that $|r_g|^2$ is equal to the ratio of the reflected to the incident power. However, on anisotropic substrates, $90°$ reflections are obtained when $l \neq l'$, and then the incident and reflected beams are of different widths. With this in mind, a consistent definition of groove reflectivity is

$$r_g = \frac{A_{out}}{A_{in}} \left(\frac{l}{l'}\right)^{1/2} \tag{9.45}$$

or

$$r_g = \frac{A_{out}}{A_{in}} (\cot \theta)^{1/2} \tag{9.46}$$

where A_{in} and A_{out} are the amplitudes of the incident and reflected waves, respectively, and θ is the grating angle as defined by (9.27). The reflectivity of a groove at oblique incidence is given by a modification of (9.5). For $90°$ reflections the reflectivity of a groove is

$$r_g = 2ir \sin \left(\frac{|\mathbf{K}_{in}| \, W}{2 \cos \theta}\right) \tag{9.47}$$

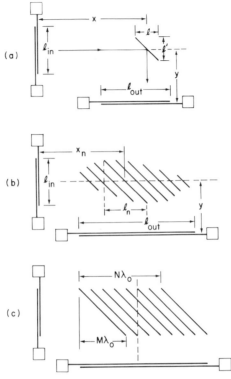

Figure 9.15 (a) 90° reflections from a single reflector. (b) 90° reflections from a grating consisting of reflectors of variable length. (c) 90° reflection from a grating with width equal to that of the aperture of one transducer.

or

$$r_g = 2ir \sin\left(\frac{|\mathbf{K}_{out}| W}{2 \sin \theta}\right) \qquad (9.48)$$

where W is the width of the groove as measured perpendicular to its length, r is the reflectivity of a step, and $\mathbf{K}_{in}$ and $\mathbf{K}_{out}$ are the wave vectors of the incident and reflected waves. Note that the groove dimension in the propagation direction is equal to $\lambda/2$ for maximum reflections.

For a single groove that lies entirely within the region illuminated by the input and output transducers (Fig. 9.15b), (9.36) to (9.39) can be used to derive the groove transfer function:

$$R(\omega) = r_g l \left(\frac{\cot \theta}{l_{in} l_{out}}\right)^{1/2} \exp\left[-i\omega\left(\frac{x}{v_{in}} + \frac{y}{v_{out}}\right)\right] \qquad (9.49)$$

Equation (9.49) can be generalized to the case of combined reflections from many grooves (Fig. 9.15*b*).

$$R(\omega) = \exp\left(\frac{-i\omega y}{v_{out}}\right)\left(\frac{\cot\theta}{l_{in}l_{out}}\right)^{1/2} \sum_n r_{g,n}l_n \exp\left(\frac{-i\omega x_n}{v_{in}}\right) \qquad (9.50)$$

Note that if any groove is translated along its length, the response of the array is unchanged, provided all grooves lie in the illuminated region.

One of the difficulties of reflection-grating devices with the geometry of Fig. 9.15*b* is that the output transducer must have a width that is larger than the length of the grating. If the desired impulse response is longer than a few hundred cycles, the required width of the output transducer may be awkwardly large.

A case of special interest is shown in Fig. 9.15*c*. Here all grooves exactly match the beam width of one transducer. M is the aperture of the input transducer measured in wavelengths at center frequency and N is the length of the grating impulse measured in signal periods at center frequency. The output transducer is $(N+M)\lambda_0$ long. Equation (9.50) becomes

$$R(\omega) = \exp\left(\frac{-i\omega y}{v_{out}}\right)\left(\frac{M}{N+M}\right)^{1/2} \sum r_{g,n} \exp\left(\frac{-i\omega x_n}{v_{in}}\right) \qquad (9.51)$$

When the impulse length is short ((i.e., $N \ll M$), the geometric factor in front of the sum approaches 1. In this case the reflected beam is essentially uniform in amplitude and each groove fully illuminates the output transducer. For this condition, $|R(\omega)|^2 =$ reflected power/incident power.

When the impulse length of the grating is long (i.e., $N \gg M$), the geometric factor $[M/(N+M)]^{1/2}$ becomes small. It is instructive to examine the special case of a long periodic grating consisting of N identical grooves located λ_0 apart along the direction of the input wave. At center frequency,

$$|R(\omega_0)| \approx (MN)^{1/2}|r_g| \qquad (9.52)$$

The reflected power at center frequency can be calculated by noting that the output wave is essentially uniform (neglecting effects at the end of the grating). At ω_0 the amplitude of the reflected wave is the coherent sum of all reflections from the grooves that intersect the dashed line in Fig. 9.15*c*, or

$$|A_{out}(\omega_0)| = M|r_gA_{in}(\omega_0)| \qquad (9.53)$$

or

$$\frac{\text{Reflected power}}{\text{Incident power}} = MN|r_g|^2 \qquad (9.54)$$

In this case $|R(\omega_0)|^2 =$ reflected power/incident power.

However such an equality does not hold away from center frequency. To see this, note that the fractional bandwidth of the grating transfer function $R(\omega)$ is equal to N^{-1}. In contrast, the local amplitude of the once-reflected wave is a sum of M reflections and thus the power reflected out of the incident beam has a fractional bandwidth of M^{-1}. For $N \gg M$ substantial power may be reflected out of the incident beam at $\omega \neq \omega_0$ even though $R(\omega)$ is small. At $\omega \neq \omega_0$ the wave incident on the output transducer is nonuniform; that is, the phase is a function of position. Because of this nonuniformity, the wave is not efficiently coupled to the output transducer and this inefficiency is expressed in the grating transfer function $R(\omega)$.

Grating geometries of the general form shown in Fig. 9.15 are useful because the grating response (9.50) is of the standard transversal filter form and the impulse response can be either length or depth weighted, as discussed previously for normal-incidence gratings. The utility of the 90° reflection gratings is that the input and output waves are easily separated and there is a natural mode-filtering action that reduces the level of bulk wave and other spurious equals. Examples of filters with this geometry are given later.

Two 90° Reflections. The effects of partial illumination and nonuniform reflected waves are more complex when two reflections occur. Consider the simple case of two grooves illustrated in Fig. 9.16a. Only the portion of the wave that reflects off both the upper and lower grooves eventually reaches the output transducer. The amplitude of this wave is the product of $r_{g,1}$, $r_{g,2}$, and the amplitude of the input wave, but the beam width is only $l \cot \theta$, where l is the "overlap" of the two grooves. The grating transfer function for two grooves is

$$R(\omega) = \exp\left(\frac{-i\omega y}{v_y}\right) r_{g,1} r_{g,2} \frac{l \cot \theta}{(l_{in} l_{out})^{1/2}} \exp\left[\frac{-i\omega(x_1 + x_2)}{v_x}\right] \quad (9.55)$$

Generalizing to the case of two arrays of grooves (Fig. 9.17b), we obtain

$$R(\omega) = \exp\left(\frac{-i\omega y}{v_y}\right) \sum_{m,n} r_{g,m} r_{g,n} \gamma_{mn} \exp\left[\frac{-i\omega(x_m + x_n)}{v_x}\right] \quad (9.56)$$

The quantity $\gamma_{m,n}$ is an overlap factor, which is a measure of the degree to which the mth reflector in the top row illuminates the nth reflector in the

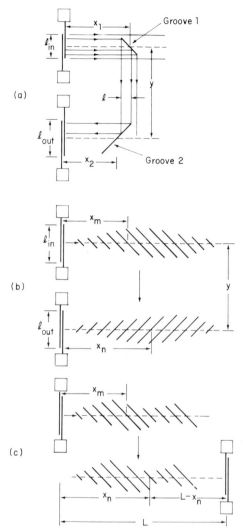

Figure 9.16 (a) Two 90° reflections from single reflectors with overlap *l*. (b) Arrangement of variable-length reflectors such that the doubly reflected wave is antiparallel to the incident wave. (c) Arrangement of variable-length reflectors such that the doubly reflected wave is parallel to the incident wave.

bottom row. As in (9.55),

$$\gamma_{mn} = \frac{l_{mn} \cot \theta}{(l_{in} l_{out})^{1/2}} \qquad (9.57)$$

where l_{mn} is the physical length of the overlap. If there is no overlap, $\gamma_{mn} = 0$. The response of the grating shown in Fig. 9.16c is the same as (9.56) except for a change of sign in the exponent.

$$R(\omega) = \exp\left[-i\omega\left(\frac{y}{v_y} + \frac{L}{v_x}\right)\right] \sum r_{g,m} r_{g,n} \gamma_{mn} \exp\left[\frac{-i\omega(x_m - x_n)}{v_x}\right] \qquad (9.58)$$

As discussed later, this change of sign drastically alters the filtering characteristics of this configuration (Fig. 9.16c) as compared to the response predicted by (9.56) (Fig. 9.16b).

Equations (9.56) and (9.58) contain double sums over the reflectors in the two sections of reflection grating. In general, these sums are not separable because of the presence of the factor γ_{mn}. As a result, $R(\omega)$ is not merely the product of the transfer functions of the two sections of grating. Also, (9.56) and (9.58) are not in the standard single-sum form for the response of a transversal filter. Because of the geometric overlap effect of the two gratings, abrupt changes in reflectivity or a rapid deviation from quasiperiodic spacing (e.g., a phase reversal) in one grating does not result in a correspondingly abrupt change within the overall impulse response of the two gratings. Changes within the impulse response occur over times comparable to the transit time across the width of the grating. For this reason, double-reflection geometries are not generally useful for phase-coded filters, large fractional-bandwidth band-pass filters, or small time-bandwidth dispersive filters, although a major exception is identified subsequently. Dispersive filters with large time-bandwidth products have impulse responses that are quasiperiodic over a large number of cycles and thus are well suited to the geometry of Fig. 9.16b. Nondispersive bandpass filters with large fractional bandwidth can be implemented in the configuration of Fig. 9.16c, provided the gratings are "chirped," that is, they are quasiperiodic with a continuously increasing (or decreasing) spacing from one end to the other. For this geometry the impulse response has an approximately $\sin x/x$ shape with many rapid changes in amplitude and phase even though the grating itself contains no abrupt changes in amplitude or phase.

The impulse response of a two-reflection device can be weighted either by changing groove reflectivity or groove length, which in turn change γ_{mn}. If depth weighting is employed, the gratings can be adjusted to span the aperture of the input transducer, in which case $l_{in} = l_{out}$ and

$$l_{mn} = l_{in} \tan \theta - |x_m - x_n| \qquad (9.59)$$

and

$$\gamma_{mn} = 1 - |x_m - x_n| \quad \text{if} \quad |x_m - x_n| < l_{in} \tan \theta \qquad (9.60)$$

$$\gamma_{mn} = 0 \quad \text{if} \quad |x_m - x_n| \geq l_{in} \tan \theta$$

Note that $l_{in} \tan \theta$ is the length of each groove in the x direction.

It is instructive to examine the response predicted by (9.56) for periodic gratings of constant width and depth. Let each section of grating be $N\lambda_0$ long and $M\lambda_0$ wide with successive grooves spaced λ_0 along the direction of propagation. For simplicity, isotropy $(\theta = 45°)$ is assumed. The geometry, envelope of the impulse response, and frequency response for the case $M \gg N$ are shown in Fig. 9.17a. Here all grooves in the first row completely illuminate all grooves in the second row, $\gamma_{mn} = 1$, and the once-reflected wave is uniform as viewed at the center line between the gratings. Thus the transfer function for two reflections is the product of the transfer functions for each section. In this case $R(\omega)$ is of the form $N^2 r_g^2 (\sin x / x)^2$ where $x = \pi N (f - f_0)/f_0$.

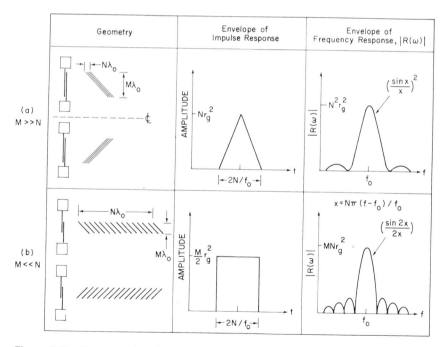

Figure 9.17 Geometry, impulse response, and frequency response for double-reflection periodic gratings in which the reflected wave is parallel to the incident wave. (a) Short, wide gratings. (b) Long, narrow gratings.

An entirely different response is obtained for the other extreme, $M \ll N$, as shown in Fig. 9.17b. Here each reflector in one grating illuminates only a few reflectors in the second grating. Because of this the maximum of the impulse response is reduced to $Mr_g^2/2$. In this case $R(\omega)$ is of the form $MNr_g^2(\sin 2x/2x)$ where $x = \pi N(f - f_0)/f_0$. Thus both the shape and amplitude of the impulse and frequency response are completely altered by changing the ratio M/N. The maximum value of $R(\omega)$, that is, when $\omega = \omega_0$, for arbitrary values of M/N has been calculated. Let us define a geometric factor $g(M/N)$ such that

$$|R(\omega)_0| = N^2 |r_g|^2 g\left(\frac{M}{N}\right) \tag{9.61}$$

The quantity $g(M/N)$ as defined by (9.61) is shown in Fig. 9.18. These results are useful in calculating the response of nonperiodic gratings.

The configuration of Fig. 9.16b has proved useful for constructing dispersive filters, or reflective array compressors (RAC). In this case the grooves have a spacing that increases (or decreases) as a function of the distance from the input transducer. The surface wave is strongly reflected at a right angle in regions where the groove spacing in the propagation

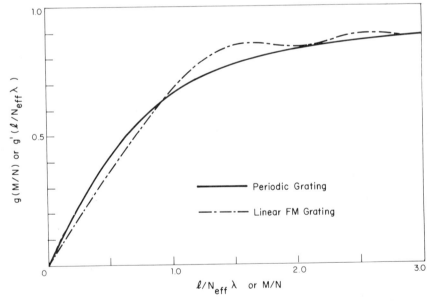

Figure 9.18 Geometric factors for periodic and linear-FM double-reflection gratings as a function of the ratio of the width to length of the gratings.

direction matches the wavelength of the surface wave. A second reflection in a symetrically placed mirror image grating sends the wave to the output transducer. The groove positions are established such that the surface wave travels from input to output along a path whose length (and delay) is an increasing or decreasing function of frequency. For a linear-FM filter, the path length is linear in frequency.

A linear-FM filter is required to have an impulse response that is approximately sinusoidal starting at an initial frequency f_1 with the instantaneous frequency changing linearly to a second frequency f_2 over the duration of the impulse. In order to satisfy this requirement for constant length reflectors in the configuration of Fig. 9.16b, the reflectors in the grating must be spaced according to

$$x_n - x_1 = \left(\frac{v_x f_1 T}{2\,\Delta f}\right)\left[1 - \left(1 - \left(\frac{4\,\Delta f}{f_1^2 T}\right)(n-1)\right)^{1/2}\right] \quad (9.62)$$

where $n = 1, 2, \ldots, f_0 T/2 + 1$, T is the duration of the impulse, Δf is the total range of frequencies (bandwidth) in the linear-FM signal or chirp, and f_0 is the center frequency. Equation (9.62) is for a down-chirp impulse response and this equation can be used for an up chirp by considering x_1 to be the last, instead of the first, groove position in the grating.

The analytic or numerical evaluation of $R(\omega)$ for a chirped grating (9.56) and (9.62) is difficult. Efficient computational procedures[50] have been developed for evaluating the double sum in (9.56), but they do not give much insight into device operation. Martin[1] has developed a closed-form analytic approximation to (9.56) for linear-FM filters that illustrates the essential features. His derivation yields an equation of the form

$$R(\omega) = (N_{\text{eff}}(\omega)\,|r_g(\omega)|)^2\,g'\left(\frac{l}{N_{\text{eff}}\lambda}\right)\exp\left[-i\left(\omega\tau_0 - \frac{T(\omega - \omega_0)^2}{2\,\Delta\omega}\right)\right] \quad (9.63)$$

where

$$N_{\text{eff}} = \frac{\omega}{\Delta\omega}\left(\frac{T\,\Delta\omega}{4\pi}\right)^{1/2} = \frac{f}{\Delta f}\left(\frac{T\,\Delta f}{2}\right)^{1/2} \quad (9.64)$$

These equations employ slightly different normalizations than in Ref. 1, but the expressions are mathematically identical. The groove reflectivity $r_g(\omega)$ is the reflectivity of those grooves that satisfy the scattering-vector condition, (9.25), at frequency ω. The group delay at center frequency is τ_0. Equation (9.63) includes a geometric factor $g'(l/N_{\text{eff}}\lambda)$, which is very similar to that defined in (9.61) for a periodic grating. Because N_{eff} is linear in frequency and λ is inversely proportional to frequency, the argument $(l/N_{\text{eff}}\lambda)$ is a constant for a grating of constant width. The dimension l is the length of each groove in the x direction. The magnitude of the geometric factor for a linear-FM grating is shown in Fig. 9.18 for comparison with the similar factor for periodic gratings.

The transfer function for a linear-FM grating, (9.63), can be interpreted in a simple fashion. Consider the case for which the reflecting lines in each section of grating are very long. In this case we can neglect effects at the ends of the reflectors and, in analogy with the situation illustrated in Fig. 9.17a, the once-reflected wave is uniform in space and the overall transfer function $R(\omega)$ is the product of the transfer functions for each section of grating. Let us define a quantity N_{eff} such that $|R(\omega)|^{1/2} = N_{\text{eff}}|r_g|$ for a grating composed of infinitely long reflectors. A summation of the waves reflected from one section of grating with spacing according to (9.63) yields an expression identical to (9.64) under the approximation $N_{\text{eff}} \gg 1$. N_{eff} can be interpreted as the effective number of grooves within a chirped grating that are reflecting at any one frequency. For a chirped grating, N_{eff} is only a fraction of the total number of grooves. Because (9.63) expresses the overall transfer function after reflection from two gratings, $R(\omega)$ is proportional to $(N_{\text{eff}}|r_g|)^2$. When the grating has finite width, $R(\omega)$ is modified by a geometric factor and the analysis illustrated in Figs. 9.17 and 9.18 suggests the approximate form for this geometric factor. Note that Martin's derivation[1] and the analysis of periodic gratings yield geometric factors with approximately the same amplitude. In both cases the geometric factor approaches 1 for large values of the argument; that is, for the condition $l \gg N_{\text{eff}}\lambda$. The initial slope of g versus M/N is unity for a periodic grating, whereas the initial slope is $2^{-1/2}$ for a linear-FM grating. In fact, $g' = l/\sqrt{2}N_{\text{eff}}\lambda$ is a good approximation for $l < N_{\text{eff}}\lambda$.

A difficulty arises when length weighting is employed in a linear-FM grating. The geometric factor for a chirped grating $g'(l/N_{\text{eff}}\lambda)$ is complex and the phase is a function of the argument.[1] The phase of g' changes by $\pi/2$ as the argument goes from zero to infinity. Therefore length weighting of the reflectors in a chirped grating causes $R(\omega)$ to have a phase response that differs from the phase response of a grating composed of reflectors of constant length. To obtain linear-FM response from length-weighted gratings, the grooves must be spaced in a fashion slightly different from the spacings specified by (9.62).

When the grooves in a grating are of uniform depth, the response is strongly skewed toward higher frequencies. The reflectivity r of any step is linear in frequency and r_g the reflectivity of a groove is approximately linear in r. N_{eff} is also linear in frequency and thus for a grating of constant depth, $|R(\omega)|$, as given by (9.63), is proportional to the fourth power of frequency. This causes a considerable skewing of the amplitude response for a device with large fractional bandwidth. One means of obtaining a constant value for $|R(\omega)|$ is to use depth weighting such that the groove depth in each region of the grating is proportional to the square of the local periodicity.

When a surface wave undergoes two 90° reflections such that the twice-reflected wave travels in the same direction as the incident wave (Fig. 9.16c), entirely different filter responses occur. The exact response can be calculated by evaluating (9.58) for a particular geometry, but some simple arguments illustrate the basic responses obtainable. It is instructive first to investigate the response of simple periodic gratings of constant width. When the width of each grating is much larger than its length, (i.e., $M \gg N$, analogous to the situation illustrated in Fig. 9.17a), the impulse response and frequency response are identical to that shown in Fig. 9.17a. However when the gratings are long, $M \ll N$, a different result from that shown in Fig. 9.16 occurs. It is shown in Fig. 9.19a. Consider the impulse response due to one groove in the upper row and all the grooves in the lower row. The wave reflected off a single groove in one row and the corresponding groove in the second row has an amplitude equal to r_g^2 because $\gamma_{mn} = 1$ in this case. This impulse arrives at a time t. All other elements of the impulse response that arrive before or after t_0 have a smaller effective amplitude due to the linear decrease of the overlap factor γ_{mn}. The triangular envelope of the resulting impulse response is shown in Fig. 9.19. Note that the paths labeled 1, 2, and 3 in Fig. 9.19a are all the same length. This means the impulse responses associated with the various grooves in the first row are identical (neglecting end effects), all peak at t_0, and the overall impulse response is a simple sum, as shown in Fig. 9.19a. The bandwidth of the frequency response Fig. 9.19a is determined solely by the width of the grating $M\lambda_0$ and not by its length.

A grating with variable spacing such as that illustrated in Fig. 9.19b can be used to obtain a bandpass filter. As an example, consider a pair of gratings with spacings given by an equation like (9.62). For simplicity, assume the grating is narrow in comparison to the length of the portion of the grating that is effectively reflecting at any one frequency, that is, $M \ll N_{\text{eff}}$, where N_{eff} is defined by (9.64). In this case the envelope of the impulse response for a single groove in the upper grating and all the grooves in the lower grating, is triangular as before (Fig. 9.19b). Although the envelope of the amplitude response associated with any single groove in the upper row is the same, the period of the individual impulses within the envelope varies, depending on the location of the particular groove in the upper row. Note that path 1, corresponding to reflection at

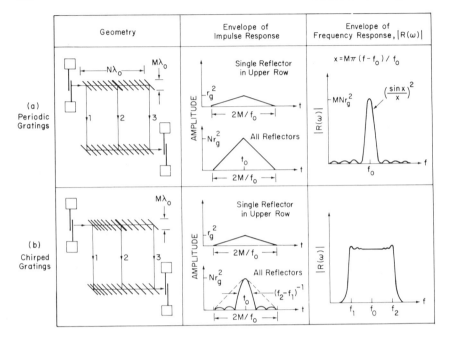

Figure 9.19 Geometry, impulse response and frequency response for double-reflection gratings in which the reflected wave is parallel to the incident wave. (*a*) Long, narrow, periodic gratings. (*b*) Long, narrow, chirped gratings.

a high frequency; path 2, for reflection at an intermediate frequency; and path 3, for reflection at a low frequency all have the same length, and thus the overall response is nondispersive. When the response of all grooves is summed, interference effects occur and the overall impulse response is of the form $(\sin x)/x$ times a triangular modulation function (Fig. 9.19*b*). This triangular modulation function tends to reduce ripples in the frequency response.[51] The net effect is a frequency response that has wider bandwidth and flatter response than obtained for a periodic grating (Fig. 9.19).

The various geometries and responses illustrated in this section cover several important cases, but the coverage is by no means complete. However, armed with the simple techniques employed in the delta function models for these geometries, the results can be readily extrapolated to a wide variety of two-dimensional arrangements of gratings and transducers.

9.3 Examples of Reflection-Grating Devices

The first known work regarding surface wave resonance phenomena was presented by Ash in 1970.[9] A resonator with a Q of 80 at 30 MHz was described in an abstract. In marked contrast to this earlier work, Staples[10] obtained resonator Q's as high as 10,000 and resonant frequencies as high as 400 MHz.

Staples employed two types of reflectors in resonators. The first consisted of periodic gratings of conducting aluminum strips on LiNbO$_3$. These strips cause $\Delta v/v$ reflections. In many cases temperature stability is important in a resonator and for this purpose ST quartz is the only known material. A second type of resonator consisting of periodic gratings of "mass-loading" strips of sputter deposited ZnO on ST quartz was fabricated. Results with this structure demonstrated that the desirable combination of high Q and temperature stability can be obtained in surface wave resonators. Arrays of grooves have not yet been used in resonators, but it is likely that the small predictable velocity shifts and precisely controllable reflectivity of grooves can be used to advantage in resonators.

The surface wave resonator response obtained by Staples is completely free of spurious responses, and this is in marked contrast to bulk mode resonators, where unwanted modes can be a problem. Spurious responses are absent because surface wave reflection occurs only over a very narrow bandwidth determined by the reflection gratings.

Figure 9.20 summarizes the Q's and resonant frequencies obtained by

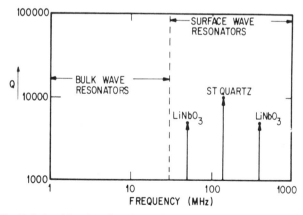

Figure 9.20 Relationship of surface acoustic wave resonator technology to that of bulk wave technology in terms of Q versus frequency of fundamental mode operation. Data points are for devices developed by Staples. Reprinted, with permission, from ref. 10.

Staples.[10] Also indicated are the frequency ranges for which surface and bulk wave resonators are best suited. The dividing line is at approximately 30 MHz.

Bandpass Filters. Melngailis et al.[7] have described development of a number of nondispersive bandpass filters that demonstrate the use of length and depth weighting, the use of chirped gratings in a nondispersive configuration, (Fig. 9.19), the use of a number of gratings on a single crystal to construct a filter bank, and a filter with a very narrow bandwidth.[8]

Reflection gratings are well suited for the construction of multichannel bandpass filter banks.[8] A schematic diagram of such a filter bank is shown in Fig. 9.21. The central transducer has bandwidth sufficient to span the range of frequencies within all the channels on a single crystal. This transducer launches waves in two directions, and these waves propagate essentially unattenuated until they reach a reflection grating with the appropriate spacing to reflect a fraction of the energy to the output transducer. In this manner there is negligible power distribution loss when addressing many channels. Although only four channels are shown in Fig. 9.21, many more channels can be added with little or no increase in insertion loss to any one channel. The fact that grooves cause a minimal perturbation of a surface wave traveling through them, particularly when off the reflection frequency, allows many channels to be stacked in this fashion. Any perturbing effects are minimized by placing channels corresponding to adjacent frequency bands on opposite sides of the input transducer. Figure 9.21 shows a configuration that reflects waves downward only. If the geometry is changed such that successive gratings reflect waves alternately upward and downward, a denser stacking of gratings can be achieved.

The performance of a filter bank[8] constructed as in Fig. 9.21 is shown in Fig. 9.22. Four separate LiNbO$_3$ substrates, each containing four

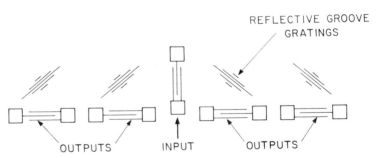

Figure 9.21 Schematic diagram of a four-channel filter bank employing length weighting.

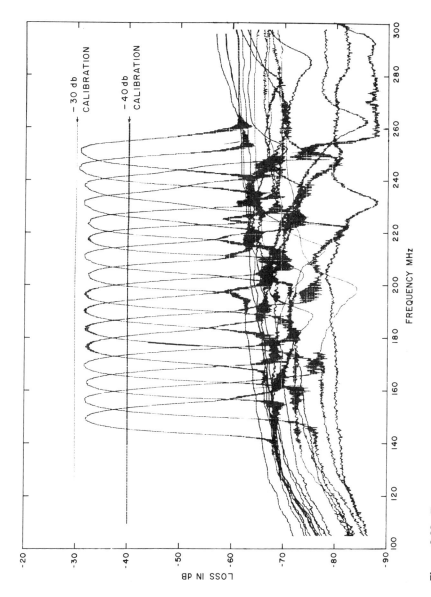

Figure 9.22 Frequency response of a 16-channel filter bank. Reprinted, with permission, from ref. 8, p. 107.

433

channels, provided a total of 16 separate channels spaced 6.7 MHz apart
with each channel having a 4 dB bandwidth of 6.7 MHz. The grating for
each channel was length weighted to achieve a Hamming weighted
impulse response. This weighting suppressed sidelobes in the frequency
response. The background level in Fig. 9.22 is almost entirely due to
electromagnetic feedthrough. It has been demonstrated that improved
packaging can reduce the feedthrough level by an additional 15 dB or
more. Because reflection gratings are especially defect tolerant, it was
possible to obtain a high yield for the filter banks.

Dispersive or Pulse Compression Filters. Historically the area of
most interest and development of reflection grating devices has been
dispersive filters. In all cases these filters had linear-FM characteristics
and the major area of application has been for pulse expansion or
compression in radar systems. Such devices have been dubbed RAC
(reflective-array compressor) devices. The successful forerunner of the
surface wave devices was the IMCON line developed by Martin.[1,13] In
recent years there has occurred a rapid development of RAC devices with
a wide range of parameters. Performance characteristics of some of the
devices that have been developed are given in Table 9.4. For these
devices the matched CW insertion losses range from 25 to 48 dB, with the
largest losses occurring for devices with the largest bandwidth and time-
bandwidth product. In all cases the reflection gratings consisted of grooves
etched into Y-cut $LiNbO_3$. Three of the many different IMCON designs
are listed for comparison. Several of the device designs listed in Table 9.4
are discussed later in more detail to illustrate various features of RAC
filters.

Because RAC filters are capable of achieving large time-bandwidth
products, one confronts a particular set of problems that become more
critical with increasing time-bandwidth product, namely, dynamic range
and temperature sensitivity.

When a dispersive filter with flat amplitude response is used as a pulse
compressor, the net insertion loss in dB from input to the compressed
output pulse is the CW insertion loss *less* $10 \log (T \Delta f)$, where $T \Delta f$ is the
time-bandwidth product of the waveform, i.e. the correlation gain of the
device increases the level of the compressed pulse relative to the noise of
the output amplifier. However the same device when used as a pulse
expander has a net insertion loss from the initial impulse to the expanded
output pulse equal to the CW insertion loss *plus* $10 \log (T \Delta f)$, that is, the
expanded pulse is stretched in time and reduced relative to the noise of
the output amplifier. Thus it is relatively easy to make large time-
bandwidth pulse compressors with adequate dynamic range but difficult to

Table 9.4 Performance Characteristics of Reflective-Array Compressors (Listed in Order of Increasing $T \Delta f$ Products)

Laboratory	Center Frequency (MHz)	Bandwidth, Δf (MHz)	Dispersion, T (μ sec)	$T \Delta f$	RMS Phase Error	Ref.
Raytheon	120	10.5	4.2	44.1	0.6	3
Raytheon	60	6	8	48	1.2	3
Raytheon	60	6	20	120	0.8	3
Raytheon	60	12	20	240	1.0	3
Andersen (IMCON)	15	6	100	600	2.5 (est.)	1
Raytheon	60	6	100	600	1.5	3
Andersen (IMCON)	10	5	250	750	1.7 (est.)	1
Radiation	100	50	20	1000	<6, not specified	5
MIT Lincoln	200	50	30	1500	3.5	
Andersen (IMCON)	20	10	250	2500	not specified	1
MIT Lincoln	1000	512	10	5120	2.6 compensated	4, 6

make expanders with good signal-to-noise ratios. Because of limiting, which is usually applied to an expanded pulse, such a pulse typically requires a signal-to-noise ratio of about 40 dB. At large bandwidths, problems of dynamic range become more severe because input powers are limited by acoustic nonlinearities and output noise is increased. For generating large time-bandwidth-product signals, particularly with large bandwidths, one must seriously consider the alternative of generating a signal with lower bandwidth and multiplying the frequencies, or using electronically generated ramps in place of a pulse expander with the full desired bandwidth.

The temperature dependence of delay in surface wave substrates requires large time-bandwidth pulse compressors to be thermostated in order to control their chirp slope. Fortunately the degree of temperature control required for well-shaped compressed pulses with low sidelobes is easily achieved. Negligible degradation occurs for velocity variations Δv as large as $\Delta v/v = (T \Delta f)^{-1}$.[52,53] For example, a filter with $T \Delta f = 5000$ on $LiNbO_3$, which has a relatively large temperature coefficient of delay, needs to be controlled to within $\pm 2°C$. A problem that is often more

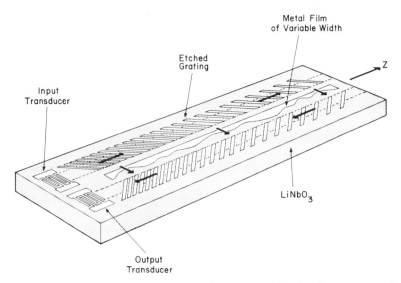

Figure 9.23 Reflective-array compressor (RAC) with a metal film for phase compensation. Copyright 1973 by The Institute of Electrical and Electronic Engineers, Inc. Reprinted, with permission, from *Proc. 1973 Ultrasonics Symposium*, 1973.

serious than stabilizing the chirp slope is keeping the delay to the compressed pulse constant. Such problems are more acute in filters with small fractional bandwidths.

The temperature dependence of delay in surface wave substrates can be used to advantage to compensate for the variations in chirp slope that arise because of variations in material properties[46] and crystal cut, as well as the differences among devices introduced by slight variations in fabrication. By thermostating each filter at its own preferred temperature, the chirp slopes of many filters can be matched.

The RAC geometry has a unique feature that allows such devices to be internally compensated to match chirp slopes and to reduce phase errors that might otherwise exist.[4,6] The possibility of internal phase compensation was suggested by Martin.[1] The technique for phase compensation is shown schematically in Fig. 9.23. Because a signal of a given frequency is dominantly reflected in a small region within the array of reflective grooves, this signal crosses the midline of the RAC device at a specific position along the midline. A metal film of width W placed in the path of this wave slows the wave and advances its phase by $\phi = 2\pi W(\Delta v/v)/\lambda$, where $\Delta v/v$ is the fractional velocity shift produced by a conducting film on the particular cut and direction of the piezoelectric substrate and λ is the wavelength of the once-reflected wave. By varying the width of the strip as a function of position along the midline a phase correction can be introduced at each frequency, such that, in principle, the net deviations from quadratic are reduced to zero. Most of the devices in Table 9.4 had a phase response so near ideal that phase compensation was unnecessary. However the ability to phase-compensate is particularly valuable at large bandwidths, where it is difficult to obtain sufficiently accurate patterns and dispersive effects in surface wave propagation become important. Phase compensation can also be applied to nondispersive configurations (Fig. 9.19b).

Specific Device Examples. In the next paragraphs four specific reflection-grating devices are described. The examples are chosen to illustrate how well reflection-grating devices meet difficult performance or fabrication requirements.

T Δf = 120, Raytheon Device (Fig. 9.24). The low fractional bandwidth of this device allows the relatively low CW insertion loss of 26 dB to be achieved.[3] Measured phase deviations with an rms value of only 0.87° are in accord with the excellent sidelobe suppression of better than 37 dB. This result was achieved in a pulse compression test circuit consisting of an expander, frequency inversion of the expanded pulse, a

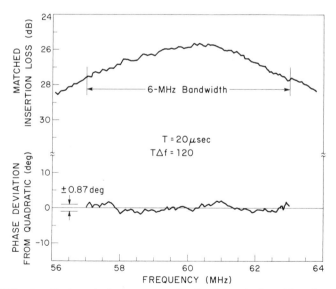

Figure 9.24 Amplitude and phase response for Raytheon device with a time-bandwidth product of 120. Reprinted, with permission, from ref. 6, p. 181.

compressor, and external Hamming weighting. The 37 dB sidelobes are close to the theoretical limit for external weighting in the frequency domain.

T Δf = 240, Raytheon Device.   To be useful for high-performance radar systems, dispersive delay lines not only must have good phase and amplitude response, but also, because they are used in pairs, must be highly reproducible. This particularly is true of the dispersive slope of the devices. For example, the dispersive slope of this device was specified to 0.5%.

In a production run of seven devices, each with a bandwidth of 12 MHz centered at 60 MHz and dispersion of 20 μsec, only one device failed and that was due to cracking of the substrate.[3] Even though the reflection gratings consisted of 1200 grooves, the grating yield was essentially 100%. Of the six good devices, all had chirp slopes identical within ±0.08%. All had an insertion loss of 30 dB and an rms amplitude ripple ranging from 0.10 to 0.13 dB. Phase errors ranged from 0.59° to 1.17° rms, thus allowing sidelobes below 40 dB to be achieved with every pair of devices.

This device had an up-chirp impulse response and the excellent performance achieved indicates that the problems of loss to bulk waves discussed previously are of no consequence for fractional bandwidth up to 20%.

T Δf = 600, Raytheon Device.   A large piece of LiNbO$_3$ allows 100 μsec of dispersion over a bandwidth of 6 MHz centered at 60 MHz to be obtained in this filter.[3] The folded RAC configurations provides twice the dispersion of an in-line interdigital filter fabricated on a substrate of the same length. For this filter the phase deviations (1.5° rms) are the major limitation on the level of the compressed-pulse sidelobes. Peak sidelobes at 37 dB are achieved for a pair of filters in a pulse compression test circuit.

T Δf = 5120, MIT Lincoln Laboratory Filter (Fig. 9.25).   In order to obtain a bandwidth of 512 MHz, this filter operates over a 51.2% bandwidth centered at 1000 MHz.[4,6] Propagation losses of about 8 dB over the 10 μsec of dispersion in this device become an important factor in the insertion loss. Because the filter was designed for compression only, the considerable roll-off in the frequency response of the 2.5-finger-pair transducers is tolerable. An additional roll-off produced by variable etching of the grating allows an overall Hamming weighting to be approached (Fig. 9.26). To achieve this response, grooves depths ranging

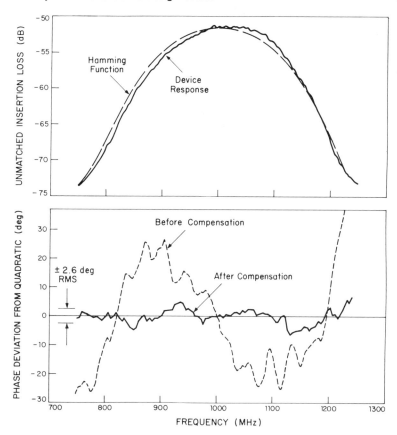

Figure 9.25   Amplitude and phase response of an MIT Lincoln Laboratory device with a time-bandwidth product of 5120. Amplitude response is within 1 dB of the desired Hamming function. Phase response before and after compensation is indicated. Copyright 1973 by The Institute of Electrical and Electronic Engineers, Inc. Reprinted, with permission, from *Proc. 1973 Ultrasonics Symposium*, 1973.

from $20\,\text{Å}$ at the high-frequency end of the grating to $400\,\text{Å}$ at the low-frequency end of the grating were required. The etch depth had to be carefully controlled with a tolerance of less than $10\,\text{Å}$ necessary at the high-frequency end of the grating. The phase response of a typical filter exhibited slowly varying phase deviations from the ideal quadratic response with a peak value of $20°$ to $30°$. The magnitude of this error is consistent with the phase distortion anticipated as a consequence of the "free-surface dispersion" on $LiNbO_3$ that has been measured by Lean and Powell.[54] Differences from the bulk elastic properties within the first few tens of angstroms of the surface presumably introduce a small dispersion in the surface wave and thereby produce phase errors in the RAC. However the slowly varying phase deviations are not reproducible from one RAC device to another and such differences may be due to differences in the surface character of each crystal, or small pattern distortions produced during fabrication.

In additon to slowly varying phase deviations, the filters had a distinct, reproducible periodic error of approximately 5° that was traceable to periodic errors in groove placement within the original pattern mask. A 5° phase error corresponds to a systematic error in groove placement of only 250 Å. All the phase errors were compensated by initially measuring the phase response of each filter and generating an appropriate compensation pattern, as discussed previously. By this means residual phase errors were reduced to approximately 3° rms.

References

1. T. A. Martin. "The IMCON pulse compression filter, and its applications." *IEEE Trans.* **MTT-21**, 186 (1973).
2. R. C. Williamson and H. I. Smith. "The use of surface elastic wave reflection gratings in large time bandwidth pulse compression filters." *IEEE Trans.* **MTT-21**, 195 (1973).
3. P. C. Meyer, R. H. Tancrell, and J. H. Matsinger. "Long time delay reflective surface wave dispersive delay line," in J. de Klerk, Ed., *Proc. 1973 IEEE Ultrasonics Symposium*, IEEE, New York, 1973, pp. 498–499.
4. R. C. Williamson, V. S. Dolat, and H. I. Smith. "L-band reflective array compressor with a compression ratio of 5120," in J. de Klerk, Ed., *Proc. 1973 IEEE Ultrasonics Symposium*, IEEE, New York, 1973, pp. 490–493.
5. H. Bush et al. "Application of chirp swd for spread spectrum communications." in J. de Klerk, Ed., *Proc. 1973 IEEE Ultrasonics Symposium*, IEEE, New York, 1973, pp. 494–497.
6. R. C. Williamson. "Large time bandwidth product devices achieved through the use of surface acoustic wave reflection gratings," in *Proc. Conf. on Component Development and Systems Applications of Surface Acoustic Wave Devices*, IEE, Stevenage, England, 1973, pp. 181–190.
7. J. Melngalis, J. M. Smith, and J. H. Cafarella. "Bandpass surface wave filters," in J. de Klerk, Ed., *Proc. 1972 IEEE Ultrasonics Symposium*, IEEE, New York, 1972, pp. 221–225.
8. J. Melngalis and G. T. Flynn. "16 channel surface acoustic wave grating filter bank for real time spectral analyser." *Electron. Lett.* **10**, 107 (1974).
9. E. A. Ash. "Surface wave grating reflectors and resonators." IEEE Symposium on Microwave Theory and Techniques, Newport Beach, Calif., May, 1970.
10. E. J. Staples. "UHF surface acoustic wave resonators," in *Proc. 28th Frequency Control Symposium*, Electronic Industries Association, Washington, D.C., 1974, pp. 280–285.
11. C. C. Tseng. "Elastic surface waves on free surfaces and metallized surfaces of CdS, ZnO, and PZT-4." *J. Appl. Phys.* **38**, 4281 (1967).

12. E. K. Sittig and G. A. Coquin. "Filters and dispersive delay lines using repetitively mismatched ultrasonic transmission lines." *IEEE Trans.* **SU-15,** 111 (1968).

13. T. A. Martin, "A new dispersive delay line." 1970 IEEE Ultrasonics Symposium, San Francisco, September, 1970.

14. M. Munasinghe and G. W. Farnell. "Finite difference analysis of Rayleigh wave scattering at vertical discontinuities." *J. Geophys. Res.* **78,** 2454 (1973).

15. M. Munasinghe and G. W. Farnell. "Acoustic surface wave scattering on a homogeneous three-quarter space." *J. Appl. Phys.* **44,** 2025 (1973).

16. M. Munasinghe and G. W. Farnell. "Rayleigh wave scattering in layered media," in J. de Klerk, Ed., *Proc.* 1973 *Ultrasonics Symposium,* IEEE, New York, 1973, pp. 506–509.

17. I. A. Viktorov. *Rayleigh and Lamb Waves,* Plenum, New York, 1967.

18. J. W. Dally and D. Lewis. "A photoelastic analysis of propagation of Rayleigh waves past a step change in elevation." *Bull. Seismol. Soc. Amer.* **58,** 539 (1968).

19. F. Gilbert and L. Knopoff, "Seismic scattering from topographic irregularities." *J. Geophys. Res.* **65,** 3436 (1960).

20. A. K. Mal and L. Knopoff. Transmission of Rayleigh waves past a step change in elevation." *Bull. Seismol. Soc. Amer.* **55,** 319 (1965).

21. A. K. Mal and L. Knopoff. "Transmission of Rayleigh waves at a corner." *Bull. Seismol. Soc. Amer.* **56,** 455 (1966).

22. A. McGarr and L. E. Alsop. "Transmission and reflection of Rayleigh waves at vertical boundaries." *J. Geophys. Res.* **72,** 2169 (1967).

23. B. A. Auld. *Acoustic Fields and Waves in Solids,* Vol. II, Wiley, New York, 1973.

24. A. A. Oliner, H. I. Bertoni, and R. C. M. Li. "A microwave network formalism for acoustic waves in isotropic media." *Proc. IEEE* **60,** 1503 (1972).

25. A. A. Oliner, H. I. Bertoni, and R. C. M. Li, "Catalog of acoustic equivalent networks for planar interfaces." *Proc. IEEE* **60,** 1513 (1972).

26. A. A. Oliner, R. C. M. Li, and H. I. Bertoni. "Microwave network approach to guided acoustic surface wave structures." Technical Report No. PIBEP-71-092, Polytechnic Institute of Brooklyn, Farmingdale, N.Y., 1971.

27. W. R. Smith, H. M. Gerard, and W. R. Jones. "Analysis and design of dispersive interdigital surface wave transducers." *IEEE Trans.* **MTT-20,** 458 (1972).

28. W. S. Jones, C. S. Hartmann, and T. D. Sturdivant. "Second order effects in surface wave devices." *IEEE Trans.* **SU-19,** 368 (1972).

29. T. L. Szabo. "Surface acoustic wave losses of thin film gratings." *Appl. Phys. Lett.* **22,** 484 (1973).

30. R. C. M. Li, "Analysis of surface wave reflection from a periodic array of grooves," in J. de Klerk, Ed., *Proc.* 1972 *Ultrasonics Symposium,* IEEE, New York, 1973, pp. 263–266.

31. H. S. Tuan and R. C. M. Li, "Rayleigh wave reflection from groove and step discontinuities." *J. Acoust. Soc. Amer.* **55,** 1212 (1974).

32. P. V. H. Sabine. "Analysis of the surface acoustic wave crossbar coupler. "*Electron. Lett.* **9,** 136 (1973).

33. P. V. H. Sabine, "Surface acoustic wave reflectors." *Electron. Lett.* **7,** 653 (1971).

34. P. V. H. Sabine. "A low loss acoustic surface wave coupler." *Proc. IEEE* **35,** 25 (1974).

35. T. Yoneyama and S. Nishida. "Reflection and transmission of Rayleigh waves by the edge of a deposited film." *J. Acoust. Soc. Amer.* **55,** 738 (1974).

36. P. C. Meyer and M. B. Schulz. "Reflective surface acoustic wave delay line material parameters," in J. de Klerk, Ed., *Proc.* 1973 *Ultrasonics Symposium,* IEEE, New York, 1973, pp. 500–502.

37. R. H. Tancrell and M. G. Holland. "Acoustic surface wave filters," *Proc. IEEE* **59,** 393 (1971).

38. P. C. Meyer and M. B. Schulz. "Temperature effects in reflective surface acoustic wave delay lines." *Electron. Lett.* **9,** 523 (1973).

39. L. M. Brekhovskikh. "Propagation of surface Rayleigh waves along uneven boundary of an elastic body." *Sov. Phys. Acoust.* **5,** 288 (1960).

40. F. Rischbieter, "Messungen an oberflachenwellen in festen korpen." *Acustica* **16,** 75 (1965).

41. P. V. H. Sabine. "Rayleigh wave propagation on a periodically roughened surface." *Electron. Lett.* **6,** 149 (1970).

42. R. F. Humphreys and E. A. Ash. "Acoustic bulk surface wave transducer." *Electron. Lett.* **5,** 175 (1969).

43. F. G. Marshall and E. G. S. Paige. "Mode conversion in surface acoustic wave reflective arrays." *Electron. Lett.* **10,** 137 (1974).

44. R. C. M. Li and J. Melngalis. "Second order effects in surface wave devices due to stored energy at step discontinuities," in J. de Klerk, Ed., *Proc.* 1973 *IEEE Ultrasonics Symposium,* IEEE, New York, 1973, pp. 503–505.

45. S. G. Joshi and R. M. White. "Dispersion of surface elastic waves produced by a conducting grating on a piezoelectric crystal." *J. Appl. Phys.* **39,** 5819 (1968).

46. R. C. Williamson. "Measurement of the propagation characteristics of surface and bulk waves in LiNbO₃," in J. de Klerk, Ed., *Proc.* 1972 *Ultrasonics Symposium,* IEEE, New York, 1972, pp. 323–327.

47. K. Blotekjaer, K. A. Ingebrigtsen and H. Skeie, "Acoustic surface waves in piezoelectric materials with periodic metal strips on the surface." *IEEE Trans.* **ED-20,** 1139 (1973).

48. C. Maerfeld and P. Tournois, "Perturbation theory for the surface wave multi-strip coupler." *Electron. Lett.* **9,** 115 (1973).

49. H. M. Gerard et al. "The design and applications of highly dispersive acoustic surface wave filters." *IEEE Trans.* **MTT-21,** 176 (1973).

50. D. P. Olsen. "A frequency and time domain analysis of the IMCON II pulse compression delay line." Technical Report No. TSC-PD-080-64, Technology Service Corporation, Santa Monica, Calif., 1972.

51. R. H. Tancrell. "Analytical design of surface wave bandpass filters." *IEEE Trans.* **SU-21,** 12 (1974).

52. J. R. Klauder et al. "The theory and design of chirp radars." *Bell System Tech. J.* **39,** 745 (1960).

53. M. B. Schulz. "Temperature effects in surface wave devices." 1972 IEEE Ultrasonics Symposium, Boston, October, 1972.

54. E. G. Lean and C. G. Powell. "Nondestructive testing of thin films by harmonic generation of dispersive Rayleigh waves." *Appl. Phys. Lett.* **19,** 356 (1971).

TEN

Surface Wave Devices for Radar Equipment

J. DENNIS MAINES

**Royal Signals and Radar Establishment,
Great Malvern, Worcestershire, England**

Radar plays a major role in both military and civil surveillance and tracking systems, and a vast array of equipment performs a variety of functions associated with the detection and location of objects. The basic radar techniques have not changed significantly since World War Two; however significant advances in radar equipment are continually being made by adoption of new technology and development of increasingly sophisticated systems.

Surface wave filters are particularly effective in processing radar signals. Their main virtues are that they are simple, cheap, and rugged structures that are compatible with other planar technologies and in some cases augment new processing techniques, including novel forms of digital processors that are at present under development.

Computers of course play a major role in new radar development and are often invaluable for storing and processing radar data (data processing). In addition digital techniques can perform complex automatic processing of individual radar returns (signal processing). Signal processing must be carried out economically, speedily, and, ideally, in real time. The digital approach uses baseband signals, that is, radar returns that have been received and detected. This video signal is converted into a binary form suitable for digital processing. Processing extracts the target echo and, to a large degree, rejects noise and other unwanted signals. At the present time the cost, size, power consumption, and computational time of a digital signal processor preclude its use for many processing radar tasks. It is clear, though, that digital techniques advance very rapidly, and there is a possibility that all future radar systems will use digital processors. However, the evidence suggests surface wave analog processors will be cheaper, smaller, and faster than their digital counterparts for at least a few more generations of radar system.

In this chapter we examine the applications of surface wave devices in radar systems that have already been accepted by systems engineers because they meet the rigid specifications for military equipment and space missions. First, though, it is necessary briefly to discuss some basic radar concepts relevant to surface wave device development. All these concepts are expanded in ref. 1.

10.1 Radar: Basic Concepts

The basic requirement for a general radar system is simple—to detect an object (target) and determine its spatial position. All methods are based on transmission of electromagnetic radiation and subsequent examination of the signal reflected from the target. The angular position of the target is usually found by measuring the direction of propagation of the return signal intercepted at the receiver. The range is found by measuring the time for the radiation to travel to the target and back. Also, the velocity of a target may be determined by measuring the Doppler shift produced by the relative motion between the target and the radar. As we shall see, surface wave processors are being used in the measurement of all target parameters.

The radar frequency can lie within the range 30 MHz to 70 GHz and is determined by operational requirements and availability of components. However the common use of microwave frequencies makes it necessary to down-convert the return signal to an intermediate frequency (IF), which is usually in the range of 10 to 400 MHz. The choice of IF is often governed by the required ability to resolve close proximity targets. This resolution is approximately proportional to the inverse bandwidth of the transmitted wave form, and the intermediate frequency is set to be several times the bandwidth. Bandwidths ranging from 100 KHz to 100 MHz permit resolution of targets separated by 5000 to 5 ft, respectively, and meet the needs of most modern radars. In simple pulsed radars this bandwidth is contained in a single transmitted pulse; the pulse duration (typically 1 μsec to 100 μsec), the bandwidth, and the intermediate frequency are admirably suited to surface wave processors. The basic compatability of surface wave processors and radar IF parameters has been a prime factor in the rapid exploitation of surface waves in radar.

The basic form of pulsed radar, shown in Fig. 10.1, consists of a short duration pulse transmission and an accurately timed reception. The received pulses are processed and displayed as a function of time so that targets can be easily identified at their particular range. The range resolution depends of course on the duration of the transmitted pulse, which, ideally, should be short enough to prevent overlap of returns from targets required to be resolved. The operating range of the radar is determined fundamentally by the power transmitted, and (10.1), a form of the well-known radar equation, predicts that the maximum range of the radar (i.e., the range R_{max} beyond which the target cannot be detected with an acceptable probability) is proportional to the fourth root of the transmitted power; in fact,

$$R_{max} = \left[\frac{P_t G^2 \lambda^2 \sigma}{(4\pi)^3 S_{min}}\right]^{1/4} \tag{10.1}$$

Here P_t denotes the transmitted power, G the antenna gain, λ the radar wavelength, S_{min} the minimum detectable signal power, and σ the target cross section. The practical limits, then, are set by the peak power capability of the transmitter and the shortest pulses it can produce. These limitations on performance have proved unacceptable for many radars; fortunately they can be overcome by practical exploitation of matched

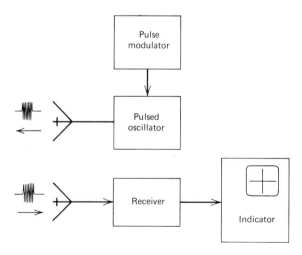

Figure 10.1 A simple pulsed radar system.

filters. The improvement is well illustrated by pulse compression radar. A simple pulse compression radar is shown in Fig. 10.2. The transmitted pulse is relatively long. In this example it is encoded by modulating the pulse carrier frequency so that it varies with time. On reception a frequency dependent delay is introduced by a filter so that all frequency components in the received pulse are detected *at the same time*. This process is illustrated in Fig. 10.2, where all the received energy in the long pulse (of duration T_E) is shown to be detected in a short time interval T_C; that is, the pulse is compressed and to a good approximation the pulse compression radar performs as though it is a simple pulsed radar having a pulse duration T_C. Thus high resolution and long pulse transmission can occur simultaneously. There is also a bonus. Because the pulse compression is achieved only for the appropriately modulated transmission pulse, this type of reception system discriminates against other signals, including noise like signals received by the antenna or generated within the receiver. The pulse compression system is in fact using matched filter reception.

Matched filter reception of any given waveform optimizes the signal to noise (S/N) at the receiver to the extent that it produces an output in which the ratio of the peak signal S to the mean noise power N is maximized. The relationship shown in (10.2), derived from matched filter theory, describes the significant result that S/N is simply proportional to the *energy* E contained in the transmitted pulse; that is

$$\frac{S}{N} = \frac{2E}{N_0} \qquad (10.2)$$

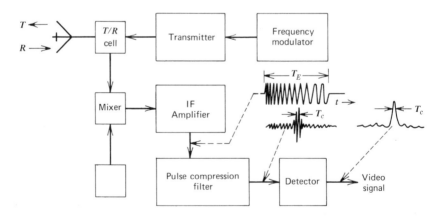

Figure 10.2 A simple pulse compression radar system.

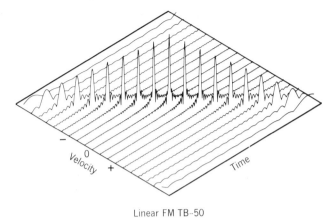

Linear FM TB-50

Figure 10.3 Cross sections of the ambiguity diagram for a linear FM waveform having a time-bandwidth product of 50.

where N_0 is the noise power per unit cycle of bandwidth. The matched filter that achieves this condition for a particular input waveform is the filter with an impulse response equal to the time inverse of the input waveform. It is significant for radar design (and incidentally for surface wave filters) that (10.2) is *independent of the signal bandwidth* so that the transmitted waveform can be chosen to meet other system requirements.

It is particularly important in long range radars that the total energy in the transmitted pulse be maximized. This consideration determines that the pulse length be long enough to insure the peak power limit is not reached before the mean power limit. The particular waveform transmitted determines the range resolution and Doppler sensitivity, parameters characterized by the ambiguity diagram.* Cross sections of the ambiguity diagram for a linearly frequency-modulated waveform (chirp) are shown in Fig. 10.3. Here, for a zero velocity shift (i.e., for the matched filter condition), the filter output takes the form of a sinc function with the main lobe having a 4 dB width equal to $1/B$, where B is the bandwidth of the chirp waveform, and the largest sidelobes peak 13 dB below the main lobe peak. Such large sidelobes are unacceptable for most pulse compression radar requirements. For linear FM the spectrum of the received waveform is weighted by a suitable filter to reduce the largest sidelobes,

---

* In a practical radar system the Doppler effect produces a shift in center frequency of the signal returned from a moving target. The pulse compression filter is a matched filter only for return signals that suffer no Doppler shift. The output from the filter for a range of fixed Doppler shift is indicated in Fig. (10.3) by cross sections of the ambiguity surface.

typically to 30 dB. The combination of weighting and matched filters is no longer optimized for signal-to-noise ratio, but the reduction in processing gain (the improvement in signal-to-noise achieved during processing) has been accepted and has led to the wide use of linear FM waveforms for pulse compression radars. Linear FM is also desirable because of its low sensitivity to Doppler shifts; note that the ambiguity diagram shows the magnitude of the main lobe varies only slowly with target velocity. The change in range with target velocity is usually acceptable for practical Doppler shifts.

The Doppler shift is itself of vital interest in radar since it is used to measure the velocity of targets. In addition, numerous systems have been built in which moving target indication (MTI) is achieved using the Doppler phenomenon. The purpose of MTI is to reject unwanted signals from fixed targets such as hills and buildings and to retain signals from moving targets such as aircraft. Figure 10.4a shows a pulsed Doppler radar, in which the phase of the transmitted pulse is established by gating and amplifying a portion of the CW oscillator. The signal returned from a moving target differs in frequency from the transmitted pulse by the

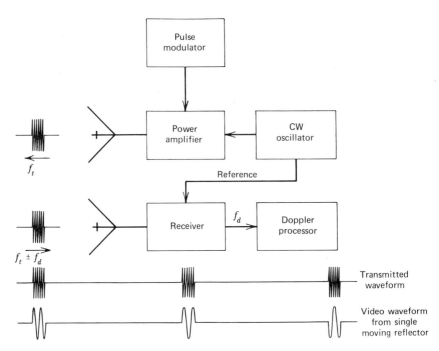

Figure 10.4 (a) Block diagram for coherent Doppler radar. (b) A common form of coherent radar.

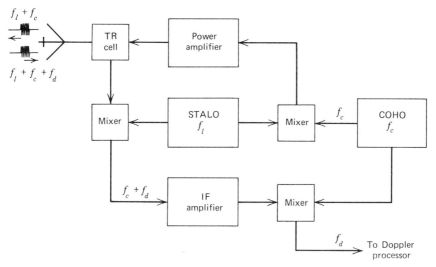

Figure 10.4 (*Contd*)

Doppler shift f_d, which is extracted by the detection system using the CW oscillator signal as a reference. This radar is *coherent* in the sense that the phase of the transmitted signal is preserved by the reference. The basic form of coherent MTI radars in common usage is shown in Fig. 10.4b. Here a coherent reference oscillator (COHO) and stable local oscillator (STALO) are used to allow the signal to be amplified at a suitable intermediate frequency, as detailed in the diagram.

For a moving target, the video output from the phase sensitive detection system oscillates at the Doppler frequency, whereas for a target that is fixed in range the constant phase difference between return and reference signals produces an unchanging output voltage. Subsequent processors remove this constant output and then measure the Doppler frequencies of the residual signals. The filter that removes the unwanted signals from stationary targets that "clutter" the display is often referred to as a *clutter filter*. The clutter filtering is usually achieved by variations of the principle exploited in the basic device shown in Fig. 10.5, the delay line canceler. Here the delay line has a delay time equal to the pulse repetition interval. The fixed target signals detected by the receiver are canceled because successive pulses are identical.

The simple delay line canceler and its derivatives have been commonly implemented in the past using bulk acoustic wave delay lines, which are able to provide the long delay times (~ 1 msec) necessary to match pulse

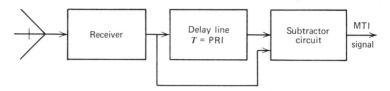

Figure 10.5　A delay line canceler circuit.

repetition intervals of long range radars. For some of the more complex configurations needed to overcome the deficiencies of the simple, single delay line canceler, these lines are inconveniently large and expensive. This situation motivates the increasing movement toward use of digital techniques for MTI.

Typical Doppler shifts cover a range of frequencies determined by the target velocity and the frequency of the radar. Application of the equation

$$f_d = 2\left(\frac{v_r}{c}\right)f_t \tag{10.3}$$

in which v_r is the relative velocity between target and radar and c is the velocity of electromagnetic radiation, shows that for the majority of MTI radars the Doppler shift is a few kilohertz. A 3 cm band radar with a 600 knot target gives rise to a Doppler shift of approximately 20 KHz.

More complex pulse Doppler radars are based on spectral analysis of the echoes rather than the delay line MTI canceler just mentioned. The signal processor may be considered a bank of narrow band filters for each range cell (the range difference between targets that are just resolved). The types of filters considered for this role are high-Q bulk wave quartz crystal filters, active filters, and digital fast Fourier transforms (FFT).

10.2　Surface Wave Devices and Their Significance in Radar Systems

Surface wave devices are now used in radar systems because they perform well many of the functions required in modern radar processing. The potential scope for application is illustrated in Fig. 10.6 which gives the basic form of a coherent pulse compression radar and includes many of the features previously discussed. Basic to the system is a surface wave oscillator operating at its fundamental frequency f_c, which is the intermediate frequency; it is used to provide the coherent reference

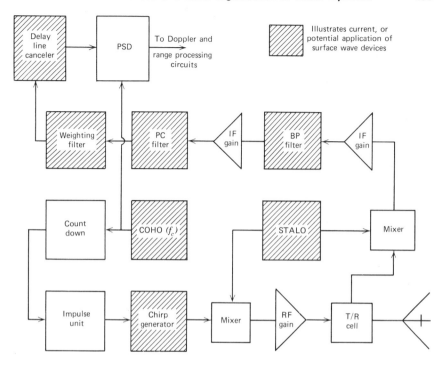

Figure 10.6 Simplified diagram of a coherent pulse compression system.

signal. The stable local oscillator (STALO) may also be a surface wave oscillator operating at about 1 GHz and followed by multipliers if necessary. The output from the coherent oscillator (COHO) can be counted down to provide the master triggering pulses for the timing unit that produces the impulse to initiate the FM waveform.* This waveform is mixed onto the RF, amplified, and transmitted. After down conversion, the received signal is amplified conventionally, but out-of-band interference can be rejected by a surface wave bandpass filter before undergoing pulse compression with range sidelobe suppression again using surface wave filters. Though not included here, phased array units that are surface wave based could also be considered. Surface wave components have not been adopted on such a scale, but this example serves to illustrate the possibility of miniaturizing radar IF units by interfacing

---

* This method of timing has the important property of operating with a pulse repetition interval matching the delay of the surface wave delay line canceler at all temperatures, providing that the temperature *differential* between the oscillator and the delay line is small.

these components with those of other modern circuit components, for example, integrated circuits and thin-film devices.

Doppler filtering could be included in Fig. 10.6 as a potential surface wave application, but for most radars Doppler shifts are relatively small (~ 1 KHz) and demand a much higher Doppler resolution than can be produced by passive surface wave filters. Exceptions include high-velocity, missile-borne radars where closing velocities can be sufficiently high to need a Doppler resolution compatible with surface wave devices (~ 10 KHz). Other radar system requirements are more compatible with surface wave filter parameters, for example, IF frequencies of 1 MHz to 600 MHz, IF bandwidths 100 KHz to 3000 MHz, transmitter pulse length 1 to 100 μsec. It is for this reason that surface wave filters have been readily accepted into radar systems and are likely to be of real significance for some years to come. It is advantageous to examine the devices themselves, stressing their properties and their limitations, so that reasoned judgments can be made of their validity in radar systems.

Nondispersive Fixed Delay Lines. The inherent advantages of surface wave components are readily exploited in fixed and tapped delay lines. They are planar, are miniature, and, for the usual radar intermediate frequencies, can be made using conventional photolithographic techniques. For applications in which delay times and bandwidths are suitable, surface wave delay lines are more economic than the equivalent bulk wave device. This is particularly true if several delay times are required and a tapped delay line can be used, or if it is desirable for the temperature coefficient of delay to be the same as that of other components in the system so that component compatibility over a wide temperature range is achieved. Fixed surface wave delay lines are suitable for many radar applications, including time ordering of multipulse radars, analog MTI processing in medium and low pulse repetition frequency radars, examination of a signal followed by a suitable delay before corrective processing, and test target simulation. Analog MTI processing requires the pulses to be stored for one pulse repetition interval. Delays up to several hundred microseconds, bandwidths in the range 10 KHz to 500 MHz, and insertion losses from 3 to 50 dB are possible for surface wave devices presently capable of being produced to general purpose delay line specifications. Delay lines with storage times of sufficient length to process long range radar signals (~ 1 msec) are still experimental, and development of such lines can in fact be questioned because of the suitability, for this application, of digital storage methods and charge coupled devices. However, the large dynamic range requirements of MTI processors (~ 80 dB) ensures increased complexity of both the purely digital method and the charge coupled devices, and use of a surface wave delay line canceler can reduce the dynamic range requirement of the subsequent digital processor. This technique is sometimes termed *prewhitening*.

Bandpass Filters. A great deal of the motivation for work on surfacewave bandpass filters was commercial pressure for a compact, economic IF filter for color television, but the attractive properties of surface wave bandpass filters were also noted by radar systems engineers. These properties have been discussed in some depth in Chapter 6. The facility for meeting a precisely defined amplitude and phase characteristic simultaneously in a single filter is particularly attractive, especially because wide-band surface wave filters may be small enough for hybrid integration. In addition, they are stable and require no adjustments. Since they can be designed to interface with standard, wide-band IC amplifiers, they also offer reliable, rugged IF amplifiers with plug-in exchangeable filters that have application in a wide variety of radar systems. A filter fabricated on the same substrate as other surface wave components—for example, the expanders and compressors in Fig. 10.6—has a bandwidth and center frequency that matches them at all temperatures, providing the unit is designed to have small thermal gradients. The temperature tracking facility is an important feature of surface wave based radar subsystems. In the case of bandpass filters it could eliminate the practice of increasing the passband beyond that ideally required by the signal to accommodate temperature drifts in conventional components. Signal-to-noise ratio considerations of course demand that the passband be kept to a minimum. In this respect it would be desirable for the IF filter also to track the local oscillator frequency with temperature—a possibility if the local oscillator is locked to a surface wave based device.

Surface wave bandpass filters are usually lossy—typically about 20 dB—and this figure is unlikely to become sufficiently low to allow the use of filters at the front end of the IF where the signal-to-noise ratio is most seriously affected by loss. However, where the radar performance is likely to be limited in operation by *interference* rather than amplifier noise, the precise passband offered by a surface wave device could prove to be advantageous.

The size of a passive surface wave device is determined by its bandwidth B and filters usually have a length approximately s/B, where s is the velocity of the acoustic wave. Thus narrow band surface wave filters are large, for example, ~ 33 cm for 10 KHz bandwidth. It is not possible to use passive surface wave filters to produce a significantly narrower bandwidth because selectivity is achieved by passing the signal through the input and output transducers once only. This is to be contrasted with "multitransit" filters (e.g., surface and bulk wave resonator filters) in which high Q is obtained using internal acoustic feedback. Where Doppler shifts are large (e.g., in high velocity missile and optical radars), surface wave filters are being considered, their advantages being more apparent for bandwidths in the range that is difficult to achieve using bulk wave devices.

Surface wave bandpass filters can be designed to have complex but specified phase and amplitude characteristics. These devices replace bulky lumped component filters, particularly where ruggedness, stability, and size are of prime importance to the radar equipment. The advantages are particularly apparent where bandwidths of the order of 10% are required and here filters produced with spurious out-of-band responses as low as -60 dB will be significant (see Fig. 10.7). These filters should prove particularly useful where low distortion is required, as in pulse compression systems, where bandpass and dispersive filters can be designed jointly, so that defects in one device can be compensated in the other. The progression of radar systems to increasingly large bandwidths provides the incentive for development of low distortion bandpass filters with fractional bandwidths up to 50%.

Surface Wave Oscillators.   The capability of producing effective surface wave oscillators with wide potential application in radar systems has been clearly demonstrated.[2] The principle is simply to use a surface wave delay line in which the output is fed back to the input with sufficient gain to overcome the loss in the acoustic line. The allowed modes of the oscillator are those for which there is excess gain and a net phase shift around the loop of $2\pi n$, where n is an integer. The phase condition is

$$\phi_{el} + \frac{2\pi f_n L}{s} = 2\pi n \qquad (10.4)$$

where L is the acoustic path length, f_n the frequency of the nth mode, s the velocity of sound, and ϕ_{el} the phase shift through the feedback loop and the reactive part of the transducers. All but one of these allowed modes are suppressed by suitable choice of filter passband, and the sensitivity of the frequency of this mode to the external circuit is dependent upon the relative size of $2\pi f_n L/s$ and ϕ_{el}. This is a key property of the oscillator; it allows a choice to be made between stability and modulation capability. For frequency stability the acoustic phase shift should dominate.

Oscillators can of course be made on a variety of substrate materials and the final choice depends on a trade-off between short term stability,

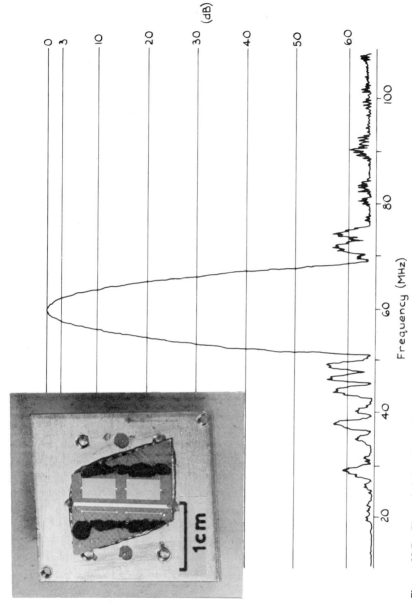

Figure 10.7 Characteristics of a surface wave bandpass filter with a Gaussian frequency response. Inset shows the size of the device. Courtesy of Mullard Research Laboratory, Redhill, England.

temperature sensitivity, and aging effects. *ST-X* quartz is commonly used because of its relative insensitivity to temperature. However lithium niobate's low transduction loss reduces the gain requirement of the external feedback amplifier and may lead to a better noise figure and improved short term stability.

A surface wave oscillator should prove effective in systems such as that shown in Fig. 10.6, particularly if a delay line canceler is used and it is necessary to match temperature coefficients. The oscillator frequency can be electronically tuned by amounts up to 1% of its center frequency, and this should be useful in airborne MTI radars where because of aircraft motion it is necessary to remove the Doppler shift by offsetting the frequency of the reference oscillator.

The attraction of the surface wave oscillators increases with intermediate frequency because they can be designed to work in the range 10 MHz to about 2 GHz without the use of multiplication stages. It is therefore likely that the major radar application of surface wave oscillators will be in large bandwidth systems where high intermediate frequencies are used.

Matched Filters.   Surface wave matched filters have made a significant impact on radar systems, particularly in pulse compression radars. The impulse response of a surface wave matched filter can be used to produce waveforms of arbitrary shape for modulation of the transmitted signal. Target returns undergo optimum processing on reception using the corresponding matched filter. As discussed in earlier chapters, conventional photolithographic processing allows time-bandwidth (TB) products of up to 600 to be produced within the constraints of bandwidths of less than 600 MHz and time of less than 60 μsec. Such performance is adequate for the majority of radar systems as presently conceived. Some specialized systems require higher TB products and here reflective array compressors (RAC) are significant.[3] The main requirement though is for modest TB products (~ 100) and the main application to date has been in linear FM systems. Other waveforms can be used with equal ease, and 13-bit Barker coded devices have, for example, been used in retrofit radar applications because the surface wave filter is considerably more economic than its bulk wave alternative.[4] The 13-bit Barker code is not a particularly good code because its sidelobe performance is poor (~ 22 dB) and it is worth examining in some detail the factors governing choice of waveform and the implications that surface wave devices have in this respect.

Many considerations influence selection of the waveform to be used in a radar system. Constraints are fixed by the power and bandwidth characteristics of available components and the specified operational requirements such as minimum and maximum operating range, range of

Doppler shifts, electronic environment, and so on. However, within these confines, the waveform may be optimized for high probability of detection, low probability of false alarm, detection of signals in clutter, and antijam capability. These considerations do not necessarily lead to a unique solution if considered simultaneously for all ranges, and the generally accepted design procedure optimizes the peak-signal-to-mean-noise ratio in order to provide an acceptable detection probability and false-alarm rate. A matched filter is therefore used for a waveform that provides an ambiguity function with good range resolution and low sensitivity to Doppler. The chirp waveform is usually chosen for mean-power limited pulsed radars. Use of a chirp waveform, although not optimum, is sufficiently close for it to be widely accepted for most radar pulse compression systems.

A chirp signal having a large TB product has a *spectrum* that to a good approximation is rectangular, as shown in Fig. 10.8. The *signal*, when received by its matched filter, produces a sinc function output in the time domain that is in fact the Fourier transform of the rectangular envelope

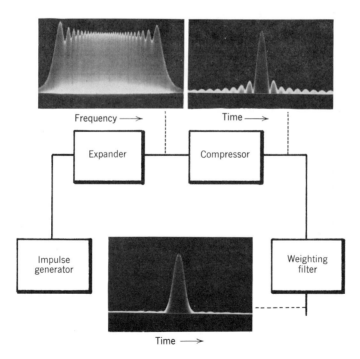

Figure 10.8 A pulse expansion/compression loop showing the frequency spectrum of the expanded pulse and sidelobe suppression by frequency weighting.

of the chirp *spectrum*. The poor time sidelobes of this waveform (-13 dB) make it necessary to change the envelope function by suitable weighting to a shape that has a more suitable Fourier transform, for example, Gaussian. The Gaussian spectrum produces no time sidelobes because its transform is also Gaussian. This solution, though, is unsatisfactory because it produces a main lobe whose width is greater by a factor of 1.9 than the -4 dB width, $1/B$, of the main lobe of an unweighted envelope function. The optimum weighting function is a function that produces a maximum suppression of sidelobes together with minimum broadening of the main lobe. Optimum weighting functions were developed for antenna design, where a similar problem arises in relation to the distribution of current across a finite width aperture—the so called *Dolph-Tschebyshev* distribution. This distribution is not, in practice, physically realizable and an approximation to it developed by Taylor[5] is commonly used. The Taylor distribution is specified by two parameters: the design sidelobe level N dB (the ratio between the main beam peak amplitude and that of the close-in sidelobes) and, n, a parameter that specifies the number of close-in sidelobes of constant height before decreasing in size. The larger the value of n the sharper is the beam. However n is not made too large; otherwise practical implementation again becomes difficult. Typical specifications require that N be 30 to 35 dB, and in this case a value of $n = 5$ proves satisfactory. In terms of the difference from the center frequency $(f - f_0)$ the complete Taylor weighting function is given by

$$Y(f, N, n) = 1 + 2 \sum F_m \cos \frac{2\pi m}{\Delta} (f - f_0) \qquad (10.5)$$

Equation (10.5) defines a weighted cosine series added to a constant (pedestal) and this function has not been easy to produce with traditional filtering methods (using *LC* circuits). For this reason the expression has been further simplified by dropping some of the higher order terms, which have small values of the co-efficient F_m.[6] A cosine squared function on a baseline pedestal is equivalent to including only the first two terms in (10.5); the Hamming function defined in (10.6) is very close to this case

$$Y_{\text{Hamm}} = 0.08 + 0.92 \cos^2 \pi \frac{(f - f_0)}{\Delta} \qquad (10.6)$$

The difference between the waveforms of the compressed pulses for the various weighting functions are not always significant in practice (see Table 10.1), but it is important to note that surface wave filters now allow greater flexibility in weighting function design than ever before and there

Table 10.1   Some Theoretical Properties of a Range of Weighting Functions for Chirp Waveforms

Weighting Function	Sidelobe Level (dB)	3 dB Pulse Width $(1/\Delta)$	Mismatch Loss (dB)
Unweighted	-13.3	0.88	0
Truncated Gaussian	35	1.27	–
Hamming	42.5	1.31	1.34
Taylor $= 30$, $n = 5$	30	1.12	0.72
Taylor 0.35, $n = 5$	35	1.19	0.95
Taylor $N = 42.5$, $n = 5$	42.5	1.29	1.3
Dolph-Tschebycheff	42.5	1.23	–

is no longer any need to restrict weighting functions to those that can be easily realized using conventional filters.

It has been common practice to weight the spectrum by suitable frequency filtering in the receiver rather than in the transmitter. Transmitter weighting is not used because the linear relationship between frequency and time for chirp signals would cause the output power to be weighted in time as well as frequency. This is inconsistent with the practical constraint of operating the transmitter at its peak power limit. Thus the *weighted* receiver is not a matched filter for the transmitted waveform and it consequently suffers a degradation of the signal-to-noise ratio from that of the *ideal* receiver. (This is known as mismatch loss but is not to be confused with the impedance mismatch loss caused by unmatched components, such as antenna feed with the antenna.) Table 10.1 also shows typical mismatch loss for several weighting functions. It would be an advantage to recover this system loss. This can be achieved by departing from the linear FM waveform and using a nonlinear relationship between frequency and time such that the amplitude of the transmitted waveform is constant with time while maintaining a weighted spectrum. The receiver is designed to be a matched filter for this waveform and achieves suitable sidelobe suppression with no degradation in processing gain. The advantages of nonlinear FM waveforms have been discussed by Cook and Bernfeld[6] and more recently in relation to surface wave filters by A. Klinger et al.[7]

The flexibility of design allowed by surface wave filters makes it possible to realize nonlinear FM waveforms with no more difficulty than linear FM waveforms. Use of such techniques, then, is not limited by device availability but by more fundamental considerations such as sensitivity to Doppler. There is likely to be considerable development work on waveforms to optimize reception for specified circumstances and filter characteristics to process particular input signals. In this respect it is significant that surface wave techniques have been used to demonstrate other optimum filters, such as the inverse filter,[8] which is capable of improving performance in high-clutter environments. Other demonstrations are likely, such as Doppler invariant waveforms (as used by the bat), and matched filters in which noise or interference other than white noise is present. Surface wave devices make these exercises possible at frequencies and bandwidths of interest to the radar engineer. The fact remains, though, that linear FM pulse compression using surface wave filters is a significant technique; it is discussed in greater detail later in this chapter.

Variable Delay Lines and Other Programmable Devices. The ability to store signals in delay lines for a limited time and subsequently use the delayed signal for calibration or comparison purposes is an important technique in radar systems. The ability to vary the delay time extends the technique, and although discretely variable delay lines can be achieved by electronically selecting from a set of transducers spaced along an acoustic beam, a delay line that is capable of controllable, continuously variable delay has important advantages. A configuration that uses two dispersive delay lines to produce variable time delay of an analog signal has been known for some time,[9] but has received little attention in the past because of difficulty obtaining dispersive delay lines with characteristics suitable for this application (e.g., cheap, low loss, compact, large TB product, and so on). Surface wave devices used with integrated circuits are now being used to produce a variable delay unit that is proving significant in radar applications, particularly for the simulation of moving targets. The principle of the variable delay line is shown in Fig. 10.9. Although illustrated for a burst input, any waveform within the bandwidth of the unit can be delayed because the system introduces no net dispersion. The input signal centered on frequency f_{in} is mixed at mixer 1 with the output of the voltage controlled oscillator (VCO) at frequency f_v. The upper sideband $(f_{in} + f_v)$ falls within the passband of the dispersive delay line DDL1 where the signal is delayed for a time that varies linearly with frequency. The delayed signal is mixed back to the frequency f_{in} by the further mixing with f_v at mixer 2. The delayed signal is then fed to the second dispersive delay line DDL2, which has the opposite dispersion to DDL1

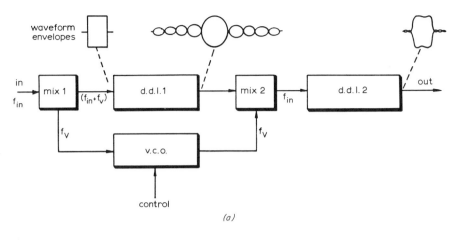

Input Pulse ; 200 nS 51 MHz

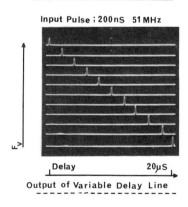

F_V

Delay   20μS

Output of Variable Delay Line

(b)

Figure 10.9 *(a)* The principle of a variable delay technique. *(b)* A photograph of the experimental unit and delayed-output pulses.

461

so that the overall system is nondispersive. Because DDL2 operates at the frequency f_{in}, independent of f_v, it introduces a constant mean delay. Here f_{in} is assumed to be constant, but in practice a signal of arbitrary frequency can be processed by introducing an additional frequency changing stage.[10]

It would be highly desirable to have a radar transmitter and receiver capable of generating and processing *any* waveform so that transmissions could be chosen to meet changing operational conditions and the receiver could be adaptive, for example, to optimally process signals with different signal-to-noise ratios or different amounts of clutter return. Two types of surface wave devices have been aimed at introducing programmability into radar and communications systems: programmable analog matched filters and "nonlinear" convolvers. These have received considerable attention in research laboratories.[11]

A programmable analog matched filter is a delay line with taps that transfer portions of a signal to a summing rail at a phase controlled by electronic circuitry. It is particularly easy to produce such devices for both generation and matched filter reception of polyphase coded signals.[12]

Polyphase coding has limited application in radar because of the poor sidelobe performance associated with pseudorandom sequences (the mean sidelobe level is -20 dB for a 100 bit code) and the sensitivity of the correlation peaks to variations in signal frequency. The conventional method of coding on a pulse-to-pulse basis is to use frequency agility so that pulses are transmitted at frequencies that are not predictable. On reception the carrier frequency is down-converted to intermediate frequency and processed using a *fixed* matched filter designed to give low sidelobe levels. Exploitation of the programmable analog matched filter in radar is limited to applications where frequency agility is not permitted and the size, low power consumption, and ruggedness of a surface wave filter justifies the poor sidelobe performance, and then only if one-bit correlations[13,14] and charge coupled devices,[15] are not proved better.

One type of surface wave convolver uses nonlinear interactions between oppositely directed surface waves ξ_a and ξ_b to produce an output signal that is the convolution of ξ_a and ξ_b. Correlation of the waveform ξ_a can be performed if the signal ξ_b is the time inverse of ξ_a. Some successful and practical approaches to convolution and correlation use interaction between surface waves and electrons[16] and nonlinearity of diodes.[17] It is tempting to argue that such devices could have far-reaching implications in radar. However a degree of caution should be exercised and several factors have to be considered.

For instance, as presently conceived the peripheral circuitry to achieve time inversion, refreshment of the reference signal, and convenient display[18] somewhat offsets the basic simplicity of the device.

Moreover, for complete generality the capability of *generating* any arbitrary waveform must also exist. In sophisticated radars where waveform generation is controlled, it seems likely that the difficulty of generating any arbitrary waveform will favor the choice of a few carefully selected waveforms (generated with fixed-coded surface wave filters) to be used with their respective matched filters in multimode capacity.

The main competition for a general surface wave signal correlator will come from a digital equivalent because such devices are already under development. These have the capability of processing signals with a wide range of times and bandwidths because of the flexibility offered by a variable clock rate device. The important parameters for comparison here are cost, size, power consumption and performance.

10.3 Systems Applications of Surface Wave Devices

Surface wave components and devices have now advanced sufficiently for them to be used in a rich variety of systems, and radar is a fruitful field for exploitation of these devices.

Pulse Compression. The most frequent application of surface wave devices in radar is in pulse compression systems. Their acceptance stems basically from the fact that they perform several functions economically, compactly, and reliably. They are used to generate the coded waveform for transmission, to compress this waveform on reception, and, in addition, to provide precise frequency filtering necessary for time sidelobe reduction. Surface wave pulse compression components are now key elements in subsystems for advanced radar applications. See, for example, the complete linear FM expansion and compression IF unit in Fig. 10.12.

The important design features of surface wave expanders and compressors have been discussed elsewhere in this book. Here the solution of practical problems associated with operational pulse compression subsystems for linear FM are discussed and reference is made to the limitations of surface wave filters and likely trends and problems for future design. Linear FM is featured here, but a large part of the discussion also applies to other coded waveforms.

The block diagram of a simple pulse compression radar is shown in Fig. 10.10. The coded IF waveform is mixed to RF for transmission and on reception the down-converted signal is amplified and then decoded by the pulse compression filter.

The chirp signal can be "actively" generated using conventional electronic circuits but cost-effective units using the amplified impulse response of a surface wave transversal filter ("passive" generation) are now

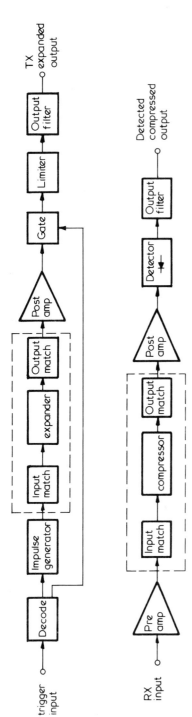

Figure 10.10 Form of pulse compression system using surface wave expanders and compressors.

preferred. This approach utilizes a key property of surface wave devices, that is, the ability, in principle, to generate *any* code. Thus engineers can optimize radar performance without introducing complex and costly code generation problems. This factor is of particular significance in multimode radars.

In the receiver (Fig. 10.10) an acoustic filter for the compressor makes possible, in principle, a matched filter for any input waveform. In practice the matched filter and weighting filter functions are successfully combined in a single surface wave device by suitably weighting the amplitude response of the pulse compressor.

Some of the technical and economic advantages of using surface wave devices for pulse compression radars are listed here.

1. Any fixed code can be generated and compressed.
2. Loss is sufficiently low to provide a passively generated chirp with satisfactory signal-to-noise performance for most radar applications.
3. With this relatively low filter loss, a large dynamic range can be achieved in the receiver.
4. Control of the filter characteristic allows other passband defects to be compensated in the filter design (e.g., known distortions in amplitude and phase introduced by external circuits such as matching networks).
5. Bandwidths are sufficiently wide for most radar applications.
6. Surface wave filters are stable with respect to temperature, vibration and time. Even if, as for lithium niobate, the temperature coefficient is not low, automatic temperature compensation is possible because the filter used in the generator and that used in the receiver can be arranged to track with temperature.

In addition to these important technical advantages there are several economic advantages:

1. Few adjustments are needed in a practical subsystem to achieve fidelity and specified performance.
2. Final design is incorporated into a single mask from which many filters, each having a nearly identical performance, can be fabricated without the use of complex jigs.

The factors influencing design of both expanders and compressors on quartz are sufficiently well understood that a computer routine can synthesize dispersive transducer design from desired device performance characteristics.[19] Since the output of such programs (e.g., on paper tape) can be used directly to drive a plotting table that produces the master artwork from which the device is ultimately derived, the design procedure can be used by systems engineers with little detailed knowledge of surface wave physics. On quartz this procedure produces a device having close to the *theoretical ideal* response, that is, close to the response of a perfect matched filter in series with a perfect weighting filter, as is illustrated in Fig. 10.11.

Unfortunately lithium niobate (LiNbO$_3$) presents special design problems because of its high electromechanical coupling constant. Reflections

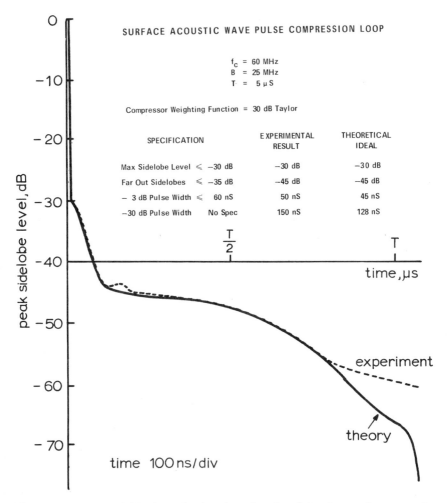

Figure 10.11 Level of sidelobe peaks plotted as a function of time for a surface wave pulse compression loop. Courtesy of the Royal Signals and Radar Establishment.

from metal fingers can be large because of the mismatch introduced by the velocity change under the fingers. In addition, a frequency f_1 at position $x(f_1)$ in the dispersive structure can also launch a strain wave at position $x(f_2)$ with sufficient intensity to distort the propagating pattern (regeneration). The double electrode structure introduced to minimize reflection effects does not significantly reduce distortions due to regeneration, and although the performance of devices using high k^2 substrates has been sugnificantly improved by such techniques, advances have not been sufficient to produce with LiNbO$_3$ the "ideal" response of a quartz device. Reflecting-array compressors (RAC) overcome this interaction problem by using a frequency dependent propagation time achieved by means of reflecting grooves (Chapter 9). This geometry eliminates the need for large transducer arrays (the source of the interaction problem).

The design procedure for reflecting-array compressors can also be automated. It is capable of giving results on LiNbO$_3$ that are similar to those achieved on quartz using dispersive transducers[3] and should prove to be significant where it is necessary to use high k^2 substrates. High k^2 material is chosen to keep insertion loss down to an acceptable level (say, below 50 dB) and has so far proved necessary for filters having TB products exceeding about 500. The performance of a reflecting-array compressor on LiNbO$_3$ having a TB product of 5000 is particularly impressive and will encourage systems engineers to specify large TB products with greater confidence.

The maximum pulse length that can be processed by a surface wave filter is limited by the physical size of the substrate material. The longest reported processing time[20] for a planar device is 100 μsec, using 300 mm of ST-cut quartz substrate. The reflecting-array structures gain a factor of 2 and have been successfully used for the bulk wave IMCON lines[21] as well as for surface wave processors.[3] The bulk wave processors are in fact available for bandwidths of less than 15 MHz and times up to 300 μsec. These bulk wave units give excellent performance, although the bulk wave lines do not have temperature coefficients as low as that of quartz.

The bandwidth of surface wave filters is of course also limited. The practical limit of "conventional" photolithographic processes confines operation of surface wave devices to below 800 MHz and hence potential bandwidths to less than 400 MHz. The essential high resolution lithography can only be achieved over small substrate areas, that is, involving times of the order of 2 to 3 μsec. Processing longer pulses is achieved only at the expense of bandwidth. Within the 100 μsec time and 400 MHz bandwidth limits, time-bandwidth products cannot exceed 1000 using standard processing techniques and a single artwork per transducer. For TB > 1000 specialized fabrication techniques are required. The TB product is a significant parameter for linear FM pulse compression systems. It is a measure of the pulse compression (in time) and also the processing gain of the compressor.

Surface wave filters are admirably suited to TB products of a few hundred but in this regime they are not without competition; digital correlation filters have been devised and demonstrated in radar pulse compression systems.[13] Typical parameters to meet a radar requirement are T of about $10 \, \mu sec$ B of about $10 \, MHz$, and a dynamic range of about $50 \, dB$. To meet these requirements a digital matched filter would require eight 200 stage shift registers operating at a 20 megabit rate and multipliers capable of performing 10-stage multiplication in less than $50 \, nsec$. At the present time the complexity of such a device makes it poor competition for the simple, but fixed code surface wave pulse compression filters. However where programmability is required digital devices compete favorably with surface wave devices. However, present radar requirements for devices having general programmability are limited, but simple fixed code filters are applicable to a large variety of systems. An example of a practical surface wave unit is shown in Fig. 10.12.

Pseudocoherent Radars. It is not always economic to produce fully coherent radars capable of extracting MTI information in the manner indicated earlier in this chapter. In man-borne systems where size, weight, cost, and complexity are prime considerations, other methods must be used and an alternative system, the clutter reference radar, has proved effective in the detection of slow moving targets such as men, vehicles, and so on. Surface wave devices extend the performance of this type of equipment.

Clutter reference radar is based on the principle that superposition of a signal from a moving target and from a fixed target at the same range produces a beat signal at the Doppler frequency. The receiver detects the presence of a beat signal using conventional Doppler filtering techniques. In an operating system returns from stationary targets, which in MTI systems would normally contribute to the "clutter" signal, are used to produce the "clutter reference." In unfavorable conditions, for example, over water or open ground, the clutter return may be so weak that the clutter reference is inadequate. A system has been devised to overcome this particular problem by generating a pseudocoherent reference signal using returns from surface wave reflectors operating at IF.

The pseudocoherent radar incorporating a surface wave device is shown in block diagram form in Fig. 10.13. Transmitter breakthrough at

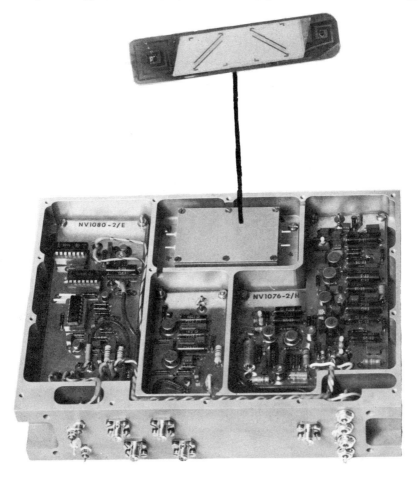

Figure 10.12 A practical pulse compression unit. Courtesy of MESL Laboratory, Edinburgh, Scotland.

the IF enters the surface wave transducer and is successively returned by reflectors spaced along the line. The resultant wave provides a reference signal of the required duration and is added to all incoming signals entering the IF amplifier. The gain of most radar receivers is swept in time (sensitivity time control) to compensate for fourth power variation in signal return as a function of range. An attraction of a surface wave line for pseudocoherent application is that reflector geometry can be designed

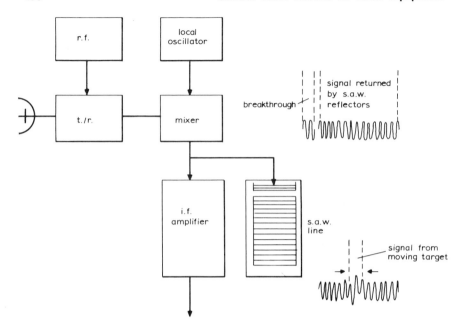

Figure 10.13   Block diagram of a pseudocoherent radar that uses a surface wave delay line.

so that the reference signal matches the swept gain characteristic of the amplifier. The reflectors in fact can be designed to match any *fixed* characteristic that optimizes the performance of this kind of radar. In other words this approach effectively puts control of fixed clutter into the hands of the radar designer. Initial experiments with a short range, ground surveillance, pseudocoherent radar and a nonoptimized surface wave delay line have shown a 10 to 12 dB improvement in the signal from a walking man situated in a site with a low clutter reference.[22]

Countermeasure Applications.   An important factor in modern radar design is the ability of equipment to operate in unfavorable signal environments. Interference with the signal may be due to many users occupying the same frequency band, or to deliberate interference—jamming. Jamming takes on a wide variety of forms but can be crudely classified into three basic types: "spot" jamming, which covers a few megahertz of bandwidth; barrage jamming, covering a wider frequency range but at a lower power per unit bandwidth; and deception techniques, where the objective is to present incorrect range information to the radar. A well-designed radar forces the jammer to spread its energy over as wide a bandwidth as possible while optimally processing the target return over as narrow a bandwidth as resolution requirements allow. Frequency agility and matched filter reception are important in this context.

In frequency agile systems the transmitter frequency is "hopped" over a wide frequency band and the received signal converted to a *constant* IF by synchronous hopping of the local oscillator in the receiver. Surface wave devices are important in pulsed radars of this type because they are wide-band, lightweight, small, rugged, and capable of generating and optimally processing sophisticated signals without significantly increasing the cost of the equipment. Other methods are often more costly and, in airborne or missile borne equipment, too bulky to be competitive. The transmitted energy per pulse should of course be as large as possible. Surface wave generators and matched filters can be used up to pulse lengths of about 150 μsec and are not the limiting factor in determining the pulse length for many radars. The advantage of the surface wave approach is seen particularly in waveform agile radars where frequency agility is not permitted (e.g., in MTI radars). Here banks of switchable, fixed code devices are used to change the transmitter code from pulse to pulse and give some protection against jammers that "play back" the radar pulse to confuse or deceive the radar.

The electronic counter-countermeasure (ECCM) considerations briefly discussed earlier are also applicable to compact, portable, and usually unsophisticated radars. Here solid-state oscillators and surface wave devices can combine to provide cheap portable radars that use relatively sophisticated transmitter codes and receiver decoders to minimize susceptibility to jamming.

The same wide-bandwidth surface wave techniques are also available for electronic countermeasure (ECM) purposes. There are requirements for acoustic delay lines in jammers that receive and repeatedly retransmit the radar signal to produce false returns intended to hide genuine target echoes at all ranges. For this purpose surface wave delay lines having bandwidths up to hundreds of megahertz and several microseconds of delay compete with bulk acoustic wave devices. At microwave frequencies bulk wave delay lines are favored, but at VHF and UHF the surface wave device offers economic advantages, particularly where large numbers are required, for example, in expendable systems. Where tapped delay lines are required the surface wave device offers clear advantages. Switchable, tapped surface wave delay lines have been reported to be applicable to repeater jammers.[23] The surface wave device is programmed to switch each tap in turn and so cause the radar to track the false target and to return to its search mode when the false target is switched off.

Surface wave devices have also been assessed for rapid frequency measurement. Here the objective is to measure as quickly as practicable the frequency of a single pulse in order to take the appropriate action—to initiate a jammer in the case of ECM or to avoid one for ECCM. Three cases have been discussed:[24] first, the use of contiguous surface wave filter banks produced on a single substrate; second, the use of a single, wide-band dispersive delay line that performs as a frequency discriminator by measuring the time delay of the detected pulse; third, the use of a compressive receiver that produces a rapid spectrum analysis of the input signal.

The three approaches using surface wave devices were compared with more conventional methods by Grasse and Gandolfo,[24] who examined performance criteria such as frequency accuracy, response time, sensitivity, and bandwidth as well as factors such as potential cost, size, and complexity. Their conclusions, which are summarized in Table 10.2, indicate that the surface wave approach represents the best combination of these characteristics. They stressed particularly the importance of the identification of signals that arrive simultaneously at the receiver.

Requirements for electronic countermeasure equipment are becoming increasingly sophisticated. The wide bandwidths and necessity of using expendable equipment suggests that surface wave devices will be of growing importance in future systems.

Table 10.2   Frequency Discriminator Trade-off Considerations

Tuning Technique	Set-on Accuracy	Set-on Time	Sensitivity	BW	Simultaneous Signal Capability	Size	Cost	Risk	Overall Assessment
1. Phase-locked Loops	Good	Exc	Poor	Good	No	Small	Low	Medium	Fair
2. Filter bank									
a. Conventional	Fair	Good	Exc	Exc	Yes	Large	High	Low	Poor
b. Active	Good	Good	Good	Fair	Yes	Medium	High	Medium	Poor
c. Acoustic	Good	Good	Good	Good	Yes	Medium	High	High	Fair
d. Coarse fine	Exc	Fair	Good	Good	Yes	Small	Medium	High	Good
3. Discriminator									
a. Open loop									
(1) Conventional	Poor	Exc	Fair	Poor	No	Small	Low	Low	Fair
(2) IFM	Fair	Exc	Fair	Exc	No	Small	Low	Low	Good
(3) Acoustic	Fair	Exc	Good	Good	Yes	Small	Low	Medium	Good
b. Closed loop									
(1) Conventional	Good	Good	Fair	Poor	No	Small	Low	Low	Good
(2) IFM	Good	Good	Fair	Exc	No	Small	Low	Low	Good
(3) Acoustic	Exc	Fair	Good	Good	Yes	Small	Low	Medium	Exc

Source: Ref. 24.

Fusing Systems. Many proximity fuses are in effect miniature radar systems. The echo from a signal transmitted from a missile, for example, can be used to initiate detonation when it coincides with a preset time. A system is required that is short range, responds only at a fixed range, and has appropriate size, weight, and ruggedness. In general, surface wave devices are suited to these requirements. For example, delay lines to provide the delayed reference for fixing the range either at intermediate or radio frequency (<3 GHz) can be considered because the time is unlikely to exceed 1 μsec. The factors governing the choice of surface wave devices rather than their bulk wave equivalents are basically economic if the devices are simple, but where the demand is for sophisticated signals to counter the effects of Doppler shift, electronic countermeasures, and so on, surface wave devices offer new opportunities for miniaturization and sophistication.

The use of surface wave devices in fusing systems receives little open discussion, but it is clear that in the future such devices will be of considerable importance, particularly because fusing systems are a large volume market compared to most military radar systems.

Air Traffic Control. The equipment and techniques used in air traffic control are primarily for communication, navigation, and surveillance. The communication systems are usually narrow band and are not in general suitable in their present form to accept surface wave filters. Surface wave devices in navigational systems are intended to improve techniques for precise timing, either of the time-of-flight of coded sequences generated by satellites in known orbits or the round-trip times to such satellites for signals generated on the aircraft. The ability of surface wave devices to encode and decode signals has obvious application here and detailed assessment will establish whether the analog approach is an improvement over competing digital techniques.

In contrast to the new possibilities offered to navigation and communication systems by the use of satellites, the basic air traffic surveillance system is a derivation of the World War Two IFF (identification of friend or foe) system and is still used on a global scale. A ground station transmits a signal to a transponder located on the target aircraft and receives a coded reply. The coded reply from the aircraft provides identity and information concerning destination, height, and so on. This type of system, having evolved over the years, is now nonideal. The use of modern techniques would certainly improve system performance but apparently logical steps cannot always be implemented because of the major economic implications of even minor changes if modification is required in *all* aircraft. Surface wave techniques offer an elegant and possibly economic solution to some of the current systems problems, and there are a wide range of approaches using surface wave encoders and decoders.[25] However it is likely that the radical system changes necessary to implement these particular ideas may prohibit their use in air traffic control.

Conclusions. It is clear that surface wave devices are useful processors of IF signals and perform a variety of functions. The rapid exploitation of these new components in radar systems is predominantly because of the compatability of surface wave devices with radar IF signal parameters.

In addition to the basic attractions of surface wave components, they also offer new possibilities for circuit design. For example, IF filters having precisely defined transfer characteristics can be designed, coded waveform generators and matched filters pairs are easily produced, and compact oscillators having good stability characteristics at high frequencies considerably simplify design of some radar subsystems. The availability of these components also affects overall radar design and performance. More complex systems can be contemplated without prohibitive increases in cost or weight factors, particularly for airborne and missile-borne equipment. Ground installations also benefit, particularly where multimode operation or complex waveform generation is desirable. In this respect surface wave devices are allowing new techniques to be investigated; see, for example, the application to a new form of 3-d radar that relies heavily on surface wave pulse compression filters.[26] The ability to build pulse compression systems with a wide range of time-bandwidth products is of course significant, and the use of phase weighting to reduce range sidelobes while maintaining matched filter conditions is particularly relevant and should receive wide acceptance in the future. The clear success of some of these simple, passive devices against digital competition has established that analog processors have a significant role to play for several generations of radar systems.

Acknowledgments. The author acknowledges with pleasure the many stimulating discussions with colleagues at the Royal Signals and Radar Establishment that have contributed to this chapter. He thanks in particular Dr J. Clarke and Dr E. G. S. Paige for critically reading and commenting on the manuscript.

References

1. M. I. Skolnik. *Introduction to Radar Systems.* McGraw-Hill, New York, 1962.
2. M. F. Lewis. "The design, performance, and limitations of SAW oscillators," in *Proc.*

Conf. on Component Performance and Systems Applications of Surface Wave Devices, IEE, Stevenage, England, 1973, pp. 63–72.

3. R. C. Williamson. "Large time bandwidth product devices achieved through the use of surface acoustic wave reflection gratings," in *Proc. Conf. on Component Performance and Systems Applications of Surface Wave Devices,* IEE, Stevenage, England, 1973, pp. 181–190.

4. R. L. Thomas, C. R. Vale, and T. M. Foster. "Design and fabrication of precise and repeatable surface wave Barker code correlators." 1971 IEEE Ultrasonics Symposium, Miami Beach, December, 1971.

5. T. T. Taylor. "Design of circular apertures for narrow beamwidth and low sidelobes." *IRE Trans.* **AP-8,** 17 (1960).

6. C. E. Cook and M. Bernfeld. *Radar Signals: An Introduction to Theory and Application,* Academic, New York, 1967, Chapter 8.

7. A. H. Klinger. "Non-linear frequency modulation waveforms and their application to radar systems," in *Proc. 19th Annual Tri-services Radar Symposium,* 1973.

8. J. D. Maines, G. R. Rich, and J. B. G. Roberts. "Inverse filters: design and performance using surface acoustic waves," in J. de Klerk, Ed., *Proc. 1973 IEEE Ultrasonics Symposium,* IEEE, New York, 1973, pp. 437–440.

9. W. S. Mortley. "Improvements in or relating to variable electrical delay arrangements." British Patent No. 994,842.

10. J. Burnsweig, W. T. Gosser, and S. H. Arneson. "Electronically controllable time dely." IEEE G-MTT International Symposium, Boulder, Colorado, 1973.

11. D. P. Morgan. "Signal processing using programmable non-linear convolvers." *Ultrasonics* **12,** 74 (1974).

12. P. J. Hagon. "Programmable analogue matched filters," in *Proc. Conf. on Component Performance and Systems Applications of Surface Wave Devices,* IEE, Stevenage, England, 1973, pp. 92–101.

13. G. C. Bagley. "Radar pulse compression by random phase coding." *Radio Electron. Eng.* **36,** 5 (1968).

14. E. G. S. Paige. "Surface acoustic wave devices: against the digital tide." in *Proc. IOP European Solid State Devices Conf.,* 1972, pp. 39–54.

15. C. S. Hartmann et al. "Programable transversal filters using surface waves, charge transfer devices, and conventional digital approaches," in *Proc. Conf. on Component Performance and Systems Appllications of Surface Wave Devices,* IEE, Stevenage, England, 1973, pp. 102–109.

16. C. W. Turner, I. M. Mason, and I. Chambers. "Acoustic convolution using non-linear surface wave interactions in a piezoelectric semiconductor." *Electron. Lett.* **7,** 696 (1971).

17. T. M. Reeder and M. Gilden. "The diode-tapped delay line correlator." 1972 IEEE Ultrasonics Symposium, Boston, October, 1972.

18. D. P. Morgan, J. H. Collins, and J. G. Sutherland, "Asynchronous operation of a surface wave acoustic coupler," in J. de Klerk, Ed., *Proc. 1972 IEEE Ultrasonics Symposium,* IEEE, New York, 1972, pp. 296–299.

19. J. D. Maines and E. G. S. Paige, "Surface acoustic wave components, devices, and applications." *Proc. IEE* **120,** 376 (1973).

20. J. Burnsweig, S. H. Arneson, and W. T. Gosser. "High performance, large time-bandwidth surface wave filters," in J. de Klerk, Ed., *Proc. 1972 IEEE Ultrasonics Symposium*, IEEE, New York, 1972, pp. 276–279.

21. T. A. Martin, "The IMCON pulse compression filter and its applications," *IEEE Trans.* **MTT-21,** 186 (1973).

22. M. A. C. S. Brown et al. "The use of a SAW delay line to provide pseudocoherence in a clutter reference pulse Doppler radar." *Electron. Lett.* **9,** 17 (1972).

23. D. A. Gandolfo, C. L. Grasse, and E. J. Schmitt. "Surface acoustic waves: new processing tools for E. W.," Microwaves **10,** 44 (1971).

24. C. L. Grasse and D. A. Gandolfo. "Acoustic surface wave dispersive delay lines as high resolution frequency discriminators," in J. de Klerk, Ed., *Proc. 1972 IEEE Ultrasonics Symposium*, IEEE, New York, 1972, pp. 233–236.

25. J. H. Collins and P. M. Grant. "The role of surface acoustic wave technology in communications systems." Ultrasonics **10,** 59 (1972).

26. J. Heighway and A. Thompson. "SAW devices and their possible implication for novel radar systems design," in *Proc. Conf. on Component Performance and Systems Applications of Surface Wave Devices*, IEE, Stevenage, England, 1973, pp. 212–211.

ELEVEN

Surface Wave Devices in Spread Spectrum Systems

MANFRED G. UNKAUF

Raytheon Company,
Sudbury, Massachusetts

Communication systems can be classed according to the form of their information transfer as either predominantly analog or digital. The surface wave devices used in analog systems are generally bandpass filters and bandpass delay lines. These replace bulky and difficult to align lumped element networks. This can result in lowering the cost of equipment manufacture. However, a development cycle with significant duration and cost is generally required to obtain a surface wave device that meets the tight performance specifications of most practical systems above VHF, and in cases where large production runs of identical equipment are not anticipated, a surface wave device will probably not be seriously considered by the system designer. On the other hand, a surface wave device sometimes permits a system with improved flexibility or performance whose equipment would otherwise be excessively bulky or expensive, and it is cost effective to develop surface wave devices even for relatively small production quantities. This characteristic generally results when a significant amount of signal processing must be performed, as in spread spectrum systems. The emphasis in this chapter is therefore on spread spectrum applications of surface wave devices.

Surface wave devices have minimum frequency and bandwidth limitations that generally restrict their use to systems operating at VHF and higher frequencies. Maximum frequency and bandwidth limitations restrict application to only a few of the most sophisticated wideband systems. The remaining parameters of surface wave devices such as insertion loss, accuracy, time-bandwidth product, and spurious response further restrict the range of applications.[1-3] However, where they can be used, surface wave devices in spread spectrum communication equipment offer the advantages of small size, simplicity, and, most important, they permit construction of modems with rapid synchronization.

The first section of this chapter discusses spread spectrum digital data transmission. Comparable modulator-demodulator (modem) implementations using both standard technology and surface wave technology are described and a table of performance characteristics is presented. The next section of the chapter deals with communication techniques as they affect the design of modems containing surface wave devices. In the third section an illustrative application of surface wave devices to digital transmission over a dispersive channel is presented, and a simple and highly efficient adaptive matched filter receiver design using surface wave devices is described.

The chapter concludes with a description of an important new communications technique employing burst transmission. This technique, made practical by the use of surface wave matched filters and delay lines, permits the asynchronous transmission of groups of spread spectrum data bits while providing nearly the accuracy of synchronous data detection, thus permitting high integrity burst communication without inefficient preambles or suboptimum detection.

11.1 Spread Spectrum Communications

Spread spectrum modulation is an important communication technique and is also the area of communication technology that has derived the greatest benefit from surface wave technology. There are many types of spread spectrum systems and many reasons for using different types of spread spectrum modulation.[4-5] For example, it is used in communication systems to provide one or more of the following features: (1) reliable information transmission in the presence of strong interference, jamming, or multipath propagation; (2) transmission with very low power per hertz of bandwidth for low interference with cochannel users or for covert operation; (3) multiplexing a number of transmissions in a common channel; (4) accurate ranging in location, detection, or navigation systems; (5) probing of dispersive channels. In all these applications there exists a common principle. Rejection of channel interference or enhanced signal detectability is achieved at the cost of increased transmission bandwidth.

Data Transmission. An important purpose of spread spectrum modulation in digital data transmission is protection against interference or jamming. A digital symbol of nominal time duration T is usually transmitted in a bandwidth $W = 2/T$ in a system without a spread spectrum. The digital pulse has only one dominant amplitude and phase state over the interval T and can be considered to have only a single "degree of freedom." Simple interference waveforms can easily simulate the digital symbol waveform on a regular basis and cause a large performance degradation.

The objective of spread spectrum modulation is to protect against interference by increasing the number of "degrees of freedom" of each digital data symbol according to some predetermined rules of signal manipulation. This requires increased transmission bandwidth. The spreading operation can take the form of direct digital phase modulation of the data bits, direct digital hopping of the carrier frequency, linear frequency (chirp) modulation, or a hybrid combination of these. Frequency hopping, chirp, and hybrid modulation can be treated as special cases of phase modulation, and only spreading by phase modulation is described in detail here.

Figure 11.1a illustrates the elements of a spread spectrum data link using bipolar phase shift keyed (PSK) modulation. Each data bit of duration T is phase modulated by a higher frequency, predetermined pseudonoise (PN) sequence of bits of duration T/N called *chips*. The required transmission bandwidth is spread by a factor N. At the receiver the known chip sequence is removed from the transmitted signal by "inverse modulation," and the original data bit is reproduced.

Simple CW interference can disrupt all standard digital communication links that do not employ spread spectrum processing if the interference power is concentrated in the bandwidth of the desired signal. However spread spectrum processing prevents concentration of interference power in the receiver bandwidth. If the despreading process (inverse modulation) is employed before bit detection, as illustrated in Fig. 11.1a, the narrowband interference spectrum is broadened while the desired signal spectrum is collapsed to its original value. The effect of the interference power is reduced by the ratio of spread spectrum and data bandwidths.

If N is large (i.e., there are many band-spreading chips per data bit), the despread data bandwidth is then about N times smaller than the broadened interference bandwidth, and there is a processing gain of N.

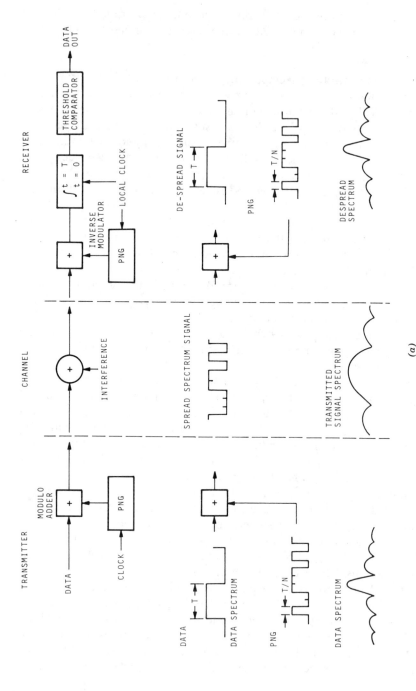

Figure 11.1 (*a*) A typical spread spectrum communications system. (*b*) The effect of spectrum spreading on a noncoherent interference waveform.

(*a*)

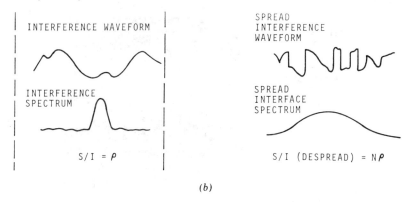

(b)

Figure 11.1 (*Contd*)

True processing gain depends on the type of spread waveform transmitted, the statistics of the interference, and the detailed characteristics of the receiver. Its computation is not trivial. However, for N reasonably large and for low intersymbol interference within the spread waveform, the processing gain can be taken as N.

It is important that the receiver in the system illustrated in Fig. 11.1a be a matched filter detector. A matched filter detector maximizes the signal-to-noise ratio at the bit decision (epoch) instant.[6] The concept of *epoch* is illustrated by Fig. 11.2, which shows the generation and matched filter reception of a 127 chip spread spectrum sequence using surface wave devices. The receiver epoch is defined as the time when the received sequence exactly fills the matched filter, in this case a surface wave filter. The filter output is maximized as shown by the large correlation peak of Fig. 11.2. In a simple data transmission system, where data is conveyed by the presence or absence of a group of PN chips, the receiver examines the matched filter output at each epoch instant for the presence or absence of a correlation peak.

Figure 11.3 illustrates the two *equivalent* baseband methods of implementing a matched filter detector. One method employs a linear filter whose impulse response is the bit-spreading sequence inverted in time. At the epoch instant the signal-to-noise ratio at the detector output is optimized. Alternatively a stored reference of the spreading sequence can be multiplied against the received waveform. The multiplier output is then integrated over the data bit duration (N chips) and the signal-to-noise ratio at the epoch instant is again optimized.

Before the advent of surface wave devices, implementation of a linear filter whose impulse response is a digital sequence was impractical for

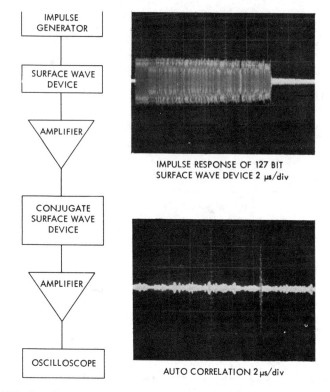

IMPULSE RESPONSE OF 127 BIT
SURFACE WAVE DEVICE 2 μs/div

AUTO CORRELATION 2 μs/div

Figure 11.2 Impulse response and autocorrelation response obtained with a 127-chip PN-coded surface wave device.

sequences with megahertz bandwidths. Approximations to such a linear filter were constructed using bulky delay lines or A/D conversion and shift register techniques, but these were limited to relatively low data rates. As a result the alternative stored reference method of matched filter detection was favored. A complicated linear filter is not required and the necessary local reference signal can usually be generated with simple logic circuitry. However the method does require a complicated synchronization procedure.

Spread spectrum data synchronization is generally a two-step process. The first step, coarse synchronization, is used to align the receiver epoch approximately with that of the incoming signal, and the second step involves time-base tracking. Consider the most general case; namely, a particular spreading (PN) sequence is used only once and discarded. Such a sequence can be thought of as a long series of pseudorandom digits that does not repeat. In a spread spectrum system the receiver has exact knowledge of the PN sequence employed by the transmitter. Because of propagation delay, clock drift, and Doppler drift, the receiver's estimate of the time at which a particular group of spreading chips will be received has a time uncertainty τ that may correspond to a large number of chip intervals. To identify coarse signal epoch in a group of N spreading chips, the receiver must detect correlation in the output of the matched filter.

Because a time uncertainty τ exists, the receiver must search for correlation by starting with the particular group of N spreading chips expected τ seconds in the future. For the linear filter implementation the filter impulse response is adjusted to match the N chip sequence expected τ seconds in the future and coarse sync is proclaimed after the first correlation peak is detected and verified. The average time-to-sync is $\tau/2$ when

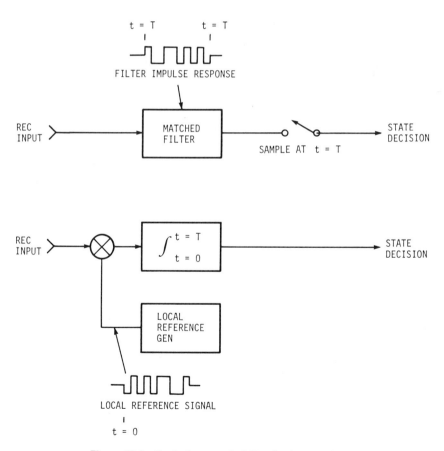

Figure 11.3 Equivalent matched filter implementations.

the correlation peak detection probability is high and the false detection probability is low.

The coarse synchronization procedure for the alternative, local reference matched filter receiver is far more complicated. The local clock reference is first advanced by τ seconds and the expected group of N spreading chips is multiplied against the incoming signal and the product integrated. If correlation is not obtained, the local clock is retarded by a fraction of a bit interval and the test is repeated. The average time-to-sync is approximately $2N\tau$ if the search proceeds in steps of one-fourth bit. This is $4N$ times longer than the average time-to-sync of the linear filter correlator. If the time uncertainty is 1 sec, for example, the linear filter correlator is expected to yield coarse sync in about $\frac{1}{2}$ sec whereas the local reference correlator with $N = 1000$ (30 dB processing gain) requires about 32 min on the average. Under degraded operating conditions, differences in time-to-sync can become even larger.

After the coarse sync operation is completed, the spread spectrum receiver enters a fine sync mode in which a delay discriminator or delay locked loop reduces the epoch error from a fraction of a bit to a very small value. To obtain equivalent performance in the white noise channel the timing precision of a spread spectrum receiver must generally be N times greater than the same receiver without spreading.

Figure 11.4 illustrates the standard approach to despreading a binary PN modulated spread spectrum transmission. A pseudonoise generator (PNG) provides a local reference and the serial bit-by-bit despreading can be performed either after demodulation, as in receiver 1 of Fig. 11.4, or before demodulation as in receiver 2. Although this approach provides high performance with few components for despreading data with a continuously changing spreading sequence, it does not provide rapid synchronization. It is, therefore, generally advantageous to combine it with a matched filter of the linear filter type whose only purpose is coarse epoch synchronization on the message preamble. A surface wave and also two conventional approaches to this preamble synchronizer are illustrated in Fig. 11.5.

Parallel despreading,* illustrated in Fig. 11.5, can also be done either before or after demodulation. The basic correlator is a delay line tapped at the chip intervals together with tap phase selectors and a combiner. The predemodulation mode is ideally suited for surface wave devices, as

---

* The term *parallel despreading* is derived from the fact that this type of correlator simultaneously processes a group of N pseudonoise chips in parallel leading to sequence recognition whenever the desired PN sequence appears. The standard synchronization approach processes PN chips sequentially, and synchronization can only occur when a time offset of the local reference PNG is found that matches that of the incoming signal.

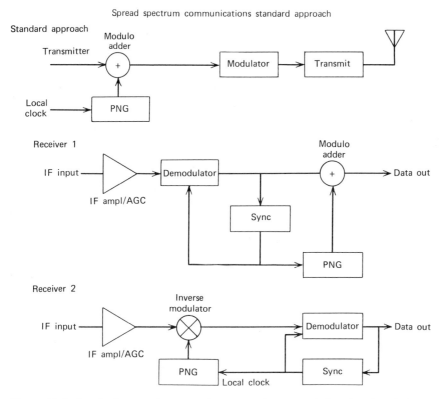

Figure 11.4 Standard approach to spread spectrum data transmission. Receiver 1 shows postdemodulation despreading and equivalent receiver 2 shows predemodulation despreading.

shown in Fig. 11.5, but difficult to implement in conventional hardware because of the need to process both in-phase and quadrature components of the IF signal when using video or digital delay lines.

The conventional postdemodulation parallel correlator either is composed of an incoherent video delay line and inverter/combiner or is realized digitally as illustrated by the two lower circuits of Fig. 11.5. The digital implementation is most attractive in many narrow bandwidth applications because of its potentially small size and compatibility with integrated circuit technology. In the digital approach the video output of the demodulator is converted to a Q bit sample (typically one to three bits per sample) at least twice per chip. The corresponding samples are delayed in shift registers and correlation is made by digitally multiplying

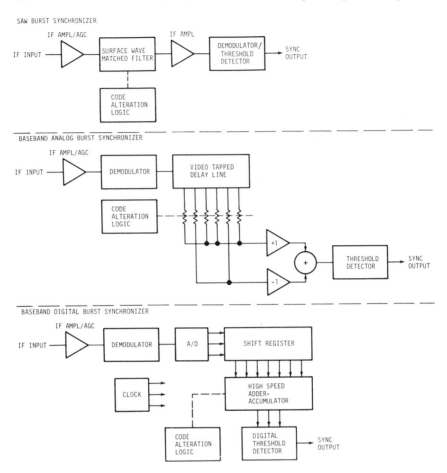

Figure 11.5 Three parallel (digital matched filter) receiver synchronization implementations.

the various taps by the anticipated chip sequence and summing the resultant.

At PN chip rates below a few megahertz implementation of the digital correlator can be accomplished with custom MOS-LSI circuitry.[8] However at chip rates between 10 and 50 MHz, a digital correlator must be constructed from individual high speed logic integrated circuits, resulting in considerable size, cost, and power consumption.

Comparison of Implementation Complexities. The most significant problem in spread spectrum systems is synchronization. Conventional technology leads to either a simple serial correlator with poor acquisition performance or a relatively complicated postdemodulation parallel correlator with rapid acquisition. However surface wave technology can lead directly to a rapid acquisition simple predemodulation parallel correlator (sequence matched filter).

A comparison of the implementation complexities and performance limits for typical conventional hardware and competitive surface wave technology is made in Table 11.1. The two conventional approaches chosen for comparison are the postdemodulation digital parallel correlator and the predemodulation analog serial correlator. Both switchable and fixed coded, PN sequence, surface wave, parallel correlators are individually compared to highlight the additional simplicity of a fixed code approach. (A fixed code correlator in the conventional hardware results in comparatively little simplification.)

It appears from Table 11.1 that the serial despread approach is not very complex from a hardware standpoint. However, relatively complicated digital hardware and multimode system operation may be required to enhance sync acquisition speed.

Table 11.1 Comparison of Spread Spectrum Correlation Detection Techniques

Parameter	Parallel Bit Detection, Q Bit Samples, Half Bit Intervals	Serial Analog Despread	Switchable-Code Surface Wave Correlator	Fixed-Code Surface Wave Correlator
Processing gain (N)	1000 Hard/Expensive	Very large Easy	1000 Hard/Expensive	1000 Easy
Maximum bit rate	50 Mb/sec	1000 Mb/sec	50 Mb/sec	200 Mb/sec
Minimum bit rate	Low	Low	1 Mb/sec	1 Mb/sec
RF frequencies	Unlimited (above bit rate)	Unlimited	Above VHF	Above VHF
Acquisition time	Short	$4N$ times longer	Short	Short
Equipment complexity (10 Mb/sec)	High	Moderate	Moderate-high	Low
Code comparison	High-speed adder-accumulator, multibit buffers, gates Hard/expensive	Analog multiplier Simple	IF analog Hard/expensive	Not needed
Digital receiver storage	High-speed multibit register Moderate/expensive	Not needed	Low-speed multibit Moderate	Not needed

In many applications the required surface wave PN correlator employs a switchable-code tapped delay line structure. That is, the surface wave device is a coherent IF delay line that is tapped at the chip interval and the various taps are switched in polarity by associated logic circuitry before IF summarization of the tap outputs.[9] At PN chip rates to 10 MHz, hybrid thin film or MSI monolithic circuits can be constructed to perform the tap code switching function for N up to 100 or greater. At these rates similar techniques can be used to implement a digital parallel correlator. However, the digitally implemented parallel correlator requires in-phase and quadrature heterodyne conversion to baseband producing two signal streams, each of which must be sampled at least twice per bit with a Q bit A/D conversion per sample. Typically eight times as much circuitry is required for similar performance using a conventional parallel correlator.

At chip rates between 10 MHz and 50 MHz, the switchable surface wave device is difficult to implement because of the small physical separation between taps, which results in potentially high signal crosstalk. The higher operating frequency associated with larger chip rates also results in a lower realizable tap-to-tap switch isolation. To achieve practical switchable surface wave devices in the region from 10 MHz to 200 MHz may require the code structure to be subdivided into a number of contiguous fixed subcodes, each of which can then be switched in polarity and combined according to an external code.

Predemodulation processors are frequency offset because of carrier instability or Doppler offset. Frequency offset results in a phase shift along the length of the device that degrades the degree of correlation achievable. The loss in processing gain is $\sin^2(2\pi FL)/2\pi FL$, where F is frequency offset and L is the length of the device. Thus a 10 μsec device will tolerate a frequency offset of 13 KHz for a 1 dB performance degradation. The loss in processing gain because of frequency offset is similar for all predemodulation despreading techniques and automatic frequency control (AFC) is generally difficult to implement. The post-demodulation despreading technique can be made less sensitive to frequency offset.

It can be concluded from the information in Table 11.1 that within their parameter limitations surface wave devices offer an efficient and economical means for synchronization of spread spectrum sequences. For bit-by-bit detection of spread spectrum data with fixed code spreading, the surface wave approach is again superior. However, where a jamming environment necessitates time variant spreading codes, continuous bit-by-bit serial despreading equipment is more desirable. In such cases a hybrid system consisting of a programmable surface wave correlator for epoch sync and a serial correlator for bit-by-bit despreading can offer the optimum system design.

11.2 Communication System Techniques

The previous section demonstrated that surface wave filters can provide significant implementation advantages in spread spectrum systems. Before describing some illustrative applications, it is useful to consider a few features of a complete communication system that are relevant to surface wave devices. These features are the modulation technique, the method of level control, the bandwidth, and the code used.

Modulation Techniques. In many spread spectrum systems used for ranging or synchronization, it is only necessary that the receiver recognize the presence of correlation between the received signal and its stored reference. The correlation processor generally consists of a matched filter followed by a demodulator and a threshold detector. The threshold level is adjusted to provide the desired false alarm and detection probabilities for the signal-to-noise ratio anticipated. Although this simple processor yields the accuracy improvement and interference rejection associated with spread spectrum ranging or synchronization, it is relatively inefficient for data transmission.

The energy utilization efficiency of the technique chosen for data modulation is very important in a spread spectrum system. The susceptibility of a communication system to interference is the difference between the explicit spread spectrum gain and the signal-to-noise ratio required by the modulation technique to achieve the desired bit error rate performance. A large variety of data modulation techniques can be effectively implemented with surface wave devices. These have different energy efficiency, complexity, and sensitivity to frequency offset.

Coherent Phase Shift Keying. It is well known that the optimum form of binary data modulation is coherent phase shift keying (CPSK).[10] In CPSK modulation, data is conveyed by the sign of the overall carrier phase during each spread spectrum data bit. It is difficult in a CPSK implementation using surface wave devices to determine the reference phase from the short duration correlation peaks at the matched filter output. That is, the signal-to-noise ratio is maximized only during the correlation peak. If a conventional phase locked loop were used for carrier phase tracking, it could be updated only during a brief fraction of each bit, and the *average* carrier-to-noise ratio component is reduced by

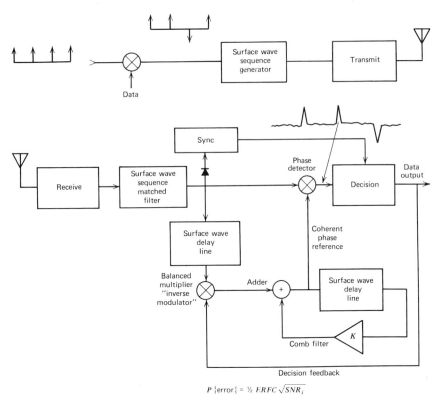

$$P\{error\} = \tfrac{1}{2}\, ERFC\,\sqrt{SNR_i}$$

Figure 11.6 Coherent phase shift keying data transmission with decision feedback carrier recovery.

the processing gain of the matched filter. Figure 11.6 illustrates a possible modulator-demodulator (modem) implementation that overcomes this difficulty by using decision feedback. The data are contained in the phase difference between adjacent correlation peaks at the matched filter output. Decision feedback is employed to *inverse modulate* the correlation peaks or restore them all to a common phase state; that is, a "0" phase state is multiplied by +1 while a "π" phase state is multiplied by −1 to yield a common phase state modulo 2π. The correlation peaks are then filtered in a broadband *comb filter* to enhance the signal-to-noise ratio of the reference waveform.

The modem illustrated in Fig. 11.6 has an inherent 180° phase ambiguity. To correct this ambiguity, differential encoding of the data is often employed, resulting in differentially coherent phase shift keying

(DCPSK) modulation. Both CPSK and DCPSK bit error rate performance is shown in Fig. 11.10 versus the peak signal-to-noise ratio at the matched filter output. The loss in performance due to differential encoding is small at low error rates.

Differential Phase Shift Keying. A somewhat simpler, but poorer performance, modulation technique employs differential phase shift keying (DPSK). Figure 11.7 illustrates the implementation of a DPSK spread spectrum modem. The modulator is the same as that for DCPSK, but the demodulator employs a simple *delay-and-compare* technique for phase detection. That is, after matched filtering, the resultant correlation peak is delayed by precisely one data bit interval and compared in phase with the following correlation peak. At each epoch instant a decision is made as to whether the adjacent bit phase is the same or opposite and these decisions are differentially decoded to recover the original data stream. The resultant DPSK error rate performance is also shown in Fig. 11.10.

CPSK, DCPSK, and DPSK modulation techniques offer the highest performance binary modulation. However they also require additional

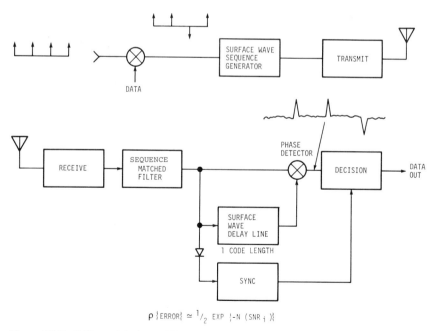

$$P\{ERROR\} \simeq \tfrac{1}{2} \; EXP \; \{-N \; (SNR_i)\}$$

Figure 11.7 Differential phase shift keying data transmission with "delay and compare" demodulation.

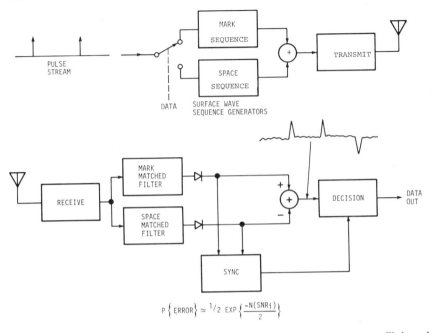

$$P\left\{ \text{ERROR} \right\} \simeq {}^{1}/{2} \ \text{EXP}\left\{ \frac{-N(\text{SNR}_i)}{2} \right\}$$

Figure 11.8 Code shift keying data transmission with noncoherent "greatest of" demodulation.

modem complexity because of the presence of additional surface wave delay lines for reference signal generation, and they are sensitive to frequency offset. If the spread spectrum data bit duration is T seconds and the frequency offset is F hertz, then a phase error of $\theta = 2\pi FT$ results over the length of a bit. The delay employed in the reference generation of the preceding PSK techniques tends to produce an error rate performance degradation that varies as $\cos^2 \theta$. This degradation is significantly more rapid than the degradation that results from loss of correlation in the matched filter, which varies as $(\sin^2 \theta/2)/(\theta/2)$.

Orthogonal Modulation Techniques. A popular alternative to PSK modulation is code shift keying (CSK). This modulation technique encodes a group of n data bits into one of 2^n nearly orthogonal codes. This approach is illustrated in Fig. 11.8 for binary modulation and incoherent detection. The corresponding receiver determines which of the two corresponding matched filter outputs is greatest at the epoch instant. Binary CSK error rate performance is exactly 3 dB poorer than DPSK performance but offers the advantage of lower sensitivity to frequency offset.

However, M' ary CSK modulation ($M = 2^n$) can actually surpass binary CPSK performance. For example, if every pair of data bits is transmitted as one of four orthogonal code sequences, performance nearly equal to that of DPSK is achieved.

Optimum M' ary CSK performance, as shown in Fig. 11.10, is obtained when the PN spreading code alternatives used are orthogonal at the epoch instant. If the codes are chosen randomly they will not be orthogonal, but they will have a cross-correlation with nearly Gaussian distribution whose variance is $1/N$, where N is the code length. For N less than 100, significant degredation of error rate performance is likely. To provide exactly orthogonal codes at the epoch instant, it is possible to select any PN sequence and superimpose on it one of a number of simple orthogonal phase modulations such as the Walsh functions. For example, the phase modulations (1 1 1 1), (1 1 −1 −1), (1 −1 −1 1), and (1 −1 1 −1) can be superimposed on any PN sequence to create four exactly orthogonal sequences at the epoch instant. The technique can easily be extended to any M' ary CSK scheme.

On-Off Keying. A simple but lowest performance technique is to transmit data by the presence or absence of a spread spectrum signal in each bit interval for binary modulation, as illustrated in Fig. 11.9. This

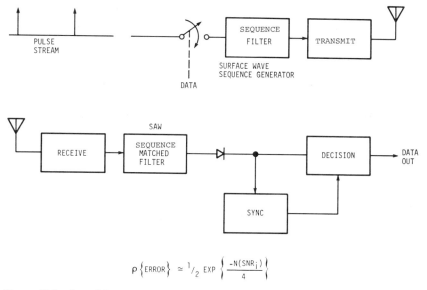

$$\rho\left\{\text{ERROR}\right\} \simeq {}^{1}/_{2} \, \text{EXP} \left\{\frac{-N(\text{SNR}_i)}{4}\right\}$$

Figure 11.9 On–off keying data transmission with simple noncoherent threshold demodulation.

modulation is similar to what is commonly called *on-off-keying*. The performance for on-off keying is also shown in Fig. 11.10 and it is 6 dB poorer than that for DPSK. The poor performance of on-off keying makes this form of modulation unsuitable for most practical communication applications.

The DPSK, CSK, and on-off keying digital modulation techniques described all require precise epoch timing for optimum performance. Normally, initial synchronization is obtained as previously described and sync maintenance can be obtained by phase-locking an oscillator to the matched filter correlation peaks. If timing recovery is not employed or if

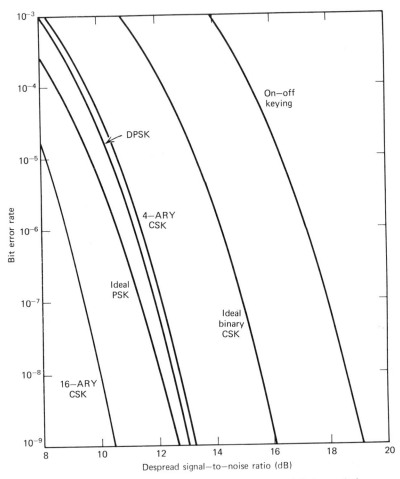

Figure 11.10 Bit error rate performance for various modulation techniques.

the communication link is asynchronous,* the detection process is significantly degraded. The probability of error is then dominated by the probability of detecting a real correlation peak or a false alarm for a given threshold detector setting. The loss in detection efficiency for this asynchronous operation is at least 6 dB at 10^{-5} bit error rate for CSK modulation, which is not tolerable in most practical applications.

Level Control. Synchronization equipment using surface wave filters requires threshold detection following the matched filter. Figure 11.11 shows the performance of a threshold detector for large spread spectrum processing gain when the code sidelobes can be neglected. A small change in the threshold level V can result in a very large change in the false alarm and detection probability of the receiver.

In many communication systems the input signal level may vary over several orders of magnitude, and a technique is required to control the signal level into the surface wave filter. The technique chosen, either limiting or automatic gain control, depends strongly on the statistics of the interference signals. The simpler techniques tend to keep the total signal plus interference power constant at the device input. When the interference power is larger than the desired signal power, suppression of the desired signal results.[11] Normally the threshold level can be set to yield the desired false alarm and detection probabilities for the smallest signal-to-interference ratio anticipated. As the signal level increases or as the interference level decreases, the detection probability improves while the false alarm probability remains relatively constant. Constant false alarm rate operation of a synchronization detector is often a suitable systems approach.

Code Selection. Another consideration in the design of a surface wave filter for PN synchronization or pattern recognition is code selection. In spread spectrum communication with time variant spreading sequences, the designer must often use segments of very long pseudorandom sequences without regard to their auto- and cross-correlation properties. In such cases the processing gain is usually very large and the probability of choosing a "bad" code segment is insignificant. However in systems with fixed codes and also in systems with a finite number of discrete address or synchronization patterns, code selection is important.

The requirements on a preamble synchronization or discrete address code are usually that it have an autocorrelation function with low time

* An asynchronous data link occurs when the data rate is variable and unknown to the receiver. A data transition is recorded whenever a correlation peak is detected.

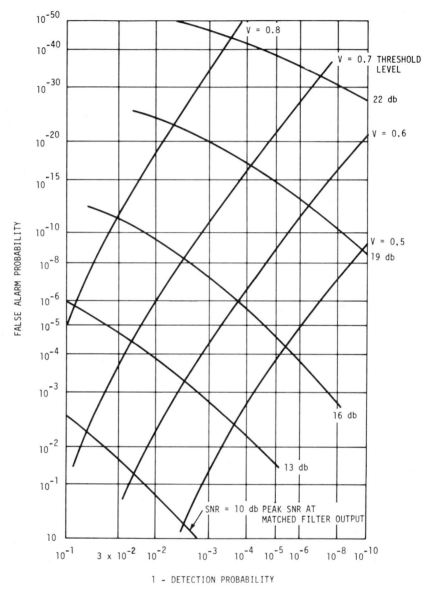

Figure 11.11 False alarm versus detection probability with threshold level and signal-to-noise ratio as parameters.

sidelobes and a small cross correlation with any other transmission code. Although the selection of "good" codes is an old problem, previous attention has been focused primarily on periodic codes (i.e., codes that continuously repeat in time). In the periodic class there are a large number of code possibilities, for a given nominal code length, that have only a two-level autocorrelation function, that is, sidelobes of maximum size 1 and a correlation peak of size N for an N chip code. Examples of periodic codes are the M sequences (maximal length shift register sequences), Legendre sequences, and Hall sequences.[13] However in the nonperiodic class of interest for most surface wave applications, very few such codes are known. The Barker codes exhibit a two-level autocorrelation but are known only to length 13. A limited number of polyphase Frank codes and complementary codes or Golay sequences also exist with good nonperiodic properties.[14]

A reasonable class of nonperiodic codes whose peak autocorrelation sidelobes are approximately $(N)^{1/2}$ are the M sequences of length $N = 2^n - 1$, where n is an integer. For $N = 127$, 18 such prime codes exist. In contrast, the cross-correlation properties of these codes appear to be random with a standard deviation of $(N)^{1/2}$ so that care must be exercised in selecting these codes for such applications as discrete addressing or orthogonal data modulation. The problem of code selection is illustrated by considering completely random PN sequences. Sequences of length N have random autocorrelation and cross-correlation sidelobes that follow the binomial probability distribution. To first order, the magnitude of the sidelobes for large N approximate a Rayleigh distribution with a mean of $1.2(N)^{1/2}$ and an rms level of $1.4(N)^{1/2}$. For example, if a computer search is performed for codes with $N = 100$ and a maximum sidelobe level of $2(N)^{1/2}$ (14 dB below the correlation peak), about 1 in 100 codes examined will display this autocorrelation property. If it is now desired to pick two such codes that also have a similar cross-correlation property, only 1 in 10,000 codes examined will display this property. Since there are nearly 10^{30} code possibilities, a large number of suitable codes can still be found. However if it is desired to find a set of 10 codes with autocorrelation and mutual cross-correlation sidelobes down 14 dB, more than 10^{20} codes must be examined, which is impractical even using a high-speed digital computer. Although this analysis is crude, it clearly demonstrates the difficulty in finding large numbers of "good" codes by random selection.

Bandwidth. Using surface wave technology an exact matched filter can be implemented for any waveform also generated by a surface wave filter. The spread spectrum processing gain realized depends mainly on the time-bandwidth product of the generated waveforms. For example, a 1000 chip PN sequence implementation will only yield a 30 dB processing gain when the device bandwidth is sufficiently wide to yield low intersymbol interference. If excess surface wave transducer finger pairs are employed to reduce insertion loss or if a number of surface wave filters are cascaded, the bandwidth is reduced, the PN chips will spread in time, and adjacent chips will overlap. The loss in processing gain varies only linearly with the bandwidth constraint but this loss is important to system performance. Phase nonlinearities also degrade the processing gain performance of the matched filter.[12]

11.3 Application to the Dispersive Channel

A number of important communication channels such as the channels that use tropospheric or ionospheric scatter are time-variant and dispersive because of the presence of multipath propagation.[15] It is difficult to achieve efficient transmission of high-speed digital data in these channels by conventional techniques. A novel modem technique that is relatively simple yet permits efficient data transmission is described in this section. At frequencies above VHF a practical modem can be realized because of the unique properties of surface wave filters.

A pulse transmitted over the dispersive channel is smeared out by multipath propagation. The pulse distortion is illustrated in Fig. 11.12 for a dispersive but time invariant channel. (The duration of the received pulse T^1 is the sum of the duration of the transmitted pulse T and the differential multipath delay spread $T^1 - T$.) When the channel is also time-variant, the pulse distortion is a function of the observation time. If a single pulse is transmitted the optimum receiver is a matched filter that adapts to the pulse distortion.[16] The modem technique described here employs this principle and can be used for channels whose differential multipath delay spread is less than the transmission symbol interval.[17]

Consider a series of PSK pulses at RF that are separated by a guard time Δ, as illustrated in Fig. 11.12. If this pulse train is passed through a dispersive channel, the received pulse train will be smeared out as shown. However, if the guard time is comparable to the differential multipath delay spread, the intersymbol interference will be small. The optimum receiver structure is then a classical matched filter in which the input pulse stream is multiplied by an identically distorted reference pulse stream and the product is operated on by an *integrate and dump* filter.

A practical adaptive matched filter demodulator needed to implement the technique is shown in Fig. 11.13 for binary PSK.[17-18] The principle of

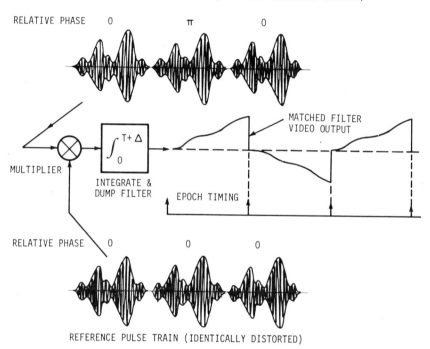

Figure 11.12 Time-gated transmission waveform and ideal matched-filter receiver for the dispersive channel.

operation is very simple. The received pulse train is delayed by precisely one symbol interval (one baud) to align with the decision feedback on the corresponding data. This decision feedback is next used to inverse-modulate or remove the PSK modulation from the distorted pulses. The resultant reference pulse stream could then be fed to the multiplier/integrater and dump circuitry of the classic matched filter. However, at this point the reference pulse stream is also corrupted by noise and is vulnerable to decision feedback errors.

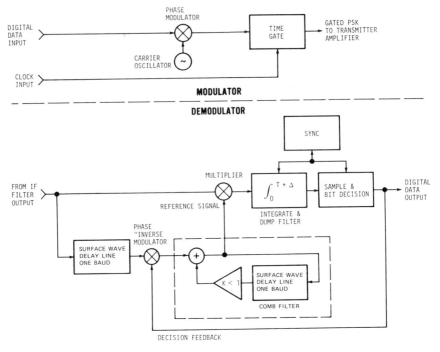

Figure 11.13 Simple surface wave matched-filter modem for dispersive channels. Shown for binary PSK modulation.

A comb filter is therefore used to stabilize the reference pulse stream. This filter consists of a positive feedback loop with a delay of precisely one symbol (at IF) and a loop gain K that is slightly less than unity. Adjacent pulses, which are similarly distorted, add on a voltage basis in the loop, whereas noise adds on a power basis. If $K = 0.9$, about 13 dB of signal-to-noise ratio improvement is achieved in the comb filter and this provides a nearly ideal reference waveform for practical demodulator operation. The underlying assumption that there is little change in the channel multipath structure over a period of several information bits is true of most applications.

This novel demodulator has several interesting features. In a fading dispersive channel it provides improved error rate performance as the pulse distortion increases because of intrinsic time diversity. Also, optimum, explicit, path-diversity combining is achieved simply by employing an adaptive matched filter for each channel, summing the video outputs of the filters to a common integrate and dump filter and providing a common decision feedback signal for each circuit. The technique is also easily extended to QPSK or higher alphabet PSK modulation. Figure 11.14 shows the calculated performance for 3.5 Mbps digital transmission over a 168 mile troposcatter link operating at 850 MHz with 28 ft diameter antennas. Also shown in the figure is the performance of the ideal ("one shot") modem and the performance for frequency flat fading

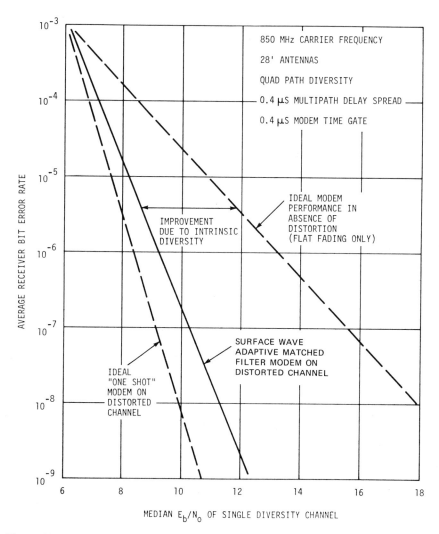

Figure 11.14 Calculated bit error rate performance of the surface wave adaptive matched-filter modem at 3.5 Mbps on a 168 mile troposcatter link.

without multipath dispersion. The presence of pulse distortion results in improved link performance because of intrinsic diversity.

The heart of this demodulator implementation for megabit data rates is a pair of identical surface wave nondispersive delay lines. For a typical troposcatter application, these delay lines must have a length of about 1 μsec and a center frequency of 70 MHz. The signal in the comb filter passes through the delay line several times as it circulates around the loop, so the delay line bandwidth must be wider than usual. A 0.3 dB bandwidth of about 7 MHz is a typical requirement. Also, since the delay line is in a positive feedback loop, its gain stability and frequency response amplitude ripple are of considerable importance. An 0.4 dB peak variation is a typical requirement.

These delay line requirements are best satisfied using surface wave technology. A temperature controlled delay line on a $LiNbO_3$ substrate easily satisfies the requirements, but a coaxial cable delay line would have an impractically large size as well as a strongly temperature dependent delay and amplitude stability. Lumped element all-pass filters would have an impractically large number of stages because of the large time-bandwidth product.

The use of surface wave devices permits sophisticated matched filter implementations directly at IF. Since these devices can be designed to hold precise phase and delay tolerances, optimum PSK modulation is easily implemented. Over the past years many ingenious signal-processing techniques have been proposed as solutions to various communication problems but have not been widely used because of implementation limitations. It is likely that some of these techniques would receive greater use if implemented by surface wave filters.

11.4 The Burst Communication Modem

Some communication systems transfer relatively small amounts of spread spectrum digital data at irregular intervals between large numbers of participants. For example, interrogation-response systems and polling systems exchange digital identities and status information. The performance goal in such systems is to transmit a small number of information bits as efficiently as possible in as short a time as possible with protection against interference.

As previously discussed, low error rate demodulation of spread spectrum data requires precise bit synchronization. A conventional approach would typically use a synchronization preamble on the transmitted burst causing a large loss in system capacity when short messages are transmitted. Surface wave devices can be used, however, to build spread spectrum burst communication modems that do not require preambles. The asynchronous transmission has nearly the error rate performance of synchronous data demodulation. Surface wave technology provides the capability to process several spread spectrum data bits simultaneously and defer a digital decision until the demodulator reference has been optimized. For example, it is possible to demodulate simultaneously a sequence of M data bits with an epoch timing precision that has M times greater signal-to-noise than a single bit. The resultant demodulator performance is then similar to the performance achieved with synchronous demodulation even though no a priori sync information is employed (such as would be obtained from a preamble).

Figure 11.15 shows the block diagram of a burst modem that transmits eight spread spectrum data bits using binary CSK modulation. The modulator consists of an eight tap surface wave delay line that drives eight pairs of surface wave PN sequence generators. When the delay line is excited by a video pulse, a corresponding pulse is sequentially generated at each tap output separated in time by precisely one bit interval. Each tap output, in turn, excites a pair of PN sequence generators that simultaneously provide orthogonal mark and space codes for binary CSK signaling. A SPDT switch selects either the mark or space code for each corresponding data bit. These coded sequences are combined to form eight contiguous PN code bursts representing a single spread spectrum message of eight bits.

The corresponding demodulator is a mirror image of the modulator employing matched filters for each of the possible transmission code sequences. Normally the same surface wave device can be used in both transmitter and receiver if it is fabricated with launching transducers at both ends of the substrate. When the received sequence of data bits completely fills the demodulator's delay line, a correlation peak appears at either the mark or space code filter output for each data bit simultaneously. If the matched filters are designed for identical propagation delay, and if the tapped delay line is designed for exactly one bit delay (modulo 2π), the correlation peaks will all be in phase coherence. Thus the individual bit correlation peaks at the 16 matched-filter outputs can be coherently summed to produce a new total correlation peak with 6 dB greater peak signal-to-noise ratio than that of a single bit. This more accurate total correlation peak can then be used as the strobe to determine whether a mark or space code was transmitted in each bit position.

In the preceding example a perfectly synchronous CSK bit decision requires 13 dB peak signal-to-noise ratio (S/N) per bit for a 10^{-5} bit error rate. The total correlation peak has a S/N of 19 dB in this case that leads to an rms timing accuracy of 0.08 of a PN chip interval. The resultant S/N

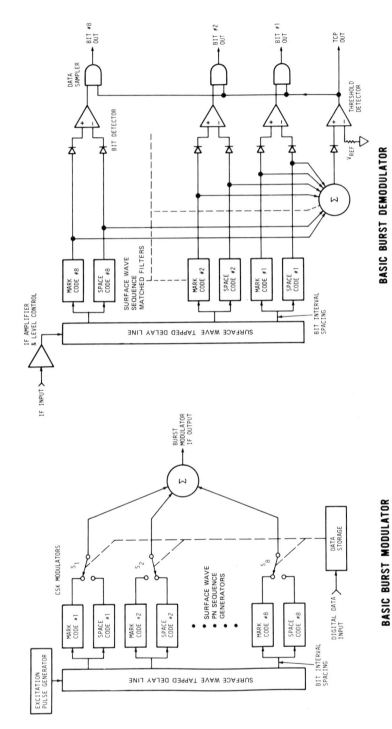

BASIC BURST DEMODULATOR

BASIC BURST MODULATOR

Figure 11.15 Basic surface wave burst modem. Shown for eight-bit binary CSK modulation.

504

degradation caused by imperfect epoch timing is less than 0.5 dB and may be considered negligible. By way of contrast, if demodulation were performed on a bit-by-bit basis using only threshold crossings of the individual bit correlation peaks, the S/N per bit required for 10^{-5} bit error rate would exceed 21 dB, or be 8 dB greater than in the deferred-decision burst technique.

In applications requiring "selective addressing" of various terminals or resistance to spoofing, it may be necessary to alter the spread spectrum codes in each transmission. For these applications it is possible to use programmable surface wave PN code generators and matched filters that allow chip-by-chip changes in the code words. However these programmable devices are expensive and complicated at chip rates above 10 MHz and for long code words. A less complex solution is to use fixed coded PN sequence matched filters for each CSK bit and to permute the order in which the CSK bits are transmitted. With an appropriate choice of threshold level, it is possible to reject any received bursts that do not possess the assigned code order permutation. In the previous example of eight data bits per burst, the addition of an 8×8 programmable switching matrix, as illustrated in Figs. 11.16 and 11.17, permits the generation of $8! = 40,320$ unique code order permutations.

An experimental programmable surface wave burst communication modem using these techniques has been built.[19] This modem transmits eight data bits in a 20 μsec burst using CSK modulation. Each data bit has a different 127 chip PN sequence with 50 MHz chip rate and the code order permutation is programmable. The data transfer rate of the modem is up to 400 Kbps with 21 dB of spread spectrum gain per bit. The implementation described provides burst length and chip rate within a factor of 2 of the current state of the art.

Conclusion. Surface wave devices have many important applications to communication technology. Circuit elements such as bandpass filters and precision bandpass delay lines can reduce the size and cost and improve the reliability of various communication systems. However, the most important applications, from the viewpoint of expanded capabilities, are in the area of spread spectrum systems.

Surface wave devices can be designed as efficient generators and corresponding linear matched filters for complicated spread spectrum waveforms, including pseudonoise (PN) sequences, frequency-hopped sequences, FM chirps, and various hybrid combinations. In a relatively narrow but important range of bandwidths from about 1 to 100 MHz, surface wave devices permit fabrication of simple, rapidly synchronized spread spectrum modems.

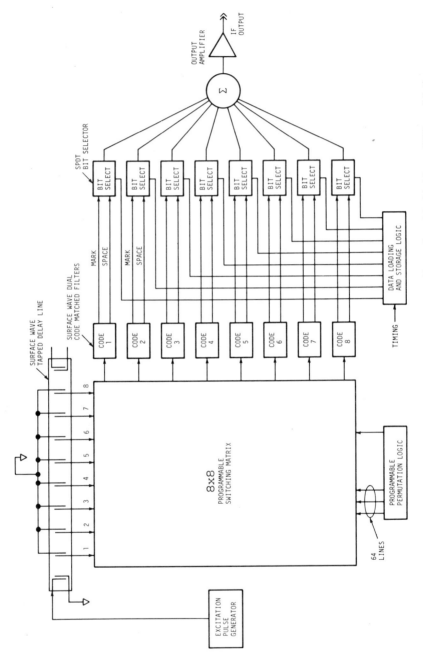

Figure 11.16 Block diagram of programmable burst modulator. Shown for eight-bit binary CSK modulation.

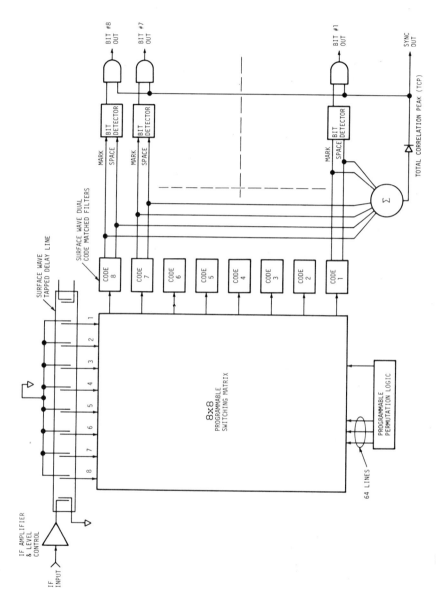

Figure 11.17 Block diagram of programmable burst receiver. Shown for eight-bit binary CSK modulation.

507

Spread spectrum processing gains up to 30 dB are easily achieved for fixed-coded devices, and, with the addition of switching circuitry, programmable surface wave sequence generators can also be built. Although the amount of processing gain available from a single matched filter is limited, its passive filter design permits rapid link synchronization and provides very important benefits in system flexibility. These devices are finding application in many areas, including data transmission, navigation systems, time division network synchronization, and command control systems.

An exciting and unique capability introduced by surface wave technology is the spread spectrum burst communication modem. This burst technique coherently combines the information in several successive data bits to provide near optimum detection of asynchronous bursts. A data link can therefore be designed that enjoys the freedom of intermittent asynchronous transmission with the performance and integrity of nearly synchronous reception. Discrete addressing, precision ranging, and code programmability are features that can be added to the burst modem to satisfy the potential requirements of future communication systems.

References

1. J. H. Collins and P. M. Brant. "The role of surface acoustic wave technology in communication systems." *Ultrasonics* **10**, 57 (1972).
2. D. T. Bell, Jr., J. D. Holmes, and R. V. Ridings. "Application of acoustic surface wave technology to spread spectrum communications." *IEEE Trans.* **MTT-21**, 263 (1973).
3. G. S. Kino and H. Matthews. "Signal processing in acoustic surface wave devices." *IEEE Spectrum* **8**(8), 22 (1971).
4. C. E. Cook. "Linear FM, spread spectrum signal formats for beacon and communication systems." 1973 URSI Conference, Boulder, Colorado, August, 1973.
5. H. Blasbalg et al. "Air-ground, ground-air communications using pseudo-noise through a satellite." *IEEE Trans.* **AES-4**, 774 (1968).
6. Special issue on matched filters, *IRE Trans.* **IT-6**, (1960).
7. G. F. Sage. "Serial synchronization of pseudonoise systems." *IEEE Trans.* **COM-12**, 123 (1964).
8. J. M. Kelly and R. A. Stein. "Charge-coupled device analog matched filters." *Electron. Lett.* **8**, 328 (1972).
9. W. C. Fifer et al. "Switchable acoustic matched filter." Final Report F30602-71-C-0199, Rome Air Defence Command, Rome, New York, 1972.
10. J. Wozencraft and J. Jacobs. *Principles of Communication Engineering*, Wiley, New York, 1965, Chapter 5.
11. J. J. Jones. "Hard limiting of two signals in random noise," *IEEE Trans.* **IT-9**, 34 (1963).

12. R. A. LeFande. "Effects of phase nonlinearities on phase shift keyed pseudonoise/spread spectrum communication systems." *IEEE Trans.* **COM-18,** 685 (1970).

13. M. P. Ristenbatt and R. S. Berkowitz. *Pseudo-random Binary Coded Waveforms in Modern Radar,* Wiley, New York, 1965.

14. R. L. Frank. "Polyphase codes with good nonperiodic correlation properties." *IEEE Trans.* **IT-9,** 43 (1963).

15. M. M. Goutmann. "Intersymbol interference as a natural code." *IEEE Trans.* **COM-20,** 1033 (1972).

16. P. Mousen. "Digital transmission performance on fading dispersive diversity channels." *IEEE Trans.* **COM-21,** 33 (1973).

17. M. Unkauf. "High speed digital tropo technology." 1973 URSI Conference, Boulder, Colorado, August, 1973.

18. M. Unkauf. "An acoustic surface wave modem for time-variant, dispersive channels." Microwave Research Institute International Symposium XXIII, New York, April, 1974.

19. M. Setrin et al. "An IFF system using block programmable surface wave signal expander and compressor." 1973 IEEE Ultrasonics Symposium, Monterey, Calif., November, 1973.

Index

Adhesives, 244, 249
Admittance, acoustic, 148, 274-275
  characteristic, 265, 268, 275, 283
  driving point, 267, 270, 278, 280-282
  input, of chirp transducer, 149-150, 369
    by delta function model, 83-85
    by equivalent circuit model, 94, 146,
      148
    by field theory, 63-67
    and Hilbert transform, 148, 364
    by impulse response model, 148-149
  internal, 267-268, 274
  load, 267, 270-271. *See also* Conductance,
    load; Impedance, load
  matrix, for apodized transducers, 100-
    101, 288-290
  of filter, 96-97, 281-290
  of inactive transmission line, 96
  representation of transducer, 91-94,
    265-268
  parameters,
    of filter, 281-290
    with split-connected transducers, 283-
      286
    with weighted transducers, 286-290
    of transducer, 265-270
  parasitic, 150. *See also* Capacitance, para-
    sitic
  transfer, 96, 281, 283, 285, 289-290
  wave, *see* Impedance, wave
  see also Conductance; Impedance; Resis-
    tance; and Susceptance
Air traffic control equipment, 473-474

Aluminum oxide, *see* Substrates
Ambiguity function, 447-448, 457
Amplitude function, 353-362, 372. *See also*
    Weighting function; Window func-
    tion
Amplitude response, *see* Frequency re-
    sponse
Anisotropy constant, 48-51, 160, 373
Antiresonant frequency, 286
Apodization, 120-123, 131-135, 351, 356-
    358, 360. *See also* Amplitude func-
    tion; Transducer weighting; and
    Window function
Array response, 84-85
Attenuation, *see* Loss, propagation
AZ 1350, 173-175. *See also* Photoresists

Bandwidth, 320, 343, 359, 368, 467
  of composite transducer, 243
  of multistrip coupled filter, 133-135
  of reflection grating, 422
  transducer fractional, and electrode resis-
    tance, 230
  and electromechanical coupling factor,
    225-226
  and insertion loss, 223-229, 238
  and radiation Q, 150, 224, 371
  of transversal filter, 112-114

Baud, 499
Beam spreading, *see* Diffraction
Beam steering, 28-30, 168, 301. *See also*
    Energy flow

511

BGO, *see* Substrates, bismuth germanium
    oxide
Bismuth germanium oxide, *see* Substrates
Bit, 308, 479
Bleustein-Gulyaev wave, 30
Boundary condition, 12, 16-17, 58
    effect on phase velocity, 26, 42-43
    for layered surface, 32
    perturbation of, 38-43
Bulk waves, 2-11, 24, 61, 71
    adverse effects of, 56, 405
    contribution to input impedance, 72-76
    distortion of filter response, 72-73, 157-
        159, 303
        reduction of, 158, 303
    distortion of reflection grating response,
        404, 406-409
    generation by transducer, 56, 65, 72-73,
        158, 303
    radiation from reflection grating, 404-406
    radiation from transducer, 73-75, 158

Cadmium sulphide, *see* Substrates
Capacitance, of finger pair on several sub-
        strates, 147
    parasitic, 150, 259, 335
        and feed structure, 257
    of transducer, 364
        approximate, 273
        chirp, 367
        equivalent circuit, 76-79, 88-89, 98,
            148, 220, 223, 265, 267, 271-272,
            332, 334-335, 368
        from field theory, 66
Chain matrices, 90-94
Chebyshev response, 135, 141, 458-459
Chip, 308, 311, 479
Clutter, filter, 449, 468
Code, Barker, 311-314, 497
    FM, 349
    frequency agile, 462, 471, 479
    Golay, 318, 487
    maximal length, 315-316, 497
    non-periodic, 497
    permuted by surface wave device, 505
    polyphase, 309, 318-319, 462, 497
    pseudonoise, 315-316, 462
        correlation properties, 497
    randomly generated, 317-318
    selection, 495-497

see also Data, modulation; Spreading
Comb filter, 239
Comb transducer, 167
Compliance, 10
Compression ratio, 150, 312
Compressor, *see* Filter, chirp
Conductance, electrode, 224, 229-231
    input, 67
    load, 234, 358, 364
        and fractional bandwidth, 225
        and insertion loss, 226
        and matching transformer, 236-238
        and network Q, 225, 237-238, 368
        and reflection loss, 220-221
        and time-bandwidth product, 231
        and transmission loss, 220-221
    radiation, 146, 223, 229, 368
        bulk wave contribution, 73
        of chirp transducer, 365-367
        and composite transducers, 240-242
        field theory of, 65-66, 70
        and fractional bandwidth, 225
        from impulse model, 149-150
        and insertion loss, 226
        and matching, 220, 236-237
        and reflection loss, 220-221
        and time-bandwidth product, 230-231
        and transmission loss, 220-221
        from various models, 104-105
        of weighted transducer, 149-150, 363-
            366
        see also Admittance; Impedance; Resis-
            tance; and Susceptance
Constitutive relations, 5, 10, 60
Contact printing, 178-186
Contracted notation, 4, 10
Convolution integral, 308
Convolver, 462. *See also* Filter, matched
Correlation integral, 118, 309
Correlation response, of chirp filter, 349,
        376-378
    function, 311, 313-314, 322-325
    of phase coded filter, 309, 313, 318,
        336-339
        effect of phase errors, 322-325
Correlators, 484-485, 487-489. *See also*
        Filter, matched
Countermeasure equipment, 470-472
Coupling coefficient, *see* Electromechanical
        coupling factor

Crosstalk, 302. *See also* Electromagnetic
feedthrough
Crystal symmetry, 5, 7, 8
and surface wave propagation, 21
Crystals, *see* Substrates

Data, modulation, 307-308, 478-479, 489-
495, 503
synchronization, 482-484, 495-497
transmission, 479-482, 489-492
Deacy coefficient, 61
Decay constant, 22
Decision feedback, 490, 496, 499
Decoder, 349. *See also* Filter, matched
Delay, group, 97, 127-128
phase, 111
temperature coefficient of, 52, 147, 326,
403
Delay line, 460-462, 471, 502
Delay line canceller, 449-451, 453, 456
Delta function model, *see* Transducer,
models of
Despreading, 479, 484, 486. *See also* Inverse modulation
Detection probability, 457, 489
Detection threshold, 495
Dielectric permittivity, 5, 7, 8, 10
Diffraction, on anisotropic substrate, 48-51,
160-161
anisotropy constant for, 160
parabolic approximation for, 48, 160
from apodized transducers, 100, 104, 120-
121
and filter performance, 44, 151, 160-161,
298, 300, 372-373
integral, 44
on isotropic substrate, 44-48
by photomasks, 179-183
effect on photoresist profile, 181-185
Dispersive transducer, *see* Transducer, chirp
Distortion, 151-162, 220, 222, 300-303,
350-353
in phase coded filters, 321-325, 329-332
in reflective grating filters, 409-411, 419
Dogleg transducer, 123-125
Dolph-Tschebyshev function, 458-459
Doppler, filtering, 452
sensitivity, 447, 457
shift, 447-450, 452, 454
Double electrodes, 156-157, 275-281, 283-

286, 330, 353, 467
Dummy electrodes, 286-287, 351-352
Dynamic range, 251, 333, 359, 434-435

Echo, spurious, 155-157
triple transit, 96-97, 153-154, 282, 302
suppression, 219-222
see also Regeneration
see also Reflection
Effective permittivity, 58-66
Eigenvector, 13-16
Elastic constants, 4-7, 26
Elastic displacement, 2, 15, 19-25, 31, 61
in layered substrates, 35-39
Electric displacement, 5, 10, 12, 24, 42-43,
60
Electric field, 5, 9, 10, 62
of transducer, 77, 115
Electric potential, 9, 12, 25-26, 31, 39-40,
60
perturbed, 39-40, 42-43
Electrodes, split connected, *see* Double electrodes
Electromagnetic feedthrough, 161, 252,
302
reduction of, 162, 246, 251-252, 302
by balanced field, 253, 303
Electromagnetic suppression, 251
Electromechanical coupling factor, 27,
65-66, 147, 226
and characteristic admittance, 265
and equivalent circuit, 77, 88-90, 272,
332
and fractional bandwidth, 225-226
and frequency response curves, 272-273
groove reflectivity compared, 410
and insertion loss, 227-228
and radiation conductance, 146, 223,
363, 366
and radiation Q, 150, 224, 332, 367
and time-bandwidth product, 231
and wave impedance, 155
see also Interaction efficiency
Encoder, 349. *See also* Filter, chirp; Filter,
phase coded
Energy flow, 20, 21, 24, 27
bulk wave, 73, 75
and slowness curve, 28-30
see also Beam steering; Poynting vector
Epoch, 481

Equation of motion, 4
Equivalent circuit, of filter, 281, 284
  of finger pair, 80-81, 264, 356-357
  Mason, 76-81
  of piezoelectric plate and bar, 76-81
  of reflection structures, 388-390, 398-
    400, 408
  of resonator, 412
  of transducer, 81-90, 266
    with weighted fingers, 97-98, 287
  of transducer electric port, 146-148, 220,
    223, 229, 234, 358, 364
    and admittance calculations, 267, 271-
      272, 332, 334
    of composite transducer, 241-242
    and matching networks, 234-236, 335,
      368
Error rate, 489, 491-494, 501
  in asynchronous modem, 503-505
Etching, chemical, 188-191
  ion beam, 210-213
  ion bombardment, 191-193
Expander, *see* Filter, chirp

False alarm, probability, 489, 496
    and detection threshold, 495
  rate, 457
Feed structures, 245, 256-260
Filter, bandpass, 290-303
    with building block transducers, 291-
      297
    with multistrip coupler, 133-135, 293
    in radar equipment, 453-454
    reflection grating, 429-430, 432-434
    with weighted fingers, 297-299
  banks, 239-243, 432-434
  chirp, 350-379
    apodization, 356-357
    electrode position, 353-356
    equivalent circuit parameters, 149-151,
      362-367
    nonlinear, 361-362
    in radar equipment, 349-350, 463-468
    see also Reflective-array compressor
  comb, 239, 490, 500
  design, bandpass, 290-299, 412-415
    chirp, 350-362, 367-375, 426-430
    equiripple, 141-145
    by Fourier transform, 138-141, 294-
      295, 416

    phase coded, 319-339
    reflection grating, 410-411, 412-430
  digital and surface wave compared, 137-
    138
  Hamming, 373, 458, 459
  high Q, 412-415
  IMCON, 383, 385, 434-435
  LC network and surface wave compared,
    109-110, 135-137, 264
  linear FM, *see* Filter, chirp
  matched, 308-310, 336-337, 349, 376-
    377, 466, 481-482, 498
    in radar, 446-447, 456-460, 465
    response function, 311-314
    signal-to-noise ratio, 311, 446, 481,
      489. *See also* Time-bandwidth
      product
    in spread spectrum communication,
      466, 481-483, 489
      adaptive, 498-502, 503
    see also Filter, chirp; Filter, phase
      coded; and Reflective-array com-
      pressor
  non-minimum phase, 136, 264
  phase coded, 312-314, 317, 319-345
    application range, 341-344
    in asynchronous modem, 503-507
    correlation response, 313-314, 318, 338
    effect of phase errors, 322-325
    equivalent circuit parameters, 332-335
    losses in, 336-339
    phase errors in, 325-329
    programmable, 339-340, 341, 462, 505-
      508
    in radar equipment, 456
    reflections in, 329-332
    in spread spectrum equipment, 481-482
  poles and zeros of, 135-136
  programmable, 339-340, 341, 462, 505-
    508
  pulse compression, *see* Filter, chirp;
    Filter, phase coded; and Reflective-
    array compressor
  reflection grating, 381-386
    distortion in, 409-411
    examples of, 431-440
    theory of, 415-430
    see also Reflective-array compressor
  television IF, 295, 299
  theory, 110-115, 135-137, 142, 264,

308-309
  of surface wave, 115-135, 281-290, 322-
    324, 348-349, 353-362
  reflection grating, 383-385, 415-430
Finger response, 84-85
Frequency characteristic, *see* Frequency
  response
Frequency hopping, 471
Frequency measurement, 471-472
Frequency response, of bandpass filters,
    293-303
  of filters, 118-119, 129-135
    by admittance parameters, 281-290
    transversal, 111-115
  Gaussian, 455
  of phase coded filters, 336-337
  of reflection grating filters, 425-426,
    430, 433, 437, 439
  ripples, 114, 139-145, 361-362, 430
  spurious causes of, 153-155, 162, 221-
    222, 302
  transition width, 139-146
  see also Admittance, transfer; Stop band;
    and Transfer function
Fresnel length, 44, 48-50. *See also* Diffrac-
    tion
Fused silica, *see* Substrates

Gallium arsenide, *see* Substrates
Gibbs oscillations, 140
Grating angle, 401-402
Grating misalignment, 401-403
Green's function, 70-71, 104

Hamming function, 458-459
Hilbert transform, 148, 364
Holography, *see* Lithography, photo, holo-
    graphic
Hooke's law, 4, 41

IMCON, 383, 385, 434, 467
Impedance, characteristic, 76, 80, 94, 102
  of dogleg structure, 124
  driving point, 286
  of finger pair, 123-124
  input, 146, 150-151, 333
    contribution of bulk waves to, 72-76
  load, 95, 332
    and distortion, 86, 152-153
  wave, 155

see also Admittance; Conductance; Resis-
    tance; and Susceptance
Impedance matching, 150, 220-233, 286,
    336, 368-371
  and transducer bandwidth, 151, 223-229,
    321, 370-371
  and transducer time-bandwidth product,
    229-233
  and triple transit echo, 152-155, 220-
    222, 371
  see also Matching networks
Impulse length, 421
Impulse response, of biphase code, 310
  of chirp filter, 376, 378, 427
  in filter design, 138-140
  of matched filter, 308-309
  of phase coded filter, 312, 318, 330
  and radiation conductance, 148-150
  of reflection grating, 397-398, 416
  of reflection grating filters, 424-425,
    429-430
  of reflection step, 394
  of reflective-array compressor, 427, 429-
    430
  of transversal filter, 118
Intensity profile, 49-51
Interaction efficiency, 26-27, 42-43, 65,
    168, 273-274
  and chirp filter finger position, 354-355
  and conducting layer reflection, 388, 389-
    390
  and transducer internal reflection, 155-
    156
  see also Electromechanical coupling
    factor
Inverse modulation, 479, 490. *See also*
    Despreading

Jamming, 471, 479

Layer, conducting, 12, 388, 389-390.
    See also Interaction efficiency
  deposition, *see* Thin films
  non-conducting, 31-40
    effect on phase velocity, 40-42
    reflection from, 387-389
    and transducer internal reflections,
      155, 352
Lead zirconium oxide, *see* Substrates
Lift-off process, 166, 193-195

Lithium niobate, etching, 191, 212-213
    filters on, 321, 370, 375, 385, 466, 467
        examples, 72-74, 312-314, 376-378,
            431, 432-433, 438-439
    physical constants, 7, 27, 147, 160, 168,
        343, 373
    reflection by discontinuities, 155, 390-
        392, 402, 407-408
    Substrate preparation, 170-171
    surface waves in, 23-30, 42, 43, 50, 61-
        62, 155
    symmetry, 5-6, 8
    temperature effects, 52, 168, 254, 300,
        403, 435
    transducers on, 63, 66-67, 71, 104-105,
        155-156, 352, 374
    YZ-out, 24, 327
Lithium tantalum oxide, see Substrates
Lithography, electron, 195-205
    photoresists for, 173, 201-204
    photo, 175-188, 341-343
        with conformable photomask, 179-186
        holographic, 186-187
    X-ray, 205-210
        photoresists for, 173, 208, 210
Loss, acoustic, see Loss, propagation
    code, 338
    conversion, 370, 410
    insertion, 97, 282
        and bandwidth, 151, 168, 223-229,
            238, 321
        and electrode resistivity, 230
        and matching conductance, 222, 226
        of particular filters, 72-76, 134, 331,
            337
        of phase coded filters, 320, 336-339
        of reflection grating filters, 409-411
        and time-bandwidth product, 229-232
        and triple transit echo, 154-155, 219-
            223
    mismatch, bandedge, 336
    matched filter, 459
    ohmic, 161. See also Resistance, elec-
        trode
    propagation, 51
        and distortion, 161, 371-372
        and insertion loss, 232
    reflection, 220-221, 369
    scattering, 405-406
    sensitivity, 326

    transfer, 271-274
    transmission, 220-221, 282
Love modes, 33-35, 167
    free, 30

Mass loading, see Layer, non-conducting
Matching, see Impedance matching
Matching networks, 151, 271-272, 336
    for comb filters, 239-240
    for composite transducers, 240-243
    connecting to transducers, 256-258
    design, 219-243, 367-371
    microstrip, 259-260
    shunt and series designs compared, 237-
        238
    simple RL, 233-234, 271-274, 368
    with transformer, 234-238, 335-336
Matrix notation, 4, 10
Microstrip, 245, 257, 259-260
Mismatch ratio, 220-222, 238
Modem, 490, 502-507
Moving target indication, 448-450, 452,
    456
Multipath propagation, 498
Multistrip coupler, 132-135, 300-301

Oscillators, 454-455
Ovens, 254

Packaging methods, 243-258
    substrate heaters, 254-257
    substrate mounting, 244-249, 326
    transducer feed, 256-258
Packaging structures, 244-247
Parseval's theorem, 149
Partial waves, 12, 32
Passband, see Frequency response, ripples
Phase compensation, 436-437
Phase error, from electromagnetic feed-
        through, 302
    from fabrication errors, 321-322, 327-
        329, 378-379
    from load impedance, 152-153, 369
    in phase coded filters, 321-329
        effect on correlation response, 322-325
        from fabrication errors, 327-329
        from temperature effects, 325-326
    in reflection grating filters, 404, 407-409,
        437, 439, 435
    compensation for, 436-437

from transducer internal reflections, 277-278

corrected by double fingers, 278, 280

from triple transit echo, 153-154

Phase response, *see* Frequency response

Photomasks, 177, 179-181

Photoresists, AZ 1350, 173-175

baking, 175, 188, 193

coating, 174-175

for electron lithography, 173, 201-204

index of refraction, 182

mathematical model of, 173-174

preparation, 173-175

relief structure in, 179-185

effect on lift-off process, 193

for X-ray lithography, 173, 208, 210

Piezoelectric ceramics, 5

Piezoelectric constant, 7, 8, 10

Piezoelectric coupling coefficient, *see* Electromechanical coupling coefficient

Piezoelectric effect, 5

Piezoelectric shorting, 352. *See also* Interaction efficiency

Piezoelectric stiffening, *see* Interaction efficiency

Plate modes, distortion by, 158

IMCON, 383

see also Bulk waves

Poisson's ratio, 390

Power, conversion by transducer, 73, 83, 94, 103, 226, 368

to bulk waves, 73, 75

reflected by transducer, 156-157, 220, 369

reflected by periodic grating, 417, 421

Poynting vector, 10-11, 19, 24, 29. *See also* Beam steering; Energy flow

Preamble, 484, 502

Predistortion, 356, 372

Prewhitening, 453

Processing gain, 349, 468, 479-481, 488, 495, 498. *See also* Time-bandwidth product

Proximity fuse, 473

Pulze compression, 349, 446-448

with chirp waveform, 447, 457-460

weighting functions for, 458-459

with nonlinear FM waveform, 459-460

systems, 450-452

chirp filters in, 349, 361-362, 463-468

Pulse compressor, *see* Filter, chirp; Reflective-array compressor

Pure mode axis, 21

PZT, *see* Substrates, lead zirconium oxide

Q, acoustic, 150

and chirp filter design, 368-375

conversion loss, 370

reflection efficiency, 371

radiation, 150-151, 224, 332-333, 367

of surface wave resonator, 405-406, 415, 431

of transducer input network, 225, 233, 234, 237

for composite transducers, 240-243

with transformer, 237-238

Quartz, etching, 191

filters on, 158-159, 321, 370, 375, 466, 467

examples, 299, 317-318, 320, 327, 331, 333, 431

fabrication of, 341-342

physical constants of, 7, 27, 147, 160, 168, 343, 373, 392

reflection by surface perturbations, 392, 402

ST-cut, 27, 327-328

surface waves in, 27-28, 51

layered, 155

symmetry, 5-7

temperature effects, 52, 168, 254, 300, 326, 403

transducers on, 155-156, 352, 374

Quasistatic approximation, 8, 13

RAC, *see* Reflective-array compressor

Radar, 444-450

ambiguity function, 447-448, 457

Doppler shift, 447-450

moving target indication, 448-450

range, 350, 444, 445

see also Pulse compression

Radar systems, clutter reference, 468

for proximity fusing, 473

pseudocoherent, 468

surface wave devices in, 450-463

bandpass filter, 453-454

chirp filter, 349, 457-458, 460-462

delay line, 452

matched filter, 456-460

oscillators, 454
programmable, 462
resonators, 454
temperature tracking of, 453
variable delay unit, 460-462
waveform selection, 456-457
Rayleigh modes, 34-38, 167
Rayleigh waves, in anisotropic substrates,
20-31
in isotropic substrated, 17-20
velocity, 17-18
in piezoelectric substrates, 23-31
stiffened, 24, 27
in YZ lithium niobate, 23-30
Reactance, input, 332, 333, 335
parasitic, 334
radiation, 229
Reciprocity, 72, 92
Reflection, by grating, 392-400
on anisotropic substrates, 401-404
of 90°, 419-422
normal incidence, 417-419
oblique incidence, 400-404
temperature effects, 402-404
two 90° reflections, 422-430
by groove, 392-393, 409, 418-420
pair of, 422-423
by step discontinuity, 386-392
by transducer, 155-157, 274-276, 329-
331, 352-353
reduction by double fingers, 156-157,
276-277, 352-353
see also Echo, triple transit
see also Reflection coefficient
Reflection coefficient, and grating filter
distortion, 409-411
of groove, 392-393, 409, 419
of periodic grating, 392-400
by delta function model, 393-398, 416-
417
frequency dependence plotted, 413-414
multiple reflections in, 396-398, 400
reactive energy storage effect, 406-409
by transmission line model, 398-400,
407-409
of step discontinuity, dependence on
height, 388-389, 409
frequency response, 394
methods of calculating, 388-391, 407
in various materials, 391-392

of transducer, 77, 94, 274-276, 369-371
voltage reflection coefficient, 277
Reflection grating, construction, 210-213
frequency of maximum reflection, 408
frequency response, 394-400
impulse length, 421
impulse response, 393-394, 416, 424
multiple reflections in, 396-398
scattering from, 400-406
into bulk waves, 404-406
temperature effects on, 402-403
transfer function, 415-430
wave velocity in, 407-408
weighting, 418-419, 424
Reflective-array compressor, 383, 434, 437
design, 426-430
examples, 437-440
insertion loss, 434
phase compensation, 436-437, 440
phase errors, 439-440
for radar equipment, 456, 467
reflector spacing, 427-428
reproducibility, 438
temperature effects, 435-436
transfer function, 427-428
geometric factor, 426, 428
weighted, 428-429
Reflectivity, *see* Reflection coefficient
Regeneration, 79-80, 153, 369, 467. *See
also* Echo, triple transit
Resistance, electrode, 161, 229-230, 235,
333, 334
in long transducers, 267
load, 335
and fractional bandwidth, 230
and insertion loss, 230
and matching network, 236, 238
with transformer, 235, 237
and reflection loss, 220-221
and transmission loss, 220-221
radiation, 229, 332, 335 ·
of composite transducers, 240-241
and fractional bandwidth, 230
and insertion loss, 230
and matching transformer, 235, 237
and network Q, 238
and reflection loss, 220-221
and transmission loss, 220-221
see also Admittance; Conductance;
Impedance; and Susceptance

Resonant frequency, of reflection grating, 408
  of transducer, 55
    symmetric, 127-128
    uniform, 128-129
Resonator, 381, 383, 406
  essential features, 412-415
  examples, 431-432
  in radar equipment, 454
Ripples, *see* Frequency response, ripples
Ritz variational method, 67-69

Sagittal plane, 11, 17, 20, 22
Sampling theorem, 84
Sapphire, *see* Substrates
Scattering, angle, 401
  loss, 405-406
  from periodic grating, 400-406
    into bulk waves, 404-406
    temperature effects, 402-403
  vector, 400-401
Secular equation, 13, 15-18, 22, 59
Series weighting, 123
Shadow printing, *see* Contact printing
Shape factor, 134
Sidelobes, in chirp radar, 447-448, 456-459
  frequency response, 112-114, 133, 292-293. *See also* Frequency response, ripples
  time response, 312-314, 333. *See also* Impulse response; Correlation response
  of various codes, 311, 316, 318, 495-497
Signal processing, 350, 443-444, 452, 477
  with matched filters, 446-450, 456-460
  see also Data, mudulation; Despreading; Processing gain; and Pulse compression
Signal-to-noise ratio, 311-312, 453, 481, 489
  in asynchronous transmission, 503-505
  in matched filter, 446-448
Silicon, *see* Substrates
Slowness, 28-29, 46, 61, 64, 66, 69-70
Source, delta function, 82, 101-103, 115
  of elastic waves, 80, 115
Spectrum analyser, 350
Spreading, 478-481. *See also* Code; Data, modulation

Sputtering, 191-193
Stiffness tensor, 4
Stopband, 133-135, 152-153, 161, 162
  and bulk waves, 158
  rejection, 297
  of resonator, 413-414
  of transversal filter, 112-115
  see also Frequency response, ripples
Straight crested wave, 12, 44
Strain, 2-4
Stress, 3-5, 12, 41
Strip line, 245, 259-260
Substrate, heaters, 254-256
  layered, 31-38
    perturbation theory of, 40-43
  orientation, 168, 327-328
    effect of errors in, 326-329
  preparation, 168-170
    cleaning, 170-172, 194
    polishing, 169-170
    work damage, 169-170
Substrates, bismuth germanium oxide, 7, 27, 147, 160, 168, 392, 402, 403
  lead zirconium oxide, 7, 68-69, 89-90, 300
  lithium niobate, *see* Lithium niobate
  physical constants of, 7, 27, 147, 168, 254, 300
    pertaining to diffraction, 160
    reflection gratings, 392, 402, 403
  quartz, *see* Quartz
  silicon, 7, 22-23
  zinc oxide, 7, 30, 167
Summation convention, 4
Surface charge, 63, 71
Surface waves, *see* Love modes; Rayleigh modes; and Rayleigh waves
Susceptance, input, 146, 148
  radiation, 146, 363-364, 369
  see also Admittance; Conductance; Impedance; and Resistance
Symmetry conditions, 21-24, 30, 32-33
Synchronization, 482-484, 495-497

Taylor weighting function, 458-459
Temperature coefficient, of delay, 147, 168, 254, 300
  in ST quartz, 147, 168, 300, 326
  of reflection grating angle, 403
Tensor notation, 4, 57

Thermal effects, 253-254, 300
  in chirp filters, 435
  in phase coded filters, 325-326
  reduction of, 254-256, 435
  in reflection grating filters, 402-403,
    435
  use of, 436, 456
Thin films, adhesion, 190, 193-194
  deposition, 172, 194
  oxidation, 250
  used in surface wvve filters, 188
Third harmonic response, 85, 88
Time-bandwidth product, and chirp filters,
    376-379, 434, 435, 467
  for radar equipment, 456, 468
  and phase coded filters, 329, 340-341,
    344
  and pulse compression, 311, 349-350,
    434, 435, 457
  and reflection grating filters, 424
  and transducer insertion loss, 229-232
  of various reflective-array compressors,
    435, 437-439
  see also Processing gain
Topografiner, 169
Transducer, chirp, 98-99, 353-356
  comb, 167
  composite, 290-297
  field theory of, 62-76
  models of, applicability, 104-106
    delta function, 82-87, 101-103, 115-
      117
    equivalent circuit, 76-82, 87-90, 97-101,
      103-104
      chain matrix analysis of, 90-97
      crossed field, 76-77, 104, 356-357
      in line, 76-77, 104
      transmission line, 264-268, 286-290
  phase coded, 319-320
  radiation from, 43-51
    bulk wave, 73, 75
  symmetric, 127-128
  uniform, 128-129
Transducer weighting, 97-103, 119-127,
    297-299, 351-352. *See also* Ampli-
    tude function; Apodization; Weight-
    ing function; and Window function
Transfer function, of filver, 96-97, 118,
    136
  via admittance matrix, 96
  with apodized transducers, 120-123
  by delta function model, 85-86, 115-
    118
  with identical transducers, 130
  poles and zeros of, 136
  of LC network, 135-137
  of reflecting grating filter, 415-416
  of reflecting grooves, 420, 422-423
  of reflection gratings, 415-417
    fractional bandwidth, 422
    geometric factor, 426
    at 90° incidence, 419-422
    at normal incidence, 417-419
    overlap factor, 422, 424-425
    with two 90° reflections, 422-430
    weighted, 418-419
  of transducer, 279, 358-359
  see also Admittance, transfer; Frequency
    response
Transformation matrix, 9
Transformation width, 139, 142
Transmission coefficient, 396
Triple transit echo, *see* Echo, triple transit
Triple transit suppression, 219-222

Velocity, group, 33-34
  phase, in anisotropic substrates, 21, 30
  of bulk waves, 16
  calculating, 13
  free-surface dispersion of, 439-440
  in layered surfaces, 33-38
    perturbation calculation, 38-43
  in periodic grating, 408
  of Rayleigh wave, 17-18, 22, 24-25, 42,
    43
  sample-to-sample variability, 300
  temperature dependence of, 52, 254.
    See also Delay, temperature coeffi-
    cient of
  variation with propagation angle, 28, 48
  in various substrates, 27, 147
  see also Slowness
Voltage reflection coefficient, 277. *See also*
    Echo, triple transit; Regeneration
Voltage triple transit contribution, 382.
    See also Echo, triple transit; Regen-
    eration
VSWR, 233, 234, 336

Walsh function, 493

Wave, equation, 9, 57
    decoupling by crystal symmetry, 21,
        30
    derivation of, 2-9
    for layered surface, 32
    solution of, 11-17
    longitudinal, 2
    straight-crested, 12
    transverse, 2
Waveform, 307-309, 447-448. *See also*
    Code; Pulse compression
Wedge transducer, 167
Weighting coefficients, for equiripple design,
    145

    of transversal filter, 111-115
Weighting function, 83-84
    in filter design, 297-298, 355-356
    for pulse compression radar, 349, 457-
        459
    See also Amplitude functions; Window
        function
Window function, 138-141. *See also*
        Weighting function
Wire bonding, 258

Zinc oxide, *see* Substrates